A7P

$\sin^2\theta + \cos^2\theta = 1$

Warren H Trester

Z89 Garner
2-6511 Ext 161
MRH

DIFFERENTIAL AND INTEGRAL

CALCULUS

THE MACMILLAN COMPANY
NEW YORK · CHICAGO
DALLAS · ATLANTA · SAN FRANCISCO

THE MACMILLAN COMPANY
OF CANADA, LIMITED
TORONTO

DIFFERENTIAL AND INTEGRAL
CALCULUS

by CLYDE E. LOVE, Ph.D.

PROFESSOR EMERITUS OF MATHEMATICS IN THE
UNIVERSITY OF MICHIGAN

and EARL D. RAINVILLE, Ph.D.

PROFESSOR OF MATHEMATICS IN THE UNIVERSITY OF MICHIGAN

FIFTH EDITION

The Macmillan Company

NEW YORK

PREFACE

For personal reasons I find myself unable to prepare a fifth edition of the calculus. I have therefore turned this task over to my colleague, Professor Earl D. Rainville, in whom I have the fullest confidence.

Clyde E. Love

In the present edition, as in the fourth edition, of this calculus, the material is so arranged that integration can be taken up early (Chapter 6) or delayed until after the customary topics in differentiation are studied. The latter arrangement is accomplished by studying Chapter 6 after Chapter 15, before Chapter 16.

New material in this edition includes the following topics: work, circle of curvature, an integral test for infinite series, the summation of power series, oblique and curvilinear asymptotes, the evaluation of iterated integrals by inversion of order and by change of coördinate system, and a short appendix introducing the student to a rigorous treatment of limits.

Several topics which were in the fourth edition have been accorded new treatment. In particular, the presentation of infinite series of constant terms and of Newton's method for solution of equations was almost completely revised. Major changes have also been made in the treatment of Wallis' Formula, plane area, limits, and the technique for obtaining derivatives in parametric form. Other changes occur throughout the book.

I have attempted to continue a most striking feature of Professor Love's books—the wealth of carefully constructed and graded exercises. The fourth edition had about 3700 exercises; the fifth has about 3900, of which only some 1500 are taken from the fourth edition. A few new types of exercises will be found here, but the essential character of the problem sets has been retained.

Throughout this revision it has been my aim to carry on in the spirit of the previous editions, to tighten up the rigor as much as seems compatible with the maturity of the student and the goal of attaining a working knowledge of calculus, and to introduce what new topics space permitted and demand recommended.

I am indebted to Professor Fred Brafman of Wayne University for an independent checking of the text and the answers to exercises, and to Professor Ralph L. Shively of Western Reserve University for an independent reading of the proofs. I wish to acknowledge the many useful suggestions on individual points of presentation made to me by Mr. Donat K. Kazarinoff of the University of Michigan. Finally, there is a more elusive, nonetheless important, contribution made to anything I write on elementary mathematics by those teachers with whom I have been in close contact regarding such exposition. For this kind of contribution I am particularly indebted to Professor Love, to Professors C. A. Hutchinson and Jack R. Britton, both of the University of Colorado, and to Professor Ruel V. Churchill of the University of Michigan.

Earl D. Rainville

CONTENTS

CHAPTER 27   OPERATIONS WITH POWER SERIES

CHAPTER 28   APPROXIMATE INTEGRATION

CHAPTER 29   PARTIAL DIFFERENTIATION

CHAPTER 30   DOUBLE INTEGRALS

CHAPTER 31   TRIPLE INTEGRALS

DIFFERENTIAL AND INTEGRAL

CALCULUS

1. Functions. In analytic geometry, the variables most frequently encountered are the rectangular coördinates (x, y) or polar coördinates (r, θ) of a point on a curve. The various applications of calculus involve, as variables, time, temperature, velocity, force, fluid pressure, air resistance, and a multitude of other quantities.

If two variables x and y are so related that, *when the value of x is given, y is thereby determined,* then y is said to be a *function of x.* The variable x, to which values may be assigned, is the *independent variable;* it is often restricted to a specific set, or range, of values.

Example (a): The area of a circle is determined by the radius—*i.e.,* the area is a function of the radius:

$$A = \pi r^2.$$

Example (b): The time required to travel 100 miles at a constant speed v depends upon the speed:

$$t = \frac{100}{v}.$$

Example (c): The cost of a quantity of gasoline is proportional to the quantity: at 30¢ per gallon (C in dollars),

$$C = 0.30Q.$$

Example (d): The temperature of the air at any point of the earth's surface is a function of the time.

In general, if y is a function of x, then x is likewise a function of y, and either may be chosen as independent variable, according to

1

convenience. Thus in (*a*), we can just as easily find the radius when the area is given:

$$r = \sqrt{\frac{A}{\pi}}.$$

In fact, this interchange of variables may be illustrated in the most ordinary, familiar way. For instance, in (*b*), with limited time available a driver may adjust his speed accordingly. And in (*c*), many would buy two dollars' worth. The only exception arises when, for some range of values of *x*, *y* is constant: *y* is still a function of *x* in that range, but *x* is not a function of *y* there.

The methods of analysis are useful, as a rule, only when the function can be expressed by a definite mathematical formula. For this reason functions such as (*d*), where no law connecting the variables is known, will not be considered in this book.

Except where the contrary is stated, the variables with which we shall have to deal are *restricted to real values*.

2. The function notation. In a study of properties held in common by many functions, it is important to have at hand a notation which expresses the fact that one variable is a function of another. We write

$$y = f(x),$$

(read "*y* equals *f* of *x*") and mean by it that *y* is a function of *x*, the symbol $f(x)$ representing the function in this instance. Other letters may be used: $F(x)$, $h(x)$, $\phi(x)$, $\psi(x)$, etc. Sometimes a specific function is designated by a function symbol, as in the examples below.

The value of $f(x)$ when $x = a$ is denoted by the symbol $f(a)$.

Example (*a*): If $f(x) = x^2 - 4x + 2$, then

$$f(a) = a^2 - 4a + 2,$$
$$f(3) = 3^2 - 4 \cdot 3 + 2 = -1,$$
$$f(0) = 2.$$

Example (*b*): If $h(\theta) = \sin \theta$, then

$$h\left(\frac{\pi}{2}\right) = \sin \frac{\pi}{2} = 1,$$
$$h(0) = 0,$$
$$h(\pi + \theta) = \sin (\pi + \theta)$$
$$= -\sin \theta = -h(\theta).$$

3. Graphic representation. The equation

(1) $y = f(x)$

assigns a value to y corresponding to every value of x under consideration. The (x, y) pairs thus determined may be considered as the Cartesian coördinates of points in a plane; the curve made up of these points is the *graph* of the function.

The graph of the function $f(x)$ is identical with the locus of equation (1) as defined in analytic geometry. Thus in (a), § 1, the graph of $A = \pi r^2$ is a parabola (Fig. 1); in (b), the graph of $t = \dfrac{100}{v}$ is an equilateral hyperbola (Fig. 2); in (c), the graph of $C = 0.30Q$ is a straight line.

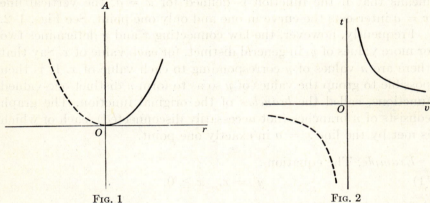

FIG. 1   FIG. 2

However, in any specific application the values assigned to x must be compatible with the conditions of the problem. In many cases x is restricted to a definite *range* or *interval:* for instance, in the above examples, negative values of the arguments r, v, Q are excluded because they would have no meaning. (See also Exs. 20–33 below.) In all such cases, we may disregard those portions of the curve lying outside the range under consideration.

4. Classification of functions. All functions are classed as either *algebraic* or *transcendental*. The algebraic functions are *rational integral functions*, or *polynomials; rational fractions*, or quotients of polynomials; and *irrational functions*, of which the simplest are those formed from rational functions by the extraction of roots. The elementary transcendental functions are *trigonometric* and *inverse* *trigonometric functions; exponential functions*, in which the variable occurs as an exponent; and *logarithms*.

$$Function$$

algebraic · · · · · · · transcendental

rational · · · irrational · · · · · elementary · · · higher

integral · · · fractional · · · trigonometric · · · exponential
inverse trig'c · · · logarithmic

5. One-valued and many-valued functions. When the relation $y = f(x)$ is such that there is only one value of y for each admissible x, then $f(x)$ is said to be a *one-valued* function of x. The equivalent term *single-valued* function is also used. Graphically this means that if the function is defined for $x = a$, the vertical line $x = a$ intersects the curve in one and only one point. See Figs. 1–2.

Frequently, however, the law connecting x and y determines two or more values of y, in general distinct, for each value of x. Say that there are n values of y corresponding to each value of x. It is then possible to group the values of y so as to form n distinct one-valued functions, called the *branches* of the original function. The graph consists of n branches (not necessarily disconnected), each of which is met by the line $x = a$ in exactly one point.

Example: The equation

(1) $y^2 = x, \quad x \geqq 0,$

defines a two-valued function whose branches are

$$y = \sqrt{x}, \quad y = -\sqrt{x}.$$

The graphs of these functions are respectively the upper and lower halves of the parabola (1). See Fig. 3.

When a many-valued function arises, we must as a rule form from it a *one-valued function* by naming the particular branch from which the value of y is to be taken. The reason is easily seen: until this has been done, there is no way to tell which of the several possible values is meant. Again we may use a homely example: if three grades of gasoline are for sale at 32¢, 30¢, 27¢, then the cost C is a three-valued function of the quantity of gasoline Q. The customer must make the function definite (*i.e.*, one-valued) by saying which kind he wants. See Fig. 4.

In the process of forming from a many-valued function a one-valued function, it is sometimes easy to make a mistake by selecting inadvertently *the wrong branch*. Warning will be given concerning the more troublesome functions as need arises, beginning with § 6.

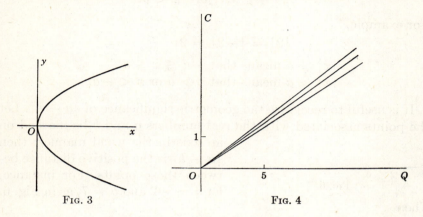

FIG. 3   FIG. 4

6. The square root. While every positive number of course has two square roots, one positive, one negative, by universal agreement the radical sign (or its equivalent the exponent $\frac{1}{2}$) is taken to mean invariably the *positive* root.* For example,

$$\sqrt{3} = 1.732 \cdots, \text{ not } \pm 1.732 \cdots; \qquad \sqrt{4} = 2, \text{ not } \pm 2;$$

$$\sqrt{a^2 - 2ab + b^2} = a - b \quad \text{if} \quad a > b,$$
$$= b - a \quad \text{if} \quad a < b;$$

$$\sqrt{x^2} = x \quad \text{if} \quad x > 0,$$
$$= -x \quad \text{if} \quad x < 0.$$

It follows that the graph of the function

$$y = \sqrt{x^2}$$

is not the 45°-line, but the two "half-lines" of Fig. 5.

FIG. 5

* The point should be emphasized that there is nothing new here; the student has always used these symbols exactly as here demanded. For instance, if $\tan \theta = \sqrt{3}$, we say that $\theta = 60°$ rather than 120°, since $\tan 120° = -\sqrt{3}$. That is, when no sign is written (implying of course the plus sign), the radical denotes invariably a positive number.

To avoid any possible confusion, let us repeat that every positive number has two square roots; but to indicate the negative root, the minus sign must be written: if $x^2 = 4$, then $x = \sqrt{4} = 2$ or $x = -\sqrt{4} = -2$.

7. The absolute-value symbol. The symbol $|x|$ is used to denote the numerical, or absolute, value of x. That is,

$$|x| = x, \quad for \quad x \geqq 0,$$
$$= -x, \quad for \quad x < 0.$$

For example,

$$|2| = |-2| = 2;$$

$$|x| \leqq a \text{ means that } -a \leqq x \leqq a;$$
$$|x| > a \text{ means that } x > a \text{ or } x < -a.$$

It is useful to recognize the geometric significance of $|a - b|$. Let the points associated with the real numbers a and b be marked on an axis in the usual manner; then $|a - b|$ is the positive distance between those points. For instance, let $a = -2$ and $b = 7$, as in Fig. 6.

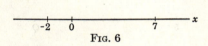
Fig. 6

Then

$$|(-2) - 7| = |-9| = 9,$$

which checks with the distance between the points $x = -2$ and $x = 7$, as shown in Fig. 6.

A fundamental property of the absolute-value symbol is that the absolute value of the sum of two numbers can never exceed the sum of their absolute values,

$$|a + b| \leqq |a| + |b|.$$

To see what lies behind this inequality, it is helpful to recall the geometric interpretation of $|a + b|$ and of $|a|$ and $|b|$.

For the one-valued square root function of § 6, it may be of interest to note that $\sqrt{x^2} = |x|$, for all real x.

EXERCISES

In Exs. 1–10, certain functions are explicitly defined. Perform the indicated operations in each exercise.

1. If $f(x) = x^3 - 2x + 1$, find $f(0)$, $f(1)$, $f(2)$, $f(-2)$, $f(\frac{1}{2})$.

Ans. $f(-2) = -3$.

2. If $f(x) = x^4 - 2x^3 + 3x^2 + 4x - 1$, find $f(0)$, $f(2)$, $f(-2)$, $f(3)$, $f(\frac{1}{2})$.

Ans. $f(3) = 65$, $f(\frac{1}{2}) = \frac{25}{16}$.

3. If $\phi(y) = y(y - 2)^2$, find $\phi(c)$, $\phi(0)$, $\phi(-2)$, $\phi(x + 2)$.

Ans. $\phi(x + 2) = x^2(x + 2)$.

4. If
$$F(a) = \frac{a^2 - a}{a^2 + 1},$$

find $F(0)$, $F(1)$, $F(2)$, $F(\tan x)$.

Ans. $F(\tan x) = \sin x(\sin x - \cos x)$.

5. If
$$f(x) = \frac{x^2 - 4x + 5}{12x - 3x^2},$$

show that $f(4 - x) = f(x)$.

6. If $H(\phi) = \cos \phi + \sin \phi$, find $H(0)$, $H\left(\frac{\pi}{6}\right)$, $H(\pi)$, $H(\pi + \phi)$,
$H(2\pi + \phi)$.   Ans. $H(\pi + \phi) = -H(\phi)$.

7. If $f(x) = \sin 2x$, find $f\left(\frac{\pi}{2}\right)$, $f(\pi - x)$, $f(-x)$, $f(0)$, $f\left(x - \frac{\pi}{2}\right)$.

Ans. $f(\pi - x) = f(-x) = f\left(x - \frac{\pi}{2}\right) = -f(x)$.

8. If $w(x) = \tan x$, find $w\left(\frac{\pi}{6}\right)$, $w\left(\frac{2\pi}{3}\right)$, $w\left(x + \frac{\pi}{2}\right)$, $w(x + \pi)$, $w(2x)$.

9. If $f(\beta) = \sin^2 \beta - \cos \beta$, find $f(\frac{1}{2}\pi)$, $f(\pi)$, $f(0)$, $f(\pi - \beta)$, $f(-\beta)$.
Ans. $f(\pi - \beta) = \sin^2 \beta + \cos \beta$.

10. If $f(x) = \cos x$, find $f(x + \frac{1}{2}\pi)$, $f(\pi - x)$, $f\left(x + \frac{3\pi}{2}\right)$, $f(-x)$.

In Exs. 11–25, express the function by a formula and draw the graph, indicating that portion of the graph which has a meaning in the problem.

11. The amount of $1 at 4% simple interest, as a function of time.
12. The volume of a sphere as a function of the radius.
13. The radius of a sphere as a function of the volume.
14. The volume of a cube as a function of the length of an edge.
15. The surface area of a cube as a function of the length of an edge.
16. The length e of an edge of a cube as a function of the surface area A

of the cube.   Ans. $e = \sqrt{\dfrac{A}{6}}$.

17. The surface area of a cube as a function of the volume of the cube.
18. The present value V of a square tract of land as a function of the length of one side k (in yards), if it will be worth $3 per sq. yd. after being inclosed by a fence costing $2 per yd., with a 12-ft. gate costing $25.
Ans. $V = 3k^2 - 8k - 17$; $k \geqq 4$.

19. Temperature in °F. as a function of temperature in °C., (*a*) in general; (*b*) for a body of water in liquid form.
Ans. (*a*) $\text{F} = \frac{9}{5}\text{C} + 32$, $\text{C} \geqq -273$.

20. The altitude of a right triangle as a function of the base, if the hypotenuse is given.
21. The hypotenuse of a right triangle as a function of the base, if the altitude is given.

22. The base of a right triangle of given altitude, in terms of the hypotenuse.

23. The height of a cylindrical cup as a function of the radius, if 4π sq. in. of sheet metal are used. What kind of curve is this?

24. In Ex. 23, the radius as a function of the height. What kind of curve is this?   *Ans.* $r = -h + \sqrt{h^2 + 4}.$

25. The current I from a battery as a function of the external resistance R, the electromotive force E and internal resistance r being constant. (Current equals electromotive force divided by the sum of the two resistances.)

26. In Ex. 25, express R as a function of I, and draw the curve. How does this compare with the graph of I?

27. A man drives from Detroit to Chicago, say 300 mi., at an average speed of 60 mi. per hr., stops 1 hr. in Chicago, and returns at a speed of 50 mi. per hr. Neglecting variations of speed en route, write formulas expressing x (distance from Detroit) as a function of t, and draw the graph.

28. In Ex. 27, graph t as a function of x.

29. In Ex. 27, graph the speed v as a function of t.

30. In Ex. 27, graph the speed v as a function of x.

31. An open-top box is made by cutting equal squares of side x out of the corners of a piece of cardboard 6 in. square and turning up the sides (Fig. 7). Plot the volume V as a function of x.

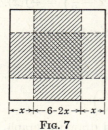

$|\!\leftarrow\!x\!\rightarrow\!|\!\leftarrow\!6-2x\!\rightarrow\!|\!\leftarrow\!x\!\rightarrow\!|$

Fig. 7

Ans. $V = 4x(3 - x)^2;\ 0 \leqq x \leqq 3.$

32. In Ex. 31, find x if $V = 12.5$ cu. in.

Ans. $x_1 = 0.5;\ x_2 = 1.60$ in.

33. Draw the graph of letter postage in the United States. What is the independent variable?

In Exs. 34–39, trace the curve (§ 6).

34. $y = \sqrt{x^2 - 2ax + a^2}.$ **35.** $y = \sqrt{x^4 - 2x^2 + 1}.$

36. $y = \dfrac{x}{\sqrt{x^2}},\ x \neq 0;\ y = 0,\ x = 0.$ **37.** $y = x\sqrt{x^2}.$

38. $y = x - \sqrt{x^2}.$ **39.** $y = \sqrt{x^4 + 2x^2 + 1}.$

40. It is shown in physics that the attraction of a thin spherical shell of radius a upon a particle at distance b from the center is

$$A = \frac{k}{b^2}\left(1 - \frac{a - b}{\sqrt{a^2 - 2ab + b^2}}\right).$$

Show that

$$A = 0, \quad\text{or}\quad A = \frac{2k}{b^2},$$

according as the particle is inside or outside the shell.

41. The sides of three squares are 1, l, x. If the area of the third square equals the difference in area of the other two, graph x as a function of l.

42. Draw the curve (a square) whose equation is $|x| + |y| = 1.$

8. Definition of a limit. Let $f(x)$ be a function of x and let a be constant. If there is a number L such that, *in order to make the value of $f(x)$ as close to L as may be desired, it is sufficient to choose x close enough to a, but different from a,* then we say that the limit of $f(x)$, as x approaches a, is L. We write

$$\lim_{x \to a} f(x) = L,$$

which is read "the limit of $f(x)$, as x approaches a, is L." The same idea is to be conveyed by writing:

$$\text{as } x \to a, \ f(x) \to L,$$

read "as x approaches a, $f(x)$ approaches L."

The above concept of a limit is the mathematical refinement of an intuitive notion which is still of importance in rough everyday use, that the limit L is a number which $f(x)$ approaches as closely as may be desired, as x creeps up on a. The idea of a moving point, x moving toward a, $f(x)$ moving toward L, is a relic of the Newtonian* calculus.

A graphical interpretation of the definition of a limit is helpful. Consider a sketch of the graph of $y = f(x)$ near $x = a$. In Fig. 8 is

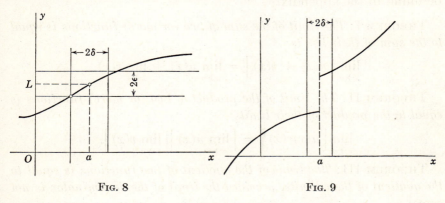

FIG. 8   FIG. 9

shown a representative graph in which $\lim_{x \to a} f(x)$ exists; in Fig. 9 is shown a graph in which $\lim_{x \to a} f(x)$ does not exist.

---

* Sir Isaac Newton (1642–1727) and Gottfried Wilhelm Leibniz (1646–1716), independently of each other, developed the calculus. Before them, the nearest approach to calculus was a set of isolated, partially developed ideas, scattered throughout the mathematical literature.

In Fig. 8, if it is desired to force $f(x)$ to differ from L by less than a prescribed quantity ϵ, $|f(x) - L| < \epsilon$, then all that is needed is to choose x anywhere within a certain amount δ of the value $x = a$, $0 < |x - a| < \delta$. That is, it is possible near $x = a$ on the curve in Fig. 8 to restrict the y variation to as little as may be desired by sufficiently narrowing the vertical band around $x = a$. For the curve of Fig. 8, $\lim_{x \to a} f(x) = L$.

Now consider the situation near $x = a$ for the curve shown in Fig. 9. There, no matter how narrow a band be chosen about $x = a$, the y variation can never be made arbitrarily small. For the curve of Fig. 9, $\lim_{x \to a} f(x)$ does not exist.

The existence or nonexistence of $f(a)$, the value of $f(x)$ at $x = a$, has nothing whatever to do with the existence or nonexistence of the limit of $f(x)$ as x approaches a.

A major difference between calculus and the subjects which usually precede it in the mathematical curriculum is that calculus uses limiting processes.

9. Theorems on limits. We shall need the following theorems on limits. Proofs are omitted, except that a proof of Theorem I can be found in the appendix.

THEOREM I: *The limit of the sum of two (or more) functions is equal to the sum of their limits:*

$$\lim_{x \to a} \Big[u(x) + v(x) \Big] = \lim_{x \to a} u(x) + \lim_{x \to a} v(x).$$

THEOREM II: *The limit of the product of two (or more) functions is equal to the product of their limits:*

$$\lim_{x \to a} \Big[u(x)v(x) \Big] = \Big[\lim_{x \to a} u(x) \Big]\Big[\lim_{x \to a} v(x) \Big].$$

THEOREM III: *The limit of the quotient of two functions is equal to the quotient of their limits, provided the limit of the denominator is not zero:*

$$\lim_{x \to a} \frac{v(x)}{u(x)} = \frac{\lim_{x \to a} v(x)}{\lim_{x \to a} u(x)}, \quad \text{if} \quad \lim_{x \to a} u(x) \neq 0.$$

In these theorems it is assumed that the limits of the two functions exist. However, even though neither function separately approaches a limit, the sum, product, or quotient may do so.

The exceptional case of Theorem III, in which the denominator approaches zero, requires further investigation. Given any quotient $\frac{v}{u}$ in which u approaches 0, two cases arise:

(a) v also approaches zero;

(b) v does not approach zero.

In case (b) the quotient $\frac{v}{u}$ may be made to assume values greater than any assignable constant by taking u sufficiently small; hence the quotient can approach no limit. But consider (a), where the numerator and the denominator both approach zero. Theorem III does not apply, since the ratio of the limits is $\frac{0}{0}$, which has no meaning whatever; nevertheless the *limit of the ratio* may exist, as will appear in many cases in the next few chapters. In fact, it will be found that the entire differential calculus is based on the determination of limits of this type.

Example (a): Evaluate $\lim\limits_{x \to 3} (x^3 + 2x)$.

By Theorem II,
$$\lim_{x \to 3} (x^3) = \lim_{x \to 3} (x \cdot x \cdot x) = 3 \cdot 3 \cdot 3 = 27.$$

By Theorem I,
$$\lim_{x \to 3} (x^3 + 2x) = \lim_{x \to 3} (x^3) + \lim_{x \to 3} (2x) = 27 + 6 = 33.$$

Example (b): Evaluate $\lim\limits_{x \to 2} \dfrac{x^3 - 2x^2 - 3x + 6}{x - 2}$.

By Theorems I and II,
$$\lim_{x \to 2} (x^3 - 2x^2 - 3x + 6) = 8 - 8 - 6 + 6 = 0, \quad \lim_{x \to 2} (x - 2) = 0.$$

Thus we have here the exceptional case (a) under Theorem III. But, for all values of x except $x = 2$,
$$\frac{x^3 - 2x^2 - 3x + 6}{x - 2} \equiv \frac{(x - 2)(x^2 - 3)}{x - 2} \equiv x^2 - 3,$$

so that
$$\lim_{x \to 2} \frac{x^3 - 2x^2 - 3x + 6}{x - 2} = \lim_{x \to 2} (x^2 - 3) = 1.$$

10. Right- and left-hand limits. Once in a while it is convenient to employ a restricted version of limit as described below. We write

(1)
$$\lim_{x \to a^+} f(x) = L,$$

and mean by $x \to a^+$ that each x involved is greater than a. A limit such as that in (1) is called a right-hand limit; the independent variable x approaches a from the right. A left-hand limit,

$$(2) \qquad \lim_{x \to a^-} f(x) = M,$$

with x remaining less than a, is also used.

If the ordinary limit, as defined in § 8, exists, then the right-hand and left-hand limits each exist and all three have the same value. If the right- and left-hand limits exist and have the same value, then the limit itself exists and has that value.

11. Limit of $\frac{\sin \alpha}{\alpha}$ as α approaches zero. The answer to Example (a), § 9, could be obtained by merely replacing x, in the function $x^3 + 2x$, by its limiting value 3. In Example (b), direct substitution produced the meaningless symbol $\frac{0}{0}$, so that a preliminary simplification was necessary, but this simplification was easily discovered. To show that the problem is not always quite so simple, and at the same time to establish a result of great intrinsic importance, we proceed to prove that, *if α is measured in radians,*

$$(1) \qquad \lim_{\alpha \to 0} \frac{\sin \alpha}{\alpha} = 1.$$

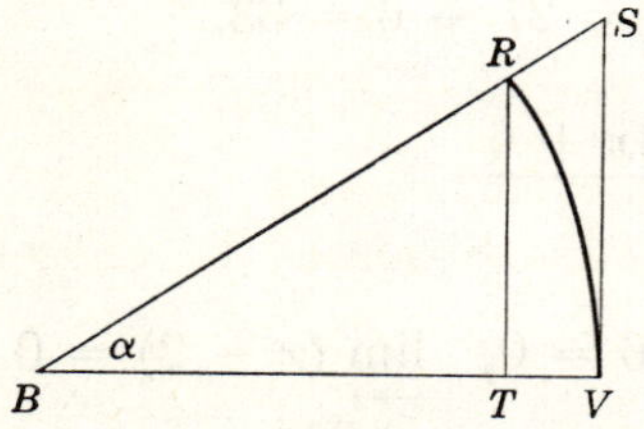

Fig. 10

Consider Fig. 10 in which RV is a circular arc with radius r and with center at B. The angles RTB and SVB are right angles. Since the triangle RTB is contained in the sector RVB, and the sector is in turn contained in the larger triangle SVB, it follows that:

Area of $\triangle RTB <$ Area of sector $RVB <$ Area of $\triangle SVB$.

Since

$$\text{Area of } \triangle RTB = \tfrac{1}{2}\overline{BT} \cdot \overline{RT} = \tfrac{1}{2}r \cos \alpha \cdot r \sin \alpha,$$

$$\text{Area of sector } RVB = \frac{\alpha}{2\pi}(\pi r^2) = \tfrac{1}{2}\alpha r^2,$$

and

$$\text{Area of } \triangle SVB = \tfrac{1}{2}\overline{BV} \cdot \overline{SV} = \tfrac{1}{2}r \cdot r \tan \alpha,$$

we may conclude that, for $0 < \alpha < \dfrac{\pi}{2}$,

$$(2) \qquad \tfrac{1}{2}r^2 \cos \alpha \sin \alpha < \tfrac{1}{2}\alpha r^2 < \tfrac{1}{2}r^2 \tan \alpha.$$

Let us divide each member of the inequalities (2) by the positive quantity $\frac{1}{2}r^2 \sin \alpha$, and thus obtain

$$\cos \alpha < \frac{\alpha}{\sin \alpha} < \frac{1}{\cos \alpha},$$

which can be rewritten, by inverting each member, in the form

$$\frac{1}{\cos \alpha} > \frac{\sin \alpha}{\alpha} > \cos \alpha.$$

As α approaches zero, both $\cos \alpha$ and $\frac{1}{\cos \alpha}$ approach unity. Then $\frac{\sin \alpha}{\alpha}$, which is hemmed in between them, must also approach unity. That is,

$$\lim_{\alpha \to 0^+} \frac{\sin \alpha}{\alpha} = 1.$$

That the left-hand limit also has the value unity follows from the fact that

$$\frac{\sin \alpha}{\alpha} = \frac{\sin (-\alpha)}{(-\alpha)}.$$

This completes the proof of (1).

It should be noted that direct substitution of $\alpha = 0$ in the expression $\frac{\sin \alpha}{\alpha}$ produces the void result $\frac{0}{0}$. Thus the difficulty here arising is the same, in kind, as the one we met in Example (b), § 9.

A variety of other important limits may be evaluated by judicious use of (1).

Example: Evaluate $\lim_{\theta \to 0} \frac{\sin 3\theta}{\theta}$.

Since

$$\frac{\sin 3\theta}{\theta} \equiv 3 \cdot \frac{\sin 3\theta}{3\theta},$$

we need merely to take $\alpha = 3\theta$ in (1):

(3) $$\lim_{\theta \to 0} \frac{\sin 3\theta}{\theta} = 3 \lim_{\theta \to 0} \frac{\sin 3\theta}{3\theta} = 3.$$

Lest anyone should think that (1) justifies us in assigning a value to the nonsense-symbol $\frac{\sin 0}{0}$, we note that the "value" suggested by (1) would be in conflict with (3); see also Exs. 43, 46, 47 below.

12. Continuity. A function $f(x)$ is said to be *continuous* for the value $x = a$ (or at the point $x = a$) if the following three conditions are satisfied:

(a) *The function is defined at $x = a$—i.e., $f(a)$ exists; and*

(b) *the function approaches a limit as x approaches a—i.e.,* $\lim_{x \to a} f(x)$ *exists; and*

(c) *the limit approached is equal to the value of the function at the point—i.e.,*

$$\lim_{x \to a} f(x) = f(a).$$

Example (a): Given $f(x) = x^3 + 2x$, we find [Example (a), § 9]

$$\lim_{x \to 3} f(x) = 33, \qquad f(3) = 27 + 6 = 33.$$

Thus (a), (b), (c) are satisfied, and the function is continuous at $x = 3$. See also Exs. 1–10 below.

Example (b): The function [Example (b), § 9]

$$f(x) = \frac{x^3 - 2x^2 - 3x + 6}{x - 2}$$

is discontinuous at $x = 2$ because $f(2)$ is not defined.

Example (c): The function

$$f(x) = \sqrt{x}$$

is discontinuous at $x = 0$ because $\lim_{x \to 0} \sqrt{x}$ does not exist. In order that the function be continuous, it is necessary that the limit exist for any manner of approach, and in this case approach through negative values is excluded.

A function is said to be *continuous in an interval* of values of the argument if it is continuous at all points of the interval. We note the following important result.*

THEOREM: *As x changes from any value a to any other value b, the function $f(x)$, if continuous in the interval $x = a$ to $x = b$, assumes every value intermediate between $f(a)$ and $f(b)$.*

When a function is continuous throughout an interval, the graph of the function is without any gap or break in that interval: it is

* This theorem, very plausible intuitively, is proved in more advanced texts.

"continuous" in the ordinary sense of the word—as simple examples, an unbroken thread is continuous, or the path of a bullet is continuous.

A fuller discussion of continuity, with examples of the commoner types of discontinuity, will be given in Chapter 7. For the present, it will suffice to say that *all the functions treated in this book are continuous*, except perhaps for certain particular values of the variable, and such values are excluded unless the contrary is indicated. The reason for this restriction will appear in § 13.

EXERCISES

Evaluate the limits in Exs. 1–30.

1. $\lim\limits_{x \to 4} (x^2 - 3x + 1)$.   *Ans.* 5.

2. $\lim\limits_{x \to -2} (x^2 + 4x + 5)$.   *Ans.* 1.

3. $\lim\limits_{z \to 1} (z^3 + 2z^2 - 4z + 1)$.

4. $\lim\limits_{v \to 3} (2y^3 - y + 10)$.

5. $\lim\limits_{t \to 1} \dfrac{t^2 + t + 1}{2t^3 - t + 3}$.   *Ans.* $\frac{3}{4}$.

6. $\lim\limits_{x \to 0} \dfrac{2x^2 - x + 3}{5x^2 + 4x + 6}$.   *Ans.* $\frac{1}{2}$.

7. $\lim\limits_{v \to 2} \dfrac{y^3 + 2y^2 - 4}{y^2 - y}$.

8. $\lim\limits_{x \to -1} \dfrac{2x^3 + 5x^2 - 3}{x^2 - x + 3}$.

9. $\lim\limits_{\phi \to \frac{1}{4}\pi} \dfrac{\sin^2 \phi}{\tan \phi}$.   *Ans.* $\frac{1}{2}$.   **10.** $\lim\limits_{\theta \to \frac{\pi}{6}} \dfrac{\cos 2\theta}{\sin \theta \tan \theta}$.   *Ans.* $\sqrt{3}$.

11. $\lim\limits_{x \to 3} \dfrac{x^2 - 9}{x^2 - x - 6}$.   *Ans.* $\frac{6}{5}$.   **12.** $\lim\limits_{x \to 1} \dfrac{x^2 - 1}{2x^2 + x - 3}$.   *Ans.* $\frac{2}{5}$.

13. $\lim\limits_{x \to -1} \dfrac{3x^2 + x - 2}{2x^2 + x - 1}$.   **14.** $\lim\limits_{x \to 2} \dfrac{3x^2 - 5x - 2}{x^2 - x - 2}$.

15. $\lim\limits_{x \to 2} \dfrac{x^3 - 2x - 4}{2x^3 - 3x^2 - 4}$.   *Ans.* $\frac{5}{6}$.   **16.** $\lim\limits_{v \to 3} \dfrac{y^3 - 10y + 3}{y^3 - 7y - 6}$.   *Ans.* $\frac{17}{20}$.

17. $\lim\limits_{x \to 1} \dfrac{2x^3 - 3x + 1}{2x^3 - 3x^2 + 1}$.   *Ans.* No limit.

18. $\lim\limits_{x \to 2} \dfrac{2x^3 - x^2 - 5x - 2}{3x^3 - 11x^2 + 8x + 4}$.   *Ans.* No limit.

19. $\lim\limits_{\beta \to -2} \dfrac{2\beta^3 + 7\beta^2 + 4\beta - 4}{\beta^3 + 2\beta^2 - 4\beta - 8}$.   *Ans.* $\frac{5}{4}$.

20. $\lim\limits_{\alpha \to \frac{1}{2}} \dfrac{8\alpha^3 - 4\alpha^2 - 2\alpha + 1}{4\alpha^2 - 4\alpha + 1}$.   *Ans.* 2.

21. $\lim\limits_{x \to 2} \dfrac{x^4 - 5x + 6}{2x^3 - 9x^2 + 12x - 4}$.

22. $\lim\limits_{x \to 3} \dfrac{x^3 + x^2 - 4x - 12}{2x^3 - 11x^2 + 12x + 9}$.

23. $\lim\limits_{x \to 0} \dfrac{\sin x}{\tan x}$.   *Ans.* 1. **24.** $\lim\limits_{\theta \to 0} \dfrac{\tan \theta}{\tan 2\theta}$.   *Ans.* $\frac{1}{2}$.

25. $\lim\limits_{\theta \to 0} \dfrac{\sin 2\theta}{\tan \theta}$.   *Ans.* 2. **26.** $\lim\limits_{\theta \to \frac{\pi}{2}} \dfrac{\cos 2\theta}{\tan \theta}$.   *Ans.* 0.

27. $\lim\limits_{x \to \pi} \dfrac{1 + \cos x}{\sin^2 x}$. **28.** $\lim\limits_{x \to 0} \dfrac{\sin^2 x}{1 - \cos x}$.

29. $\lim\limits_{\alpha \to 0} \dfrac{\sin \alpha - \tan \alpha}{\sin^3 \alpha}$. *Ans.* $-\frac{1}{2}$. **30.** $\lim\limits_{\alpha \to 0} \dfrac{\sin 2\alpha \tan \alpha}{1 - \cos \alpha}$. *Ans.* 4.

31. Show that, if $P(x)$ is a polynomial in x,

$$\lim_{x \to a} P(x) = P(a).$$

32. Show that, if $P_1(x)$ and $P_2(x)$ are polynomials,

$$\lim_{x \to a} \frac{P_1(x)}{P_2(x)} = \frac{P_1(a)}{P_2(a)}, \qquad P_2(a) \neq 0.$$

33. Under what circumstances may the limit in Ex. 32 exist when $P_2(a) = 0$? Give examples.

34. Show, by means of an example, that the limit in Ex. 32 does not always exist when $P_1(a) = P_2(a) = 0$.

35. Prove that

$$\lim_{x \to a} \sqrt{u} = \sqrt{\lim_{x \to a} u}, \qquad u > 0.$$

(Put $u = v^2$ and apply Theorem II, § 9.)

36. Prove that, if p and q are integers,

$$\lim_{x \to a} (u^{\frac{p}{q}}) = (\lim_{x \to a} u)^{\frac{p}{q}}, \qquad u > 0.$$

Evaluate the limits in Exs. 37–42.

37. $\lim\limits_{x \to 2^+} \dfrac{\sqrt{x - 2}}{\sqrt{x^2 - 4}}$.   *Ans.* $\frac{1}{2}$. **38.** $\lim\limits_{x \to 3^+} \dfrac{x - 3}{\sqrt{x^2 - 9}}$.   *Ans.* 0.

39. $\lim\limits_{x \to 1} \dfrac{(1 - x^2)^{\frac{1}{3}}}{(1 - x^3)^{\frac{1}{3}}}$.   *Ans.* $(\frac{2}{3})^{\frac{1}{3}}$. **40.** $\lim\limits_{x \to 1^-} \dfrac{\sqrt{1 - x^3}}{\sqrt{1 - x^2}}$.   *Ans.* $\frac{1}{2}\sqrt{6}$.

41. $\lim\limits_{x \to 2^+} \dfrac{(x^4 - 4x^3 + 5x^2 - 4x + 4)^{\frac{1}{4}}}{(x^2 - 3x + 2)^{\frac{1}{2}}}$.   *Ans.* $5^{\frac{1}{4}}$.

42. $\lim\limits_{x \to 1^+} \dfrac{(x^2 + 4x - 5)^{\frac{1}{2}}}{(x^2 - 4x + 3)^{\frac{1}{3}}}$.   *Ans.* 0.

Use the result $\lim\limits_{\alpha \to 0} \left(\dfrac{\sin \alpha}{\alpha}\right) = 1$ to evaluate the limits in Exs. 43–50.

43. $\lim\limits_{\alpha \to 0} \dfrac{\sin k\alpha}{\alpha}$.   *Ans.* k.   44. $\lim\limits_{\theta \to 0} \dfrac{\sin^2 \theta}{\theta}$.   *Ans.* 0.

45. $\lim\limits_{\alpha \to 0} \dfrac{\tan \alpha}{\alpha}$.   *Ans.* 1.   46. $\lim\limits_{\alpha \to 0} \dfrac{\sin \alpha^2}{\alpha}$.   *Ans.* 0.

47. $\lim\limits_{\theta \to 0} \dfrac{\sin \theta}{\theta^2}$.   *Ans.* No limit.   48. $\lim\limits_{x \to 0} x \csc x$.   *Ans.* 1.

49. $\lim\limits_{x \to 0} \dfrac{\tan ax}{\sin bx}$.   *Ans.* $\dfrac{a}{b}$.   50. $\lim\limits_{x \to \frac{1}{2}\pi} \dfrac{\cos x}{x - \frac{1}{2}\pi}$.   *Ans.* -1.

51. Let $\alpha°$ denote the measure in degrees of an angle whose radian measure is α. Use the fact that $\sin \alpha° = \sin \alpha$, and that $\alpha° = \dfrac{180°}{\pi}\alpha$, together with the result of § 11, to show that

$$\lim_{\alpha° \to 0} \frac{\sin \alpha°}{\alpha°} = \frac{\pi}{180°}.$$

CHAPTER 2 THE DERIVATIVE.
SLOPE. RATE OF CHANGE

13. The derivative. Given a continuous function

(1) $$y = f(x),$$

let us choose some fixed value of x, the corresponding value of y being given by (1). Now consider another value of x, differing from the first one by an amount (positive or negative) which we will call the *increment* of x, and will denote by the symbol Δx. For this value of x, y will have a new value, differing from the original by an amount Δy. In other words, *when x changes to the value $x + \Delta x$, y changes to the value $y + \Delta y$*, and we have

$$y + \Delta y = f(x + \Delta x),$$
(2) $$\Delta y = f(x + \Delta x) - f(x).$$

Now let us form the ratio $\frac{\Delta y}{\Delta x}$, and investigate the behavior of this ratio when Δx approaches zero. Since $f(x)$ is continuous, the Δy of equation (2) also approaches zero. We have found that when both numerator and denominator of a fraction approach zero, the fraction itself may, or may not, approach a limit. In Fig. 11, let the curve AB represent the graph of the given function. The ratio $\frac{\Delta y}{\Delta x}$ is the slope of the line joining the points $P : (x, y)$ and $P' : (x + \Delta x, y + \Delta y)$. As Δx approaches zero, P' approaches P along the curve, and in all ordinary cases the line PP' approaches a certain straight line (PT in the figure) as a limiting position. That is, for a sufficiently well-behaved curve, the ratio $\frac{\Delta y}{\Delta x}$ *approaches a limit,* viz. the slope of the line PT. This limit is called the *derivative* of y with respect to x.

FUNDAMENTAL DEFINITION: *The* **derivative** *of y with respect to x is the limit of the ratio* $\dfrac{\Delta y}{\Delta x}$ *when Δx approaches zero.*

The derivative is designated by the symbol $\dfrac{dy}{dx}$:

$$\frac{dy}{dx} = \lim_{\Delta x \to 0} \frac{\Delta y}{\Delta x} = \lim_{\Delta x \to 0} \frac{f(x + \Delta x) - f(x)}{\Delta x}.$$

Other symbols for the derivative are y', $f'(x)$, $D_x y$, $\dfrac{d}{dx} f(x)$. But since the symbol y' does not explicitly indicate the independent variable, this notation should be used only when no confusion or ambiguity can arise.

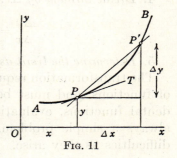

FIG. 11

Functions can be found which, though continuous, do not possess a derivative for any value of x. Such functions, being extremely artificial, are very unlikely to occur in any application, so that their importance is theoretical rather than practical.

The operation of finding the derivative is called **differentiation.** *Only differentiable functions (i.e.,* those having a derivative) *are studied in this book.* When the derivative fails to exist for particular values of x, those values are either excluded or specially investigated. (See § 77.)

We have now listed three fundamental requirements of the calculus. Each function to be studied must, for some range of values of the independent variable, be *continuous, one-valued,* and *differentiable.* These basic properties may be most easily kept in mind by memorizing the initial letters C.O.D.

14. Determination of the derivative. Our first problem is to prove, for the elementary functions, the existence of the derivative — *i.e.,* to prove that when Δx approaches zero, $\dfrac{\Delta y}{\Delta x}$ approaches a definite limit—and at the same time to derive formulas for the derivative in terms of x, for the various functions. This problem will occupy us extensively for some time.

To obtain the derivative of any function, the general process is as follows:

1. *Replace x by $x + \Delta x$, and y by $y + \Delta y$:*

(1) $$y = f(x),$$
(2) $$y + \Delta y = f(x + \Delta x).$$

2. *By subtraction, eliminate y between (1) and (2), thus obtaining a formula for Δy in terms of x and Δx:*

(3) $$\Delta y = f(x + \Delta x) - f(x).$$

3. *By some suitable transformation, throw the right member of (3) into a form which contains Δx explicitly as a factor.*

4. *Divide through by Δx:*

$$\frac{\Delta y}{\Delta x} = \frac{f(x + \Delta x) - f(x)}{\Delta x}.$$

5. *Determine the limit as Δx approaches zero.*

The transformation required in step 3 varies with different classes of functions, and must be discovered by trial. For the transcendental functions, evaluation of the limit in the final step is not always a simple problem. We shall see how to overcome these difficulties as they arise.

15. Derivative of a polynomial. When the given function is a *polynomial*, the formula for Δy will contain certain powers of the binomial $x + \Delta x$. The transformation required in step 3 above is obvious: we merely *expand the powers of $x + \Delta x$ by the Binomial Theorem, and simplify the result.*

Example: Differentiate the function $y = x^3 - 2x$.

1. $y + \Delta y = (x + \Delta x)^3 - 2(x + \Delta x).$
2. $\quad \Delta y = (x + \Delta x)^3 - 2(x + \Delta x) - x^3 + 2x$
3. $\quad\quad = x^3 + 3x^2\,\Delta x + 3x\,\overline{\Delta x}^2 + \overline{\Delta x}^3 - 2x - 2\,\Delta x - x^3 + 2x$

$\quad\quad = 3x^2\,\Delta x + 3x\,\overline{\Delta x}^2 + \overline{\Delta x}^3 - 2\,\Delta x.$

4. $\dfrac{\Delta y}{\Delta x} = 3x^2 + 3x\,\Delta x + \overline{\Delta x}^2 - 2.$
5. $y' = 3x^2 - 2.$ \hfill (Theorems I, II, § 9.)

16. Derivative of a rational algebraic fraction. When the function is a *quotient of two polynomials*, Δy appears in step 2 as the difference of two fractions. The transformation of step 3 is to *reduce the two fractions to a common denominator, and simplify the numerator of the resulting fraction.*

Example: Find the derivative of the function $x = \dfrac{1}{t}$.

1. $x + \Delta x = \dfrac{1}{t + \Delta t}$.

2. $\Delta x = \dfrac{1}{t + \Delta t} - \dfrac{1}{t}$

3. $\quad = \dfrac{t - (t + \Delta t)}{(t + \Delta t)t} = \dfrac{-\Delta t}{(t + \Delta t)t}$.

4. $\dfrac{\Delta x}{\Delta t} = \dfrac{-1}{(t + \Delta t)t}$.

5. $\dfrac{dx}{dt} = -\dfrac{1}{t^2}$.

(Theorem III, § 9.)

17. Derivative of a square root. When the function is the *square root of a polynomial,* Δy comes out as the difference of two radicals. Step 3 then requires that we *multiply and divide by the sum of these radicals,* thus obtaining a fraction with rational numerator, *and simplify the numerator.*

When the function is the *square root of a rational fraction,* a combination of this method with that of § 16 is employed.

Detailed treatment of more complicated functions will be given in later chapters.

Example: Differentiate the function

$$y = \sqrt{x} \qquad\qquad (x > 0).$$

1. $y + \Delta y = \sqrt{x + \Delta x}$.

2. $\Delta y = \sqrt{x + \Delta x} - \sqrt{x}$

3. $\quad = (\sqrt{x + \Delta x} - \sqrt{x}) \cdot \dfrac{\sqrt{x + \Delta x} + \sqrt{x}}{\sqrt{x + \Delta x} + \sqrt{x}}$

$\quad = \dfrac{(x + \Delta x) - x}{\sqrt{x + \Delta x} + \sqrt{x}}$

$\quad = \dfrac{\Delta x}{\sqrt{x + \Delta x} + \sqrt{x}}$.

4. $\dfrac{\Delta y}{\Delta x} = \dfrac{1}{\sqrt{x + \Delta x} + \sqrt{x}}$.

5. $\dfrac{dy}{dx} = \dfrac{1}{2\sqrt{x}}$.

(Ex. 35, p. 16.)

EXERCISES

Differentiate the functions in Exs. 1–28.

1. $y = 3x^2 - x + 1$.   *Ans.* $y' = 6x - 1$.

2. $y = 4 + 2x - x^2$.   *Ans.* $y' = 2 - 2x$.

3. $y = \frac{1}{2}x^2 - 4x$.

4. $x = y^2 + 4y - 1$.   *Ans.* $\dfrac{dx}{dy} = 2y + 4$.

5. $y = x^3 - 2x + 3$.   *Ans.* $y' = 3x^2 - 2$.

6. $x = 2t^3 - t^2 + 5$.   *Ans.* $\dfrac{dx}{dt} = 6t^2 - 2t$.

7. $z = \frac{1}{2}x^4 - 7x + 4$.

8. $y = t^4 - 3t^3$.   *Ans.* $\dfrac{dy}{dt} = 4t^3 - 9t^2$.

9. $y = \frac{1}{2}(x^2 + 1)^2$.   *Ans.* $y' = 2x(x^2 + 1)$.

10. $y = \frac{1}{2}(3x^2 - 1)^2$.   *Ans.* $y' = 6x(3x^2 - 1)$.

11. $y = \dfrac{1}{x + c}$.   *Ans.* $\dfrac{dy}{dx} = \dfrac{-1}{(x + c)^2}$.

12. $y = \dfrac{1}{3 - x}$.   *Ans.* $\dfrac{dy}{dx} = \dfrac{1}{(3 - x)^2}$.

13. $x = \dfrac{3t}{t + 2}$.

14. $x = \dfrac{y}{4 - y}$.

15. $y = 1 + 3x - \dfrac{1}{x}$.   *Ans.* $y' = 3 + \dfrac{1}{x^2}$.

16. $y = \dfrac{2x - 1}{3x + 4}$.   *Ans.* $\dfrac{dy}{dx} = \dfrac{11}{(3x + 4)^2}$.

17. $y = \dfrac{1}{x^2}$.   *Ans.* $\dfrac{dy}{dx} = \dfrac{-2}{x^3}$.

18. $v = \dfrac{2}{t^3}$.   *Ans.* $\dfrac{dv}{dt} = \dfrac{-6}{t^4}$.

19. $y = \sqrt{x + 4}$.   *Ans.* $\dfrac{dy}{dx} = \dfrac{1}{2\sqrt{x + 4}}$.

20. $y = \sqrt{3 - 4x}$.   *Ans.* $\dfrac{dy}{dx} = \dfrac{-2}{\sqrt{3 - 4x}}$.

21. $y = \sqrt{a^2 - x^2}$.   *Ans.* $\dfrac{dy}{dx} = \dfrac{-x}{\sqrt{a^2 - x^2}}$.

22. $u = \sqrt{a^2 + y^2}$.   *Ans.* $\dfrac{du}{dy} = \dfrac{y}{\sqrt{a^2 + y^2}}$.

23. $y = 2x + \sqrt{x}$.   *Ans.* $y' = 2 + \dfrac{1}{2\sqrt{x}}$.

24. $x = t^2 - \sqrt{t}.$ *Ans.* $x' = 2t - \dfrac{1}{2\sqrt{t}}.$

25. $y = \dfrac{1}{\sqrt{x}}.$ *Ans.* $\dfrac{dy}{dx} = \dfrac{-1}{2x^{\frac{3}{2}}}.$

26. $u = t^{\frac{3}{2}}.$ *Ans.* $\dfrac{du}{dt} = \dfrac{3}{2}t^{\frac{1}{2}}.$

27. $y = \dfrac{1}{\sqrt{x+3}}.$ *Ans.* $\dfrac{dy}{dx} = \dfrac{-1}{2(x+3)^{\frac{3}{2}}}.$

28. $y = x\sqrt{x+1}.$ *Ans.* $\dfrac{dy}{dx} = \dfrac{3x+2}{2\sqrt{x+1}}.$

29. For the function $y = \sqrt{3 - 4x}$, show that the derivative does not exist at the point $x = \frac{3}{4}$. (Ex. 20.)

30. For the function $u = t^{\frac{3}{2}}$, show that the derivative does not exist at the point $t = 0$. (Ex. 26.)

18. Tangents to plane curves. A straight line that intersects a curve in two or more distinct points is called a *secant*.

Let P be a fixed point of a plane curve, and P' a neighboring point. If P' be made to approach P along the curve, the secant PP' approaches, in general, a definite limiting position, PT in Fig. 12. If the secant line has such a limiting position, then the straight line which is that limit, PT in Fig. 12, is called the *tangent to the curve at P*, or is said to *touch the curve at P*. The point P is the *point of contact*.

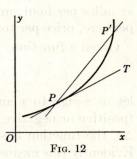
FIG. 12

The slope of the tangent to the curve at any point is called simply the *slope of the curve* at that point. When P' approaches P, the slope of the secant *approaches as its limit the slope of the curve*.

19. Derivative interpreted as slope. In Fig. 11, the slope of the secant PP' is $\dfrac{\Delta y}{\Delta x}$. As Δx approaches zero, P' approaches P along the curve, so that by § 18 the slope of the secant approaches as its limit the slope of the curve at P. But this limit has been defined as the derivative of y with respect to x.

THEOREM: *The derivative of a function is identical with the slope of the graph.*

More explicitly, this means that if, in the formula for y', we substitute any given value of x, the *number* thus obtained is the slope of the curve at the point whose abscissa is the given x.

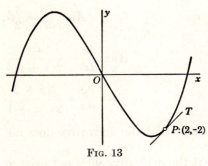

FIG. 13

Example: Find the slope of the curve $y = \frac{1}{4}x^3 - 2x$ at the point P : $(2, -2)$.

By the method of § 15, the derivative is

$$y' = \tfrac{3}{4}x^2 - 2.$$

When $x = 2$, this takes the value

$$y' = 1,$$

which is the slope at the given point (slope of the tangent PT, Fig. 13).

20. Rate of change. The idea of *rate of change* of a function occurs constantly in everyday experience. Such familiar expressions as miles per hour, miles per gallon, pressure per square inch, value per acre, price per ton, all represent rates.

Given a function

$$y = f(x),$$

let us assign to x an arbitrary increment Δx, thus causing in y a (positive or negative) change Δy. When Δy is merely *proportional to* Δx, the function is said to change *uniformly*, or *at a uniform rate*. Evidently this means that the change in y, corresponding to a given change in x, will always be the same regardless of the value of x. In such cases the rate is the change in the function divided by the change in the argument:

$$\frac{\Delta y}{\Delta x} = m,$$

where m is a constant. The graph of the function is a straight line of slope m:

$$y = mx + k.$$

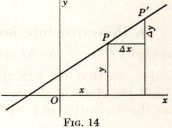

FIG. 14

Frequently, however, the function does not change in this way. Both cases are illustrated below.

Example (a): When a sum of money is placed at simple interest, the increase in the amount, in any interval of time, is proportional to the length of the interval. But at compound interest, the amount increases more and more rapidly as time goes on.

Example (b): When a tank is kept filled, water runs out with constant velocity through a hole in the bottom. But if there is no influx of water, the velocity of escape diminishes as the level falls.

Now, when the function does not vary uniformly, the ratio $\dfrac{\Delta y}{\Delta x}$ is merely the *average* rate of change over the interval Δx. If we let Δx approach zero, this ratio in general approaches a definite limiting value, which is defined as the *rate of change of y corresponding to the given value of x*, or the *instantaneous rate:*

$$\frac{dy}{dx} = \lim_{\Delta x \to 0} \frac{\Delta y}{\Delta x} = \textit{rate of change of y with respect to x.}$$

We might point out that, in order to understand and appreciate these ideas, nothing more than ordinary experience is needed. As an illustration, suppose that two posts, at a measured distance apart, are set up beside a highway, and that a car is driven past them. Let Δx be the distance between the posts, and Δt the time required to pass. Then, if the car travels at a uniform speed, that speed is merely $\dfrac{\Delta x}{\Delta t}$. But if the speed is variable, this ratio is the *average* speed. If we wish to know the speed at a particular instant, say when passing the first post, common sense would suggest that the posts be placed close together. For then Δt will be small, and there will not be time for the speed to change a great deal, so that the average will be nearly equal to the instantaneous speed. While in practice, of course, this process could not be pushed beyond a certain point, it is clear that our ordinary idea of instantaneous speed is expressed exactly by $\dfrac{dx}{dt}$, the *limit* of $\dfrac{\Delta x}{\Delta t}$ as Δt approaches zero.

21. Derivative interpreted as a rate. Comparing the definitions of derivative (§ 13) and rate of change (§ 20), we have another fundamental relation as expressed in the theorem below.

THEOREM: *The derivative of a function is identical with its rate of change.*

Thus in our future work it must always be borne in mind that the three quantities—derivative, slope of graph, rate of change—are all equal to each other.

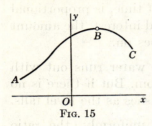

FIG. 15

It is geometrically evident that when the slope of a curve is positive (as on the arc AB), the ordinate y is increasing (as x increases); when the slope is negative (as on BC), the ordinate is decreasing. This merely says that a function increases or decreases according as its rate of change is positive or negative.

Example (a): Find the rate at which the reciprocal of a number changes as the number increases.

Let n equal the number, r its reciprocal:

$$r = \frac{1}{n}.$$

By the method of § 16 (or directly from the example of that section) we find

$$\frac{dr}{dn} = -\frac{1}{n^2}.$$

At the instant, say, when n passes through the value 2, the reciprocal is diminishing one-fourth as fast as the number is increasing.

Example (b): The surface area of a sphere, initially zero, increases uniformly at the rate of 4 sq. in. per sec. Find the rate at which the radius is increasing at the end of 2 sec.

Let: t = time (sec.),
     r = radius of sphere (in.),
     S = surface area (sq. in.).

Since S is increasing at a constant rate, S is proportional to the elapsed time; indeed,

$$S = 4t.$$

But also, $S = 4\pi r^2$, so that $4t = 4\pi r^2$, from which it follows that

$$r = \frac{\sqrt{t}}{\sqrt{\pi}}.$$

By the method of § 17, we find

$$\frac{dr}{dt} = \frac{1}{2\sqrt{\pi} \cdot \sqrt{t}}.$$

When $t = 2$,

$$\frac{dr}{dt} = \frac{1}{2\sqrt{2\pi}} = 0.20 \text{ in. per sec.}$$

EXERCISES

In Exs. 1–10, find the slope of the curve at the given point.

1. $y = x^2 - 4x$, $(3, -3)$.   *Ans.* 2.
2. $y = 1 - 2x^2$, $(1, -1)$.   *Ans.* -4.
3. $y = 2x^3 + x$, $(1, 3)$.   *Ans.* 7.
4. $y = x^3 - x^2$, $(1, 0)$.   *Ans.* 1.

5. $y = \dfrac{1}{x^2}$, $(1, 1)$.   *Ans.* -2.   6. $y = \dfrac{1}{x + 1}$, $(1, \frac{1}{2})$. *Ans.* $-\frac{1}{4}$.

7. $y^2 = 4x$, $(1, -2)$.   *Ans.* -1.
8. $y^2 = x - 4$, $(5, 1)$.   *Ans.* $\frac{1}{2}$.
9. $y^2 = 2x + 1$, $(4, 3)$.   *Ans.* $\frac{1}{3}$.
10. $y^2 = 6x - 2$, $(1, -2)$.   *Ans.* $-\frac{3}{2}$.

11. The dimensions of a box are b, $b + 1$, $b + 3$. Find how fast the total surface area A increases as b increases.   *Ans.* $\dfrac{dA}{db} = 12b + 16$.

12. For the box of Ex. 11, find how fast the volume increases as b increases.

13. Find how fast (a) the circumference, (b) the area, of a circle increases when the radius increases.

14. Find how fast (a) the volume, (b) the surface area, (c) the diagonal, of a cube increases when the length of the edge increases.

15. Find how fast (a) the volume, (b) the surface area, of a sphere increases as the radius increases.

16. The radius of a sphere, initially zero, increases at the rate of 3 ft. per sec. Find how fast the volume is increasing after $\frac{1}{2}$ sec.
Ans. 27π cu. ft. per sec.

17. The base of a box is a square of side l; the volume V is constant. How fast does l change as the depth h changes?   *Ans.* $\dfrac{dl}{dh} = -\dfrac{V^{\frac{1}{2}}}{2h^{\frac{3}{2}}}$.

18. A right circular cylinder has a fixed height of 4 units. Find the rate of change of its volume V with respect to the radius r of its base.
Ans. $\dfrac{dV}{dr} = 8\pi r$.

19. In Ex. 18, find the rate of change of the total surface area A with respect to r.   *Ans.* $\dfrac{dA}{dr} = 4\pi(r + 2)$.

CHAPTER 3 ALGEBRAIC FUNCTIONS

22. Introduction. In this and later chapters (8–10) we develop certain *standard formulas* by means of which any elementary function may be differentiated. The use of these formulas obviates the necessity of evaluating a special limit in every problem, thus effecting a great saving of time.

At present we confine our attention to algebraic functions. However, the formulas of §§ 24, 26 are direct consequences of the definition of the derivative, and are valid for all functions that are *continuous*, *one-valued*, and *differentiable;* see §§ 12, 5, 13.

23. Derivative of a constant. We note first that *the derivative of a constant is zero:*

(1)
$$\frac{dc}{dx} = 0.$$

This result appears geometrically from the fact that the curve $y = c$ is a straight line parallel to Ox, so that the slope is everywhere zero. Likewise, since a constant never changes in value, its rate of change is always zero. Formally, if $y = c$, then $y + \Delta y = c$, and hence

$$\Delta y = 0, \qquad \frac{\Delta y}{\Delta x} = 0,$$

$$\frac{dy}{dx} = \lim_{\Delta x \to 0} \frac{\Delta y}{\Delta x} = 0.$$

24. Derivative of a sum; a product; a quotient. If u and v are functions of x, the following formulas are true by the definition of the derivative (see proofs below):

(2)
$$\frac{d}{dx}(u + v) = \frac{du}{dx} + \frac{dv}{dx},$$

(3)
$$\frac{d}{dx}(uv) = u\,\frac{dv}{dx} + v\,\frac{du}{dx},$$

(4)
$$\frac{d}{dx}\left(\frac{u}{v}\right) = \frac{v\,\dfrac{du}{dx} - u\,\dfrac{dv}{dx}}{v^2}.$$

These formulas may be stated in words as follows:

(2) *The derivative of the sum of two functions is equal to the sum of their derivatives.*

(3) *The derivative of the product of two functions is equal to the first function times the derivative of the second plus the second times the derivative of the first.*

(4) *The derivative of the quotient of two functions is equal to the denominator times the derivative of the numerator minus the numerator times the derivative of the denominator, all divided by the square of the denominator.*

Proof of (2): Let x assume an increment Δx, and denote by Δu and Δv the corresponding increments of u and v. Then

$$y = u + v,$$
$$y + \Delta y = u + \Delta u + v + \Delta v,$$
$$\Delta y = \Delta u + \Delta v,$$
$$\frac{\Delta y}{\Delta x} = \frac{\Delta u}{\Delta x} + \frac{\Delta v}{\Delta x},$$
$$\frac{dy}{dx} = \lim_{\Delta x \to 0} \frac{\Delta y}{\Delta x} = \frac{du}{dx} + \frac{dv}{dx}.$$

Proof of (3):

$$y = uv,$$
$$y + \Delta y = (u + \Delta u)(v + \Delta v),$$
$$\Delta y = u\,\Delta v + v\,\Delta u + \Delta u\,\Delta v,$$
$$\frac{\Delta y}{\Delta x} = u\,\frac{\Delta v}{\Delta x} + v\,\frac{\Delta u}{\Delta x} + \Delta u\,\frac{\Delta v}{\Delta x},$$
$$\frac{dy}{dx} = \lim_{\Delta x \to 0} \frac{\Delta y}{\Delta x} = u\,\frac{dv}{dx} + v\,\frac{du}{dx}.$$

Proof of (4):

$$y = \frac{u}{v},$$
$$y + \Delta y = \frac{u + \Delta u}{v + \Delta v},$$

$$\Delta y = \frac{u + \Delta u}{v + \Delta v} - \frac{u}{v} = \frac{uv + v\,\Delta u - uv - u\,\Delta v}{(v + \Delta v)v},$$

$$\frac{\Delta y}{\Delta x} = \frac{v\dfrac{\Delta u}{\Delta x} - u\dfrac{\Delta v}{\Delta x}}{(v + \Delta v)v},$$

$$\frac{dy}{dx} = \lim_{\Delta x \to 0} \frac{\Delta y}{\Delta x} = \frac{v\dfrac{du}{dx} - u\dfrac{dv}{dx}}{v^2}.$$

Formulas (2) and (3) can be extended to the case where n functions are involved. For three functions, (3) becomes

$$\frac{d}{dx}uvw = vw\frac{du}{dx} + wu\frac{dv}{dx} + uv\frac{dw}{dx}$$

In the special case when $u = c$, a constant, (3) and (4) become

(3′)
$$\frac{d}{dx}cv = c\frac{dv}{dx},$$

(4′)
$$\frac{d}{dx}\frac{c}{v} = -\frac{c\dfrac{dv}{dx}}{v^2}.$$

All the formulas appearing in heavy type should be carefully memorized, preferably in words.

25. Derivative of x^n. If

$$y = x^n,$$

then

(1)
$$\frac{dy}{dx} = nx^{n-1}.$$

When n is a positive integer, this formula may be established as follows:

$$y + \Delta y = (x + \Delta x)^n$$

$$= x^n + nx^{n-1}\,\Delta x + \frac{n(n-1)}{2!}x^{n-2}\,\overline{\Delta x}^2 + \cdots + \overline{\Delta x}^n,$$

$$\Delta y = nx^{n-1}\,\Delta x + \frac{n(n-1)}{2!}x^{n-2}\,\overline{\Delta x}^2 + \cdots + \overline{\Delta x}^n,$$

$$\frac{\Delta y}{\Delta x} = nx^{n-1} + \frac{n(n-1)}{2!}x^{n-2}\,\Delta x + \cdots + \overline{\Delta x}^{n-1},$$

$$\frac{dy}{dx} = \lim_{\Delta x \to 0}\frac{\Delta y}{\Delta x} = nx^{n-1}.$$

In particular, if $n = 1$, *i.e.*, if $y = x$,

$$\frac{dx}{dx} = 1.$$

Although the above proof is valid only for positive integral values of n, formula (1) is true for all values of the exponent. The general proof will be given later; meanwhile the truth of the statement will be assumed.

Example (*a*): The derivative of

$$y = 2x^3 - 5x^2 + 3x + 2$$

is

$$y' = 6x^2 - 10x + 3.$$

Example (*b*): The derivative of

$$y = \frac{x^2 + 1}{4x + 3}$$

is

$$y' = \frac{(4x + 3)2x - (x^2 + 1)4}{(4x + 3)^2}$$
$$= \frac{4x^2 + 6x - 4}{(4x + 3)^2}.$$

Example (*c*): To differentiate

$$y = \frac{1}{\sqrt{x}},$$

we write

$$y = x^{-\frac{1}{2}},$$

whence

$$\frac{dy}{dx} = -\frac{1}{2}x^{-\frac{3}{2}} = \frac{-1}{2x^{\frac{3}{2}}}.$$

EXERCISES

Differentiate the functions in Exs. 1–28.

1. $y = x^3 - 6x + 2$.

2. $y = x^4 + 2x^3 - x + 1$.

3. $y = 3x^2 - x^4 - 3x^5$.

4. $y = 4 - 2x + x^3 - 2x^6$.

5. $y = 2x^{-1} - 3x^{-2}$.

    Ans. $y' = -2x^{-2} + 6x^{-3}$.

6. $y = 4x^{-2} + x^{-3}$.

    Ans. $y' = -8x^{-3} - 3x^{-4}$.

7. $y = \frac{2}{t^2} - \frac{1}{t^4}$. See Ex. 5.

    Ans. $\frac{dy}{dt} = -\frac{4}{t^3} + \frac{4}{t^5}$.

8. $x = \frac{1}{t} - \frac{3}{t^2}$. See Ex. 5.

    Ans. $\frac{dx}{dt} = -\frac{1}{t^2} + \frac{6}{t^3}$.

9. $z = \dfrac{1}{5} + \dfrac{2x}{7} - \dfrac{x^2}{4}.$ *Ans.* $\dfrac{dz}{dx} = \dfrac{2}{7} - \dfrac{x}{2}.$

10. $x = \dfrac{3}{4} - \dfrac{y^2}{3} + \dfrac{2y^3}{5}.$ *Ans.* $\dfrac{dx}{dy} = -\dfrac{2y}{3} + \dfrac{6y^2}{5}.$

11. $y = x^{\frac{1}{2}} - x^{-\frac{3}{2}}.$ **12.** $y = x^{-\frac{1}{2}} - x^{\frac{1}{2}}.$

13. $x = \sqrt{t} - 4\sqrt{t^3}.$ **14.** $x = t\sqrt{t} - \dfrac{2}{\sqrt{t}}.$

15. $y = 2x^{\frac{1}{3}} + x^2.$ **16.** $y = 4 - x^{-\frac{3}{4}}.$

17. $y = (1 - x^2)(2 + 3x).$

18. $y = (t^3 + 2)(t^2 - t + 1).$ *Ans.* $\dfrac{dy}{dt} = 5t^4 - 4t^3 + 3t^2 + 4t - 2.$

19. $y = \dfrac{1}{2 - 3x}.$ Use (4′), § 24.   *Ans.* $y' = \dfrac{3}{(2 - 3x)^2}.$

20. $y = \dfrac{4}{1 + 2x}.$ Use (4′), § 24.   *Ans.* $y' = \dfrac{-8}{(1 + 2x)^2}.$

21. $z = \dfrac{3}{t^2 - 1}.$ *Ans.* $\dfrac{dz}{dt} = \dfrac{-6t}{(t^2 - 1)^2}.$

22. $x = \dfrac{5}{1 - 3t^2}.$ *Ans.* $\dfrac{dx}{dt} = \dfrac{30t}{(1 - 3t^2)^2}.$

23. $y = \dfrac{x^2}{1 - x}.$ *Ans.* $\dfrac{dy}{dx} = \dfrac{2x - x^2}{(1 - x)^2}.$

24. $y = \dfrac{2x}{x^2 + 1}.$ *Ans.* $\dfrac{dy}{dx} = \dfrac{2(1 - x^2)}{(x^2 + 1)^2}.$

25. $f(x) = \dfrac{x^2 - 1}{x^2 + 1}.$ *Ans.* $f'(x) = \dfrac{4x}{(x^2 + 1)^2}.$

26. $F(t) = \dfrac{1 + 2t}{4 - t^2}.$ *Ans.* $F'(t) = \dfrac{2(4 + t + t^2)}{(4 - t^2)^2}.$

27. $\phi(t) = \dfrac{t^2 + 2t}{1 - 2t}.$ *Ans.* $\phi'(t) = \dfrac{2(1 + t - t^2)}{(1 - 2t)^2}.$

28. $f(v) = \dfrac{v^2 + v - 1}{v^2 - v}.$ *Ans.* $f'(v) = \dfrac{-2v^2 + 2v - 1}{(v^2 - v)^2}.$

In Exs. 29–34, find the slope at the point indicated.

29. $y = x^3 - 4x^2 + 3x + 5,$ at $x = 2.$ *Ans.* $-1.$

30. $y = 1 + 9x - 2x^3,$ at $x = -1.$ *Ans.* $3.$

31. $y = \dfrac{x}{x^2 + 4},$ at $x = 1.$ *Ans.* $\frac{3}{25}.$

32. $y = \dfrac{x - 2}{1 - x^2},$ at $x = 3.$ *Ans.* $-\frac{1}{32}.$

33. $y = x^3 - x^2 + 2,$ where the curve crosses $Ox.$ *Ans.* $5.$

34. $y = x^4 - 3x^3 - x^2 + 13x - 10,$ where the curve crosses $Ox.$

Ans. $-51; 6.$

In Exs. 35–38, find the vertex of the parabola by means of the derivative. Check by completing the square and putting the equation of the parabola in standard form.

35. $y = x^2 + 4x + 2$.   **36.** $y = 3x^2 - 2x + 1$.
37. $3x^2 - 9x + 7y + 5 = 0$.   **38.** $2x^2 + x + 5y + 2 = 0$.

In Exs. 39–46, find the points where the tangent is parallel to Ox.

39. $y = x^3 + 3x^2 + 1$.   *Ans.* $(0, 1)$, $(-2, 5)$.
40. $y = 3x^4 + 4x^3 - 12x^2 + 2$.   *Ans.* $(0, 2)$, $(1, -3)$, $(-2, -30)$.
41. $y = x^4 - 2x^3 - 3x^2 + 4x + 3$.   *Ans.* $(-1, -1)$, $(\frac{1}{2}, \frac{65}{16})$, $(2, -1)$.
42. $5y = x^4 - 14x^2 - 24x + 7$.   *Ans.* $(-2, 3)$, $(-1, \frac{18}{5})$, $(3, -22)$.
43. $y = x^4 + 2x^3 + 8x^2 - 10x + 3$.   *Ans.* $(\frac{1}{2}, \frac{5}{16})$.
44. $y = x^4 + 2x^2 - 40x + 36$.   *Ans.* $(2, -20)$.

45. $y = \dfrac{x + 1}{x^2 + 2x + 5}$.   *Ans.* $(1, \frac{1}{4})$, $(-3, -\frac{1}{4})$.

46. $y = \dfrac{x + 2}{x(x + 3)}$.   *Ans.* None.

47. Find the rate at which the radius r of a sphere increases as the volume V increases.

$$Ans. \quad \frac{dr}{dV} = (4\pi)^{-\frac{1}{3}}(3V)^{-\frac{2}{3}}.$$

48. A body of gas is contained in a vessel of volume v; the pressure is given by the formula $p = \dfrac{k}{v}$. Find the rate at which pressure increases with decreasing volume, at the instant when $v = 3$.

49. Suppose the container of Ex. 48 is a cube with its edge c units in length. Find the rate at which the pressure p varies with varying edge length, when $c = 2$ units. $Ans.\ \dfrac{dp}{dc} = -\dfrac{3k}{16}.$

50. Use (4′) of § 24 to prove that (1) of § 25 holds for negative integral values of n.

51. The force between two magnetic poles at a distance r apart is $F = \dfrac{k}{r^2}$. Find the rate at which F changes with respect to r, when $r = 4$.

26. Derivative of a function of a function. Given y as a function of x, it is frequently convenient to think of y as a function of an auxiliary variable u, where u in turn is a function of x. For example, the formula of § 25 would fail entirely to find the derivative of such a function as

$$y = \sqrt{x^2 + 1};$$

it will appear presently that the difficulty may be overcome by merely putting $y = \sqrt{u}$, where $u = x^2 + 1$.

Let
$$y = f(u), \text{ where } u = \phi(x).$$

Assign to x an increment Δx, and denote by Δu and Δy the corresponding changes in u and y. Then

$$\frac{\Delta y}{\Delta x} = \frac{\Delta y}{\Delta u} \cdot \frac{\Delta u}{\Delta x},$$

and when Δx approaches zero, we find (assuming that the limits of all three ratios exist)

$$\lim_{\Delta x \to 0} \frac{\Delta y}{\Delta x} = \lim_{\Delta x \to 0} \frac{\Delta y}{\Delta u} \cdot \lim_{\Delta x \to 0} \frac{\Delta u}{\Delta x},$$

or

(5)
$$\frac{dy}{dx} = \frac{dy}{du} \cdot \frac{du}{dx}.$$

Two other formulas follow very quickly. Writing (5) in the form

$$\frac{dy}{du} = \frac{\dfrac{dy}{dx}}{\dfrac{du}{dx}},$$

let us interchange u and x:

(5′)
$$\frac{dy}{dx} = \frac{\dfrac{dy}{du}}{\dfrac{dx}{du}} \qquad \left(\frac{dx}{du} \neq 0\right).$$

In (5′), put $u = y$:

(5″)
$$\frac{dy}{dx} = \frac{1}{\dfrac{dx}{dy}} \qquad \left(\frac{dx}{dy} \neq 0\right).$$

Formula (5″) says that the rate of change of y with respect to x and the rate of change of x with respect to y are reciprocals. This fact appears constantly in ordinary experience. Say that a car is traveling at a speed (time-rate of change of distance) of 30 mi. per hr. Then time is elapsing at a rate (distance-rate of change of time) of 2 min. ($\frac{1}{30}$ hr.) per mile:

$$\frac{dx}{dt} = 30,$$

$$\frac{dt}{dx} = \frac{1}{30}.$$

27. The general power formula. Formula (1) of § 25 enables us to differentiate any power of x. By means of (5), we are able to differentiate *any power of any function of* x. To do this, let

$$y = u^n, \text{ where } u = \phi(x).$$

Then by (1), § 25,

$$\frac{dy}{du} = nu^{n-1},$$

and we have by (5)

(6) $$\frac{d}{dx}u^n = nu^{n-1}\frac{du}{dx}.$$

An important special case of this formula is the case $n = \frac{1}{2}$:

(6′) $$\frac{d}{dx}\sqrt{u} = \frac{\dfrac{du}{dx}}{2\sqrt{u}}.$$

Example (*a*): Find the derivative of

$$y = (3x^2 + 1)^4.$$

This function is of the form u^n, with $u = 3x^2 + 1$, $n = 4$. Hence (6) gives

$$y' = 4(3x^2 + 1)^3 \cdot 6x$$
$$= 24x(3x^2 + 1)^3.$$

Example (*b*): Differentiate the function

$$x = \sqrt{t^2 + 1}.$$

By (6′), we have

$$\frac{dx}{dt} = \frac{2t}{2\sqrt{t^2 + 1}} = \frac{t}{\sqrt{t^2 + 1}}.$$

Example (*c*): Differentiate

$$y = (4x + 1)^2(x^2 - 2)^3.$$

By (3) and (6), we have

$$y' = (4x + 1)^2 3(x^2 - 2)^2 2x + (x^2 - 2)^3 2(4x + 1)4$$
$$= (4x + 1)(x^2 - 2)^2[6(4x + 1)x + 8(x^2 - 2)]$$
$$= (4x + 1)(x^2 - 2)^2(32x^2 + 6x - 16).$$

28. Higher derivatives. The derivative of y with respect to x is itself a function of x, and may in turn be differentiated. The derivative of the first derivative is called the *second derivative*, and is written $\dfrac{d^2y}{dx^2}$; further differentiations give $\dfrac{d^3y}{dx^3}$, $\dfrac{d^4y}{dx^4}$, etc. Other symbols for the higher derivatives are y'', y''', $y^{(4)}$, $\cdots$, and $f''(x)$, $f'''(x)$, $f^{(4)}(x)$, $\cdots$.

Since y'' is the derivative of y', we see by § 21 that *the second derivative of a function is the rate of change of slope of the graph.*

Example: In Example (*b*), § 27,

$$\frac{dx}{dt} = \frac{t}{\sqrt{t^2+1}},$$

so that, by (4),

$$\frac{d^2x}{dt^2} = \frac{\sqrt{t^2+1}\cdot 1 - \dfrac{t\cdot 2t}{2\sqrt{t^2+1}}}{t^2+1}$$

$$= \frac{1}{(t^2+1)^{\frac{3}{2}}}.$$

It is sometimes necessary to express $\dfrac{d^2y}{dx^2}$ in terms of the derivatives of x with respect to y. To do this, let us in (5′), § 26, replace u by y and y by y':

$$(1) \qquad \frac{dy'}{dx} = \frac{\dfrac{dy'}{dy}}{\dfrac{dx}{dy}}.$$

But by (5″),

$$\frac{dy'}{dy} = \frac{d}{dy}\left(\frac{1}{\dfrac{dx}{dy}}\right) = -\frac{\dfrac{d^2x}{dy^2}}{\left(\dfrac{dx}{dy}\right)^2}.$$

Substituting in (1), we find

$$(2) \qquad \frac{d^2y}{dx^2} = -\frac{\dfrac{d^2x}{dy^2}}{\left(\dfrac{dx}{dy}\right)^3} \qquad \left(\frac{dx}{dy} \neq 0\right).$$

EXERCISES

In Exs. 1–40, find the first derivative.

1. $y = (1 + 2x)^3$. *Ans.* $y' = 6(1 + 2x)^2$.

2. $y = (2 - x)^4$. *Ans.* $y' = -4(2 - x)^3$.

3. $y = (4 - 3t)^5$. *Ans.* $\dfrac{dy}{dt} = -15(4 - 3t)^4$.

4. $x = \frac{1}{2}(5t - 1)^8$. *Ans.* $\dfrac{dx}{dt} = 20(5t - 1)^7$.

5. $y = (a - x)^{-2}$. *Ans.* $\dfrac{dy}{dx} = 2(a - x)^{-3}$.

6. $x = 4\sqrt{3 + y}$. *Ans.* $\dfrac{dx}{dy} = \dfrac{2}{\sqrt{3 + y}}$.

7. $y = 6(1 - 3x)^{\frac{3}{2}}$. *Ans.* $y' = -27(1 - 3x)^{\frac{1}{2}}$.

8. $y = \dfrac{2}{(1 + 3x)^2}$. *Ans.* $y' = \dfrac{-12}{(1 + 3x)^3}$.

9. $a^2 y = (x^2 + a^2)^{\frac{3}{2}}$. *Ans.* $a^2 \dfrac{dy}{dx} = 3x(x^2 + a^2)^{\frac{1}{2}}$.

10. $x = \sqrt{2ay - y^2}$. *Ans.* $\dfrac{dx}{dy} = \dfrac{a - y}{\sqrt{2ay - y^2}}$.

11. $x = (16 - t^4)^{-\frac{3}{2}}$. *Ans.* $\dfrac{dx}{dt} = 6t^3(16 - t^4)^{-\frac{5}{2}}$.

12. $u = (v^4 + 3v^2 - 1)^{\frac{5}{2}}$. *Ans.* $\dfrac{du}{dv} = 5v(2v^2 + 3)(v^4 + 3v^2 - 1)^{\frac{3}{2}}$.

13. $y = x^3(x + 1)^2$. *Ans.* $y' = x^2(x + 1)(5x + 3)$.

14. $f(x) = x(x^2 - a^2)^{\frac{1}{2}}$. *Ans.* $f'(x) = (2x^2 - a^2)(x^2 - a^2)^{-\frac{1}{2}}$.

15. $f(t) = t^3(t^2 + b^2)^{-\frac{1}{2}}$. *Ans.* $f'(t) = t^2(2t^2 + 3b^2)(t^2 + b^2)^{-\frac{3}{2}}$.

16. $y = \dfrac{(1 + x)^2}{x}$. *Ans.* $y' = \dfrac{x^2 - 1}{x^2}$.

17. $y = \dfrac{(2x + 1)^3}{x^2}$. *Ans.* $y' = 8 - 6x^{-2} - 2x^{-3}$.

18. $y = \dfrac{(x - 2)^3}{x^2}$. Use three methods and check your answers against one another. *Hint:* consider y as a product, as a quotient, or with the binomial expanded.

19. $x = \dfrac{t}{\sqrt{a^2 - t^2}}$. *Ans.* $\dfrac{dx}{dt} = \dfrac{a^2}{(a^2 - t^2)^{\frac{3}{2}}}$.

20. $y = (a^{\frac{2}{3}} - x^{\frac{2}{3}})^{\frac{3}{2}}$. *Ans.* $y' = -x^{-\frac{1}{3}}(a^{\frac{2}{3}} - x^{\frac{2}{3}})^{\frac{1}{2}}$.

21. $y = \dfrac{1}{(3 - 4x)^5}$. *Ans.* $\dfrac{dy}{dx} = \dfrac{20}{(3 - 4x)^6}$.

22. $\phi = \dfrac{7}{\sqrt{9 + t^4}}.$

$Ans. \dfrac{d\phi}{dt} = \dfrac{-14t^3}{(9 + t^4)^{\frac{3}{2}}}.$

23. $y = x\sqrt{(a^2 - x^2)^3}.$ $Ans. \; y' = (a^2 - 4x^2)\sqrt{a^2 - x^2}.$

24. $y = \dfrac{\sqrt{a^2 + x^2}}{x}.$ $Ans. \; y' = -a^2 x^{-2}(a^2 + x^2)^{-\frac{1}{2}}.$

25. $y = (1 + x)^2(2 - x)^3.$ $Ans. \; y' = (1 + x)(2 - x)^2(1 - 5x).$

26. $y = (x^2 + 1)^3(x^2 - 2)^2.$ $Ans. \; y' = 2x(x^2 + 1)^2(x^2 - 2)(5x^2 - 4).$

27. $f(x) = (2 + 3x)^4(5 - 2x)^3.$

$Ans. \; f'(x) = 6(2 + 3x)^3(5 - 2x)^2(8 - 7x).$

28. $\phi(t) = (4 + 3t)^2(2 - 5t)^3.$

$Ans. \; \phi'(t) = -3(4 + 3t)(2 - 5t)^2(16 + 25t).$

29. $y = (2x + 1)^3(x^2 - 1)^{\frac{3}{2}}.$

$Ans. \; y' = 3(2x + 1)^2(x^2 - 1)^{\frac{1}{2}}(4x^2 + x - 2).$

30. $y = (x^2 - 1)^{\frac{1}{2}}(3x - 2)^2.$

$Ans. \; y' = (x^2 - 1)^{-\frac{1}{2}}(3x - 2)(9x^2 - 2x - 6).$

31. $F(y) = \dfrac{(y^2 + 1)^2}{y^2 - 1}.$ $Ans. \; F'(y) = 2y(y^2 + 1)(y^2 - 3)(y^2 - 1)^{-2}.$

32. $\psi(x) = \dfrac{2x}{\sqrt{x + 1}}.$ $Ans. \; \psi'(x) = (x + 2)(x + 1)^{-\frac{3}{2}}.$

33. $y = \dfrac{1}{x^3(x + 2)^2}.$ $Ans. \; y' = -(5x + 6)x^{-4}(x + 2)^{-3}.$

34. $y = \dfrac{1}{(x + 2)^2(2x - 1)^3}.$

$Ans. \; y' = -10(x + 1)(x + 2)^{-3}(2x - 1)^{-4}.$

35. $x = \left(\dfrac{t}{1 + t}\right)^{\frac{1}{2}}.$ $Ans. \; \dfrac{dx}{dt} = \dfrac{1}{2}t^{-\frac{1}{2}}(1 + t)^{-\frac{3}{2}}.$

36. $y = \left(\dfrac{z^3}{a + z}\right)^{\frac{1}{2}}.$ $Ans. \; \dfrac{dy}{dz} = \dfrac{1}{2}(3a + 2z)z^{\frac{1}{2}}(a + z)^{-\frac{3}{2}}.$

37. $y = x^3(x + 1)^2(2x - 3)^2.$

$Ans. \; y' = x^2(x + 1)(2x - 3)(14x + 9)(x - 1).$

38. $z = [1 + (x^2 - 1)^3]^{\frac{1}{2}}.$ $Ans. \; z' = 9x(x^2 - 1)^2\sqrt{1 + (x^2 - 1)^3}.$

39. $f(x) = \sqrt{1 + \sqrt{1 - x}}.$ $Ans. \; f'(x) = \dfrac{-1}{4\sqrt{1 - x}\sqrt{1 + \sqrt{1 - x}}}.$

40. $y = \dfrac{1}{(1 + \sqrt{1 - x})^2}.$ $Ans. \; y' = \dfrac{1}{\sqrt{1 - x}(1 + \sqrt{1 - x})^3}.$

In Exs. 41–44, find the slope of the curve at the given point.

41. $y = (3x + 1)^2, (-1, 4).$ $Ans. \; -12.$

42. $y = \sqrt{25 - x^2}, (3, 4).$ $Ans. \; -0.75.$

43. $y = \dfrac{x}{(x^2 + 1)^2}, \left(1, \dfrac{1}{4}\right).$ $Ans. \; -0.25.$

44. $6y = (2x + 1)^2(x - 3)^3, (1, -12).$ $Ans. \; 2.$

In Exs. 45–49, find the second derivative.

45. $y = x(x + 1)^3$.   *Ans.* $y'' = 6(x + 1)(2x + 1)$.

46. $y = x^2(2x - 1)^2$.   *Ans.* $y'' = 2(24x^2 - 12x + 1)$.

47. $y = \dfrac{-1}{\sqrt{a^2 + x^2}}$.   *Ans.* $y'' = (a^2 - 2x^2)(a^2 + x^2)^{-\frac{5}{2}}$.

48. $x = \dfrac{(1 + t)^2}{t^2}$.   *Ans.* $\dfrac{d^2x}{dt^2} = \dfrac{6}{t^4} + \dfrac{4}{t^3}$.

49. $u = (1 - 3v)^2(2 + v)^3$.   *Ans.* $\dfrac{d^2u}{dv^2} = 6(2 + v)(1 + 36v + 30v^2)$.

50. Find $\dfrac{d^2y}{dx^2}$ from the equation

$$y = \sqrt{1 - 2xt + t^2}.$$

Ans. $\dfrac{d^2y}{dx^2} = -t^2(1 - 2xt + t^2)^{-\frac{3}{2}}$.

51. Find $\dfrac{d^2y}{dt^2}$ from the equation of Ex. 50.

Ans. $\dfrac{d^2y}{dt^2} = (1 - x^2)(1 - 2xt + t^2)^{-\frac{3}{2}}$.

52. For the curve $y = (2x + 1)^3$, find the rate of change of slope at $(1, 27)$.   *Ans.* 72.

53. For the curve $y = \dfrac{(1 + x)^2}{x}$, find the rate of change of slope at $(1, 4)$.
                    Ans. 2.

54. Given any parabola with axis parallel to Oy, show that the rate of change of slope is constant.

55. If $y = x(x + 1)^3$, find y'''.   *Ans.* $y''' = 24x + 18$.

56. If $\phi(x) = \sqrt{ax + b}$, find $\phi^{(4)}(x)$.   *Ans.* $\phi^{(4)}(x) = -\frac{15}{16}a^4(ax + b)^{-\frac{7}{2}}$.

57. If $y = uv$, where u and v are any functions of x, derive the formula $y'' = uv'' + 2u'v' + u''v$. Obtain the formula for y'''.

58. Prove the following result.

THEOREM: *If $f(x)$ contains the factor $(x - a)^n$, then $f'(x)$ contains the factor $(x - a)^{n-1}$, $f''(x)$ contains the factor $(x - a)^{n-2}$; etc.*

29. Implicit functions. In general, an equation of any form involving x and y determines a value (or values) of y corresponding to each value of x, and therefore determines y as a function of x. Hitherto we have been concerned with functions defined *explicitly* by an equation of the form

$$y = f(x).$$

It may happen, however, that x and y are connected by an equation not solved for y; for example,

$$x^3 + y^3 = 3axy.$$

In such a case y is called an *implicit function* of x, and the relation is expressed by writing

$$F(x, y) = 0.$$

The definition becomes explicit if we solve for y; *e.g.*, if

$$x^2 + y^2 = a^2, \text{ then } y = \pm \sqrt{a^2 - x^2}.$$

Frequently, however, it is not desirable to change to the explicit form, even when such a change is feasible.

30. Derivatives in implicit form. To find the derivative of a function defined implicitly, we apply the following procedure.

RULE: *Differentiate each term of the equation*

$$F(x, y) = 0$$

with respect to x, bearing in mind that y is a function of x.

In this connection it must be remembered that, by **(6)**, the derivative of y^n with respect to x is $ny^{n-1}\dfrac{dy}{dx}$.

Example (a): Find y', if

$$x^3 + y^3 - 3axy = 0.$$

Differentiating each term in turn, we have

$$3x^2 + 3y^2y' - 3a(xy' + y) = 0,$$

whence

$$(y^2 - ax)y' + x^2 - ay = 0,$$

$$y' = - \frac{x^2 - ay}{y^2 - ax}.$$

Example (b): Find y'', if $x^2 - y^2 = a^2$.

Differentiating, we get

$$2x - 2yy' = 0,$$

whence

(1) $$y' = \frac{x}{y}.$$

A second differentiation gives

$$y'' = \frac{y - xy'}{y^2},$$

or, after substituting the value of y' from (1),

$$y'' = \frac{y - \dfrac{x^2}{y}}{y^2} = \frac{y^2 - x^2}{y^3};$$

since $x^2 - y^2 = a^2$, this reduces to

$$y'' = -\frac{a^2}{y^3}.$$

31. Parametric equations. Instead of the Cartesian equation of a curve, it is sometimes more convenient to represent the curve by two equations giving x and y in terms of some third variable:

(1) $$x = u(t), \quad y = v(t).$$

The auxiliary variable t is called a *parameter*, and equations (1) are *parametric equations* of the curve. In an application, the parameter may have a geometric or physical meaning, depending on the nature of the problem.

If it happens to be algebraically feasible, we may eliminate the parameter from (1), thus obtaining the Cartesian equation,

(2) $$F(x, y) = 0.$$

But one point is to be noted: due to the form of equations (1) or the physical meaning of the variables involved, the given equations may represent only a portion of the curve (2). This of course is not surprising. From the fact that every (x, y)-pair satisfying (1) also satisfies (2), it does not follow, conversely, that every pair satisfying (2) must satisfy (1).

32. Derivatives in parametric form. Because of algebraic difficulties, it may not be possible to eliminate the parameter from a given pair of parametric equations; or, the resulting Cartesian equation may be so awkward that little can be done with it. One method for obtaining derivatives in terms of the parameter is illustrated below.

Example: Find $\dfrac{dy}{dx}$ and $\dfrac{d^2y}{dx^2}$ from

$$x = t^3 + 2t - 4, \qquad y = t^3 - t + 2.$$

First we obtain the derivatives of x, and of y, with respect to t:

$$\frac{dx}{dt} = 3t^2 + 2, \qquad \frac{dy}{dt} = 3t^2 - 1.$$

Then, by (5′) of § 26, the ratio of these gives the desired first derivative,

(1)
$$\frac{dy}{dx} = \frac{3t^2 - 1}{3t^2 + 2}.$$

Equation (1) exhibits $\frac{dy}{dx}$ in terms of t. We wish to differentiate both members of (1) with respect to x, and t is a function of x. Therefore we need to use the formula for a derivative of a function of a function,

(2)
$$\frac{dF}{dx} = \frac{dF}{dt} \cdot \frac{dt}{dx},$$

which is (5) of § 26, except for changes in notation. Employing the idea in (2) when differentiating the right member of equation (1), we get

(3)
$$\frac{d^2y}{dx^2} = \frac{(3t^2 + 2)(6t) - (3t^2 - 1)(6t)}{(3t^2 + 2)^2} \cdot \frac{dt}{dx}.$$

But $\frac{dt}{dx}$ is the reciprocal of $\frac{dx}{dt}$, as shown in (5″) of § 26. Hence (3) yields

$$\frac{d^2y}{dx^2} = \frac{18t}{(3t^2 + 2)^2} \cdot \frac{1}{3t^2 + 2}$$
$$= \frac{18t}{(3t^2 + 2)^3}.$$

EXERCISES

In Exs. 1–12, find the derivative of y with respect to x.

1. $x^2 + y^2 = a^2$.   Ans. $y' = -\dfrac{x}{y}$.

2. $x^3 - y^3 = a^3$.   Ans. $y' = \dfrac{x^2}{y^2}$.

3. $y^2(x + y) = b^3$.   Ans. $y' = -\dfrac{y}{2x + 3y}$.

4. $4x^2 + y^2 = 4cy$.   Ans. $y' = \dfrac{4x}{2c - y}$.

5. $x^2 + xy + y^2 = 1$.   Ans. $y' = -\dfrac{2x + y}{x + 2y}$.

6. $x^2 - 3xy + y^2 = 6x - 2y$.   Ans. $y' = \dfrac{2x - 3y - 6}{3x - 2y - 2}$.

7. $(x - y)^2 = 2ay$.   Ans. $\dfrac{dy}{dx} = \dfrac{x - y}{x - y + a}$.

8. $(x + y)^2 = 2ax.$ *Ans.* $\dfrac{dy}{dx} = \dfrac{a - x - y}{x + y}.$

9. $x^{\frac{1}{2}} + y^{\frac{1}{2}} = a^{\frac{1}{2}}.$ *Ans.* $y' = -x^{-\frac{1}{2}}y^{\frac{1}{2}}.$

10. $x^{\frac{2}{3}} + y^{\frac{2}{3}} = a^{\frac{2}{3}}.$ *Ans.* $y' = -x^{-\frac{1}{3}}y^{\frac{1}{3}}.$

11. $(x^2 + y^2)^2 = ay^3.$ *Ans.* $\dfrac{dy}{dx} = \dfrac{4x(x^2 + y^2)}{y(3ay - 4x^2 - 4y^2)}.$

12. $(x^2 + y^2)^3 = a^4x^2.$ *Ans.* $\dfrac{dy}{dx} = \dfrac{x[a^4 - 3(x^2 + y^2)^2]}{3y(x^2 + y^2)^2}.$

13. If $x = t^3 - 3t^2$, find $\dfrac{dt}{dx}.$ *Ans.* $\dfrac{dt}{dx} = \dfrac{1}{3t(t - 2)}.$

14. If $y = (x^3 + 1)^2$, find $\dfrac{dx}{dy}.$ *Ans.* $\dfrac{dx}{dy} = \dfrac{1}{6x^2(x^3 + 1)}.$

15. If $z^2 - 2zy + 3y^2 = 4$, find $\dfrac{dz}{dy}.$ *Ans.* $\dfrac{dz}{dy} = \dfrac{z - 3y}{z - y}.$

16. If $4c^2\theta t = (\theta^2 - t^2)^2$ find $\dfrac{d\theta}{dt}.$ *Ans.* $\dfrac{d\theta}{dt} = \dfrac{t\theta^2 - t^3 + c^2\theta}{\theta^3 - t^2\theta - c^2t}.$

17. If $y^2 = 4ax$, find $y''.$ *Ans.* $y'' = \dfrac{-4a^2}{y^3}.$

18. If $x^2 = 4ay$, find $y''.$

19. If $x^2 + y^2 = a^2$, find $y''.$ *Ans.* $y'' = \dfrac{-a^2}{y^3}.$

20. If $x^3 - y^3 = a^3$, find $y''.$ *Ans.* $y'' = -2a^3xy^{-5}.$

21. If $x^3 = a^2t$, find $\dfrac{d^2x}{dt^2}.$ *Ans.* $\dfrac{d^2x}{dt^2} = -\dfrac{2a^4}{9x^5}.$

22. If $x^3 = az^2$, find $\dfrac{d^2x}{dz^2}.$ *Ans.* $\dfrac{d^2x}{dz^2} = -\dfrac{2a}{9x^2}.$

23. If $x^{\frac{1}{2}} + y^{\frac{1}{2}} = a^{\frac{1}{2}}$, find $\dfrac{d^2y}{dx^2}.$ *Ans.* $\dfrac{d^2y}{dx^2} = \frac{1}{2}a^{\frac{1}{2}}x^{-\frac{3}{2}}.$

24. If $x^{\frac{2}{3}} + y^{\frac{2}{3}} = a^{\frac{2}{3}}$, find $\dfrac{d^2y}{dx^2}.$ *Ans.* $\dfrac{d^2y}{dx^2} = \frac{1}{3}a^{\frac{2}{3}}x^{-\frac{4}{3}}y^{-\frac{1}{3}}.$

In Exs. 25–34, find the slope of the curve at the given point.

25. $x^2 + y^2 + 4x - 2y - 5 = 0$ at $(1, 0)$.   *Ans.* 3.

26. $x^2 + 2y^2 - 6x + 4y - 13 = 0$ at $(-1, 1)$.   *Ans.* 1.

27. $(x + y)^2 + 3x - 15 = 0$ at $(2, 1)$.   *Ans.* -1.5.

28. $(x - y)^2 = 4y$ at $(0, 4)$.   *Ans.* 2.

29. $x(y^2 - x^2) = 3$ at $(1, 2)$.   *Ans.* -0.25.

30. $y(x - y^2) = 3$ at $(4, 1)$.   *Ans.* -1.

31. $y(x - y^2) = 2$ at $(3, 1)$.   *Ans.* Slope does not exist.

32. $y^2 = \dfrac{b^3}{2x + b}$ at $(0, b)$.   *Ans.* -1.

33. $y^2 = \dfrac{2a^3x}{x^2 + a^2}$ at (a, a).   *Ans.* 0.

34. $y^3 = \dfrac{2ax^3}{x + a}$ at (a, a).   *Ans.* $\frac{5}{6}$.

In Exs. 35–46, find the first and second derivatives of y with respect to x from the parametric equations given.

35. $x = 1 + t^2,\ y = 4t - 3.$ *Ans.* $y'' = -t^{-3}.$

36. $x = t^3 + 7,\ y = 6t^2 - 1.$ *Ans.* $y'' = -\frac{4}{3}t^{-4}.$

37. $x = t^3 - 1,\ y = t^2 + t.$ *Ans.* $y'' = \dfrac{-2(t + 1)}{9t^5}.$

38. $x = 3(t - 2)^2,\ y = 9t^2 + 4.$ *Ans.* $y'' = -(t - 2)^{-3}.$

39. $x = \dfrac{1}{t^2},\ y = t^2 - 4t + 1.$ *Ans.* $y'' = t^5(2t - 3).$

40. $x = \dfrac{1}{t^2},\ y = t^2 - t.$ *Ans.* $y'' = \frac{1}{4}t^5(8t - 3).$

41. $x = \dfrac{1}{t^3},\ y = t^3 + 3t.$ *Ans.* $y'' = \frac{2}{3}t^7(3t^2 + 2).$

42. $x = \dfrac{1}{(t + 1)^2},\ y = t^2 + 3.$ *Ans.* $y'' = \frac{1}{2}(t + 1)^5(4t + 1).$

43. $x = \sqrt{1 - t},\ y = t^3 - 3t.$ *Ans.* $y'' = 6(1 + 4t - 5t^2).$

44. $x = \sqrt{t + 2},\ y = t^2 - 3.$ *Ans.* $y'' = 4(3t + 4).$

45. $x = (t - 2)^{\frac{3}{2}},\ y = t^2 - 1.$ *Ans.* $y'' = \dfrac{4(t - 4)}{9(t - 2)^2}.$

46. $x = \dfrac{1}{(t - 1)^2},\ y = \dfrac{1}{t + 2}.$ *Ans.* $y'' = \dfrac{-(t - 1)^5(t + 8)}{4(t + 2)^3}.$

CHAPTER *4* APPLICATIONS OF THE DERIVATIVE

33. Tangents and normals to plane curves. The equation of a line of slope m through the point (x_1, y_1) is

$$(1) \qquad y - y_1 = m(x - x_1).$$

Hence, to find the tangent at any point of a plane curve we have only to find the slope of the curve (*i.e.*, the value of y') at that point, and substitute for m in the above formula.

The equation of the normal is found from that of the tangent by recalling that if two lines are perpendicular, the slope of one is the negative reciprocal of the slope of the other.

Example (*a*): Find the tangent and normal to the ellipse

$$4x^2 + 9y^2 = 25$$

at the point $P : (2, -1)$.

Differentiation of both members of the equation of the ellipse yields

$$8x + 18yy' = 0,$$

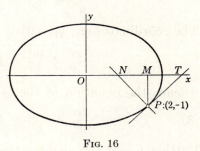

Fig. 16

from which, at the point of contact $(2, -1)$,

$$16 - 18y' = 0,$$

so that the slope of the tangent line is found to be

$$y' = m = \tfrac{8}{9}.$$

Thus the equation of the tangent is, by (1),

$$y + 1 = \tfrac{8}{9}(x - 2),$$

or
$$8x - 9y = 25;$$
that of the normal is
$$9x + 8y = 10.$$

Example (b): Find the tangent to the ellipse

(2)
$$\frac{x^2}{a^2} + \frac{y^2}{b^2} = 1$$

at any point (x_1, y_1) on the curve.

Differentiating (2), we get
$$\frac{2x}{a^2} + \frac{2yy'}{b^2} = 0, \quad y' = -\frac{b^2 x}{a^2 y}.$$

Substituting the coördinates of the given point, we find
$$y' = m = -\frac{b^2 x_1}{a^2 y_1}.$$

Substitute in (1):
$$y - y_1 = -\frac{b^2 x_1}{a^2 y_1}(x - x_1),$$

or, after clearing of fractions, dividing by $a^2 b^2$ and rearranging,
$$\frac{x_1 x}{a^2} + \frac{y_1 y}{b^2} = \frac{x_1^2}{a^2} + \frac{y_1^2}{b^2}.$$

The coördinates (x_1, y_1) satisfy (2), so that
$$\frac{x_1^2}{a^2} + \frac{y_1^2}{b^2} = 1,$$

whence the equation of the tangent at any point of the ellipse is

(3)
$$\frac{x_1 x}{a^2} + \frac{y_1 y}{b^2} = 1.$$

Putting $b = a$, we deduce the further result that the tangent at any point (x_1, y_1) of the circle
$$x^2 + y^2 = a^2$$
is

(4)
$$x_1 x + y_1 y = a^2.$$

Example (c): Find the tangents of slope 2 to the circle

(5)
$$x^2 + y^2 = 5.$$

From equation (5) it follows that

(6) $x + yy' = 0.$

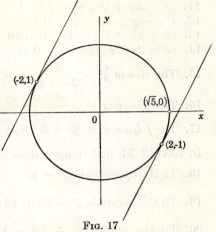

The slope of the tangent line is to be 2. Therefore, the coördinates of the point of contact must satisfy the equation

(7) $x + 2y = 0,$

found by using $y' = 2$ in equation (6).

FIG. 17

The coördinates of the point of contact must also satisfy the equation of the original curve (5). By solving the simultaneous equations (5) and (7), we determine the points of contact $(-2, 1)$ and $(2, -1)$.

Each point of contact, together with the given slope 2, yields the equation of one of the desired tangent lines. With the aid of the point-slope form (1) of the equation of a line, the desired tangents may now be found to be

$$2x - y = -5, \qquad 2x - y = 5.$$

EXERCISES

In Exs. 1–17, find the equations of the tangent and the normal at the point indicated.

1. $y = 3x^2 - x + 1$ at $(1, 3)$. *Ans.* Tangent: $5x - y = 2$; Normal: $x + 5y = 16.$

2. $y = 2x^3 - x^2 + 1$ at $(1, 2)$. *Ans.* Tangent: $4x - y = 2.$

3. $y = 3 + 2x - x^3$ at $x = 1$. *Ans.* Normal: $x - y = -3.$

4. $x^2 - 4x + 2y - 5 = 0$ at $x = 3$.

5. $y = (2x + 1)^3$ at $x = -1$. *Ans.* Normal: $x + 6y = -7.$

6. $y = (1 - x^2)^2$ at $x = 0$.

7. $y = x^2 + x$ at its points of intersection with the line $y = 6$.
  Ans. Tangents: $5x - y = 4, 5x + y = -9.$

8. $y = x^3 + 3x^2 - x - 3$ at its points of intersection with the x-axis.
  Ans. Tangents: $8x - y = -24, 4x + y = -4, 8x - y = 8.$

9. $a^2y = x^3$ at (a, a). *Ans.* Normal: $x + 3y = 4a.$

10. $xy^2 = a^3$ at its points of intersection with the line $x = \frac{1}{4}a$.
  Ans. Tangents: $4x - y = 3a, 4x + y = 3a.$

11. $xy - 3x + y = 0$ at $x = 2$.   *Ans.* Tangent: $x - 3y = -4$.

12. $x^2 - xy + 3y - 9 = 0$ at $x = -1$.

13. $(x + y)^2 + 3x - 1 = 0$ at $(0, 1)$.   *Ans.* Tangent: $5x + 2y = 2$.

14. $(x - 2y)^2 + 4y - 4 = 0$ at $(-2, 0)$.

15. The *cissoid* $y^2 = \dfrac{x^3}{2a - x}$ at (a, a).   *Ans.* Tangent: $2x - y = a$.

16. The *trisectrix* $y^2 = \dfrac{x^2(3a - x)}{a + x}$ at (a, a).

17. The *folium* $x^3 + y^3 = 3axy$ at $(\frac{3}{2}a, \frac{3}{2}a)$.   *Ans.* Normal: $x - y = 0$.

In Exs. 18–34, find tangent lines as directed.

18. To the hyperbola $9y^2 - 4x^2 = 36$ parallel to the line $2x - 5y = -3$.
                                     Ans. $2x - 5y = \pm 8$.

19. To the parabola $y^2 = 8x + 12$ perpendicular to the line $x + 2y = 5$.
                                     Ans. $y - 2x = 4$.

20. To the ellipse $x^2 + 4y^2 = 1$ parallel to the line $3x + 8y = 15$.

21. To the ellipse $x^2 - xy + 2y^2 - x - 3y = 0$ perpendicular to the
line $4x + y = 7$.   *Ans.* $x - 4y = 1$, $x - 4y = -7$.

22. To the parabola $(x + 2y)^2 + 2x - y - 8 = 0$ parallel to the line
$4x + 3y = 2$.   *Ans.* $4x + 3y = 9$.

23. To the curve $y = x^3 - 2x + 4$ parallel to the line $y = x$.
                          Ans. $y = x + 2$, $y = x + 6$.

24. To the curve $y = x^4 - 14x^2 + 19x + 4$ parallel to the line
$5x + y = 4$.   *Ans.* $5x + y = 15$, $5x + y = 12$, $5x + y = -113$.

25. To the curve $y = x^4 + 2x^3 - 2x^2 - 3x + 3$ perpendicular to the
line $x - 3y = 2$.   *Ans.* $3x + y = 3$, $3x + y = -5$, $48x + 16y = 45$.

26. To the curve $y = x^4 - 4x^3 + 2x^2 - 4x + 15$ perpendicular to the
line $x + 8y = 7$.   *Ans.* $8x - y = 30$.

27. To the curve $y = x^4 - 4x^3 - 2x^2 + 16x - 10$ parallel to the line
$y = 4x - 1$.   *Ans.* $4x - y = 3$, $4x - y = 19$ (twice).

28. To the curve $y = \frac{1}{4}x^4 + x^3 + x^2 - 2x - 3$ parallel to the line
$2x + y = 1$.   *Ans.* $8x + 4y = -11$, $2x + y = -3$ (twice).

29. To the curve $y = x^4 - 4x^3 + 6x^2 - 4x + 3$ with slope zero.
                          Ans. $y = 2$ (three times).

30. To the curve $y = x^4 + 4x^3 - 8x^2 + 3x + 70$ with slope 3.
                Ans. $3x - y = -70$, $3x - y = -67$, $3x - y = 58$.

31. To the curve $y = x^2(x^2 + 2x - 2)$ parallel to the x-axis.
                Ans. $y = 0$, $y = -8$, $y = -\frac{3}{16}$.

32. To the parabola $y^2 = 4ax$, with slope m.   *Ans.* $y = mx + \dfrac{a}{m}$.

33. To the ellipse $\dfrac{x^2}{a^2} + \dfrac{y^2}{b^2} = 1$, with slope m.

                                 Ans. $y = mx \pm \sqrt{a^2m^2 + b^2}$.

34. To the hyperbola $2xy = a^2$, with slope m; $(m < 0)$.
                                 Ans. $y = mx \pm a\sqrt{-2m}$.

35. Find a normal of slope 4 to the ellipse $x^2 + 2y^2 = 9$.

$$Ans. \ 4x - y = \pm 2.$$

36. Find a normal of slope $(-\frac{2}{9})$ to the hyperbola $9x^2 - 4y^2 = 32$.

$$Ans. \ 2x + 9y = \pm 13.$$

37. Find a normal of slope $(-\frac{1}{2})$ to the cubic $y = x^3 - 10x - 7$.

$$Ans. \ x + 2y = 8, \ x + 2y = -36.$$

38. Find a normal of slope $\frac{1}{3}$ to the cubic $ay^2 = x^3$.

$$Ans. \ x - 3y = 28a.$$

39. Determine a, b, c so that the parabola $y = ax^2 + bx + c$ shall touch (be tangent to) the line $3x - y = 5$ at $(2, 1)$ and shall also pass through $(3, -1)$. $Ans. \ y = -5x^2 + 23x - 25.$

40. Make the parabola $y = ax^2 + bx + c$ touch the line $2x - y = 3$ at $(3, 3)$ and also pass through $(-1, 3)$.

$$Ans. \ y = \tfrac{1}{2}x^2 - x + \tfrac{3}{2}.$$

41. Make the curve $y = ax^3 + bx^2 + cx + d$ touch the line $y = 4(x + 1)$ at $(1, 8)$ and also touch the line $y = 4(2x + 3)$ at $(-1, 4)$.

$$Ans. \ y = 2x^3 - x^2 + 7.$$

42. Make the curve $y = ax^3 + bx^2 + cx + d$ touch the line $3x - y = 3$ at the point $(1, 0)$ and also pass through $(-1, -6)$ and $(0, -2)$.

$$Ans. \ y = x^3 - x^2 + 2x - 2.$$

43. Find the equation of a circle tangent to the line $3x + y = -5$ at $(-1, -2)$ and also passing through $(1, 2)$.

$$Ans. \ x^2 + y^2 - 4x + 2y - 5 = 0.$$

44. Find the equation of a circle tangent to the line $3x + y = 1$ at $(-1, 4)$, and also passing through $(-1, 2)$.

$$Ans. \ x^2 + y^2 + 8x - 6y + 15 = 0.$$

45. Find the x-intercept of each of the lines (3), (4), § 33; hence deduce a ruler-and-compass construction for the tangent at any point of an ellipse.

In Exs. 46–51, (a) plot the curve; (b) get the equation of the tangent at (x_1, y_1); (c) find the x-intercept of the tangent; (d) from the result of (c), show how to construct the tangent by ruler and compass.

46. The parabola $y^2 = 4ax$. $Ans. \ (b) \ y_1 y = 2ax + 2ax_1.$

47. The hyperbola $2xy = a^2$. $Ans. \ (b) \ y_1 x + x_1 y = a^2; \ (c) \ 2x_1.$

48. $a^2 y = x^3$. $Ans. \ (c) \ \tfrac{2}{3}x_1.$

49. $y^3 = ax^2$. $Ans. \ (c) \ -\tfrac{1}{2}x_1.$

50. $a^{n-1} y = x^n$. Cf. Exs. 46–49. $Ans. \ (c) \ \dfrac{n-1}{n} x_1.$

51. The hyperbola $\dfrac{x^2}{a^2} - \dfrac{y^2}{b^2} = 1$. $Ans. \ (b) \ \dfrac{x_1 x}{a^2} - \dfrac{y_1 y}{b^2} = 1.$

52. Find (a) the normal to the parabola $y^2 = 4ax$ at (x_1, y_1), and (b) its x-intercept; hence construct the normal and tangent.

$$Ans. \ (a) \ y_1 x + 2ay = y_1(x_1 + 2a).$$

53. Show that the tangent to the hyperbola $2xy = a^2$ forms with the axes a triangle of constant area. (Ex. 47.)

34. Graphs. In constructing the graph of a given function, the beginner relies chiefly on the rudimentary method of plotting by separate points. This method, although useful in giving an accurate detail of some portion of the curve in which we may be specially interested, fails to exhibit the general properties of the function. In analytic geometry, by observing the algebraic properties of the equation and then interpreting these properties geometrically, we are able to discover the general appearance of the curve, in many cases, with very little point-plotting. We are now in position to develop still stronger methods for attacking the problem. These methods will rest chiefly on a study of the first and second derivatives of the function.

For simplicity, we shall in this chapter confine our attention to the graphs of polynomials. A fuller treatment of the subject of curve tracing will be given in Chapter 14.

In tracing a curve, it is well to begin by finding the points of intersection with the axes, provided this can be done without great difficulty.

The behavior of a function for large values of x, both positive and negative, can usually be determined at once by inspection. This question should always be investigated, since the result is of great value in interpreting the meaning of other data.

35. Increasing and decreasing functions. We proceed to show how calculus may be used to obtain important information concerning the graph. While the results will at present be employed in the study of polynomials only, they apply in general.

Given any function

$$y = f(x)$$

having a continuous derivative, we note first that, as x increases, *the curve rises if the slope is positive*, as on the arc AB, Fig. 18; *it falls if the slope is negative*, as along BD:

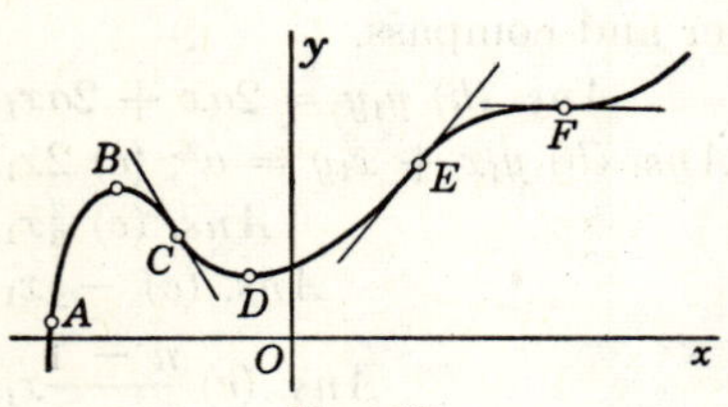

Fig. 18

If $y' > 0$, y increases; y' is positive

If $y' < 0$, y decreases. y' is negative

Of course this also appears at once from the fact that y' is the rate of change of y.

36. Maxima and minima. At a point such as B (Fig. 18), where the function is algebraically greater than at any neighboring point, the function is said to have a *maximum value*, and the point is called a *maximum point*. Similarly, at D the function has a *minimum value*. It is evident that *at such points the tangent is parallel to Ox; i.e.,*

$$y' = 0.$$

But the vanishing of the derivative does not mean that the function is necessarily a maximum or a minimum; the tangent is parallel to Ox at F, yet the function is neither a maximum nor a minimum there. From the figure, we deduce the following test:

At a point where $y' = 0$, if y' changes from positive to negative (as x increases), y is a maximum; if y' changes from negative to positive, y is a minimum; if y' does not change sign, y is neither a maximum nor a minimum.

The points at which $y' = 0$ are called *critical points*, and the corresponding values of x are the *critical values* of x: in Fig. 18, B, D, F are critical points. Maxima and minima collectively are called *extremes*: in the figure, B and D are extremes.

It should be clearly understood that an extreme is not necessarily the greatest (or least) value that the function attains anywhere in its range—the ordinate of F, for example, is greater than that of B. An extreme is merely greater (or less) than any *neighboring* value. The greatest value that the function can assume anywhere in its range (if such a value exists) is the *absolute maximum;* a maximum (such as at B) that is merely greater than any other in the neighborhood is a *relative maximum.* Evidently there is no absolute maximum or minimum in Fig. 18.

In the majority of applications, we are concerned with the absolute maximum or minimum. It is clear that when the function is a polynomial there can never be an absolute extreme if x is unrestricted; but even in the case of polynomials such extremes frequently occur in practical problems, owing to the fact that x is limited in its range. This matter will be discussed more fully in §§ 78–79.

Example: Locate and classify the critical points of

$$y = \tfrac{1}{3}x^3 - \tfrac{1}{2}x^2 - 2x + 2.$$

We find

$$y' = x^2 - x - 2 = (x + 1)(x - 2).$$

Setting
$$y' = 0,$$
we get the critical values $x = -1$ or 2, and the critical points
$(-1, \frac{19}{6})$, $(2, -\frac{4}{3})$. Now as x (increasing) passes through -1,
y' changes from positive to negative: thus y assumes the maximum
value $\frac{19}{6}$. As x passes through 2, y' changes from negative to positive: y assumes the minimum value $-\frac{4}{3}$. The curve is shown in
Fig. 19, p. 55.

37. Concavity. The second derivative is the rate of change of
the first derivative. It follows that when y'' is positive, y' is increasing; as x increases the tangent turns in counterclockwise
sense and the curve is *concave upward*. When y'' is negative, y'
decreases; the curve is *concave downward*.

At a maximum point the curve is concave downward, and hence
y'', if it is not zero, must be negative. At a minimum y'', if not
zero, must be positive. If the second derivative is easily obtained
and if it does not happen to be zero at the critical point in question,
it is usually more convenient to determine whether we have a
maximum or a minimum by finding the sign of y''; but the test
of § 36 has the advantage of being perfectly general.

In summary, the test is as follows:

*At a point where $y' = 0$, if $y'' < 0$, y is a maximum; if $y'' > 0$,
y is a minimum; if $y'' = 0$, the test fails.*

Example (a): Examine the function
$$y = \tfrac{1}{3}x^3 - \tfrac{1}{2}x^2 - 2x + 2$$
for maxima and minima. (See the example, § 36.)
We have
$$y' = x^2 - x - 2 = (x + 1)(x - 2),$$
$$y'' = 2x - 1.$$
At $x = -1$, $y'' = -3$: a maximum. At $x = 2$, $y'' = 3$: a minimum.

Example (b): Examine the function
$$y = x(x - 1)^3$$
for maxima and minima.
We find
$$y' = 3x(x - 1)^2 + (x - 1)^3 = (x - 1)^2(4x - 1),$$
$$y'' = 4(x - 1)^2 + 2(x - 1)(4x - 1) = 6(x - 1)(2x - 1).$$

The critical points $(y' = 0)$ are $(\frac{1}{4}, -\frac{27}{256})$, $(1, 0)$. When $x = \frac{1}{4}$, $y'' = \frac{9}{4}$: a minimum. When $x = 1$, $y'' = 0$: the test fails. Turning to the test of § 36, we find that as x passes through 1, y' does not change sign: the point is neither a maximum nor a minimum. The curve is shown in Fig. 20, p. 56.

The results of this and the preceding section give useful information regarding the behavior of a function as determined by the behavior of its derivatives. However, we shall find (§§ 40–41) that in specific applications of the theory the nature of the various critical values can often be determined very easily by inspection. In such a case, of course, it is unnecessary to apply either of the above tests, except perhaps as a check.

In the exercises below, it is advised that no attempt be made to trace the curve; this is better postponed until our analysis is complete (§§ 38–39).

EXERCISES

In Exs. 1–15, locate the critical points, and determine the maxima and minima by the tests of §§ 36–37.

1. $y = 7 - 8x + x^2$.   **2.** $y = 3x^2 + 12x - 1$.

3. $y = (3x - 1)^2$.   **4.** $y = -4(x + 3)^2$.

5. $y = 2x^3 + 3x^2 - 12x + 7$.

                   Ans. $(1, 0)$ minimum; $(-2, 27)$ maximum.

6. $y = 5 + 9x - \frac{1}{3}x^3$.   *Ans.* $(3, 23)$ maximum; $(-3, -13)$ minimum.

7. $y = x^3 + 3x^2 + 30x - 4$.   *Ans.* No critical point.

8. $y = -20 + 18x - \frac{3}{2}x^2 - x^3$.

               Ans. $(2, 2)$ maximum; $(-3, -60.5)$ minimum.

9. $y = x^3 + 3x^2 + 3x - 4$.   *Ans.* No extreme.

10. $y = \frac{1}{4}x^4 - x^3 + 4x + 3$.   *Ans.* $(-1, \frac{1}{4})$ minimum.

11. $y = x^2(x - 2)^2$.   *Ans.* $(0, 0)$ and $(2, 0)$ minima; $(1, 1)$ maximum.

12. $a^3y = x^4$.   *Ans.* $(0, 0)$ minimum.

13. $9a^3y = x(4a - x)^3$.   *Ans.* $(a, 3a)$ maximum.

14. $a^3y = x^2(2a^2 - x^2)$.

         Ans. $(0, 0)$ minimum; (a, a) and $(-a, a)$ maxima.

15. $a^3y = x^3(4a - 3x)$.   *Ans.* (a, a) maximum.

16. Determine a, b, c, d so that the curve $y = ax^3 + bx^2 + cx + d$ shall have critical points at $(-1, -1)$ and $(-3, 3)$.

                   Ans. $y = x^3 + 6x^2 + 9x + 3$.

17. Make the curve $y = ax^3 + bx^2 + cx + d$ have critical points at $(0, 2)$ and $(-2, 6)$.   *Ans.* $y = x^3 + 3x^2 + 2$.

18. Make the curve $y = ax^3 + bx^2 + cx + d$ pass through the points $(0, 6)$ and $(3, 0)$ and have a critical point at $(2, 2)$.

              Ans. $y = -x^3 + 5x^2 - 8x + 6$.

19. Make the curve $y = ax^3 + bx^2 + cx + d$ have a critical point at $(0, -2)$ and also be tangent to the line $3x + y + 3 = 0$ at $(-1, 0)$.

Ans. $y = x^3 + 3x^2 - 2$.

20. Make the curve $y = ax^4 + bx^3 + cx^2 + dx + e$ pass through $(2, -36)$, with critical points at $(0, -4)$, $(1, 0)$.

Ans. $y = -4(x^2 - 1)^2$.

21. Make the curve $y = ax^4 + bx^3 + cx^2 + dx + e$ pass through $(-1, 8)$, touch the line $y = 11x - 5$ at $(1, 6)$, and have a critical point at $(0, 3)$.

Ans. $y = 3x^4 - x^3 + x^2 + 3$.

22. What is the condition that the cubic $y = ax^3 + bx^2 + cx + d$ shall have two extremes?

Ans. $b^2 - 3ac > 0$.

38. Points of inflection. A *point of inflection* is a point at which the curve changes from concave upward to concave downward, or vice versa (the points C, E, F in Fig. 18, p. 50).

At a point of inflection the tangent reverses the sense in which it turns, which means that y' changes from an increasing to a decreasing function, or vice versa. Hence at such a point y'' changes sign, and, if it is continuous, must vanish. (By the theorem of § 12, a continuous function, in passing from a negative to a positive value, must pass through the value zero.) Conversely, *a point at which y'' vanishes is a point of inflection, provided y'' changes sign at that point.*

Since y''—*i.e.* the rate of change of the slope—is zero at a point of inflection, the tangent is sometimes said to be *stationary for an instant* at such a point, and in the neighborhood of the point it turns very slowly. Hence the inflectional tangent agrees more closely with the curve near its point of contact than does an ordinary tangent; it is therefore especially useful in tracing the curve to *draw the tangent at each point of inflection.*

A point at which y'' vanishes without changing sign is not a point of inflection; the result merely means that near that point the tangent turns even more slowly than near a point of inflection.

As noted in §§ 36–37, a point where $y' = 0$ is a maximum or a minimum, provided $y'' \neq 0$. If y' and y'' both equal zero, the point is in general a point of inflection with a horizontal tangent (the point F in Fig. 18); but if y'' vanishes without changing sign, the point is a maximum or minimum.

It follows from the theorem of Ex. 58, p. 39, that:

If $x = a$ is a root of odd order—simple, triple, etc.—of the equation $y' = 0$, then $x = a$ is a maximum or minimum; if $x = a$ is a root of even order, $x = a$ is a point of inflection with horizontal tangent.

39. Summary. The theory of §§ 34–38 may now be summarized in the form of a definite sequence of steps, as follows:

1. *Find the points of intersection with the axes.*
2. *Determine the behavior of y for large values of x.*
3. *Locate the points where $y' = 0$, and determine the maxima and minima.*
4. *Locate the points where $y'' = 0$ (points of inflection, in most cases), and draw the tangent at each of those points.*
5. *If necessary, plot a few additional points.*

In a given case, any step that leads to serious algebraic difficulties may be omitted provided sufficient information is obtainable without it.

Example (*a*): Trace the curve

$$y = \tfrac{1}{3}x^3 - \tfrac{1}{2}x^2 - 2x + 2.$$

1. When $x = 0$, $y = 2$. The x-intercepts are irrational, and will not be determined.

2. When x is numerically large, the sign of y is the same as the sign of the highest-degree term in x. Hence, when x is large and negative, y is large and negative; when x is large and positive, y is large and positive.

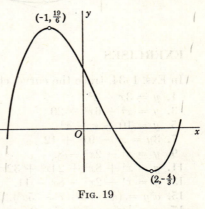

3. $y' = x^2 - x - 2$
   $= (x + 1)(x - 2)$:

the critical points are $(-1, \tfrac{19}{6})$, $(2, -\tfrac{4}{3})$. Without reference to previous examples (§§ 36–37), the situation at once becomes clear when the result of step 2 is considered: since y is large and negative when x is large and nega-

Fig. 19

tive, the curve must come up through the third quadrant, rise to a maximum at $(-1, \tfrac{19}{6})$, fall to a minimum at $(2, -\tfrac{4}{3})$, and then rise indefinitely (since when x is large and positive y is large and positive).

4. $y'' = 2x - 1$.

Equating this to zero, we get $x = \tfrac{1}{2}$; the point $(\tfrac{1}{2}, \tfrac{11}{12})$ is a point of inflection, the slope at that point being $-\tfrac{9}{4}$.

Example (*b*): Trace the curve $y = x(x - 1)^3$.

1. When $x = 0$, $y = 0$; when $y = 0$, $x = 0$ or 1.

2. When x is large and either positive or negative, y is large and positive.

3. $y' = (x - 1)^3 + 3x(x - 1)^2 = (x - 1)^2(4x - 1)$.

Thus the critical points are $(\frac{1}{4}, -\frac{27}{256})$, $(1, 0)$. The result of step 2 shows that the former point is a minimum, the latter a point of inflection with horizontal tangent. This last is verified by the fact that $x = 1$ is a *double root* of $y' = 0$ (§ 38, last paragraph).

4. $y'' = 2(x - 1)(4x - 1) + 4(x - 1)^2$
   $= 6(x - 1)(2x - 1)$.

The points of inflection are $(\frac{1}{2}, -\frac{1}{16})$, with slope $\frac{1}{4}$, and $(1, 0)$, with slope zero.

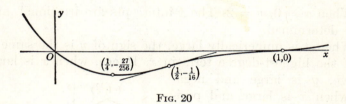

Fig. 20

EXERCISES

In Exs. 1–34, trace the curve, choosing a suitable scale in each problem.

1. $y = 3x - x^3$.
2. $y = 3x^2 - x^3$.
3. $y = x^3 - 6x^2 - 20$.
4. $y = x^3 + 3x^2 + 3x - 7$.
5. $y = 10 - x - x^3$.
6. $y = (x - 6)^2(9 - x)$.
7. $3y = x^3 - 9x^2 + 12$.
8. $y = x^3 + 6x^2 + 15x + 18$.
9. $y = x^4 - 2x^2 - 8$.
10. $y = x^2(3x^2 + 8x + 6)$.
11. $y = x^4 + 8x^3 + 24x^2 + 32x$.
12. $y = 8x(2x^3 - 4x^2 + 3x - 1)$.
13. $y = x^4 - 2x^3 - 8x - 11$.
14. $y = x^4 - 8x^3 + 18x^2 - 24$.
15. $a^3y = (a^2 - x^2)(x^2 - 5a^2)$.
16. $a^3y = (x^2 - a^2)(x^2 - 23a^2)$.
17. $y = \frac{1}{2}x^4 - x^3 + x - 2$.
18. $y = x^4 - 4x^3 + 16x - 16$.
19. $y = x^4 - 8x^3 + 18x^2 - 16x + 5$.
20. $y = x^5 - 5x$.
21. $a^4y = x^4(5a - 4x)$.
22. $y = x^5 - 20x^2$.
23. $y = 3x^5 - 20x^3$.
24. $y = (2x + 1)^5 - 32$.
25. $8y = 3x^5 - 50x^3 + 135x$.
26. $y = 3x^5 - 10x^3 + 15x$.
27. $y = \frac{1}{4}x^4 - \frac{3}{2}x^2 - 2x + 2$.
28. $120y = 3x^5 + 40x^3 + 240x$.
29. $y = x^5 - 10x^3 - 20x^2 - 15x - 4$.
30. $y = 6x^5 - 15x^4 + 20x^3 - 30x^2 + 30x$.
31. $y = 64x^3(x - 1)^3$.

32. $a^4y = x(x^2 - 15a^2)^2$.

33. $y = x^2(x - 1)^4$.

34. $a^5y = x^5(6a - 5x)$; $[(0.8)^5 = 0.33]$.

35. Plot the curves $y = x$, $y = x^2$, $y = x^3$, $y = x^4$, $y = x^5$, all on the same axes, in the interval $-1 \leqq x \leqq 1$.

36. Make the curve $y = ax^3 + bx^2 + cx + d$ have at $(-1, 2)$ a point of inflection with a horizontal tangent, and also pass through $(0, 4)$.

Ans. $y = 2(x^3 + 3x^2 + 3x + 2)$.

37. Make the curve $y = ax^3 + bx^2 + cx + d$ pass through $(1, 5)$ and have a point of inflection at $(2, 1)$, with inflectional tangent $3x + y = 7$.

Ans. $y = 15 - 15x + 6x^2 - x^3$.

38. Make the curve $y = ax^4 + bx^3 + cx^2 + dx + e$ have a critical point at $(0, 0)$ and an inflection point at $(-1, 2)$ with inflectional tangent $2x + y = 0$.

Ans. $y = 2x^2(x^2 + 3x + 3)$.

39. Make the curve $y = ax^4 + bx^3 + cx^2 + dx + e$ pass through the points $(0, 0)$, $(2, 24)$, and also have an inflection point with horizontal tangent at $(1, 9)$.

Ans. $y = 3x(x^3 - 6x + 8)$.

40. Prove that the cubic $y = ax^3 + bx^2 + cx + d$ is symmetric with respect to its point of inflection. (Find the point of inflection; translate to that point as new origin.)

40. Applications of the theory of maxima and minima. It was shown in § 36 that, at a point where its first derivative vanishes, a function assumes an extreme value, provided the derivative changes sign at that point. This result finds application in a great variety of problems, some of which will now be considered.

When the derivative is equated to zero, it may happen, of course, that several critical values are obtained. In practice, the value that gives the desired maximum or minimum can often be selected at once by inspection.

Example (a): A box is to be made of a piece of cardboard 16×10 in. by cutting equal squares out of the corners and turning up the sides. Find the volume of the largest box that can be made in this way. (Fig. 21.)

Let x be the length of the side of each of the squares cut out. Then the volume of the box is

$$V = x(10 - 2x)(16 - 2x), \qquad 0 \leqq x \leqq 5$$
$$= 160x - 52x^2 + 4x^3,$$

whence

$$V' = 160 - 104x + 12x^2$$
$$= 4(x - 2)(3x - 20).$$

Setting

$$V' = 0,$$

we get the critical values $x = 2, 6\frac{2}{3}$. By the nature of the problem x is restricted to values between 0 and 5, so that the value $6\frac{2}{3}$ must be rejected. Since the volume is zero when $x = 0$ and again when $x = 5$, it must reach a maximum at some intermediate point; it

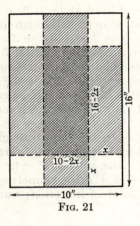

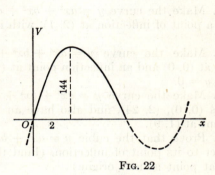

FIG. 21   FIG. 22

therefore follows without the application of further tests that the critical value $x = 2$ gives the required maximum volume (Fig. 22):

$$V_{\max.} = 2(10 - 4)(16 - 4) = 144 \text{ cu. in.}$$

The minimum volume, of course, is $V = 0$, occurring at the endpoints $x = 0$, $x = 5$. The reason why our analysis fails to show these minima is that V is discontinuous (§ 12) at $x = 0, 5$, and all our present theory rests on the assumption that $f(x)$ and $f'(x)$ are continuous. Extremes occurring in connection with discontinuities will be discussed in § 79.

Example (b): Find the area of the largest rectangle that can be inscribed in a given circle.

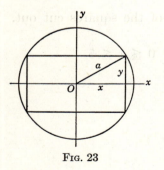

The area of the rectangle is

(1) $A = 4xy,$

where x and y are connected by the relation

(2) $x^2 + y^2 = a^2.$

Substituting $y = \sqrt{a^2 - x^2}$ in (1), we find

FIG. 23   (3) $A = 4x\sqrt{a^2 - x^2},$

whence

$$A' = 4\sqrt{a^2 - x^2} - \frac{4x^2}{\sqrt{a^2 - x^2}} = \frac{4a^2 - 8x^2}{\sqrt{a^2 - x^2}}.$$

Setting $A' = 0$, we get $4a^2 - 8x^2 = 0,$ $x = \frac{1}{2}\sqrt{2}\,a.$

Substitute in (3):

$$A_{\text{max.}} = 2a^2.$$

Let us obtain a geometric interpretation of the situation in this example. Examination of Fig. 23 shows that the "half-dimensions" x, y, of the inscribed rectangle are to satisfy the relation

(2) $$x^2 + y^2 = a^2,$$

with fixed a. Therefore, x and y, both positive, may be interpreted as rectangular coördinates of a point on the circle (2) and in the first quadrant.

At the same time, we wish to force the area of the rectangle,

(1) $$A = 4xy,$$

to be a maximum. We can think of equation (1) as the equation of a family of hyperbolas, one for each positive A.

The point (x, y) is to be in the first quadrant, to satisfy both of the equations (1) and (2), and is to be chosen so that the A in (1) is as large as possible.

Figure 24 exhibits the circle (2) and several elements of the family of hyperbolas (1). The vertices of the rectangular hyperbolas (1) recede from the origin as the value of A increases. Hence, as can be seen from Fig. 24, the largest A for which a point of intersection with the circle exists is found when the intersection point is on the 45° line; that is, when $x = y = \dfrac{a}{\sqrt{2}}.$ This again yields

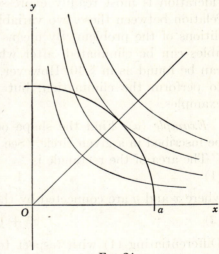

Fig. 24

$$A_{\text{max.}} = 4\frac{a}{\sqrt{2}} \cdot \frac{a}{\sqrt{2}} = 2a^2.$$

Example (c): Find the altitude of the largest circular cylinder that can be inscribed in a circular cone of radius r and height h. The volume of the cylinder is

$$V = \pi x^2 y.$$

Figure 25 shows a section by a plane through the axis. By similar triangles,

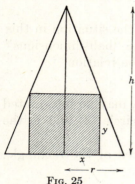

$$\frac{x}{r} = \frac{h - y}{h}, \qquad x = \frac{r}{h}(h - y),$$

so that

$$V = \frac{\pi r^2}{h^2}(h - y)^2 y,$$

$$\frac{dV}{dy} = \frac{\pi r^2}{h^2}[(h - y)^2 - 2(h - y)y]$$

$$= \frac{\pi r^2}{h^2}(h - y)(h - 3y) = 0,$$

$$y = \tfrac{1}{3}h.$$

FIG. 25

(The value $y = h$ makes $x = 0$ and therefore $V = 0$: an obvious, and trivial, minimum.)

41. Use of an auxiliary variable. If the function under consideration is most readily expressed in terms of two variables, a relation between these two variables must be found from the conditions of the problem. By means of this relation one of the variables can be eliminated, after which the maximum or minimum can be found as in § 40. However, it is often more convenient not to perform the elimination, but to proceed as in the following examples.

Example (a): Find the shape of the largest rectangle that can be inscribed in a given circle. (See Fig. 23.)

The area of the rectangle is

(1) $$A = 4xy,$$

where x and y are connected by the relation

(2) $$x^2 + y^2 = a^2.$$

Differentiating (1) with respect to x and equating the derivative to zero, we have

$$A' = 4(xy' + y) = 0,$$

or

$$y' = -\frac{y}{x}.$$

Differentiating (2), we get, since a is constant,

$$2x + 2yy = 0, \qquad y' = -\frac{x}{y}.$$

Equating values of y', we find

$$-\frac{y}{x} = -\frac{x}{y},$$

whence

(3) $$y = x:$$

the maximum rectangle is a square.

If it is desired to find the actual maximum value of A, we solve the simultaneous equations (2), (3), whence

$$x = y = \tfrac{1}{2}\sqrt{2}\,a,$$

and

$$A_{\text{max.}} = 2a^2.$$

Example (b): A cylindrical tin boiler, open at the top, has a copper bottom. If sheet copper is five times as expensive as tin, per unit area, find the most economical proportions.

Let r denote the radius, h the height; let k be the unit cost of tin. Then the cost C, which is to be a minimum, is

(4) $$C = 2\pi krh + 5\pi kr^2 = \pi k(2rh + 5r^2).$$

It is clearly implied that the volume, viz.

(5) $$V = \pi r^2 h,$$

is given* (constant). Differentiate (4) and (5) with respect to either h or r — say with respect to r:

(6) $$\frac{dC}{dr} = \pi k\Big(2r\frac{dh}{dr} + 2h + 10r\Big) = 0,$$

(7) $$\frac{dV}{dr} = \pi\Big(r^2\frac{dh}{dr} + 2rh\Big) = 0.$$

(We set $\dfrac{dC}{dr} = 0$ to give a minimum, and $\dfrac{dV}{dr} = 0$ automatically, since V is constant.) Eliminating $\dfrac{dh}{dr}$ between (6) and (7), we find $h = 5r$.

---

* An alternative assumption would be that V is to be a maximum for a given C. Unless either V or C is given, there is no problem; for if not, then obviously the most economical dimensions would be $r = h = 0$. The alternative assumption just mentioned leads to the same equations as in the text, merely reversing the reasons for the vanishing of $\dfrac{dC}{dr}$ and $\dfrac{dV}{dr}$.

That this gives an actual minimum (rather than a maximum, or neither) is evident; for by taking r very large and h correspondingly small, or vice versa, any amount of sheet metal could be used up.†

Example (c): A man in a rowboat 6 mi. from shore desires to reach a point on the shore at a distance of 10 mi. from his present position. If he can walk 4 mi. per hr. and row 2 mi. per hr., in what direction should he row in order to reach his destination in the shortest possible time?

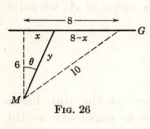

FIG. 26

Let x and y be distances defined by Fig. 26, with the man starting at M. Since he rows the distance y at 2 mi. per hr. and walks the distance $(8 - x)$ at 4 mi. per hr., the time required for him to reach his goal G is

$$T = \frac{y}{2} + \frac{8 - x}{4},$$

with

$$y^2 = x^2 + 36.$$

To find the minimum time, we have

$$T' = \tfrac{1}{2}y' - \tfrac{1}{4} = 0, \qquad y' = \tfrac{1}{2};$$

$$2yy' = 2x, \qquad y' = \frac{x}{y}.$$

Equating the values of y' and noting that

$$\frac{x}{y} = \sin \theta,$$

we find

$$\theta = 30°.$$

EXERCISES

1. The sum of two numbers is k. Find the minimum value of the sum of their squares.   *Ans.* $\tfrac{1}{2}k^2$.

2. What number exceeds its square by the maximum amount?
    Ans. $\tfrac{1}{2}$.

3. What positive number added to its reciprocal gives the minimum sum?

† Or, if not quite obvious when r is small, h large, it is easily shown: substitute the value of r from (5) in (4), then let h increase.

4. The sum of two positive numbers is fixed at 4. Find the smallest value possible for the sum of the cube of one number and the square of the other.   *Ans.* $\frac{256}{27}$.

5. Find two numbers whose sum is a, if the product of one by the square of the other is to be maximum.   *Ans.* $\frac{1}{3}a$, $\frac{2}{3}a$.

6. Find two numbers whose sum is a, if the product of one by the cube of the other is to be a maximum.   *Ans.* $\frac{1}{4}a$, $\frac{3}{4}a$.

7. Find two numbers whose sum is a, if the product of the square of one by the cube of the other is to be a maximum.   *Ans.* $\frac{2}{5}a$, $\frac{3}{5}a$.

8. A rectangular field is to be inclosed and divided into five lots by parallels to one of the sides. What should be the shape of the field of fixed area to make the amount of fencing a minimum?

Ans. Width $= \frac{1}{3} \times$ length.

9. What should be the shape of a rectangular field of given area, if it is to be inclosed by the least amount of fencing?   *Ans.* A square.

10. A rectangular field of given area is to be fenced off along the bank of a river. If no fence is needed along the river, what is the shape of the rectangle requiring the least amount of fencing?

Ans. Width $= \frac{1}{2} \times$ length.

11. A rectangular lot is to be fenced off along a highway. If the fence on the highway costs m dollars per yd., on the other sides n dollars per yd., find the area of the largest lot that can be fenced off for k dollars.

Ans. $\dfrac{k^2}{8n(m+n)}$.

12. A rectangular lot is bounded at the back by a river. No fence is needed along the river and there is to be a 20 ft. opening in front. If the fence along the front costs $3 per ft., along the sides $1 per ft., find the dimensions of the largest lot which can be thus fenced in for $600.

Ans. 110 by 165 ft.

13. Find the rectangle of maximum perimeter inscribed in a given circle.   *Ans.* A square.

14. If the hypotenuse of a right triangle is given, show that the area is a maximum when the triangle is isosceles.

15. Find the most economical proportions for a covered box of fixed volume whose base is a rectangle with one side three times as long as the other.   *Ans.* Altitude $= \frac{3}{2} \times$ shorter side of base.

16. Solve Ex. 15 if the box has an open top.

Ans. Altitude $= \frac{3}{4} \times$ shorter side of base.

17. Find the most economical proportions for a quart can.

Ans. Diameter $=$ height.

18. Find the most economical proportions for a cylindrical cup.

Ans. Radius $=$ height.

19. Find the most economical proportions for a box with an open top and a square base.   *Ans.* Side of base $= 2 \times$ altitude.

20. A box is to be made of a piece of cardboard 12 in. square by cutting equal squares out of the corners and turning up the sides. Find the volume of the largest box that can be made in this way.   *Ans.* 128 cu. in.

21. Find the volume of the largest box that can be made by cutting equal squares out of the corners of a piece of cardboard of dimensions 6 in. by 16 in., and then turning up the sides.   *Ans.* $\frac{1600}{27}$ cu. in.

22. Find the depth of the largest box that can be made by cutting equal squares of side x out of the corners of a piece of cardboard of dimensions $6a$, $6b$, $(b \leqq a)$, and then turning up the sides. To select that value of x which yields a maximum volume, apply the test of § 37; or, as an exercise in algebra, show that $(a + b + \sqrt{a^2 - ab + b^2}) \geqq 3b$. Check Exs. 20, 21.   *Ans.* Depth $= a + b - \sqrt{a^2 - ab + b^2}$.

23. The perimeter of an isosceles triangle is P in. Find the maximum area.   *Ans.* $P^2 \dfrac{\sqrt{3}}{36}$ sq. in.

24. The sum of the length and girth of a container of square cross section is a in. Find the maximum volume.   *Ans.* $\frac{1}{108}a^3$ cu. in.

25. Find the proportions of the largest circular cylinder that can be inscribed in a given sphere.   *Ans.* Diameter $= \sqrt{2} \times$ height.

26. In Ex. 25, find the shape of the cylinder if its convex surface is to be a maximum.   *Ans.* Diameter $=$ height.

27. The strength of a rectangular beam is proportional to the breadth and the square of the depth. Find the shape of the strongest beam that can be cut from a log of given size.   *Ans.* Depth $= \sqrt{2} \times$ breadth.

28. The stiffness of a rectangular beam is proportional to the breadth and the cube of the depth. Find the shape of the stiffest beam that can be cut from a log of given size.   *Ans.* Depth $= \sqrt{3} \times$ breadth.

29. Compare for strength and stiffness, against both edgewise and sidewise thrust, two beams of equal length, one 2×8 in., the other 4×6 in. (See Exs. 27–28.) Which shape is more often used for floor joists? For what principal reason?

30. A cylindrical glass jar has a plastic top. If the plastic is half as expensive as glass, per unit area, find the most economical proportions for the jar.   *Ans.* Height $= \frac{3}{2} \times$ radius of the base.

31. Find the dimensions of the largest rectangular building that can be placed on a right-triangular lot, facing one of the perpendicular sides. (Fig. 27.)   *Ans.* $x = \frac{1}{2}a$.

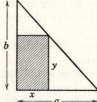
FIG. 27

32. A Norman window consists of a rectangle surmounted by a semicircle. What shape gives the most light for a given perimeter?   *Ans.* Breadth $=$ height.

33. Solve Ex. 32 if the semicircle is of stained glass admitting only half the normal amount of light.

34. Given a point on the conjugate axis of an equilateral hyperbola, find the shortest distance to the curve.   *Ans.* For curve $x^2 - y^2 = a^2$, point $(0, k)$, ordinate of nearest point is $y = \frac{1}{2}k$.

35. Find the point on the curve $a^2 y = x^3$ that is nearest the point $(4a, 0)$.   *Ans.* (a, a).

36. Find the shortest distance from the point $(0, 8a)$ to the curve $ax^2 = y^3$.   *Ans.* $2a\sqrt{11}$.

37. Find the shortest distance from the point $(4, 2)$ to the ellipse $x^2 + 3y^2 = 12$.   *Ans.* $\sqrt{2}$.

38. A cylindrical tin boiler, open at the top, has a copper bottom. If sheet copper is m times as expensive as tin, per unit area, find the most economical proportions.   *Ans.* Height $= m \times$ radius.

39. Solve Ex. 38 if the boiler is to have a tin cover. Deduce the answer directly from that of Ex. 38.

40. The base of a covered box is a square. The bottom and back are made of pine, the remainder of oak. If oak is m times as expensive as pine, find the most economical proportions.
$$Ans.\ \text{Side of base} = \frac{3m+1}{2m+2} \times \text{height.}$$

41. A silo consists of a cylinder surmounted by a hemisphere. If the floor, walls, and roof are equally expensive per unit area, find the most economical proportions.   *Ans.* Diameter $=$ total height.

42. For the silo of Ex. 41, find the most economical proportions, if the floor is twice as expensive as the walls, per unit area, and the roof is three times as expensive as the walls, per unit area.
$$Ans.\ \text{Diameter} = \tfrac{2}{7} \times \text{total height.}$$

43. Two posts, one 10 ft. high and the other 15 ft. high, stand 30 ft. apart. They are to be stayed by wires attached to a single stake at ground level, the wires running to the tops of the posts. Where should the stake be placed, to use the least amount of wire?
$$Ans.\ \text{12 ft. from the shorter post.}$$

44. A lot has the form of a right triangle, with perpendicular sides 90 and 120 ft. long. Find the length and width of the largest rectangular building that can be erected, facing the hypotenuse of the triangle.
$$Ans.\ \text{36 by 75 ft.}$$

45. Solve Ex. 44 if the lengths of the perpendicular sides are a, b.
$$Ans.\ \frac{ab}{2\sqrt{a^2+b^2}}, \frac{\sqrt{a^2+b^2}}{2}.$$

46. An oil can consists of a cylinder surmounted by a cone. If the diameter of the cone is five-sixths of its height, find the most economical proportions.   *Ans.* Height of cone $= 2 \times$ height of cylinder.

47. A ship lies 8 mi. from shore, and opposite a point 15 mi. farther along the shore another ship lies 12 mi. offshore. A boat from the first ship is to land a passenger and then proceed to the other ship. What is the least distance the boat can travel?   *Ans.* 25 mi.

48. A trapezoidal gutter is to be made from a strip of tin by bending up the edges. If the cross-section has the form shown in Fig. 28, what width across the top gives maximum carrying capacity?   *Ans* 2a.

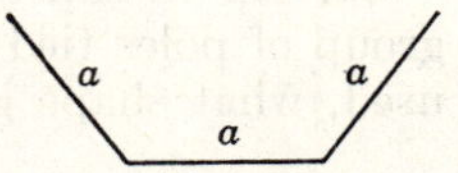

Fig. 28

49. Solve Ex. 48, if the strip is 11 in. wide and the base 7 in. wide.   *Ans.* 8 in.

50. In Ex. 48, if the strip is L in. wide, and the width across the top is T in. ($T < L$), what base width gives the maximum capacity?

Ans. $\frac{1}{3}L$ in.

51. From a strip of tin 14 in. wide a trapezoidal gutter is to be made by bending up the sides at an angle of 45°. Find the width of the base, for greatest carrying capacity. *Ans.* 3.17 in.

52. A page is to contain 24 sq. in. of print. The margins at top and bottom are $1\frac{1}{2}$ in., at the sides 1 in. Find the most economical dimensions for the page. *Ans.* Printed portion 4 × 6 in.

53. A light is to be placed above the center of a circular area of radius a. What height gives the best illumination on a circular walk surrounding the area? (When light from a point-source strikes a surface obliquely, the intensity of illumination is $I = \dfrac{k \sin \theta}{d^2}$, where θ is the angle of incidence and d the distance from the source.) *Ans.* $h = \frac{1}{2}\sqrt{2}\,a$.

54. It is shown in the theory of attraction that a wire bent in the form of a circle of radius a exerts upon a particle in the axis of the circle (*i.e.*, in the line through the center of the circle perpendicular to its plane) an attraction proportional to $\dfrac{h}{(a^2 + h^2)^{\frac{3}{2}}}$, where h is the height of the particle above the plane of the circle. Find h, for maximum attraction. (Compare Ex. 53.) *Ans.* $h = \frac{1}{2}\sqrt{2}\,a$.

55. In Ex. 54, if the wire has instead the form of a square of side $2l$, the attraction is proportional to $\dfrac{h}{(h^2 + l^2)\sqrt{h^2 + 2l^2}}$. Find h, for maximum attraction. *Ans.* $h = 0.786l$.

56. Inscribe a circular cylinder of maximum convex surface in a given circular cone. *Ans.* Diameter of cylinder = radius of cone.

57. Find the circular cone of maximum volume inscribed in a sphere of radius a. *Ans.* Altitude = $\frac{4}{3}a$.

58. A sphere is cut to the shape of a circular cone. How much of the material can be saved? (Ex. 57.) *Ans.* 30%.

59. Find the circular cone of minimum volume circumscribed about a sphere of radius a. *Ans.* Altitude = 4a.

60. Find the largest right pyramid with a square base that can be inscribed in a sphere of radius a. *Ans.* Altitude = $\frac{4}{3}a$.

61. An Indian tepee is made by stretching skins or birch bark over a group of poles tied together at the top. If poles of given length are to be used, what shape gives maximum volume?

Ans. Radius = $\sqrt{2}$ × height.

62. Solve Ex. 61 if poles of any length can be found, but only a limited amount of covering material is available. *Ans.* Height = $\sqrt{2}$ × radius.

63. Cut the largest possible rectangle from a circular quadrant, as shown in Fig. 29.   *Ans.* $x = 0.54a$.

64. One corner of a leaf of width a is folded over so as just to reach the opposite side of the page. Find the width of the part folded over when the length of the crease is a minimum. See Fig. 30.   *Ans.* $\frac{3}{4}a$.

65. Solve Ex. 64 if the area folded over is to be a minimum.   *Ans.* $\frac{2}{3}a$.

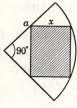

FIG. 29

FIG. 30

66. A man on an island a mi. south of a straight beach wishes to reach a point on shore b mi. east of his present position. If he can row r mi. per hr. and walk w mi. per hr., in what direction should he row, to reach his destination as soon as possible? See Fig. 31.

$$Ans. \text{ If } r < w, \text{ and if } b > \frac{ra}{\sqrt{w^2 - r^2}}, \sin \theta = \frac{r}{w};$$

otherwise, directly toward his destination.

67. A man on an island 12 mi. south of a straight beach wishes to reach a point on shore 20 mi. east. If a motorboat, making 20 mi. per hr., can be hired at a rate of $2.00 per hr. for the time it is actually used, and the cost of land transportation is $0.06 per mi., how much must he pay for the trip?   *Ans.* $2.16.

68. A man in a motorboat at A (Fig. 32) receives a message at noon, calling him to B. A bus making 40 mi. per hr. leaves C, bound for B, at 1:00 P.M. If $AC = 40$ mi., what must be the speed of the boat to enable the man to catch the bus?   *Ans.* At least 28.3 mi. per hr.

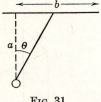

FIG. 31

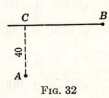

FIG. 32

69. In Ex. 68, if the speed of the boat is 30 mi. per hr., what is the greatest distance offshore from which the bus can be caught?

$$Ans. \tfrac{120}{7}\sqrt{7} = 45.3 \text{ mi.}$$

42. Time-rates. The fact that the derivative of a function is identical with its rate of change leads to a great variety of applications; those in which time is the independent variable are especially important.

If the quantity whose rate of change is to be found can be expressed directly as a function of time, the result may be obtained at once by differentiating with respect to the time.

Example (a): A balloon, leaving the ground 60 ft. from an observer, rises vertically at the rate of 10 ft. per sec. How fast is the balloon receding from the observer, after 8 sec.?

In time t, the balloon rises a distance $10t$, so that

$$s = \sqrt{3600 + 100t^2},$$

$$\frac{ds}{dt} = \frac{100t}{\sqrt{3600 + 100t^2}}.$$

When $t = 8$,

$$\frac{ds}{dt} = \frac{800}{\sqrt{3600 + 6400}} = 8 \text{ ft. per sec.}$$

Fig. 33

Note that the given value of t, viz. $t = 8$, is employed only *after the differentiation has been performed.*

Example (b): As a man walks across a bridge at the rate of 5 ft. per sec. a boat passes directly beneath him at 10 ft. per sec. If the bridge is 30 ft. above the water, how fast are the man and the boat separating 3 sec. later?

In t sec., the man covers a distance $5t$, the boat a distance $10t$. By elementary geometry, the distance between them is

$$s = \sqrt{(5t)^2 + (10t)^2 + (30)^2}$$

$$= \sqrt{125t^2 + 900};$$

$$\frac{ds}{dt} = \frac{125t}{\sqrt{125t^2 + 900}}.$$

After 3 sec.,

$$\frac{ds}{dt} = \frac{375}{\sqrt{2025}} = 8\tfrac{1}{3} \text{ ft. per sec.}$$

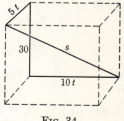

Fig. 34

Frequently, the problem of rates is most conveniently solved by expressing the variable whose rate of change is to be found, in terms of another variable whose rate is *known*, and then differentiating *with respect to time* the equation connecting them. It will be recalled that a similar device was employed in § 41.

Example (c): A man on a wharf 20 ft. above the water pulls in a rope, to which a boat is attached, at the rate of 4 ft. per sec. At what rate is the boat approaching the wharf when there is 25 ft. of rope out?

Let x denote the distance of the boat from the wharf, r the length of rope. Then, *given* $\frac{dr}{dt}$, we have *to find* $\frac{dx}{dt}$. To do this, as suggested above, we express x in terms of r (implicitly or explicitly) and differentiate with respect to t:

$$x = \sqrt{r^2 - 400}, \qquad \frac{dx}{dt} = \frac{r\frac{dr}{dt}}{\sqrt{r^2 - 400}}.$$

Substitute $r = 25$, $\frac{dr}{dt} = -4$:

$$\frac{dx}{dt} = \frac{-100}{\sqrt{225}} = -6\tfrac{2}{3} \text{ ft. per sec.}$$

FIG. 35

Example (d): Water is flowing into a conical reservoir 20 ft. deep and 10 ft. across the top, at the rate of 15 cu. ft. per min. Find how fast the surface is rising when the water is 8 ft. deep.

The volume of water is

$$V = \tfrac{1}{3}\pi r^2 h.$$

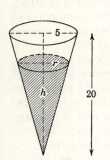

FIG. 36

By similar triangles,

$$\frac{r}{h} = \frac{5}{20}, \qquad r = \frac{1}{4}h.$$

Hence

$$V = \frac{\pi h^3}{48}, \qquad \frac{dV}{dt} = \frac{\pi h^2}{16}\frac{dh}{dt}.$$

But we have given that

$$\frac{dV}{dt} = 15,$$

so that

$$\frac{\pi h^2}{16}\frac{dh}{dt} = 15, \qquad \frac{dh}{dt} = \frac{240}{\pi h^2}.$$

When $h = 8$,

$$\frac{dh}{dt} = \frac{15}{4\pi} = 1.19 \text{ ft. per min.}$$

EXERCISES

1. Water is flowing into a vertical cylindrical tank at the rate of 12 cu. ft. per min. If the radius of the tank is 3 ft., how fast is the surface rising?   *Ans.* 0.42 ft. per min.

2. Water flows into a vertical cylindrical tank at 6 cu. ft. per min.; the surface rises 6 in. per min. Find the radius of the tank.   *Ans.* 1.95 ft.

3. A rectangular trough is 10 ft. long and 3 ft. wide. Find how fast the surface rises, if water flows in at the rate of 6 cu. ft. per min.

Ans. 0.2 ft. per min.

4. A triangular trough 10 ft. long is 4 ft. across the top, and 4 ft. deep. If water flows in at the rate of 6 cu. ft. per min., find how fast the surface is rising when the water is 6 in. deep.   *Ans.* 1.2 ft. per min.

5. A man 6 ft. tall walks away from a lamp post 10 ft. high at the rate of 4 mi. per hr. How fast does the end of his shadow move?

Ans. 10 mi. per hr.

6. In Ex. 5, how fast does the shadow lengthen?

7. A boy on a bike rides north 5 mi., then turns east (Fig. 37). If he rides 10 mi. per hr., at what rate was his distance to the starting point S changing 2 hr. after he left that point?

Ans. $3\sqrt{10}$ mi. per hr.

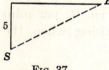

Fig. 37

8. A train, starting at noon, travels north at 40 mi. per hr. Another train, starting from the same point at 2 P.M., travels east at 50 mi. per hr. Find, to the nearest mile per hour, how fast the two trains are separating at 3 P.M.   *Ans.* 56 mi. per hr.

9. In Ex. 8, how fast are the trains separating after a long time?

Ans. 64 mi. per hr.

10. A 15-ft. ladder leans against a vertical wall. If the top slides downward at the rate of 2 ft. per sec., find how fast the lower end is moving, when it is 12 ft. from the wall.   *Ans.* 1.5 ft. per sec.

11. In Ex. 10, find the rate of change of the slope of the ladder.

Ans. $\frac{-25}{96}$ per sec.

12. A trapezoidal trough is 12 ft. long, 6 ft. wide at the top, 3 ft. wide at the bottom, and 3 ft. deep. If water flows in at 6 cu. ft. per min., find how fast the water surface is rising, when the water is one foot deep.

Ans. $\frac{1}{8}$ ft. per min.

13. For the trough of Ex. 12, find how fast the water surface is rising, when the water is 2 ft. deep.   *Ans.* 0.1 ft. per min.

14. A light at eye level stands 20 ft. from a house, and 15 ft. from the path leading from the house to the street. A man walks along the path at 6 ft. per sec. How fast does his shadow move along the wall, when he is 10 ft. from the house?   *Ans.* 18 ft. per sec.

15. In Ex. 14, when the man is 10 ft. from the house, find the time-rate of change of that portion of his shadow which lies on the ground.
                                                     Ans. 18.3 ft. per sec.

16. A light is placed on the ground 40 ft. from a building. A man 6 ft. tall walks from the light toward the building at the rate of 5 ft. per sec. Find the rate at which the length of his shadow on the wall is changing, when he is 20 ft. from the building.   *Ans.* −3 ft. per sec.

17. Solve Ex. 16, if the light is 8 ft. above the ground.
                                                     Ans. 1 ft. per sec.

18. One city, A, is 30 mi. north and 55 mi. east of another city, B. At noon, a car starts west from A at 40 mi. per hr.; at 12:10 P.M., another car starts east from B at 60 mi. per hr. Find, in two ways, when the cars will be nearest together.   *Ans.* 12:39 P.M.

19. For the conditions of Ex. 18, draw the appropriate figures for times before 12:39 P.M., and after that time. Show that, in terms of time after noon, the formulas for distance between the two cars (one formula associated with each figure) are equivalent.

20. For Ex. 18, compute the time-rate of change of the distance between the cars at: (a) 12:15 P.M.; (b) 12:30 P.M.; (c) 1:15 P.M.
                      Ans. (a) −80 mi. per hr.; (c) 89.4 mi. per hr.

21. One city, C, is 30 mi. north and 35 mi. east of another city, D. At noon, a car starts north from C at 40 mi. per hr.; at 12:10 P.M., another car starts east from D at 60 mi. per hr. Find when the cars will be nearest together.   *Ans.* 12:17 P.M.

22. For the conditions of Ex. 21, draw the appropriate figures for times before 12:45 P.M., and after that time. Show that, in terms of time after noon, the formulas for distance between the two cars (one formula associated with each figure) are equivalent.

23. For Ex. 21, compute the time-rate of change of the distance between the cars at: (a) 12:15 P.M.; (b) 12:45 P.M.   *Ans.* (a) −4 mi. per hr.

24. One city, E, is 20 mi. north and 20 mi. east of another city, F. At noon, a car starts south from E at 40 mi. per hr.; at 12:10 P.M., another car starts east from F at 60 mi. per hr. Find the rate at which the cars approach each other between 12:10 P.M. and 12:30 P.M. What happens at 12:30 P.M.?   *Ans.* 72.1 mi. per hr.

25. A kite is 120 ft. high, with 130 ft. of cord out. If the kite moves horizontally 6.5 mi. per hr. directly away from the boy flying it, how fast is the cord being paid out?   *Ans.* 2.5 mi. per hr.

26. In Ex. 25, find the rate at which the slope of the cord is decreasing.
                                                     Ans. $\frac{286}{625}$ per sec.

27. A car drives from A toward C at 30 mi. per hr. Another car, starting from B at the same time, drives toward A at 20 mi. per hr. If $AB = 20$ mi., find when the cars will be nearest together. See Fig. 38.   *Ans.* $\frac{7}{19}$ hr.

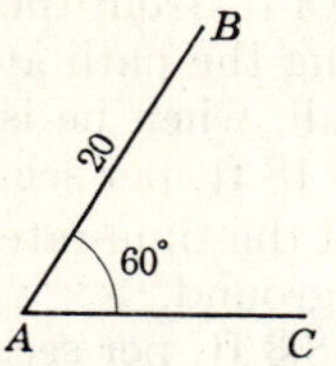

28. Solve Ex. 27 if the second car starts 30 min. later.
Ans. $\frac{1}{19}$ hr. after the second car starts.

29. Two railroad tracks intersect at right angles. At noon there is a train on each track approaching the crossing at 40 mi. per hr., one being 100 mi., the other 200 mi. distant. Find (a) when they will be the nearest together, and (b) what will be their minimum distance apart.
Ans. (a) 3:45 P.M.; (b) 70.7 mi.

Fig. 38

30. An elevated train on a track 30 ft. above the ground crosses a street at the rate of 20 ft. per sec. at the instant that a car, approaching at the rate of 30 ft. per sec., is 40 ft. up the street. Find how fast the train and the car are separating 1 second later.
Ans. $\frac{5}{7}\sqrt{14} = 2.67$ ft. per sec.

31. In Ex. 30, find when the train and the car are nearest together.
Ans. $1\frac{2}{3}$ sec.

32. From a car traveling east at 40 mi. per hr., an airplane traveling horizontally north at 100 mi. per hr. is visible 1 mi. east, 2 mi. south, and 2 mi. up. Find when the two will be nearest together.
Ans. $1\frac{7}{29}$ min.

33. In Ex. 32, find how fast the two will be separating after a long time.
Ans. $20\sqrt{29} = 107.7$ mi. per hr.

34. An arc light hangs at a height of 30 ft. above the center of a street 60 ft. wide. A man 6 ft. tall walks along the sidewalk at the rate of 4 ft. per sec. How fast is his shadow lengthening when he is 40 ft. up the street?
Ans. 0.8 ft. per sec.

35. In Ex. 34, how fast is the tip of the shadow moving?
Ans. 5 ft. per sec.

36. A ship sails east 20 mi. and then turns N. 30° W. If the ship's speed is 10 mi. per hr., find how fast it will be leaving the starting point 5 hr. after the start.   *Ans.* $\frac{20}{7}\sqrt{7}$ mi. per hr.

37. In Ex. 36, find when the ship will be nearest the starting point.
Ans. 3 hr.

38. In Ex. 36, when would the ship have been nearest the starting point if it had turned N. 45° W.?   *Ans.* 3 hr. 25 min.

39. Solve Ex. 36 if the ship turns N. 30° E.

CHAPTER 5 THE DIFFERENTIAL

43. Infinitesimals. When a variable, at some stage of the problem, is to *approach zero*, it is called an *infinitesimal*. Such variables are omnipresent in calculus, due to the fact that, in the problem of differentiation, both Δx and Δy approach zero — *i.e.*, they are infinitesimals.

A concept of fundamental importance in the theory of infinitesimals is that of *order*. Let one infinitesimal be defined as a function of another—say β as a function of α. If

$$(1) \qquad \lim_{\alpha \to 0} \frac{\beta}{\alpha} = k \quad (k \neq 0),$$

then β is said to be *infinitesimal of the first order* with respect to α. If

$$(2) \qquad \lim_{\alpha \to 0} \frac{\beta}{\alpha} = 0,$$

β is of *higher order than* α: precisely, if

$$(3) \qquad \lim_{\alpha \to 0} \frac{\beta}{\alpha^n} = k \quad (k \neq 0),$$

then β is *infinitesimal of the n-th order* with respect to α. Thus $k\alpha$, $k\alpha^2$, $k\alpha^3$, etc., are infinitesimal of first order, of second order, of third order, etc.

By the very definition of "limit," it follows from (3) that when α is small, $\dfrac{\beta}{\alpha^n}$ is nearly equal to k, so that β is approximately *proportional to* α^n. Since the square of a small quantity diminishes much

73

more rapidly than the quantity itself, the cube more rapidly than the square, etc., we see that *the higher the order of an infinitesimal, the more rapidly it approaches zero.*

Example: The surface and volume of a cubical box are infinitesimal of second and third orders, respectively, with respect to the length of the edge:

$$S = 6l^2, \qquad V = l^3.$$

If $l = 0.1$, $S = 0.06$, $V = 0.001$; if $l = 0.01$, $S = 0.0006$, $V = 0.000\,001$. Dividing l by 10 divides S by 100 and V by 1000.

The case of greatest importance is that in which β consists of a term of first order plus a term or terms of higher order:

(4) $$\beta = k\alpha + \epsilon \quad (k \neq 0),$$

where ϵ is a function of α (of any form, including the possibility $\epsilon \equiv 0$) subject to the single condition that it is infinitesimal of order higher than the first. Then, *the entire infinitesimal β is of first order.* Since ϵ is of order higher than one,

$$\lim_{\alpha \to 0} \frac{\epsilon}{\alpha} = 0.$$

It follows, therefore, that

$$\lim_{\alpha \to 0} \frac{\beta}{\alpha} = \lim_{\alpha \to 0} \left(k + \frac{\epsilon}{\alpha} \right) = k,$$

which means that β itself is of order one with respect to α.

THEOREM: *The product of any number of infinitesimals is infinitesimal; the order of the product is equal to the sum of the orders of the factors.*

Proof: Let β, γ be infinitesimal of respective orders m, n with respect to α. Then by (3),

$$\lim_{\alpha \to 0} \frac{\beta}{\alpha^m} = k_1, \qquad \lim_{\alpha \to 0} \frac{\gamma}{\alpha^n} = k_2,$$

whence by Theorem II, § 9,

$$\lim_{\alpha \to 0} \frac{\beta\gamma}{\alpha^{m+n}} = k_1 k_2,$$

so that, again by (3), $\beta\gamma$ is of order $m + n$.

44. Principal part of an infinitesimal. When an infinitesimal is the sum of several terms of different orders, the term of lowest order is called the *principal part*. Near the limit, the lowest-ordered term, although small, is *relatively* very large compared to the other terms; thus the word "principal" as used here has exactly its ordinary meaning—largest, most important.

Example (a): If $A = l^2$, then

$$A + \Delta A = (l + \Delta l)^2 = l^2 + 2l\,\Delta l + \overline{\Delta l}^2,$$
$$\Delta A = 2l\,\Delta l + \overline{\Delta l}^2.$$

Thus with l fixed, Δl infinitesimal, ΔA consists of a term of first order plus a term of second order, the former being the principal part.

Note that nothing is involved here beyond the most rudimentary common sense. For instance, in laying a 5-ft. sidewalk along two sides of a corner lot 100 ft. square, the bulk of the expense is due to the two long stretches, of combined area

$$2l\,\Delta l = 2 \times 100 \times 5 = 1000 \text{ sq. ft.;}$$

the little corner, of area

$$\overline{\Delta l}^2 = 5^2 = 25 \text{ sq. ft.,}$$

does not amount to much.

Example (b): If $y = x^3 - 2x$,

$$\Delta y = (3x^2 - 2)\,\Delta x + 3x\,\overline{\Delta x}^2 + \overline{\Delta x}^3.$$

(See the example, § 15.) Thus Δy is infinitesimal of first order, with principal part $(3x^2 - 2)\,\Delta x$.

45. The differential. By definition,

$$(1) \qquad\qquad \lim_{\Delta x \to 0} \frac{\Delta y}{\Delta x} = y'.$$

It follows at once that we may always write

$$(2) \qquad\qquad \Delta y = y'\,\Delta x + \epsilon,$$

where ϵ is infinitesimal of higher order. Let us verify this in Example (b), § 44:

$$\Delta y = (3x^2 - 2)\,\Delta x + 3x\,\overline{\Delta x}^2 + \overline{\Delta x}^3.$$

Thus the coefficient of Δx is y', as it should be according to (2), and ϵ is the second-order infinitesimal $3x\,\overline{\Delta x}^2 + \overline{\Delta x}^3$.

The term $y'\,\Delta x$ is called the *differential* of y, denoted by dy:

$$(3) \qquad\qquad\qquad\qquad dy = y'\,\Delta x.$$

Thus, except at particular points where $y' = 0$, *dy is the principal part of* Δy, and for small values, *dy and* Δy *are nearly equal.*

Theoretically, we are still at liberty to define dx—i.e., the differential of the independent variable—in any way we please. But if in (3) we put

$$y = x, \qquad y' = 1,$$

the result is

$$(4) \qquad\qquad\qquad\qquad dx = \Delta x.$$

Thus in order to avoid conflict when (3) is applied to the function $y = x$, we adopt (4) as our definition. That is, *the differential of the independent variable is equal to the increment of that variable.*

We may therefore write

$$(5) \qquad\qquad\qquad dy = y'\,dx = y'\,\Delta x,$$

and state the definition as follows:

The **differential** *of any function is equal to its derivative multiplied by the differential of the independent variable.*

It follows from this definition that *all the fundamental formulas for derivatives become differential formulas if we merely multiply through by* dx. For instance, the product formula is

$$d(uv) = u\,dv + v\,du:$$

in words, the differential of the product of two functions is equal to the first function times the differential of the second plus the second times the differential of the first.

Example (a):
$$y = x^3 - 2x,$$
$$dy = 3x^2\,dx - 2dx.$$

Example (b):
$$s = (1 + 2t)^3 - \sqrt{1 - t^2} + 4,$$
$$ds = 3(1 + 2t)^2\,2dt - \frac{-2t\,dt}{2\sqrt{1 - t^2}}$$
$$= 6(1 + 2t)^2\,dt + \frac{t\,dt}{\sqrt{1 - t^2}}.$$

Example (c): $y = \dfrac{z^2 - 1}{z^2 + 1}$,

$$dy = \frac{(z^2 + 1)2z\,dz - (z^2 - 1)2z\,dz}{(z^2 + 1)^2}$$

$$= \frac{4z\,dz}{(z^2 + 1)^2}.$$

Example (d): $x^3 + y^3 - 3axy = 0$,

$$3x^2\,dx + 3y^2\,dy - 3ax\,dy - 3ay\,dx = 0,$$

$$(y^2 - ax)\,dy + (x^2 - ay)\,dx = 0,$$

$$dy = -\frac{(x^2 - ay)\,dx}{y^2 - ax}.$$

We see now that the technique of differentiation is the same, except for a slight change in form, whether derivatives or differentials are used. It follows that differentials would hardly be worth bothering with, if they were to be used merely as an additional tool in differentiation. The importance of differentials lies elsewhere, as will begin to appear very shortly.

The geometric meaning of the differential is easily seen. The slope at the point $P : (x, y)$ on the curve

$$y = f(x)$$

(either Fig. 39 or Fig. 40) is

$$\frac{QR}{PQ} = \frac{QR}{\Delta x} = y',$$

so that

$$QR = y'\,\Delta x = dy.$$

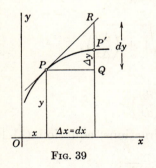

FIG. 39

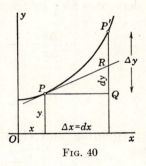

FIG. 40

It appears from the sketches that, in general, $dy < \Delta y$ or $dy > \Delta y$ according as the curve is concave upward or concave downward.

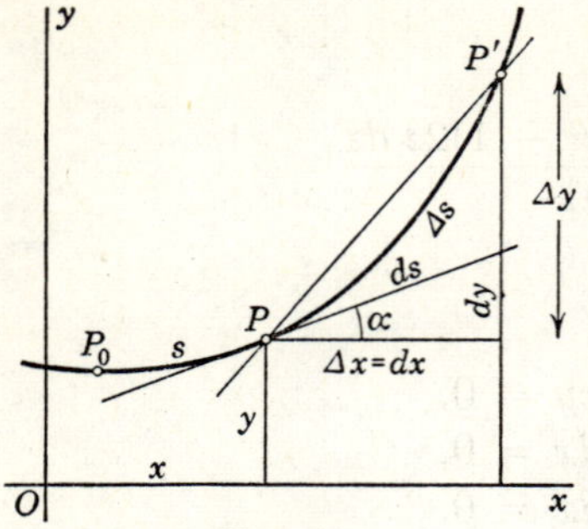

FIG. 41

46. Differential of arc. Let s denote the length of the arc of the plane curve

$$y = f(x)$$

measured from some initial point P_0 to the point $P : (x, y)$, and suppose for definiteness that s increases as x increases. The arc s is evidently a function of x. Its derivative $\dfrac{ds}{dx}$ may be found as follows:

$$\frac{\Delta s}{\Delta x} = \frac{\Delta s}{\overline{PP'}} \cdot \frac{\overline{PP'}}{\Delta x} = \frac{\Delta s}{\overline{PP'}} \cdot \frac{\sqrt{\overline{\Delta x^2} + \overline{\Delta y^2}}}{\Delta x}$$

$$= \frac{\Delta s}{\overline{PP'}} \cdot \sqrt{1 + \left(\frac{\Delta y}{\Delta x}\right)^2},$$

where Δs is the length of the arc, $\overline{PP'}$ the length of the chord, from $P : (x, y)$ to $P' : (x + \Delta x, y + \Delta y)$. Since

$$\lim_{\Delta x \to 0} \frac{\Delta s}{\overline{PP'}} = 1,$$

we have

(1) $$\frac{ds}{dx} = \lim_{\Delta x \to 0} \frac{\Delta s}{\Delta x} = \sqrt{1 + \left(\frac{dy}{dx}\right)^2}.$$

If s decreases as x increases, then

$$\frac{\Delta s}{\Delta x} = -\frac{\Delta s}{\overline{PP'}} \cdot \sqrt{1 + \left(\frac{\Delta y}{\Delta x}\right)^2},$$

and

(2) $$\frac{ds}{dx} = -\sqrt{1 + \left(\frac{dy}{dx}\right)^2}.$$

After squaring and clearing of fractions, equation (1) [or (2)] becomes

$$\overline{ds}^2 = \overline{dx}^2 + \overline{dy}^2;$$

i.e., ds is the hypotenuse of the right triangle whose sides are dx and dy.

If the tangent to the curve at P makes an angle α with Ox, then

$$\cos \alpha = \frac{dx}{ds}, \qquad \sin \alpha = \frac{dy}{ds}.$$

Right now we are not in position to make any application of these results, but they will be needed in the next chapter and many times later.

EXERCISES

In Exs. 1–24 find the differential of the given function.

1. $y = 2x^4 - 7x^3 + x - 3.$
$\qquad$ *Ans.* $dy = 8x^3\,dx - 21x^2\,dx + dx = (8x^3 - 21x^2 + 1)\,dx.$

2. $z = (1 - 2t + t^3)^{-\frac{3}{2}}.$ $\qquad$ *Ans.* $dz = \frac{3}{2}(2 - 3t^2)(1 - 2t + t^3)^{-\frac{5}{2}}\,dt.$

3. $x = (3t + 2)^4.$ $\qquad\qquad\qquad$ **4.** $y = (1 - x^3)^2.$

5. $z = \sqrt{4 - 3x}.$ $\qquad\qquad\qquad$ **6.** $\beta = \dfrac{3}{\sqrt{1 - 2\alpha}}.$

7. $u = \sqrt{2y - y^2}.$ $\qquad$ *Ans.* $du = (1 - y)(2y - y^2)^{-\frac{1}{2}}\,dy.$

8. $x = \frac{1}{3}t^3 - \sqrt{t} + \dfrac{1}{t^2}.$ $\qquad$ *Ans.* $dx = \left(t^2 - \dfrac{1}{2\sqrt{t}} - \dfrac{2}{t^3}\right)dt.$

9. $y = x(3 + 2x)^4.$ $\qquad\qquad$ **10.** $w = x^2(1 - x^2)^{\frac{1}{2}}.$

11. $u = \dfrac{v^3}{v + 2}.$ $\qquad\qquad$ **12.** $x = \dfrac{t^2}{\sqrt{1 - t}}.$

13. $y = \sqrt{x^2 - a^2},$ a held constant. $\qquad$ *Ans.* $dy = \dfrac{x\,dx}{\sqrt{x^2 - a^2}}.$

14. $y = \sqrt{x^2 - a^2},$ x held constant. $\qquad$ *Ans.* $dy = \dfrac{-a\,da}{\sqrt{x^2 - a^2}}.$

15. $x = t^2(t^2 + 4)^{\frac{3}{2}}.$ $\qquad\qquad$ **16.** $x = y^3(9 - y^2)^{\frac{1}{2}}.$

17. $r = \dfrac{s}{\sqrt{1 - s^2}}.$ $\qquad\qquad$ **18.** $r = \dfrac{\sqrt{1 - s^2}}{s}.$

19. $y = (1 + \sqrt{x})^4.$ $\qquad\qquad$ **20.** $y = \sqrt{1 + \sqrt{x}}.$

21. $x = \dfrac{t}{(2 - 3t)^4}.$ $\qquad$ *Ans.* $dx = \dfrac{(9t + 2)\,dt}{(2 - 3t)^5}.$

22. $y = \dfrac{(1 - x)^2}{(1 - 2x)^2}.$ $\qquad$ *Ans.* $dy = \dfrac{2(1 - x)\,dx}{(1 - 2x)^3}.$

23. $r = \sqrt{\dfrac{1 - s}{1 + s}}.$ $\qquad$ *Ans.* $dr = \dfrac{-ds}{(1 - s)^{\frac{1}{2}}(1 + s)^{\frac{3}{2}}}.$

24. $y = \dfrac{(x^3 - x)^2}{x + 1}.$ $\qquad$ *Ans.* $dy = x(x - 1)(5x^2 + x - 2)\,dx.$

In Exs. 25–32, find dy.

25. $y^2 = 4ax$. $\qquad\qquad$ *Ans.* $dy = \dfrac{2a\,dx}{y}.$

26. $\dfrac{x^2}{a^2} - \dfrac{y^2}{b^2} = 1$. $\qquad$ *Ans.* $dy = \dfrac{b^2x\,dx}{a^2y}.$

27. $x^2 + xy + y^2 = 4$.

28. $3x^2 - 6xy + 3y^2 - 7x + 2y - 1 = 0$.

29. $x^{\frac{2}{3}} + y^{\frac{2}{3}} = a^{\frac{2}{3}}$. $\qquad\qquad$ **30.** $y^2 = \dfrac{x^2}{x^2 - a^2}.$

31. $y^2 = \dfrac{x^3}{2a - x}.$ $\qquad\qquad$ **32.** $y^3 = \dfrac{x^2}{a - x}.$

From the parametric equations in each of Exs. 33–37, find $y' = \dfrac{dy}{dx}$ from the quotient dy divided by dx.

33. $x = 1 + t^2$, $\quad y = t^3 - 2$. $\qquad$ *Ans.* $y' = \frac{3}{2}t.$

34. $x = 2 - 3t + t^3$, $\quad y = 3t^2 - 7$. $\qquad$ *Ans.* $y' = \dfrac{2t}{t^2 - 1}.$

35. $x = (\beta^2 - 1)^2$, $\quad y = 4\beta^3$. $\qquad$ *Ans.* $y' = \dfrac{3\beta}{\beta^2 - 1}.$

36. $x = \dfrac{1}{u^2}$, $\quad y = u^4 - 2u^2 + \dfrac{4}{u}$. $\quad$ *Ans.* $y' = 2u(1 + u^3 - u^5).$

37. $x = \dfrac{1}{t + 1}$, $\quad y = \dfrac{1}{t - 1}$. $\qquad$ *Ans.* $y' = \left(\dfrac{t + 1}{t - 1}\right)^2.$

In each of Exs. 38–44, find $y'' = \dfrac{d^2y}{dx^2}$ by first obtaining y' and then $\dfrac{dy'}{dx}$.

38. Ex. 33. $\qquad\qquad\qquad\qquad$ *Ans.* $y'' = \dfrac{3}{4t}.$

39. Ex. 34. $\qquad\qquad$ *Ans.* $y'' = \dfrac{-2(t^2 + 1)}{3(t^2 - 1)^3}.$

40. Ex. 35. $\qquad\qquad$ *Ans.* $y'' = \dfrac{-3(\beta^2 + 1)}{4\beta(\beta^2 - 1)^3}.$

41. Ex. 36. $\qquad\qquad$ *Ans.* $y'' = u^3(6u^5 - 4u^3 - 1).$

42. Ex. 37. $\qquad\qquad$ *Ans.* $y'' = 4\left(\dfrac{t + 1}{t - 1}\right)^3.$

43. $x = t^2 - 3$, $\quad y = t^3 + t + 1$. $\qquad$ *Ans.* $y'' = \dfrac{3t^2 - 1}{4t^3}.$

44. $x = 1 - \dfrac{1}{t}$, $\quad y = 6 - \dfrac{7}{t} + \dfrac{2}{t^2}$. $\qquad$ *Ans.* $y'' = 4.$

47. Approximate formulas. Very often we wish to compute, or to estimate within safe limits, the change in the value of a function caused by a small change in the value of the independent variable. As noted in § 45, when Δx is small, dy and Δy are, in general, nearly equal, and in many cases *the value of dy furnishes a sufficiently good approximation to the value of* Δy.

In any approximate computation, the amount by which the computed value of the function differs from the true value is called the *error* of the computation. Of course in using any approximate formula, we should make sure that the error committed is within the allowable limit of error for the problem in hand. This question will be considered more fully in § 208.

Example (a): Find an approximate formula for the area of a narrow circular ring.

The area of a circle of radius r is

$$A = \pi r^2.$$

When the radius increases by an amount Δr, the area increases by an amount ΔA whose principal part is

$$dA = 2\pi r\, dr = 2\pi r\, \Delta r.$$

(Since r is the independent variable, $dr = \Delta r$.) Hence the area of a narrow circular ring is approximately the *product of the circumference by the width*.

Example (b): Find approximately the change in the square root of a number produced by a small change in the number.

Here

$$y = \sqrt{x}, \qquad dy = \frac{dx}{2\sqrt{x}} = \frac{\Delta x}{2\sqrt{x}}.$$

That is, the change in the square root is approximately the change in the number divided by twice the square root. The result fails when $\sqrt{x}$ is small in comparison with Δx, owing to the fact that Δy is no longer small.

The above formula may be used to find the square root of a number.

Example (c): Extract the square root of 9.12.

In Example (b), take $x = 9$, $\Delta x = 0.12$:

$$\frac{\Delta x}{2\sqrt{x}} = 0.02, \qquad \sqrt{9.12} = 3.02.$$

To four places, the correct value is 3.0199.

EXERCISES

1. Find approximately the volume of a thin spherical shell.

Ans. Surface area $\times$ *thickness.*

2. Find an approximate formula for the volume of a thin cylindrical shell of given height.   *Ans. Circumference* $\times$ *height* $\times$ *thickness.*

3. Find approximately the volume of wood required to make a cubical box, of edge length 5 ft., using boards $\frac{1}{2}$ in. thick.   *Ans.* 6.25 cu. ft.

4. The base of a right triangle is fixed at 3 ft., the hypotenuse is 5 ft. long and subject to change. Find the approximate change in altitude when the hypotenuse is changed by a small amount Δh.   *Ans.* 1.25 Δh.

5. The diameter of a circle is measured and found to be 4 ft. with a maximum error of 0.1 in. Find the approximate maximum error in the computed area.   *Ans.* 7.54 sq. in.

6. The diameter of a sphere is measured and found to be 4 ft. with a maximum error of 0.1 in. Find the approximate maximum error in the computed volume.   *Ans.* 362 cu. in.

7. Find the approximate maximum error in computing the surface area of the sphere of Ex. 6.   *Ans.* 30.2 sq. in.

8. Find approximately the change in the reciprocal of a number x produced by a small change in the number. Investigate also the case when the number itself is small.   *Ans.* $\dfrac{-\Delta x}{x^2}$.

9. Divide 1 by 9.83. Use Ex. 8.   *Ans.* 0.1017.

10. Divide 1 by 25.3.   *Ans.* 0.0395.

11. The diameter of a circle is to be measured, and its area computed. If the diameter can be measured with a maximum error of 0.001 in., and the area must be accurate to within 0.1 sq. in., find the largest diameter for which the process can be used.   *Ans.* Nearly 64 in.

12. The diameter of a sphere is to be measured, and its volume computed. If the diameter can be measured with a maximum error of 0.001 in., and the volume must be accurate to within 0.1 cu. in., find the largest diameter for which the process can be used.   *Ans.* Nearly 8 in.

13. A closed cylindrical tank of circular cross-section has a radius of 2 ft. and a height of 6 ft. Find the approximate volume of asbestos required to line the tank completely with a lining one inch thick.

Ans. 8.4 cu. ft.

14. A bin is 10 $\times$ 9 $\times$ 8 ft. Find approximately the change in the volume when the bin is completely lined with paper $\frac{1}{16}$ in. thick.

Ans. -2.52 cu. ft.

15. The volume of a body of gas is measured; the pressure is then computed from the formula

$$p = \frac{k}{v}.$$

If the allowable error in p is $0.001k$, and the maximum error in measuring v is 0.4 cu. ft., what is the volume of the smallest container to which the process can be applied?   *Ans.* 20 cu. ft.

16. Suppose that the container in Ex. 15 is a cube of edge length s. Find the approximate error in the computed value of p due to a small error in measuring s.

17. In Ex. 16, if $s = 10 \pm 0.3$, how accurately can p be determined?

Ans. $dp \leqq 9(10)^{-5}k$.

18. The attraction between two magnetic poles is inversely proportional to the square of the distance between them: $F = \dfrac{k}{r^2}$. If the distance is slightly increased, how is the attraction affected?

19. The attraction between two magnetic poles is measured, and the distance between them computed (cf. Ex. 18). If $k = 1$ and $F = 6.3 \pm 0.1$, find r.

Ans. 0.398 ∓ 0.003 in.

20. A 16-lb. shot is made of iron weighing 444 lbs. per cu. ft. If the weight must be accurate within 1 oz., find the radius.

Ans. 2.459 ± 0.003 in.

21. A hollow sphere of outer radius 1 ft. is made of metal weighing about 400 lbs. per cu. ft. The volume of metal is found by weighing to be 2 cu. ft., with an uncertainty of 0.1 cu. ft. due to the uncertain density. Find the inner radius.

Ans. $9.67 + 0.15$ in.

In Exs. 22–29, use differentials to approximate to the desired number.

22. The square root of 623.   Ans. 24.96.
23. The square root of 286.   Ans. 16.91.
24. The square root of 36.3.   Ans. 6.025.
25. The square root of 101.2.   Ans. 10.06.
26. The cube root of 9.   Ans. 2.083.
27. The cube root of 339.   Ans. 6.973.
28. The cube root of 3.4.   Ans. 1.504.
29. The fourth root of 17.   Ans. 2.031.

30. Find the change in the lateral surface of a right circular cone, with radius of base fixed as r, when the altitude h changes by a small amount Δh.

Ans. $\dfrac{\pi r h \, \Delta h}{\sqrt{r^2 + h^2}}$.

31. Solve Ex. 30 if the radius changes (altitude fixed).

Ans. $\dfrac{\pi(h^2 + 2r^2) \, \Delta r}{\sqrt{r^2 + h^2}}$.

32. Find the lateral surface of a circular cone of radius 5 ft., height 12 ft., if the radius is uncertain by $\frac{1}{4}$ in. (Ex. 31.)   Ans. $(65 \pm 0.3)\pi$ sq. ft.

33. For what values of x may $\sqrt[3]{x + 1}$ be replaced by $\sqrt[3]{x}$, if the allowable inaccuracy is 0.01?

Ans. $x > 192$.

CHAPTER 6 INTEGRATION

48. Integration. We have been occupied up to this point with the problem: Given a function, to find its derivative (or differential). Many of the most important applications of the calculus lead to the inverse problem: *Given the derivative of a function, to find the function.* The required function is called an *integral* of the given derivative, and the process of finding it is called *integration.* The given function is the *integrand.*

If $f(x)$ is a given function and $F(x)$ is a function whose derivative is $f(x)$, the relation between them is expressed by writing

$$F(x) = \int f(x)\, dx,$$

where the symbol $\int$, called the *integral sign*, indicates that we are to perform the operation of integration upon $f(x)\, dx$: that is, we are to find a function whose derivative is $f(x)$, or whose differential is $f(x)\, dx$. For reasons that will appear later, we always write after the integral sign the differential $f(x)\, dx$ rather than the derivative $f(x)$.

Example (a): Evaluate $\int x^2\, dx$.

Since differentiation reduces the exponent by 1, integration must *increase* the exponent by 1 (in order that, upon differentiating our answer, we may return to the original exponent). Thus our first guess at the answer might be x^3. But

$$d(x^3) = 3x^2\, dx:$$

an unwanted factor 3 presents itself. To correct this, we amend our first guess by dividing by 3. Now, $d(\frac{1}{3}x^3) = x^2\, dx$, but the addition of any constant whatever to $(\frac{1}{3}x^3)$ does not alter the differential. Hence

(1)
$$\int x^2 \, dx = \tfrac{1}{3}x^3 + C,$$

where C is an arbitrary constant. Equation (1) is equivalent to the statement that $d(\frac{1}{3}x^3 + C) = x^2 \, dx$.

It is natural to inquire whether there may be other correct, and essentially different, functions for the right member of (1); that is, whether any function can have the differential $(x^2 \, dx)$ and differ from $\frac{1}{3}x^3$ by other than a constant. The answer, contained in the following theorem, is "No!".

THEOREM: *Two functions having the same derivative differ only by a constant.*

Let $\phi(x)$ and $\psi(x)$ be the two functions, and place

$$y = \phi(x) - \psi(x).$$

By hypothesis,

$$y' = \phi'(x) - \psi'(x) = 0.$$

The rate of change of y with respect to x is everywhere zero, hence y is constant.

In the following examples, the student should try to obtain the answer for himself, by intelligent guesswork, and should finally verify by differentiation.

Example (b): $\int \sqrt{1 + 5x} \, dx = \tfrac{2}{15}(1 + 5x)^{\frac{3}{2}} + C.$

Example (c): $\int (a^2 - y^2)^6 \, y \, dy = -\tfrac{1}{14}(a^2 - y^2)^7 + C.$

Example (d): $\int \dfrac{dt}{\sqrt{1 - t}} = \int (1 - t)^{-\frac{1}{2}} \, dt = -2(1 - t)^{\frac{1}{2}} + C.$

It is now clear that a function whose derivative is given is not completely determined, since it contains an arbitrary additive constant, the *constant of integration*. For this reason, the function $\int f(x) \, dx$ is called the *indefinite integral* of $f(x)$.

49. General properties of indefinite integrals. The following properties of indefinite integrals are easily verified by differentiation.

$$\int du = u + C.$$

$$\int (du + dv + \cdots + dz) = \int du + \int dv + \cdots + \int dz.$$

$$\int c \, du = c \int du.$$

The first formula is merely the definition of an integral.

The second formula shows that if the integrand consists of a sum of terms, each term may be integrated separately.

The third formula says that if the integrand contains a constant factor, that factor may be written before the integral sign. As a corollary, we may *introduce a constant factor into the integrand,* provided we place its reciprocal before the integral sign. But it is *never* allowable to introduce variable factors by this rule, for the reason that an answer obtained in this way cannot possibly be correct.*

50. The power formula. In the formula

$$d(u^n) = nu^{n-1} \, du,$$

let us replace n by $n + 1$:

$$d(u^{n+1}) = (n + 1)u^n \, du.$$

Divide by $n + 1$ (since this is impossible when $n = -1$, that value must be excluded), and reverse the equation:

$$u^n \, du = \frac{d(u^{n+1})}{n + 1}.$$

* Given

(1) $$F(x) = \int f(x) \, dx,$$

write

(2) $$F(x) = \frac{1}{u} \int uf(x) \, dx,$$

or

$$uF(x) = \int uf(x) \, dx.$$

Differentiate:

(3) $$uF'(x) \, dx + F(x) \, du = uf(x) \, dx.$$

But, from (1), $F'(x) = f(x)$, so that (3) becomes

$$F(x) \, du = 0.$$

Since $F(x) \neq 0$, we must have $du = 0$, $u = C$ if (2) is to be true.

Integrating, we obtain the *general power-formula of integration:*

(1) $$\int u^n\, du = \frac{u^{n+1}}{n+1} + C \qquad (n \neq -1).$$

This formula, *correctly applied*, serves to evaluate each of the examples of § 48, and in fact every integral occurring in this chapter. (In Chapter 16, analogous formulas will be developed for the other types of elementary integrals.) Thus the hit-or-miss method of § 48 may now be replaced by straightforward use of the formula. But aside from mere algebraic mistakes, it often happens, especially at first, that the student interprets the formula incorrectly: thus it is just as important as ever that each answer be checked by differentiation.

Example (a):

$$\int \left(3x^3 + 1 + \frac{1}{2x^2}\right) dx = 3\int x^3\, dx + \int dx + \frac{1}{2}\int x^{-2}\, dx$$
$$= \frac{3x^4}{4} + x - \frac{1}{2}x^{-1} + C$$
$$= \frac{3x^4}{4} + x - \frac{1}{2x} + C.$$

After a little practice the answer can be written at once, both intermediate steps being omitted.

Example (b): Evaluate $\int (a^2 - y^2)^5 y\, dy.$

This resembles (1) with $u = a^2 - y^2$, $n = 5$. Since

$$d(a^2 - y^2) = -2y\, dy,$$

we introduce the factor -2 under the integral sign, with its reciprocal in front:

$$\int (a^2 - y^2)^5 y\, dy = -\frac{1}{2}\int (a^2 - y^2)^5 (-2y)\, dy = -\frac{(a^2 - y^2)^6}{12} + C.$$

This integral could also be evaluated by expanding $(a^2 - y^2)^5$ and integrating the resulting row of powers; but this would be an exceedingly slow and tiresome method.

Example (c): Evaluate $\int (a^2 - x^2)^2\, dx.$

This resembles Example (b), but only superficially. In any attempt to use Formula (1) directly, it is found that when we choose

$u = a^2 - x^2$, $n = 2$, then the differential

$$du = d(a^2 - x^2) = -2x \, dx$$

is not present in our integrand. The (-2) can be inserted, but nothing can be done about that missing factor x.

We are therefore forced to have recourse to expansion of $(a^2 - x^2)^2$, followed by a term-by-term integration. Thus the integral can be evaluated as follows:

$$\int (a^2 - x^2)^2 \, dx = \int (a^4 - 2a^2x^2 + x^4) \, dx$$
$$= a^4x - \tfrac{2}{3}a^2x^3 + \tfrac{1}{5}x^5 + C.$$

Example (*d*): Evaluate $\int (2x + 3) \, dx$.

First method: $\int (2x + 3) \, dx = x^2 + 3x + C.$

Second method:

$$\int (2x + 3) \, dx = \frac{1}{2} \int (2x + 3)2 \, dx = \frac{(2x + 3)^2}{4} + C_1.$$

This simple example is introduced to exhibit a very common phenomenon. We shall meet plenty of cases where two answers, both correct, differ widely in appearance; yet it will always be possible to show that they differ at most by a constant, however improbable this may seem at first sight. Here, we have only to expand the second form:

$$\frac{(2x + 3)^2}{4} + C_1 = x^2 + 3x + \tfrac{9}{4} + C_1 = x^2 + 3x + C.$$

This shows that the arbitrary constants C, C_1 merely differ by $\tfrac{9}{4}$. In the exercises, when the result of an integration is given, it is not implied that the one given is the only correct form, or even necessarily better than any other.

EXERCISES

Evaluate the following integrals; check by differentiation.

1. $\int (x^3 - 2x) \, dx.$ 2. $\int (4x - x^2) \, dx.$

3. $\int (6x^3 - 3x + 1) \, dx.$ 4. $\int (10x^4 + 6x^2 - 1) \, dx.$

5. $\int \dfrac{dv}{v^2}.$ Ans. $-\dfrac{1}{v} + C.$

6. $\int \dfrac{6\,dz}{z^4}.$ Ans. $-\dfrac{2}{z^3} + C.$

7. $\int (4 - y^{-2})\,dy.$

8. $\int \left(\dfrac{1}{y^3} - y \right) dy.$

9. $\int \left(\sqrt{t} - \dfrac{1}{\sqrt{t}} \right) dt.$ Ans. $\frac{2}{3}t^{\frac{3}{2}} - 2t^{\frac{1}{2}} + C.$

10. $\int \left(u^{\frac{3}{2}} + \dfrac{1}{u^{\frac{3}{2}}} \right) du.$ Ans. $\frac{2}{5}u^{\frac{5}{2}} - 2u^{-\frac{1}{2}} + C.$

11. $\int (y - 2)^3\,dy.$

12. $\int (a + x)^4\,dx.$

13. $\int \dfrac{dx}{(x + 1)^3}.$

14. $\int \dfrac{du}{(u - 4)^2}.$

15. $\int (4x + 1)^2\,dx.$

Ans. $\frac{1}{12}(4x + 1)^3 + C.$

16. $\int \dfrac{dx}{(2x - 7)^4}.$

Ans. $-\frac{1}{6}(2x - 7)^{-3} + C.$

17. $\int \dfrac{dx}{\sqrt{3x - 4a}}.$

18. $\int \dfrac{dv}{(4v + 3a)^{\frac{3}{2}}}.$

19. $\int (x^4 + a^4)^2\,dx.$

20. $\int (x^4 - 2a^2x^2)\,dx.$

21. $\int \left(x - \dfrac{1}{x} \right)^2 dx.$

22. $\int x(4 - x)^2\,dx.$

23. $\int \dfrac{dy}{\sqrt{1 - 3y}}.$

24. $\int \dfrac{dz}{(4 - z)^3}.$

25. $\int x(1 + x^2)^4\,dx.$

26. $\int \dfrac{y\,dy}{(1 + y^2)^2}.$

27. $\int (1 + x^2)^3\,dx.$

28. $\int y^2(a^2 - y^2)\,dy.$

29. $\int \dfrac{u\,du}{\sqrt{a^2 + u^2}}.$

30. $\int u^2(a^2 - u^2)^2\,du.$

31. $\int x(x^3 + 2)^2\,dx.$

32. $\int x^2(x^3 + 2)^4\,dx.$

33. $\int \dfrac{x^3 + a^3}{x^2}\, dx.$ **34.** $\int \dfrac{a^2 - y^2}{y^2}\, dy.$

35. $\int (x^7 + 3x)^5\, dx.$

In Exs. 36–39, integrate by two different methods and show that your answers are equivalent.

36. $\int x(2 - x^2)\, dx.$ **37.** $\int y^2(1 - y^3)^2\, dy.$

38. $\int u^{\frac{1}{2}}(u^{\frac{3}{2}} - 5)^2\, du.$ **39.** $\int \dfrac{(\sqrt{x} - 1)^2\, dx}{\sqrt{x}}.$

51. Rectilinear motion. Consider a point P moving in a straight line. Choose as origin any convenient fixed point in the line of motion, and denote the distance OP by x, positive on one side of O, negative on the other. In accordance with

FIG. 42

the argument of § 20 (last paragraph), the *velocity* at any instant is defined as

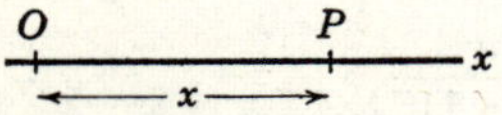

$$(1) \qquad\qquad v = \frac{dx}{dt};$$

that is, *velocity is time-rate of change of distance, measured from a fixed point in the line of motion.*

When the velocity is constant, the motion is said to be *uniform*, and the distance covered in any time is merely proportional to the time. When the velocity changes from instant to instant, the motion is *accelerated*.

Acceleration, denoted in this book by a, is defined by the formula

$$(2) \qquad\qquad a = \frac{dv}{dt};$$

that is, *acceleration is time-rate of change of velocity.*

Since we may write

$$\frac{dv}{dt} = \frac{dv}{dx} \cdot \frac{dx}{dt} = v\frac{dv}{dx},$$

an alternative form of (2) is

$$(3) \qquad\qquad a = v\frac{dv}{dx}.$$

Of course the moving "point" may be a body of any size or shape, provided the motion of a single point determines the motion of the whole mass: for instance, a locomotive on a straight track if we neglect the internal motions—wheels, pistons, etc.

When a particle of mass m moves with an acceleration a, the motion is said to be due to the action of *force*. Force is defined as the *product of mass by acceleration:*

$$F = ma.$$

If there is no force acting (or if all the forces balance), the particle is *in equilibrium*. A particle in equilibrium is either at rest or moving uniformly in a straight line.

In view of the relation $F = ma$, equations (2) and (3) yield

(4) $$F = m\,\frac{dv}{dt} = m\,\frac{d^2x}{dt^2},$$

and

(5) $$F = mv\,\frac{dv}{dx}.$$

When the acceleration (or force) is given as a function of time, the velocity and position can be found by successive integrations. For, by (2),

$$dv = a\,dt, \qquad v = \int a\,dt + C_1;$$

by (1),

$$dx = v\,dt, \qquad x = \int v\,dt + C_2.$$

Since two constants of integration are introduced, we must always have given the initial position and velocity, the position at two different times, or some other pair of conditions enabling us to determine the constants. The given data are called *initial conditions*, or *boundary conditions*.

52. Falling body. When the acceleration is constant, the motion is *uniformly accelerated*. An important instance of uniformly accelerated motion arises when a body moves near the earth's surface in a vertical straight line. The attraction of the earth gives it an acceleration, denoted by g, roughly equal to *32 ft. per sec. per sec.

---

* A more nearly correct value is 32.16 ft. per sec. per sec. Since we are interested in methods, rather than in numerical refinement, the value 32 ft. per sec. per sec. will be used.

Take the starting point as origin, and the distance x and velocity v as positive downward. If the body starts, at $x = 0$, with an initial velocity v_0, then

$$a = \frac{dv}{dt} = g; \qquad \text{when } t = 0, \text{ then } x = 0, v = v_0.$$

From

$$dv = g \, dt,$$

we get

$$v = gt + C_1.$$

The condition $v = v_0$, $t = 0$ gives $C_1 = v_0$, so that

(1) $$v = gt + v_0.$$

Replacing v by $\dfrac{dx}{dt}$ and integrating again, we get

$$x = \tfrac{1}{2}gt^2 + v_0 t + C_2;$$

since $x = 0$ when $t = 0$, $C_2 = 0$ and

(2) $$x = \tfrac{1}{2}gt^2 + v_0 t.$$

By eliminating t between equations (1) and (2), we arrive at the useful result:

(3) $$v^2 = v_0{}^2 + 2gx.$$

In all motion problems, we shall disregard negative values of t, assuming the motion to start at $t = 0$.

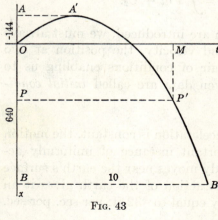

FIG. 43

Example (a): A ball is dropped from a balloon at a height of 640 ft. If the balloon is rising 96 ft. per sec., find the highest point reached by the ball, and the time of flight.

By (2), with $g = 32$,

(4) $$x = 16t^2 - 96t.$$

From (4), we obtain

(5) $$v = 32t - 96.$$

At the highest point, $v = 0$, hence

$$t = 3, \qquad x = 144 - 288 = -144 \text{ ft.}$$

Thus the height above the starting point is 144 ft.; the distance above the ground is $640 + 144 = 784$ ft. To find the time of flight (time when the ball strikes the ground), put $x = 640$ in (4):

$$640 = 16t^2 - 96t,$$
$$16(t^2 - 6t - 40) = 0,$$
$$t = -4 \quad \text{or} \quad t = 10.$$

Thus the ball is in the air for 10 sec.

The graph of x as a function of t is the parabolic arc $OA'B'$ (Ox positive downward). The actual path of the ball, of course, is from O to A, then down to the ground at B. To find graphically the position at any time, say $t = OM$, erect the ordinate MP' and project P' to P. To find the time corresponding to any position P, draw the abscissa PP' and project P' to M. For $x < 0$ (ball above the starting point), t of course is two-valued.

With different initial conditions, a different line of attack may be indicated. In particular, when a (v, x)-pair is given—velocity at a certain position—it is best to start with (3).

Example (b): The velocity 2 ft. below the starting point is 18 ft. per sec. If the start is made from a height of 200 ft., when and with what velocity does the body strike the earth?

With $g = 32$, and the starting point as origin, we have

$$a = v\frac{dv}{dx} = 32; \qquad x = 0 \text{ when } t = 0, \quad v = 18 \text{ when } x = 2.$$

A first integration gives

$$v^2 = 64x + C_1.$$

The reason for starting with (3) is now apparent: we can use $v = 18$, $x = 2$ to find C_1:

$$C_1 = 324 - 128 = 196,$$
(6) $$v^2 = 64x + 196.$$

When $x = 200$, $v = \sqrt{12800 + 196} = 114$ ft. per sec. (The negative sign of course must be rejected.) Now by (6), when $x = 0$, $v = \pm 14$. Starting over again, we have

$$\frac{dv}{dt} = 32, \qquad v = \pm 14 \text{ when } t = 0;$$
$$v = 32t \pm 14.$$

The final value of v just found, viz., $v = 114$, gives

$$32t = 114 \mp 14, \qquad t = 3\tfrac{1}{8} \text{ or } 4 \text{ sec.}$$

Thus the body strikes the ground after $3\tfrac{1}{8}$ or 4 sec., with a velocity of 114 ft. per sec.

In this problem it could be foreseen that t must turn out as a two-valued function. For, the given data do not tell whether the initial velocity of 14 ft. per sec. is upward or downward—either one will produce a velocity of 18 ft. per sec. 2 ft. below the starting point; yet obviously the time of reaching the earth will be different in the two cases.

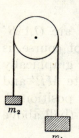

m_2

m_1

Fig. 44

53. Atwood's Machine. In the apparatus called *Atwood's Machine*, two masses m_1, m_2 are joined by a cord hung over a pulley, as in Fig. 44. Suppose for definiteness that $m_1 > m_2$. The total mass moved (if the masses of the cord and pulley can be neglected) is

$$m = m_1 + m_2,$$

while the force producing the motion is

$$F = m_1 g - m_2 g.$$

Hence equation (4) of § 51 becomes

$$(m_1 + m_2)\frac{dv}{dt} = (m_1 - m_2)g,$$

or

$$\frac{dv}{dt} = \frac{m_1 - m_2}{m_1 + m_2}g.$$

From this point the discussion proceeds as in § 52.

EXERCISES

In Exs. 1–21, a body moves in a vertical line under gravity alone, air resistance, etc. being neglected.

1. If the initial velocity is 16 ft. per sec. upward, how far and for how long a time does the body rise?   *Ans.* 4 ft.; 0.5 sec.

2. If the initial velocity is 40 ft. per sec. upward, how far and for how long a time does the body rise?   *Ans.* 25 ft.; 1.25 sec.

3. If the velocity after one second is 8 ft. per sec. downward, find (a) the initial velocity and (b) the greatest distance above the starting point.   *Ans.* (a) 24 ft. per sec. upward; (b) 9 ft.

4. If the velocity after one second is 8 ft. per sec. upward, find (a) the initial velocity and (b) the greatest distance above the starting point.
Ans. (a) 40 ft. per sec. upward; (b) 25 ft.

5. If the body rises 49 ft. before starting to fall, find the initial velocity, and the time required to return to the starting point.
Ans. $v_0 = -56$ ft. per sec.; $t = \frac{7}{4}$ sec.

6. During the third second, the body falls 70 ft. Find the initial velocity.
Ans. -10 ft. per sec.

7. During the third second, the body falls 100 ft. Find the initial velocity.
Ans. 20 ft. per sec.

8. During the third second, the velocity doubles. Find the initial velocity.
Ans. -32 ft. per sec.

9. A ball is thrown upward and rises 9 ft. before starting to fall. Find the total time taken for the ball to return to the starting point.
Ans. 1.5 sec.

10. At what times was the ball of Ex. 9 at a distance 8 ft. above its starting point?
Ans. $\frac{1}{2}$ sec., 1 sec.

11. From a point 36 ft. above the ground, with what velocity must a stone be thrown to reach the ground in 1 sec.?
Ans. 20 ft. per sec.

12. From a point 36 ft. above the ground, with what velocity must a stone be thrown to take 4 sec. to reach the ground?
Ans. 55 ft. per sec. upward.

13. From a point 128 ft. above the ground, a stone is thrown in such a way that it is at the same point, 4 sec. after it was thrown, as it was 3 sec. after it was thrown. How long does it take the stone to reach the ground?
Ans. 8 sec.

14. A ball is thrown upward from the ground with a speed of 40 ft. per sec.; at the same instant another ball is dropped (from rest) from a height of 100 ft. Show that they strike the ground at the same time.

15. The velocity 1 ft. below the starting point is 10 ft. per sec. If the starting point is at a height of 76 ft., when and with what velocity does the body strike the earth?
Ans. $t = 2$ or $2\frac{3}{8}$ sec.

16. The velocity 4 ft. above the starting point is 12 ft. per sec. If the starting point is at a height of 176 ft., when and with what velocity does the body reach the earth?
Ans. $t = 4$ sec.

17. A stone is thrown vertically upward from the top of a tower. At the end of 2 sec. it is 400 ft. above the ground, and is still rising, with velocity 10 ft. per sec. Find the height of the tower and time of flight.
Ans. 316 ft.; 7.3 sec.

18. A stone thrown upward from the top of a tower with a velocity of 100 ft. per sec. reaches the ground with a velocity of 140 ft. per sec. Discuss the motion. Find the height of the tower, and the time of flight.
Ans. 150 ft.; 7.5 sec.

19. If a stone dropped from a balloon while ascending at the rate of 20 ft. per sec. reaches the ground in 10 sec., find the initial height and the final velocity.
Ans. 1400 ft.; 300 ft. per sec.

20. A body falls under gravity. Find the distance covered in 6 sec. if at the end of 2 sec. the distance below the starting point is 84 ft.

Ans. 636 ft.

21. A stone is thrown upward from the top of a tower. At the end of 2 sec. it is 84 ft., at the end of 3 sec. 36 ft., above the ground. Find the height of the tower.

Ans. 84 ft.

22. What uniform acceleration will bring an automobile, running at 40 mi. per hr., to rest in 120 ft.? What time will be required?

Ans. -14.3 ft. per sec^2.; 4.1 sec.

23. If a car running at 20 mi. per hr. can be brought to rest in 20 ft., what distance will be required (under the same conditions) at 40 mi. per hr.?

Ans. 80 ft.

24. The motion of a railroad train is uniformly accelerated. If when the train is 250 ft. past a station the velocity is 30 ft. per sec., when 600 ft. past the station it is 40 ft. per sec., find the acceleration, and the velocity when passing the station.

Ans. $v_0 = 20$ ft. per sec.

25. A cord hangs over a vertical pulley and carries equal weights of 10 lbs. at each end. If a 1-lb. weight be added at one end, discuss the motion of the system. Find v when the system has moved 6 ft. (§ 53.)

Ans. 4.3 ft. per sec.

26. The weights in Atwood's Machine are 8 and 10 lbs. If the smaller weight is originally falling 4 ft. per sec., discuss the motion.

27. The weights in Atwood's Machine are 4 and 10 lbs.; the cord is 3 ft. long. If the weights are initially equidistant from the pulley, what velocity must be given the system to make the heavier weight strike the pulley?

Ans. 6.4 ft. per sec.

28. In Atwood's Machine, show that the acceleration can be expressed as a function of the ratio $\dfrac{m_1}{m_2}$; hence that the motion depends only on the ratio of the masses, not on their actual values.

29. The weights in Atwood's Machine, starting from rest, attain a velocity of 2 ft. per sec. in 1 sec. Find the ratio of the masses. *Ans.* 17 : 15.

30. The weights in Atwood's Machine, starting from rest, attain a velocity of 4 ft. per sec. in the first 2 ft. Find the ratio of the masses.

Ans. 9 : 7.

31. Find the ratio of the weights, and the initial velocity, if $v = 4$ when $t = 1$, $v = 6$ when $t = 2$. *Ans.* 17 : 15; 2 ft. per sec.

32. Find the ratio of the weights, and the initial velocity, if $v = 2$ when $x = 3$, $v = 3$ when $x = 8$. *Ans.* 65 : 63; ± 1 ft. per sec.

33. A mass of 12 lbs. rests on a smooth horizontal table. A cord attached to this mass runs over a pulley on the edge of the table; from the cord a mass of 4 lbs. is suspended. Discuss the motion. If the 12-lb. mass is originally 5 ft. from the edge of the table, find when and with what velocity it reaches the edge. *Ans.* 1.1 sec.; 8.9 ft. per sec.

34. In Ex. 33, find the initial velocity if the 12-lb. mass reaches the edge in 1 sec. *Ans.* 1 ft. per sec.

54. Discussion of the motion. In studying a motion, the integrations are really only a preliminary step. When x has been found as a function of t, we proceed to develop the character of the motion. The analysis is very similar to that for plane curves. A minimum discussion should answer the following questions:

1. *Where, in what direction, and with what velocity does the motion begin?* $(t = 0.)$

2. *When and where does the body come to rest, and in what direction does it start after each stop?* $(v = 0.)$

3. *What happens after a long time?* $(t \to \infty.)$

Example (a): Investigate the motion

$$a = 6t - 18; \qquad x = 0, v = 15 \text{ when } t = 0.$$

The first integration gives

$$v = 3t^2 - 18t + C_1,$$

or, since $v = 15$ when $t = 0$,

$$v = 3t^2 - 18t + 15$$
$$= 3(t - 1)(t - 5).$$

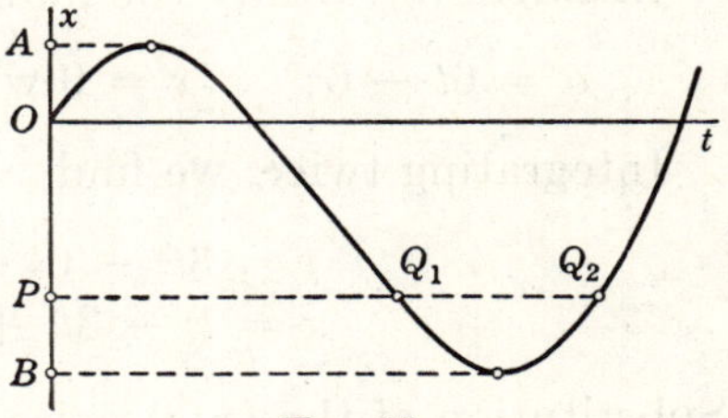

Integrating again, we get

$$x = t^3 - 9t^2 + 15t + C_2,$$

where $x = 0$, $t = 0$ gives $C_2 = 0$:

$$x = t^3 - 9t^2 + 15t.$$

Fig. 45

Since x is a polynomial, its graph may be drawn by the method of § 39. The questions above are answered as follows.

1. $t = 0$: $x = 0$, $v = 15$, $a = -18$. The motion starts at O, with a velocity of 15 ft. per sec. in the positive direction (as given); the velocity is diminishing.

2. $v = 0$: when $t = 1$ (the stops must of course be taken *in chronological order*), $x = 7$, $a = -12$; since $a < 0$, the body turns back in the negative direction. When $t = 5$, $x = -25$, $a = 12$. Thus the body moves out to A $(OA = 7)$, turns back to B $(OB = -25)$, then turns in the positive direction.

3. $t \to \infty$: When t increases indefinitely, both x and v become indefinitely large and positive. The body goes indefinitely far and indefinitely fast in the positive direction.

From Fig. 45 the position at any time, also the time (or times) corresponding to any position, may be read off at once.

When time is not available for drawing the graph of x, the general character of the motion may be exhibited visually by the device shown in Fig. 46. The three "legs" of which this motion

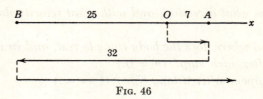

FIG. 46

consists are shown by directed lines drawn at successively lower levels: from O to A, from A to B, from B indefinitely to the right.

Example (b): Study the motion

$$a = 6t - 6; \qquad x = 0 \text{ when } t = 0, \quad x = 1 \text{ when } t = 1.$$

Integrating twice, we find

$$v = 3t^2 - 6t + C_1,$$
$$x = t^3 - 3t^2 + C_1 t + C_2.$$

Substitution of the (x, t)-pairs gives

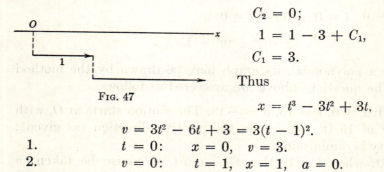

FIG. 47

$$C_2 = 0;$$
$$1 = 1 - 3 + C_1,$$
$$C_1 = 3.$$

Thus

$$x = t^3 - 3t^2 + 3t,$$
$$v = 3t^2 - 6t + 3 = 3(t - 1)^2.$$

1. $\qquad t = 0: \qquad x = 0, \quad v = 3.$
2. $\qquad v = 0: \qquad t = 1, \quad x = 1, \quad a = 0.$

Since v and a vanish together, the direction of the ensuing motion may be determined by noting that, for $t > 1$, $v > 0$. The same conclusion follows from the fact that

$$\frac{da}{dt} = 6:$$

thus a will become positive, and v will do likewise.

EXERCISES

Discuss fully the rectilinear motions of Exs. 1–16.

1. $a = 2$; when $t = 2$, $x = 3$ and $v = 2$.   *Ans.* $x = t^2 - 2t + 3$.

2. $a = -1$; when $t = 2$, $x = 4$ and $v = 0$.   *Ans.* $x = -\frac{1}{2}t^2 + 2t + 2$.

3. $a = 6(2t - 3)$; when $t = 0$, $x = 2$ and $v = 12$.

$$Ans.\ x = 2t^3 - 9t^2 + 12t + 2.$$

4. $a = 6(2t - 1)$; when $t = 0$, $x = 13$ and $v = -12$.

$$Ans.\ x = 2t^3 - 3t^2 - 12t + 13.$$

5. $a = 6(t - 2)$; when $t = 1$, $x = 0$ and $v = 3$.

$$Ans.\ x = t^3 - 6t^2 + 12t - 7.$$

6. $a = 6(t - 1)$; when $t = 0$, $x = 0$, and when $t = 4$, $x = 16$.

$$Ans.\ x = t^2(t - 3).$$

7. $a = 12t^2 - 48t + 44$; when $t = 0$, $x = 10$ and $v = -24$.

$$Ans.\ x = t^4 - 8t^3 + 22t^2 - 24t + 10.$$

8. $a = 12t^2 - 8$; when $t = 0$, $x = 25$, and when $t = 1$, $v = -20$.

$$Ans.\ x = t^4 - 4t^2 - 16t + 25.$$

9. $a = 12t^2 - 24t - 16$; when $t = 0$, $v = 48$, and when $t = 1$, $x = -3$.

$$Ans.\ x = t^4 - 4t^3 - 8t^2 + 48t - 40.$$

10. $a = 12t^2 - 48t + 20$; when $t = 0$, $x = 40$, and when $t = 1$, $v = 0$.

$$Ans.\ x = t^4 - 8t^3 + 10t^2 + 40.$$

11. $a = 12(t - 1)(t - 3)$; when $t = 0$, $x = 5$, and when $t = 1$, $x = 0$.

$$Ans.\ x = t^4 - 8t^3 + 18t^2 - 16t + 5.$$

12. $a = 3(t - 2)^2$; when $t = 0$, $x = 5$, and when $t = 1$, $v = 3$.

$$Ans.\ x = \tfrac{1}{4}(t - 2)^4 + 4t + 1.$$

13. $a = 12t^2 - 48t + 36$; when $t = 0$, $v = 0$, and when $t = 1$, $x = -9$.

$$Ans.\ x = t^4 - 8t^3 + 18t^2 - 20.$$

14. $a = 12(t - 2)(t - 4)$; when $t = 0$, $x = 15$, and when $t = 1$, $x = -12$.

$$Ans.\ x = t^4 - 12t^3 + 48t^2 - 64t + 15.$$

15. $a = \dfrac{2}{(t + 2)^3}$; when $t = 0$, $x = \dfrac{1}{2}$ and $v = -\dfrac{1}{4}$.   *Ans.* $x = \dfrac{1}{t + 2}$.

16. $a = \dfrac{2}{(t + 2)^3}$; when $t = 0$, $x = -\dfrac{1}{2}$ and $v = \dfrac{3}{4}$.

$$Ans.\ x = \frac{t^2 + t - 1}{t + 2}.$$

17. A body moves under an acceleration which increases uniformly at the rate of 6 ft. per sec³. If at the end of 1 sec. the body is 1 ft., at the end of 2 sec. 2 ft., from the starting point, discuss the motion.

$$Ans.\ x = t^3 - 3t^2 + 3t.$$

55. Vectors. A straight line segment of definite *length*, *direction*, and *sense* is called a *vector*.

Any quantity that is fully characterized when we know its magnitude, direction, and sense may be represented geometrically by a vector (or, as we say for brevity, *is* a vector). The importance of vectors in physics is due to the fact that velocity, acceleration, force, etc., are vector quantities.

Two vectors are said to be *equal* if they have the same magnitude, direction, and sense, even though they do not lie in the same straight line. This agrees with our ordinary ideas. For instance, if two bodies are falling under gravity, they are both subject to the same acceleration, whether or not they happen to be in the same vertical line.

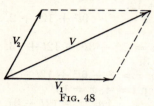

Fig. 48

56. Geometric addition. The sum of two vectors V_1, V_2 is called their *resultant*. It is defined as *the diagonal of the parallelogram having V_1, V_2 as adjacent sides.* This is the *Parallelogram Law.* Composition by this law is called *geometric addition,* or *vector addition.* The sum of two vectors is defined in this way for the reason that in any application the vector V is actually equivalent to the vectors V_1, V_2 combined.

Example: A ship is moving N. at 10 mi. per hr.; a man walks S.E. across the deck at 5 mi. per hr. In what direction and how fast is the man moving, relative to the earth's surface? (Fig. 49.)

By the Cosine Law,

$$v = \sqrt{100 + 25 - 2 \times 50 \cos 45°} = \sqrt{54.3}$$
$$= 7.4 \text{ mi. per hr.}$$

Fig. 49

By the Sine Law,

$$\frac{\sin \alpha}{5} = \frac{\sin 45°}{7.4}, \qquad \sin \alpha = 0.48, \qquad \alpha = 29°.$$

Thus the man is actually moving 29° E. of N., at 7.4 mi. per hr.

In Fig. 48, the vectors V_1, V_2 are *components* of V. Frequently, having given a vector V, we wish to resolve it into components. Obviously, this can be done in an infinite number of ways: if we draw any triangle with V as one side, the other sides, directed as in Fig. 48, are components of V.

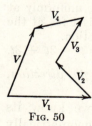

Fig. 50

By repeated application of the Parallelogram Law, the resultant of any number of vectors is easily found. Lay off the vectors end to end to form an open polygon: the closing line, directed from the initial to the terminal point, is the resultant. In Fig. 50, V is the resultant of V_1, V_2, V_3, V_4.

57. Algebraic addition. For various reasons, it may happen in a particular problem that geometric addition of vectors is not feasible; we then have recourse to *algebraic addition*.

From the definition of vector sum, it follows at once that two vectors may be added algebraically if and only if they have *the same direction*. (For instance, in the above example, if the man were to walk due north or south, his net velocity would be 15 or 5 mi. per hr. respectively.) Thus, to add a number of vectors having different directions:

1. *Resolve all the vectors into components parallel to Ox and Oy.*
2. *Add (algebraically) all the x-components to form V_x, all the y-components to form V_y.*
3. *Compound V_x and V_y by the Parallelogram Law: i.e., draw the vector V of magnitude*

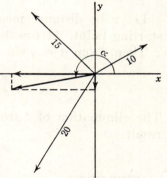

$$V = \sqrt{V_x{}^2 + V_y{}^2},$$

inclined to Ox at an angle α such that

$$\tan \alpha = \frac{V_y}{V_x}.$$

Of course the quadrant in which α lies must be determined as in trigonometry, by examining the signs of V_x and V_y.

Fig. 51

Example: Three forces act on a particle: 10 lbs. inclined at 30° to Ox, 15 lbs. at 135°, 20 lbs. at 240°. Find the resultant.

We have (Fig. 51)

$$F_x = 10 \cos 30° + 15 \cos 135° + 20 \cos 240°$$
$$= 10 \cdot \tfrac{1}{2}\sqrt{3} - 15 \cdot \tfrac{1}{2}\sqrt{2} - 20 \cdot \tfrac{1}{2} = -11.9;$$

$$F_y = 10 \sin 30° + 15 \sin 135° + 20 \sin 240°$$
$$= 10 \cdot \tfrac{1}{2} + 15 \cdot \tfrac{1}{2}\sqrt{2} - 20 \cdot \tfrac{1}{2}\sqrt{3} = -1.7.$$

Thus

$$F = \sqrt{(11.9)^2 + (1.7)^2} = 12.0 \text{ lbs.};$$

$$\tan \alpha = \frac{-1.7}{-11.9} = 0.143, \qquad \alpha = 188°.$$

58. Inclined plane. Consider a body of mass m on a smooth plane inclined at an angle α to the horizontal. At any instant the

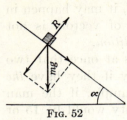

Fig. 52

body is subject to two forces: the attraction of gravity, of magnitude mg, and the reaction R of the plane. Resolve the vertical force mg into components $mg \cos \alpha$ and $mg \sin \alpha$ respectively normal and parallel to the plane. The normal component is exactly balanced by the reaction R. Assume that the body is released from rest, or with an initial velocity either directly down or directly up the slope. Then, rectilinear motion occurs, due to the "effective component" $mg \sin \alpha$:

$$ma = mg \sin \alpha,$$
$$a = g \sin \alpha.$$

Let x be distance measured down the inclined plane from the starting point. At $t = 0$, let $x = 0$ and $v = v_0$.

Then, from $a = g \sin \alpha$, we obtain

$$v = gt \sin \alpha + v_0,$$
$$x = \tfrac{1}{2}gt^2 \sin \alpha + v_0 t.$$

The elimination of t from these two equations yields the useful result

$$v^2 = 2xg \sin \alpha + v_0^2.$$

EXERCISES

1. A man can row a boat 5 mi. per hr. He pulls at right angles to the course of a river 2 mi. wide, having a current of 3 mi. per hr. Where and when will he reach the opposite shore?

Ans. 1.2 mi. downstream; 24 min.

2. In Ex. 1, if the man wishes to land directly opposite his starting point, in what direction must he row, and how long will it take him to cross? *Ans.* 30 min.

3. Suppose the man in Ex. 1 wishes to reach a point on the opposite shore, but 3 mi. downstream from his starting point. At what angle downstream, the α of Fig. 53, should he row, and how long will it take him?

Ans. $\alpha = 36° 52'$; 30 min.

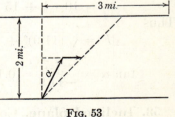

Fig. 53

4. A steamship is moving at the rate of 12 mi. per hr. A man walks across the deck at right angles to the ship's course, at the rate of 5 mi. per hr. If the deck is 40 ft. wide, how far is he finally from his starting point? In what direction?

5. Across the deck of a vessel going S. at 10 ft. per sec., a man walks S. 30° E. at 6 ft. per sec. If the deck is 15 ft. wide, how long does it take him to cross, and how far does he travel?   *Ans.* 5 sec.; 77.4 ft.

6. A river flows S. at 5 mi. per hr. A ferryboat, headed E., is making forward progress at 10 mi. per hr. A man sprints across the deck 30° W. of N. at 20 mi. per hr. How fast and in what direction is he actually moving?

7. A river flows S. at 5 mi. per hr. A boat, headed E., is making forward progress at 20 mi. per hr. On the deck is a man capable of sprinting 100 yd. in 10 sec. Can he hold himself motionless, relative to the earth's surface?   *Ans.* No.

8. Find the resultant of a plane system of forces, $F_1 = 10$ lbs., $F_2 = 7$ lbs., $F_3 = 3$ lbs., $F_4 = 15$ lbs., acting as in Fig. 54, where $\tan \alpha = \frac{4}{3}$.
                    Ans. $F = 10.8$ lbs.; angle with $Ox = 146° 19'$.

9. Six forces, of 1, 2, 3, 4, 5, 6 lbs. respectively, act at the same point, making angles of 60° with each other. Find their resultant.

                    Ans. 6 lbs., along the line
                            of the 5-lb. force.

In Exs. 10–12, a body moves on a plane inclined 30° to the horizontal. All distances and velocities are measured along the inclined plane.

10. If the body rises 18 ft. before starting to fall, what was its initial velocity?   *Ans.* −24 ft. per sec.

11. A body is given an initial velocity of 20 ft. per sec. upward. How far, and for how long, does it travel before starting to fall?

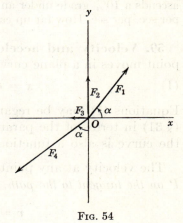

Fig. 54

                    Ans. 12.5 ft.; $\frac{5}{4}$ sec.

12. A body is given an initial velocity of 16 ft. per sec. upward. How long does it take the body to reach a point 4.5 ft. below its starting point?
                    Ans. $\frac{9}{4}$ sec.

13. A body moves on an inclined plane. After one second, the body is 3 ft. below its starting point and has a velocity of 7 ft. per sec., distance and velocity being measured along the plane. Find the angle of inclination of the plane.   *Ans.* About 14° 30′.

14. If the initial velocity is 16 ft. per sec. upward along an inclined plane and the body moves 12 ft. before starting to return, find the angle of inclination of the plane.   *Ans.* About 19° 30′.

15. It is known that the gravitational attraction of the moon at its surface is approximately 0.165g, in terms of the gravitational attraction of the earth at its surface. Find the angle of inclination of a plane near the earth's surface which will yield the same equations of motion, along that plane, as the equations of motion of a freely falling body near the surface of the moon.   *Ans.* About 9° 30′.

16. A bead is strung on a smooth straight wire inclined at 45° to the horizontal. What initial velocity must the bead be given to raise it to a vertical height of 10 ft.? *Ans.* 25.3 ft. per sec.

17. Show that it takes a body twice as long to slide down a plane of 30° inclination as it would take to fall through the "height" of the plane.

18. A hillside slopes gently on one face, steeply on another. Toboggans start at the same time down the two faces. If friction is negligible, find (*a*) which will reach level ground first, and (*b*) which will acquire the greater velocity.

19. A car, starting with a velocity of 10 mi. per hr., coasts for 20 sec. down a 2% grade, and then ascends a 3% grade. Neglecting friction, find how far it will go up the grade. *Ans.* 393 ft.

20. A car, starting from rest, coasts 200 ft. down a 2% grade and then ascends a 10% grade under an acceleration, due to its own power, of 2 ft. per sec. per sec. How far up can it go? *Ans.* 107 ft.

59. Velocity and acceleration in curvilinear motion. If a point moves in a plane curve, its coördinates are functions of time:

(1) $$x = \phi(t), \quad y = \psi(t).$$

Equations (1) may be regarded as *parametric equations of the path* (§ 31) in terms of the parameter *t*. The distance *s* described along the curve is also a function of time.

The velocity at any point *P* is defined as the *vector, laid off from P on the tangent to the path*, of magnitude

$$v = \lim_{\Delta t \to 0} \frac{\Delta s}{\Delta t} = \frac{ds}{dt}.$$

The components of velocity parallel to the axes are

$$v_x = v \cos \alpha, \quad v_y = v \sin \alpha,$$

where α is the angle between Ox and the tangent at *P*. By § 46,

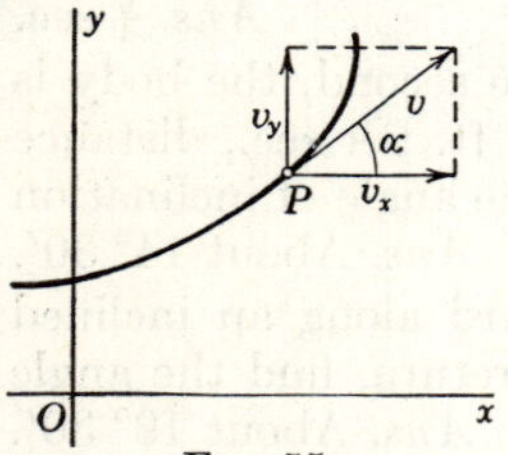

$$v \cos \alpha = \frac{ds}{dt} \cdot \frac{dx}{ds} = \frac{dx}{dt},$$

$$v \sin \alpha = \frac{ds}{dt} \cdot \frac{dy}{ds} = \frac{dy}{dt},$$

so that

$$v_x = \frac{dx}{dt}, \quad v_y = \frac{dy}{dt}.$$

Fig. 55

Thus the total velocity is the vector sum of the velocities parallel to the axes (or in any two perpendicular directions—see Ex. 16 below).

By § 57, the magnitude of the velocity is

$$v = \sqrt{v_x^2 + v_y^2} = \sqrt{\left(\frac{dx}{dt}\right)^2 + \left(\frac{dy}{dt}\right)^2},$$

inclined to the x-axis at an angle α such that

$$\tan \alpha = \frac{v_y}{v_x}.$$

The *acceleration* is the vector a whose components, parallel to the axes, are

$$(2) \qquad a_x = \frac{dv_x}{dt} = \frac{d^2x}{dt^2}, \qquad a_y = \frac{dv_y}{dt} = \frac{d^2y}{dt^2}.$$

The total acceleration is

$$a = \sqrt{a_x^2 + a_y^2},$$

inclined to the x-axis at an angle β such that

$$\tan \beta = \frac{a_y}{a_x}.$$

When multiplied by m, equations (2) give the components of force:

$$F_x = m\frac{dv_x}{dt}, \qquad F_y = m\frac{dv_y}{dt}.$$

60. Projectiles. A simple example of curvilinear motion is furnished by a projectile moving under gravity alone—*i.e.*, in a medium whose resistance can be neglected. This is only a first approximation to actual fact, since in the majority of practical cases the resistance of the medium affects the results materially. (See § 265.)

Let a particle be projected with an initial velocity v_0 inclined at an angle α to the horizontal. With the starting point as origin and the y-axis *positive upward*, the initial conditions are

$$x = 0, \quad y = 0, \quad v_x = v_0 \cos \alpha, \quad v_y = v_0 \sin \alpha \qquad \text{when } t = 0.$$

The force of gravity acts vertically downward; there is no horizontal force. Hence the equations of motion are

$$\frac{d^2x}{dt^2} = 0, \qquad \frac{d^2y}{dt^2} = -g.$$

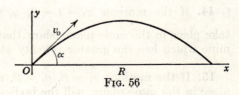

Fig. 56

These may be integrated and the constants determined precisely as in our earlier work; the results are as follows:

(1) $\qquad\qquad v_x = v_0 \cos \alpha, \qquad v_y = -gt + v_0 \sin \alpha;$

(2) $\qquad\qquad x = v_0 t \cos \alpha, \qquad y = -\tfrac{1}{2}gt^2 + v_0 t \sin \alpha.$

EXERCISES

1. Obtain equations (1) and (2), § 60.

2. By eliminating t from (2), show that the path is a parabola opening downward.

3. Show that a projectile whose initial velocity is horizontal will strike the ground in the same time as a body let fall from rest from the same height.

4. The *time of flight* is the time from the starting point until the projectile strikes the ground. Show that on a horizontal plane the time of flight is

$$T = \frac{2v_0}{g} \sin \alpha.$$

5. The *range* of a projectile is the distance from the starting point to the point where it strikes the ground. Show that the range on a horizontal plane is

$$R = \frac{v_0^2}{g} \sin 2\alpha.$$

6. What elevation gives the greatest range on a horizontal plane? (Ex. 5.)

In Exs. 7–12, a point moves in a plane curve, its coördinates being determined by the given formulas. Discuss the motion, for $t \geqq 0$, and draw the path of the point.

7. $x = 3t, \quad y = 9t(2 - t).$

8. $x = 3(t^2 - 2t + 2), \quad y = 3(t - 2).$

9. $x = \dfrac{1}{t + 2}, \, y = \dfrac{2(t + 2)}{t + 1}.$

10. $x = t, \quad y = t(4 - t^2).$

11. $x = 2(t - 1), y = \sqrt{t(2 - t)}.$

12. $x = 5 - t, y = \sqrt{t(10 - t)}.$

13. If the motions in Exs. 7 and 8 take place in the same plane, will the bodies collide? *Ans.* At $(6, 0)$.

14. If the motions $x_1 = t - 2$, $y_1 = t^2$, and $x_2 = t^2 - 8$, $y_2 = \dfrac{4t^2}{t + 1}$, take place in the same plane, show that the bodies will collide, and determine which has the greater velocity at the moment of collision.

Ans. At $(1, 9)$; $v_2 > v_1$.

15. If the motions $x_1 = t^2$, $y_1 = t^3$, and $x_2 = 3t - 2$, $y_2 = t^2 + 4$, take place in the same plane, will the bodies collide? *Ans.* At $(4, 8)$.

16. A point moves in a plane curve, the rectangular coördinates x, y, being functions of the time t. If the axes are rotated to a new system x_1, y_1, by the usual formulas,

$$x = x_1 \cos \phi - y_1 \sin \phi, \qquad y = x_1 \sin \phi + y_1 \cos \phi,$$

prove that

$$\sqrt{\left(\frac{dx}{dt}\right)^2 + \left(\frac{dy}{dt}\right)^2} = \sqrt{\left(\frac{dx_1}{dt}\right)^2 + \left(\frac{dy_1}{dt}\right)^2},$$

and interpret the result physically.

17. A point describes the parabola $y^2 = 4x + 1$, with a constant vertical velocity, $v_y = 4$. Find v_x, a_x, a_y, at $(2, 3)$.   *Ans.* $v_x = 6$; $a_x = 8$.

18. A point describes the parabola $y^2 = 4x + 1$, with a constant horizontal velocity, $v_x = 3$. Find v_y, a_y, a_x, at $(2, 3)$.

$$\text{\textit{Ans.} } v_y = 2; a_y = -\tfrac{4}{3}.$$

19. A particle moves on the circle $x^2 + y^2 = 25$, with a constant horizontal velocity $v_x = -2$. Find v_y, a_y, a_x, at $(3, 4)$.

$$\text{\textit{Ans.} } v_y = \tfrac{3}{2}; a_y = -\tfrac{25}{16}.$$

20. A particle starts at the point $(0, -4)$ and moves along the parabola $y = x^2 - 4$, with a variable horizontal velocity given by $v_x = 2t - 1$. At time $t = 2$, find the position of the particle, and its various components of velocity and acceleration.

$$\text{\textit{Ans.} } (2, 0); v_x = 3; v_y = 12; a_x = 2; a_y = 26.$$

21. In Ex. 20, let the particle start at the point $(-2, 0)$, but leave the rest of the problem unchanged.

$$\text{\textit{Ans.} } (0, -4); v_x = 3; v_y = 0; a_x = 2; a_y = 18.$$

22. The motion of a certain body is determined by its components of acceleration, $a_x = 2$ and $a_y = -6t$, together with the initial conditions that, when $t = 0$, then $x = 0$, $y = 0$, $v_x = 0$, and $v_y = 1$. Find the equation of the path of the motion.   *Ans.* $y = (1 - x)\sqrt{x}$.

23. The motion of a certain body is determined by its components of acceleration, $a_x = 1 - t$ and $a_y = 0$, together with the initial conditions that, when $t = 0$, then $x = 1$, $y = 0$, $v_x = 0$, and $v_y = -\tfrac{1}{2}$. Find the equation of the path of the motion.   *Ans.* $3(x - 1) = 2y^2(3 + 2y)$.

24. Starting at the origin, initially at rest $(v = 0)$, a particle is subjected to a constant horizontal acceleration b, and a constant vertical acceleration c. Find the equation of the path of motion.   *Ans.* $by = cx$.

25. In Ex. 24, let the particle have an initial velocity $v_0 \neq 0$, but leave the remainder of the problem unchanged. Show that the path of motion is, in general, a parabola.

26. Prove that when a point traverses a curve with constant velocity $v = k$, the acceleration is always directed along the normal to the path. (Differentiate both members of the equation $v_x^2 + v_y^2 = k^2$.)

27. A pitcher throws a ball with a speed of 120 ft. per sec., the ball leaving his hand horizontally at a height of 5 ft. If the distance from pitcher to batter is 60 ft., at what height will the ball pass the batter?

28. A stone is thrown horizontally from the top of a tower 400 ft. high, with a velocity of 20 ft. per sec. (*a*) When, (*b*) where, and (*c*) with what velocity does it strike the ground?

Ans. (*a*) 5 sec.; (*c*) 161.2 ft. per sec., at 7° 8′ to the vertical.

29. A man on a cliff 160 ft. high throws a stone, with velocity 100 ft. per sec., directly toward a point 120 ft. out from the foot of the cliff. By what distance does the stone miss the mark?   *Ans.* 28.1 ft.

61. The definite integral. Let $f(x)$ be a given continuous function, $F(x)$ an integral of $f(x)$, and $x = a$ and $x = b$ two given values of x. The *change in the value of the integral* $F(x)$ *as* x changes from a to b, *i.e.*, the quantity $F(b) - F(a)$, is called the *definite integral of* $f(x)$ *between the* "*limits*" a *and* b, or simply the *definite integral from a to b*, and is denoted by the symbol $\int_a^b f(x)\,dx$. It is called the *definite* integral because its value is independent of the constant of integration.

The numbers a and b are called the *lower limit* and the *upper limit* respectively. Thus the definite integral is merely *the value of the indefinite integral at the upper limit, minus its value at the lower limit.* The symbol $\left[F(x) \right]_a^b$ means $F(b) - F(a)$:

(1) $$\int_a^b f(x)\,dx = \left[F(x) \right]_a^b = F(b) - F(a).$$

Since the constant of integration disappears, there is no object in writing it at all.

The assumption of continuity is introduced temporarily for simplicity. See § 154.

Example (a): $\displaystyle \int_0^1 (x + 1)^2\,dx = \left[\frac{(x + 1)^3}{3} \right]_0^1 = \frac{8}{3} - \frac{1}{3} = \frac{7}{3}.$

Example (b): $\displaystyle \int_{-a}^a (a^2 - t^2)\,dt = \left[a^2 t - \tfrac{1}{3} t^3 \right]_{-a}^a$

$$= a^3 - \tfrac{1}{3} a^3 - (-a^3 + \tfrac{1}{3} a^3) = \tfrac{4}{3} a^3.$$

Example (c): $\displaystyle \int_0^a z(a^2 - z^2)^3\,dz = -\left[\frac{(a^2 - z^2)^4}{8} \right]_0^a = \frac{a^8}{8}.$

The variable whose differential occurs—respectively x, t, z, in the examples—is called the *variable of integration*.

62. General properties of definite integrals. The following properties are possessed by all definite integrals:

(1)
$$\int_a^b f(x)\,dx = -\int_b^a f(x)\,dx;$$

(2)
$$\int_a^b f(x)\,dx = \int_a^c f(x)\,dx + \int_c^b f(x)\,dx;$$

(3)
$$\int_a^b f(x)\,dx = \int_a^b f(z)\,dz.$$

In words, these formulas say respectively:

(1) Interchanging the limits changes the sign of the integral.

(2) The interval of integration may be broken up into any number of sub-intervals, and the integration performed over each interval separately. (While the theorem is usually employed in this way, it is true whether or not c lies between a and b.)

(3) It makes no difference what letter is used for the variable of integration: that is, *the definite integral of a given integrand is independent of the variable of integration.*

The first two are established very easily by writing out, by the defining formula (1), § 61, the values of the various integrals. The truth of (3) appears from a glance at that same formula, where the result involves the limits a and b, but not the variable of integration x. Thus in Example (a), § 61,

$$\int_0^1 (x+1)^2\,dx = \int_0^1 (y+1)^2\,dy = \int_0^1 (t+1)^2\,dt = \tfrac{7}{3}.$$

63. Even and odd functions. A function that *remains unchanged* when x is replaced by $-x$, *i.e.*, such that

$$f(-x) = f(x),$$

is called an *even function*. This means geometrically that the curve

$$y = f(x)$$

is symmetric with respect to the y-axis. Familiar examples of even functions are x^{2n} (n an integer), $\cos\theta$, $t\sin t$, etc.

A function such that

$$f(-x) = -f(x)$$

is called an *odd function*. Geometrically, the curve $y = f(x)$

is symmetric with respect to the origin. Examples are x^{2n+1}, $x^{\frac{1}{3}}$, $\sin \theta$, $\tan \theta$.

Two properties of these functions will be stated now, to make them available for immediate use; the proofs will appear presently (§ 68).

Theorem I: *If $f(x)$ is an even function, then*

$$\int_{-a}^{a} f(x)\, dx = 2 \int_{0}^{a} f(x)\, dx.$$

Theorem II: *If $f(x)$ is an odd function, then*

$$\int_{-a}^{a} f(x)\, dx = 0.$$

Since many integrals of these precise types occur, the theorems are frequently applicable. Theorem I saves time and reduces the danger of mistake; Theorem II is even more useful, since whenever it applies there is no need to find the indefinite integral at all.

When the integrand consists of several terms, some odd, some even (the limits being, of course, $-a$ to a), the odd terms may be dropped at once.

Example (a):

$$\int_{-a}^{a} (a^2 - t^2)\, dt = 2 \int_{0}^{a} (a^2 - t^2)\, dt$$

$$= 2\left[a^2 t - \tfrac{1}{3} t^3 \right]_{0}^{a} = \tfrac{4}{3} a^3.$$

[Cf. Example (*b*), § 61.]

Example (b): $\displaystyle \int_{-1}^{1} \frac{x\, dx}{\sqrt{2 - x^8}} = 0.$

This is a so-called "elliptic integral": the indefinite integral is not only beyond our present reach—it can never be evaluated in terms of elementary functions. But Theorem II gives the value of the definite integral at a glance.

Example (c):

$$\int_{-2}^{2} (x^5 - 3x^3 + 2x^2 - x)\, dx = 4 \int_{0}^{2} x^2\, dx$$

$$= \left[\frac{4x^3}{3} \right]_{0}^{2} = \frac{32}{3}.$$

EXERCISES

Evaluate the definite integrals in Exs. 1–20.

1. $\int_1^2 x^3\, dx.$ *Ans.* $\frac{15}{4}$.   **2.** $\int_0^2 (y-1)^2\, dy.$ *Ans.* $\frac{2}{3}$.

3. $\int_{-1}^2 (3 - 2v + 6v^2)\, dv.$ *Ans.* 24.

4. $\int_{-1}^2 (1 - 3x^2)\, dx.$ *Ans.* -6.

5. $\int_0^3 z(1 + 2z)\, dz.$ *Ans.* $\frac{45}{2}$.   **6.** $\int_0^2 \sqrt{4\beta + 1}\, d\beta.$ *Ans.* $\frac{13}{3}$.

7. $\int_{-2}^{-3} (5 + 2w)^5\, dw.$ *Ans.* 0.   **8.** $\int_{-2}^0 x^2(3 - x)\, dx.$ *Ans.* 12.

9. $\int_1^2 (x - 4)(3x - 2)\, dx.$ **10.** $\int_1^2 (3x - 4)(x + 2)\, dx.$

11. $\int_1^2 \dfrac{dy}{(3 - y)^3}.$ *Ans.* $\frac{3}{8}$.   **12.** $\int_1^2 \dfrac{du}{(2 + u)^2}.$ *Ans.* $\frac{1}{12}$.

13. $\int_0^2 (1 - \alpha^2)^2\, d\alpha.$ *Ans.* $\frac{46}{15}$.   **14.** $\int_{\frac{1}{2}}^1 \left(1 - \dfrac{1}{x^2}\right)^2 dx.$ *Ans.* $\frac{5}{6}$.

15. $\int_0^1 \dfrac{dy}{(1 + 4y)^3}.$ *Ans.* $\frac{3}{25}$.   **16.** $\int_1^3 \dfrac{v^4 + 1}{v^2}\, dv.$ *Ans.* $\frac{28}{3}$.

17. $\int_1^4 \dfrac{1 + y}{\sqrt{y}}\, dy.$ *Ans.* $\frac{20}{3}$.

18. $\int_0^a \dfrac{x^3\, dx}{\sqrt{a^4 + x^4}}.$ *Ans.* $\frac{1}{2}a^2(\sqrt{2} - 1).$

19. $\int_{\frac{1}{4}}^1 \dfrac{\sqrt{1 - \sqrt{y}}}{\sqrt{y}}\, dy.$ *Ans.* $\frac{1}{3}\sqrt{2}.$

20. $\int_0^1 (1 - x^{\frac{3}{2}})^4 \sqrt{x}\, dx.$ *Ans.* $\frac{2}{15}$.

In Exs. 21–29, use the properties of integrals with odd, or even, functions as integrands, to simplify the evaluation of the integral.

21. $\int_{-2}^2 (x^3 - 7x^5)\, dx.$ *Ans.* 0.   **22.** $\int_{-a}^a x^3\sqrt{a^2 - x^2}\, dx.$ *Ans.* 0.

23. $\int_{-1}^1 (6y^2 - 5y^4)\, dy.$ *Ans.* 2.   **24.** $\int_{-2}^2 (1 - \frac{1}{4}t^2)^2\, dt.$ *Ans.* $\frac{32}{15}$.

25. $\int_{-4}^{4} (2v^3 + \frac{3}{8}v^2 - 17v - 3)\, dv.$ *Ans.* −8.

26. $\int_{-a}^{a} x^2(7x^3 + 15ax^2 - 13a^2x + 6a^3)\, dx.$ *Ans.* $10a^6$.

27. $\int_{-2}^{2} x(9 - x^6)^{\frac{1}{2}}\, dx.$ *Ans.* 0.

28. $\int_{-1}^{1} (u^7 + 1)(3u^2 + 1)\, du.$ *Ans.* 4.

29. $\int_{-2}^{2} (x^5 - x^3 + 3x^2 - 4)\, dx.$ *Ans.* 0.

30. Show that the product or quotient of two odd functions is even.

64. The Sigma-notation. We shall have frequent occasion to speak of *sums* of a considerable number of terms, usually an unspecified number n −say

$$u_1 + u_2 + u_3 + \cdots + u_n.$$

To save the bother of writing out such expressions always in full, a single symbol is commonly used in mathematics. The symbol $\sum_{i=1}^{n}$ means that we are to substitute $i = 1, 2, 3, \cdots, n$ successively in the expression following, and add the results: for example,

$$\sum_{i=1}^{n} u_i = u_1 + u_2 + u_3 + \cdots + u_n,$$

$$\sum_{k=0}^{n} a_k x^{n-k} = a_0 x^n + a_1 x^{n-1} + \cdots + a_{n-1}x + a_n.$$

65. Plane area. Calculus grew out of the attempts, eventually successful in the seventeenth century, of mathematicians* to solve two major problems. The first problem was to obtain the tangent line to a curve at a given point on it; that was solved by introducing and applying the notion of a derivative. The second problem was to obtain the area bounded by a curve $y = f(x)$, the x-axis, and two ordinates $x = a$ and $x = b$.

This second problem is solved by a judicious extension of the elementary concept of the area of a rectangle as the product of its base and its altitude.

---

* Particularly Sir Isaac Newton, 1642–1727, and Gottfried Wilhelm Leibnitz, 1646–1716; these two men, independently of each other, produced the great bulk of basic ideas and techniques which form the elementary calculus.

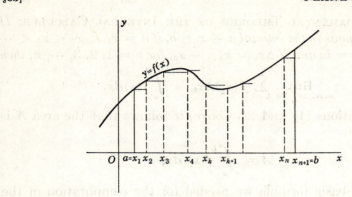

In Fig. 57, let the interval $a \le x \le b$ be divided into n parts in any manner, the divisions being at $x_1, x_2, x_3, \cdots, x_{n+1}$, with $x_1 = a$, $x_{n+1} = b$. Erect rectangles using the ordinates at $x_1, x_2, x_3, \cdots, x_n$, as shown in the figure. In order to have a simple notation for the width of the bases of these rectangles, let $\Delta x_1 = x_2 - x_1$, $\Delta x_2 = x_3 - x_2$, $\cdots$; that is, let $\Delta x_k = x_{k+1} - x_k$, for $k = 1, 2, 3, \cdots, n$.

It is reasonable that, if the maximum width of the rectangles shown be taken sufficiently small, and the number of rectangles correspondingly large, then the sum of the areas of the rectangles will approximate, as closely as desired, a quantity which agrees with our intuitive concept* of the required area.

Therefore, we proceed to lay down as our definition of the area A bounded by the curve $y = f(x)$, the x-axis, and the ordinates $x = a$ and $x = b$, the following:

$$(1) \qquad\qquad A = \lim_{\max. \Delta x_k \to 0} \sum_{k=1}^{n} f(x_k)\,\Delta x_k,$$

in which, since the widths Δx_k of the rectangles approach zero, the number of them, n, must approach infinity.

At once we are confronted with the question of whether the limit in (1) exists, and, if it does exist, with the problem of determining how to compute that limit. A sufficient condition for the existence of the limit in (1), together with a remarkably simple method for obtaining its value, is contained in the following theorem:

---

* Even the oft-quoted average man on the street would, if presented with the curve $y = f(x)$ drawn carefully on graph paper, obtain an approximation to the area we wish by counting the squares enclosed by its boundaries. We wish to replace his rough idea by a specific formula.

THE FUNDAMENTAL THEOREM OF THE INTEGRAL CALCULUS: *If
$f(x)$ is continuous in the interval $a \le x \le b$, if $a = x_1 < x_2 < x_3 < \cdots
< x_n < x_{n+1} = b$, and if $\Delta x_k = x_{k+1} - x_k$, for $k = 1, 2, 3, \cdots, n$, then*

$$\text{(2)} \qquad \lim_{\text{max. } \Delta x_k \to 0} \sum_{k=1}^{n} f(x_k)\Delta x_k = \int_a^b f(x)dx.$$

From equations (1) and (2) above, it follows that the area A is
given by

$$\text{(3)} \qquad A = \int_a^b f(x)\ dx,$$

which is the basic formula we needed for the computation of the
area shown in Fig. 57.

Proof of the Fundamental Theorem will be omitted; a rigorous
analytic approach to our subject properly belongs in Advanced
Calculus, or in a course in Functions of a Real Variable. Here we
content ourselves with the discussion in the next section, a treatment intended to make the Fundamental Theorem plausible, not
to prove it.

66. Plane area: an intuitive approach. Consider the area

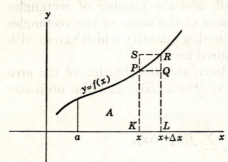

FIG. 58

bounded by the continuous
curve $y = f(x)$, the x-axis, the
fixed ordinate $x = a$, and a
variable ordinate, $x = x$, as
shown in Fig. 58. For the moment, let the function $f(x)$ be
increasing with increasing x.
Then, when x is increased by
an amount Δx, the area A will
increase by an amount ΔA,
the area $KLRP$. Now,

$$\text{Area } KLQP < \text{Area } KLRP < \text{Area } KLRS,$$

and

$$\text{Area } KLQP = \overline{KP} \cdot \overline{KL} = f(x)\ \Delta x,$$
$$\text{Area } KLRP = \Delta A,$$
$$\text{Area } KLRS = f(x + \Delta x)\ \Delta x.$$

Therefore, we have

$$f(x)\ \Delta x < \Delta A < f(x + \Delta x)\ \Delta x,$$
$$\text{(1)} \qquad f(x) < \frac{\Delta A}{\Delta x} < f(x + \Delta x).$$

In the inequalities (1), let $\Delta x \to 0$. Then $f(x)$ stays fixed and $f(x + \Delta x) \to f(x)$, because $f(x)$ is continuous. Since $\dfrac{\Delta A}{\Delta x}$ is pinned in between two quantities, $f(x)$ and the quantity $f(x + \Delta x)$ which approaches $f(x)$ (because of continuity), then $\dfrac{\Delta A}{\Delta x}$ must also approach $f(x)$. Since $\dfrac{\Delta A}{\Delta x} \to \dfrac{dA}{dx}$, as $\Delta x \to 0$, we can conclude that

$$(2) \qquad \frac{dA}{dx} = f(x).$$

Because the derivative of A is $f(x)$, it follows that

$$A = \int f(x)\, dx = F(x) + C.$$

Since the position of the fixed ordinate $x = a$ is given, the constant of integration may be determined by the fact that $A = 0$ when $x = a$:

$$0 = F(a) + C, \qquad C = -F(a),$$
$$(3) \qquad A = F(x) - F(a).$$

For the area bounded by $y = f(x)$, the x-axis, and the ordinates $x = a$ and $x = b$, equation (3) becomes

$$(4) \qquad A = F(b) - F(a).$$

In view of the definition of the definite integral, equation (4) yields

$$(5) \qquad A = \int_a^b f(x)\, dx,$$

in agreement with the formula for area as dictated by the Fundamental Theorem.

The above discussion is readily modified to apply to a function which steadily decreases with increasing x, or which remains constant. If the interval between the ordinates $x = a$ and $x = b$ can be broken up into sub-intervals, on each of which the function increases, decreases, or remains constant, the argument leading to (5) goes through just as easily.

For brevity and simplicity in this first course, we shall make free use of intuitive reasoning. All of the many formulas that we shall obtain will fall into one or the other of two classes: first, definitions, based always on our conception of the quantity in hand; second, consequences of other definitions or theorems. For these we shall usually omit formal proofs, being content merely to show the meaning and reasonableness of the result; but every formula or theorem that we accept on this basis can be shown to rest on the firm foundation of analysis.

67. Computation of plane areas. The formula for area in § 65, properly extended, enables us to compute areas bounded, in any manner whatever, by curves whose equations are given in Cartesian coördinates. We merely take an element, parallel to either axis according to convenience, express its area in terms of the coördinates, and integrate over the whole region. The process is best explained by means of examples.

In plane-area problems, a rough check on the answer may be obtained by circumscribing about the area a rectangle with its sides parallel to the axes and comparing the area of the rectangle with the result obtained by integration. In problems where the numerical work is simple, so that the answer is apt to be either correct or widely incorrect, this check is especially valuable.

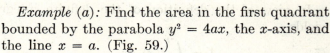

In every problem the student should *make a sketch of the area to be found, draw an element in a general position, and obtain the area of the element directly from the figure.*

Example (a): Find the area in the first quadrant bounded by the parabola $y^2 = 4ax$, the x-axis, and the line $x = a$. (Fig. 59.)

Fig. 59

With the element parallel to Oy, we have

$$A = \int_0^a y \, dx = 2a^{\frac{1}{2}} \int_0^a x^{\frac{1}{2}} \, dx = \tfrac{4}{3} a^{\frac{1}{2}} \left[x^{\frac{3}{2}} \right]_0^a = \tfrac{4}{3} a^2.$$

Since the area $OABC$ is $2a^2$, the result is roughly checked.

Example (b): Find the above area by another method.

Take the element parallel to Ox (Fig. 60). The base of the rectangle is evidently $a - x$, the altitude dy, whence

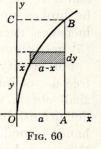

$$A = \int_0^{2a} (a - x) \, dy = \int_0^{2a} \left(a - \frac{y^2}{4a} \right) dy$$

$$= \left[ay - \frac{y^3}{12a} \right]_0^{2a} = \frac{4}{3} a^2.$$

Fig. 60

68. Integral with negative integrand. In the definite integral $\int_a^b f(x)\, dx$, let the limits be so chosen that the lower limit is algebraically less than the upper limit. With this convention x increases, so that dx is positive.

Suppose first that the integrand $f(x)$ keeps the same sign, either positive or negative, throughout the interval. Then, when the integral is evaluated, the result will have the same sign as $f(x)$. For, in the Fundamental Theorem, each of the terms occurring in the summation will have the same sign as $f(x)$, and the limit of the sum must have that same sign.

Now, if we are using the integral to compute an area in the ordinary sense of elementary geometry, the formula must always be so written that the element is positive, since area is essentially positive.

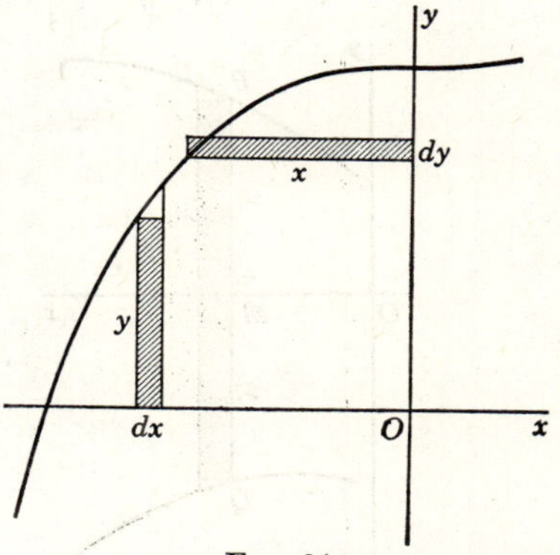

Example: Find the area in the second quadrant bounded by the curve

$$y = x^3 + 1.$$

With vertical rectangles,

Fig. 61

$$A = \int_{-1}^{0} y\, dx = \int_{-1}^{0} (x^3 + 1)\, dx = \left[\frac{1}{4}x^4 + x\right]_{-1}^{0} = \frac{3}{4}.$$

With horizontal rectangles, since x is negative, the area of the element is $(-x)\, dy$, and

$$A = \int_{0}^{1} (-x)\, dy = -\int_{0}^{1} (y - 1)^{\frac{1}{3}}\, dy = -\frac{3}{4}\left[(y - 1)^{\frac{4}{3}}\right]_{0}^{1} = \frac{3}{4}.$$

If the curve crosses the axis within the interval of integration, and we wish to find the area in the above sense, the procedure is obvious: we must integrate over the positive and negative regions separately, changing the sign in the latter. (Of course, considerations of symmetry may enable us to shorten the process.)

By interpreting the integrals as limits of sums, it is very easy to prove geometrically the theorems of § 63. (Formal analytic proofs are easily written out by a method to be developed in § 148.) If the curve is symmetric to Oy, then for every element $y_i\, \Delta x$ on the right there will be an equal $y_i \, \Delta x$ on the left. Thus the area on the left equals that on the right, so that the total area is twice either one of them. From the remarks of this section Theorem II also follows at once.

69. Area between two curves. In finding the area between two curves, uncertainty as to signs sometimes arises when some of the coördinates are negative. It need not, if we merely remember that in analytic geometry all coördinates are *directed* line segments. In Fig. 62, the height of the element is

$$QP = QM + MP = MP - MQ = y_h - y_l.$$

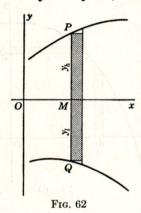

Fig. 62   Fig. 63

In Fig. 63, the height is

$$QP = QM - PM = MP - MQ = y_h - y_l.$$

Always, a vertical element will be positive, if we use the *higher y minus the lower y* as the length of the element. See Examples (*a*) and (*b*) below.

In a similar manner, a horizontal element is always made positive by taking the *right-hand x minus the left-hand x*, as is done in Example (*c*) below.

Example (a): Find the area between the curves (Fig. 64)

$$x^2 = 2ay, \qquad x^2 = 4ay - a^2.$$

We easily find that these parabolas intersect at $(\pm a, \frac{1}{2}a)$. The area of a vertical element is $(y_h - y_l) \, dx$, where y_h and y_l are the ordinates of the higher and lower curves respectively. Instead of integrating from $-a$ to a, we may, due to the symmetry with respect to Oy (Theorem I, § 63), integrate from 0 to a and multiply by 2:

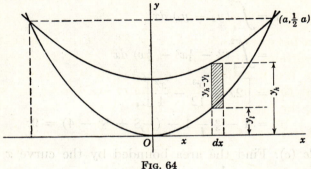

FIG. 64

$$A = \int_{-a}^{a} (y_h - y_l)\, dx = 2 \int_{0}^{a} \left(\frac{x^2}{4a} + \frac{a}{4} - \frac{x^2}{2a} \right) dx$$

$$= 2 \int_{0}^{a} \left(\frac{a}{4} - \frac{x^2}{4a} \right) dx = \frac{1}{2} \left[ax - \frac{x^3}{3a} \right]_{0}^{a} = \frac{1}{3} a^2.$$

The area of the circumscribing rectangle is a^2, which yields a rough check on our result.

Example (b): Find the area bounded by the curve $x^2 + 4y - 8 = 0$ and the line $x = 2y$.

First, put the parabola in standard form, $x^2 = -4(y - 2)$, in order to sketch it. Obtain the intersections of the given curves, by solving their equations simultaneously. In this example, the intersections are found to be at $(2, 1)$ and $(-4, -2)$. Then sketch the

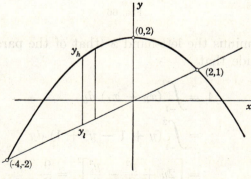

FIG. 65

curves, Fig. 65, and draw in an appropriate element, as shown. Using that element, we arrive at the desired area as follows:

$$A = \int_{-4}^{2} (y_h - y_l)\, dx$$

$$= \int_{-4}^{2} (2 - \tfrac{1}{4}x^2 - \tfrac{1}{2}x)\, dx$$

$$= \left[2x - \frac{x^3}{12} - \frac{x^2}{4} \right]_{-4}^{2}$$

$$= 4 - \tfrac{2}{3} - 1 - (-8 + \tfrac{16}{3} - 4) = 9.$$

Example (c): Find the area bounded by the curve $x = y^2 - 1$ and the line $y = x - 1$.

As in Example (*a*), we find the intersections, and sketch the figure, Fig. 66. This time a horizontal element is suggested by the figure. The length of the element is the right-hand x (that of the

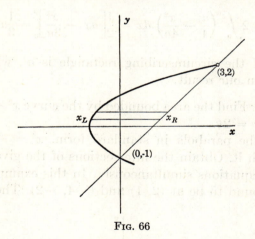

Fɪɢ. 66

straight line) minus the left-hand x (that of the parabola). Therefore we conclude that

$$A = \int_{-1}^{2} (x_R - x_L)\, dy$$

$$= \int_{-1}^{2} (y + 1 - y^2 + 1)\, dy$$

$$= \left[2y + \frac{y^2}{2} - \frac{y^3}{3} \right]_{-1}^{2} = \frac{9}{2}.$$

EXERCISES

1. Find the area bounded by the curve $y = 4 - x^2$ and the x-axis. Solve in two ways. *Ans.* $\frac{32}{3}$.

2. Find the area bounded by the curve $a^2y = x^3$, the x-axis, and the line $x = 2a$. Solve in two ways. *Ans.* $4a^2$.

3. Find the area bounded by the curve $y^2 - 3x + 3 = 0$ and the line $x = 4$. *Ans.* 12.

4. Find the area bounded by the curve $ay = x^2$ and the lines $y = a$ and $y = 4a$. *Ans.* $\frac{28}{3} a^2$.

5. Find the area bounded by the curve $y = 8 - x^3$ and the axes. Solve in two ways.

6. Find the area of a right triangle by integration. Deduce the general formula by considering a scalene triangle as the sum (or difference) of two right triangles.

7. Find the area bounded by a parabola and any right chord. (Use the parabola $y^2 = 4ax$, chord $x = x_1$.)
Ans. Two-thirds of the circumscribing rectangle.

8. Solve Ex. 7 by another method.

9. Find the area in the third quadrant bounded by the curve $x = y^2 + 2y$. *Ans.* $\frac{4}{3}$.

10. Find the area bounded by the curve $x = y^2 + 2y$ and the line $x = 3$.

11. Find the area bounded by the curve $y^2 + 2x - 2y - 3 = 0$ and the y-axis. *Ans.* $\frac{16}{3}$.

12. Find the area bounded by the curve $y = 3x(x - 2)^2$ and the x-axis. *Ans.* 4.

13. Find the area bounded by the curve $y = x(x - 1)^2$, the y-axis, and the line $y = 2$. *Ans.* $\frac{10}{3}$.

14. Find the area in the second quadrant bounded by the curve $2x^2 + 4x + y = 0$. *Ans.* $\frac{8}{3}$.

15. Find the area bounded by the curve $y = 4x - x^2$ and the line $y = 3$. *Ans.* $\frac{4}{3}$.

16. Find the area bounded by the curve $y = 4x - x^2$ and the lines $x = 0$ and $y = 4$. Solve in two ways. *Ans.* $\frac{8}{3}$.

17. Find the area bounded by the curve $y = 4x - x^2$ and the lines $x = -2$ and $y = 4$. *Ans.* $\frac{64}{3}$.

18. Find the area bounded by the curve $y = 12x - x^3$ and the line $y = 16$. *Ans.* 108.

19. Find each of the two areas bounded by the curves $y = x^3 - 4x$ and $y = x^2 + 2x$. *Ans.* $\frac{16}{3}$, $\frac{63}{4}$.

20. Find the area bounded by the curve $a^3y = (x^2 - a^2)^2$ and the x-axis. *Ans.* $\frac{16}{15} a^2$.

21. Find the area, in the first quadrant, bounded by the curve $x^2y = a^3$, the lines $x = 2a$, $y = 4a$, and the axes. *Ans.* $\frac{7}{2} a^2$.

In Exs. 22–37, find the area between the two curves.

22. $2x^2 + 4x + y = 0$, $y = 2x$. *Ans.* 9.

23. $y^2 = -4x$, $y = 2(x + 2)$. *Ans.* 9.

24. $y^2 = 2x + 3$, $y = x$.   *Ans.* $\frac{16}{3}$.

25. $y = x^4$, $y = 5x + 6$.   *Ans.* 18.9.

26. A parabola and a chord through the vertex. (Use $y^2 = 4ax$, $y = mx$.)

Ans. $\dfrac{8a^2}{3m^3}$.

27. $x^2 = ay$, $a^2y = x^3$.

28. $y = x$, $a^2y = x^3$.

29. $y^2 = 1 - x$, $y = 1 + x$.   *Ans.* $\frac{9}{2}$.

30. $y^2 = -x$, $x^2 = 6 - 5y$.   *Ans.* 5.4.

31. $y^2 = -x$, $x^2 + 3y + 4x + 6 = 0$.   *Ans.* $\frac{5}{3}$.

32. $y = x^2 - 2x$, $x + 2y + 1 = 0$.   Check by Ex. 26.

33. $y = x^2(x - 3)$, $y = x^2$.   *Ans.* $\frac{64}{3}$.

34. $y = x^2(x - 3)$, $y = 4(x - 3)$; the total area.   *Ans.* 32.75.

35. $x^2 = y + 1$, $x = (y + 1)^2$. Solve in two ways.   *Ans.* $\frac{1}{3}$.

36. $y = x^2(x - 3)$, $y^2 + 8y - 16x + 48 = 0$.   *Ans.* $\frac{17}{12}$.

37. $y = x^3 + 3x^2 - 4$, $y = 2x^3$.   *Ans.* $\frac{27}{4}$.

38. Find the area bounded by $y^2 = 4a(y - x)$, $y^2 = 2a(x + 2y - 3a)$, and the x-axis.   *Ans.* $2a^2$.

39. Evaluate $\int_0^a \sqrt{a^2 - x^2}\, dx$ by considering the geometric meaning of the integral.   *Ans.* $\frac{1}{4}\pi a^2$.

40. Find the area of an ellipse. (Set up the integral; then see Ex. 39.)

Ans. πab.

In Exs. 41–46, find the area of the section of the surface by the plane. (Use the answer to Ex. 40.)

41. Surface $\dfrac{x^2}{4} - \dfrac{y^2}{9} - \dfrac{z^2}{1} = 1$, plane $x = 3$.   *Ans.* $\frac{15}{4}\pi$.

42. Surface $\dfrac{x^2}{3} - \dfrac{y^2}{1} + \dfrac{z^2}{12} = 1$, plane $y = 1$.   *Ans.* 12π.

43. Surface $x^2 + 2y^2 = 4$, plane $y = z$.   *Ans.* 4π.

44. Surface $5x^2 + 4z^2 = 20$, plane $y = 2x$.   *Ans.* 10π.

45. Surface $4x^2 + 4y^2 = z^2$, plane $y + z = 3$.   *Ans.* $2\sqrt{6}\pi$.

46. Surface $x^2 + y^2 = z$, plane $z = 2y + 3$.   *Ans.* $4\sqrt{5}\pi$.

70. Continuity. In calculus the idea of continuity is always in the foreground, for the reason (§ 13) that our theory breaks down at a point where the given function is discontinuous. Thus, of necessity, all the functions treated are continuous except perhaps at isolated points; those points are excluded from the general discussion, and must be specially investigated. Such investigation is the purpose of this chapter: we shall illustrate the types of discontinuity most likely to arise, and discuss the ways in which discontinuities affect our procedures and results. Before proceeding, the student should review § 12.

For convenient reference, we re-state the definition of continuity:

A function $f(x)$ is said to be *continuous* for the value $x = a$ (or at the point $x = a$) if the following three conditions are satisfied:

(a) *The function is defined at $x = a$—i.e., $f(a)$ exists; and*

(b) *the function approaches a definite limit as x approaches a— i.e.,* $\lim_{x \to a} f(x)$ *exists; and*

(c) *the limit approached is equal to the value of the function at the point — i.e.,*

$$\lim_{x \to a} f(x) = f(a).$$

71. Missing-point discontinuities. Consider a function $f(x)$ which is not defined when $x = a$, but such that $\lim_{x \to a} f(x)$ exists,

$$(1) \qquad\qquad \lim_{x \to a} f(x) = l.$$

The function is discontinuous at $x = a$ because condition (a), § 70, is not satisfied. Graphically the curve appears, to the eye, to be continuous, but the single point $x = a$ is missing—like a wire that is broken, but with the ends in contact.

It is always possible to repair such missing-point discontinuities by replacing the original function $f(x)$ with another function $\phi(x)$, defined as follows:

$$
(2) \quad
\begin{cases}
\phi(x) = f(x); & x \neq a, \\[2mm]
\phi(x) = l; & x = a.
\end{cases}
$$

The function $\phi(x)$ is the same as $f(x)$ wherever $f(x)$ was defined, but $\phi(x)$ is continuous at $x = a$.

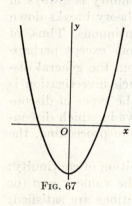

Example: In Example (*b*), §9, we found that the function

$$
(3) \qquad f(x) = \frac{x^3 - 2x^2 - 3x + 6}{x - 2}
$$

is undefined when $x = 2$, but that

$$
\lim_{x \to 2} \frac{x^3 - 2x^2 - 3x + 6}{x - 2} = 1.
$$

Since

$$
\frac{x^3 - 2x^2 - 3x + 6}{x - 2} = x^2 - 3, \qquad x \neq 2,
$$

FIG. 67

the graph of $y = f(x)$ is the parabola $y = x^2 - 3$, except for an invisible break at $x = 2$.

The function $\phi(x)$ of equations (2) is, in this instance,

$$
\phi(x) = x^2 - 3,
$$

for all x. That is, the complete parabola $y = x^2 - 3$ differs from the curve $y = f(x)$, in that the parabola is continuous at $x = 2$.

72. Finite discontinuities. It may happen that, at $x = a$, the function has both a left-hand and a right-hand limit, but the two are not equal:

$$
\lim_{x \to a^-} f(x) = l_1, \qquad \lim_{x \to a^+} f(x) = l_2, \qquad l_1 \neq l_2.
$$

At such a point the function has a *finite discontinuity:* the curve takes a vertical jump of width $l_2 - l_1$.

Example: The first-class postage P (in cents) is defined in terms of the weight W (in ounces) as follows:

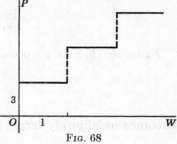

$$P = 0, \qquad W = 0;$$
$$P = 3, \qquad 0 < W \leqq 1;$$
$$P = 6, \qquad 1 < W \leqq 2; \text{ etc.}$$

The function has finite discontinui- ties at $W = 0, 1, 2,$ etc.*

Fig. 68

73. Infinite discontinuities. A frequently-occurring type of discon- tinuity is that in which the function *increases numerically without limit* as x approaches a: we say that the function has an *infinite discontinuity* at $x = a$. Graphically this means that the curve approaches the line $x = a$, usually without ever reaching it, at the same time receding indefinitely from the x-axis. It may happen that $f(x)$ becomes large and positive, or large and negative, on both sides of the line $x = a$ (Fig. 69); if so, we write

$$\lim_{x \to a} f(x) = \infty \quad \text{or} \quad \lim_{x \to a} f(x) = -\infty,$$

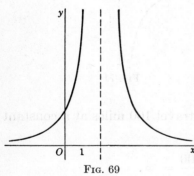

Fig. 69

as the case may be. Other possi- bilities are shown in Figs. 70, 74.

It should be clearly understood, however, that any "equation" such as those above is not an equation at all, in the true sense, for the reason that *the symbol ∞ does not represent a number*. The symbols written tell us, not that $f(x)$ ap- proaches some vague, indefinite, very large limiting value, but that it increases numerically beyond any limit whatever.

Example (a): As x approaches 1, the function (Fig. 69)

$$y = \frac{1}{(x - 1)^2}$$

---

* Many familiar functions have a great number of relatively small finite discontinu- ities — *e.g.*, the cost of a quantity of gasoline at 30 cents per gallon, jumping by 1 cent at intervals of $\frac{1}{30}$ gallon; price of a stock on the New York Exchange, changing by eighths at irregular time-intervals; etc. For most purposes such a function may be replaced by a function varying continuously: see, for instance, Example (*c*), § 1.

increases without limit: that is,

$$\lim_{x \to 1} \frac{1}{(x-1)^2} = \infty.$$

Example (b): As x approaches 2, the function (Fig. 70)

$$y = \frac{x^2}{x-2}$$

becomes indefinitely large, positive if $x > 2$, negative if $x < 2$:

$$\lim_{x \to 2+} \frac{x^2}{x-2} = \infty, \qquad \lim_{x \to 2-} \frac{x^2}{x-2} = -\infty.$$

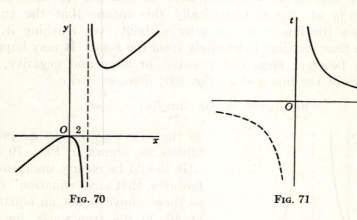

FIG. 70   FIG. 71

Example (c): The time required to travel 100 miles at a constant speed v is (Fig. 71)

$$t = \frac{100}{v}; \quad \lim_{v \to 0+} \frac{100}{v} = \infty.$$

This merely states the obvious fact that by moving slowly enough we could, theoretically at least, take any conceivable amount of time to cover the distance.*

74. Function with argument approaching infinity. We frequently have to investigate the behavior of a function as the independent variable increases, or decreases, without bound.

* A glacier would require many centuries to travel 100 miles.

If there is a constant c, such that $|f(x) - c|$ can be made as small as desired by choosing x sufficiently large, we write

$$\lim_{x \to \infty} f(x) = c.$$

Graphically this means that the curve $y = f(x)$ approaches the line $y = c$, as $x \to \infty$.

In a similar manner, if there is a constant k, such that $|f(x) - k|$ can be made arbitrarily small by choosing x negative and of sufficiently great magnitude, we say that

$$\lim_{x \to -\infty} f(x) = k.$$

As x increases indefinitely, it may happen that $f(x)$ does likewise. If both are positive, we write

$$\lim_{x \to \infty} f(x) = \infty,$$

with appropriate changes in notation when either or both are negative.

Finally, it may be that $f(x)$ approaches no limit, finite or infinite, as $x \to \infty$, or as $x \to -\infty$. Consider the behavior of the curve $y = \tan x$, as x recedes from the y-axis in either direction.

Example (a): To evaluate

$$\lim_{x \to \infty} \frac{x^2 - 1}{x^2 + 1},$$

divide numerator and denominator by x^2:

$$\lim_{x \to \infty} \frac{x^2 - 1}{x^2 + 1} = \lim_{x \to \infty} \frac{1 - \dfrac{1}{x^2}}{1 + \dfrac{1}{x^2}} = 1.$$

The graph of the function is shown in Fig. 72.

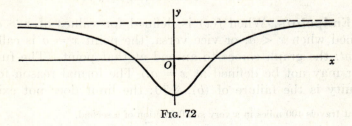

FIG. 72

Example (b):

$$\lim_{x \to \infty} \frac{x^2}{x-2} = \lim_{x \to \infty} \frac{x}{1 - \frac{2}{x}} = \infty,$$

$$\lim_{x \to -\infty} \frac{x^2}{x-2} = -\infty.$$

Thus in this case no limit is approached as x increases in either direction. (Fig. 70.)

Example (c): In Example (c), § 73,

$$t = \frac{100}{v}; \qquad \lim_{v \to \infty} \frac{100}{v} = 0.$$

This merely says that if the speed could be made great enough we could cover the distance in any desired time, no matter how short.* (Fig. 71.)

75. Rational algebraic functions. In regard to rational algebraic functions, the question of continuity is completely covered by the following theorems.

THEOREM I: *A polynomial is continuous for all values of x.*

THEOREM II: *A rational algebraic fraction is continuous except for those values of x for which the denominator vanishes.*

These theorems are immediate consequences of Exs. 31–32, p. 16. Under Theorem II, at a point where the denominator vanishes, only two kinds of discontinuity are possible: a missing-point discontinuity (§ 71), or an infinite discontinuity (§ 73).

In the above, it is understood that x is free to assume any real value. In applications where, owing to the nature of the problem, the variable is restricted in range, an entirely different situation may arise. This matter will be discussed in § 79.

76. Endpoints. When $f(x)$ is defined for values of $x > a$, but undefined when $x < a$, or vice versa, the point $x = a$ is called an *endpoint;* the graph comes to an end at that point. (The function may or may not be defined at $x = a$.) The formal reason for discontinuity is the failure of (b), § 70: the limit does not exist for

* Light travels 100 miles in a very small fraction of a second.

left-hand or for right-hand approach as the case may be.* The simplest examples are furnished by irrational algebraic functions where roots of even order are involved. Also, we shall see later that end-points are of frequent occurrence among certain classes of transcendental functions.

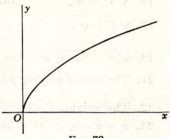

FIG. 73

Example (a): The function

$$(1) \qquad\qquad y = \sqrt{x}$$

has an endpoint at $x = 0$. Its graph, of course, is the upper half of the parabola $y^2 = x$, Fig. 73.

Example (b): The function

$$(2) \qquad\qquad y = \sqrt{\frac{1 - x}{1 + x}}$$

is imaginary for $x > 1$ and $x < -1$. It has an infinite discontinuity at $x = -1$ and an endpoint at $x = 1$. See Fig. 74.

FIG. 74

Technically, a function is discontinuous at every point of an interval where it is not defined. We shall disregard intervals of non-definition as of no possible interest. With this understood, we may say that the functions (1) and (2) have no discontinuities except those noted.

EXERCISES

Find the points of discontinuity of the functions in Exs. 1–24.

1. $\dfrac{x^2 + 5}{x^2 - 9}$. *Ans.* $x = \pm 3$.

2. $\dfrac{2x + 1}{x^2 - 4x + 4}$. *Ans.* $x = 2$.

3. $\dfrac{x - 1}{x^2 + 4}$.

4. $\dfrac{x + 2}{3x^2 - 2x + 1}$.

5. $\dfrac{x^2 - 2x}{x^3 - 2x^2 + 2x}$. *Ans.* $x = 0$.

6. $\dfrac{4(x + 1)^2}{2x^3 - 5x^2 - 4x + 3}$.

7. $\dfrac{x^4 - x + 2}{x^3 - 12x + 16}$.

8. $\dfrac{3}{2x^3 + 5x^2 + 4}$.

9. $\sin \theta$. *Ans.* None.

10. $\cot \theta$. *Ans.* $n\pi$, n any integer.

*When the function is defined at $x = a$, and $\lim\limits_{x \to a^+} f(x) = f(a)$, the function is said to possess *right-hand continuity;* similarly for left-hand continuity.

11. $\csc \theta$.   **12.** $\sec \theta$.   **13.** $(1 - x)^{\frac{1}{3}}$.

14. $\sqrt{x^2 - a^2}$.   **15.** $(1 - x)^{-\frac{1}{4}}$.   **16.** $(1 - x)^{-\frac{1}{2}}$.

17. $\sqrt{1 + \sqrt{x}}$.   **18.** $\dfrac{\sqrt{a + x}}{x^2 - a^2}$.

19. $\sqrt{x^2 - 2ax + a^2}$. *Ans.* None.   **20.** $\dfrac{\sqrt{2ax - x^2}}{a^2 - x^2}$.

21. The cost of sending a telegram, as a function of the number of words.
Ans. Everywhere discontinuous.

22. The weight of a U. S. coin, as a function of the value.

23. $y = x - \sqrt{x^2}$. (Ex. 38, p. 8.)   *Ans.* None.

24. $y = \dfrac{x}{\sqrt{x^2}}$, $x \neq 0$; $y = 0$, $x = 0$. (Ex. 36, p. 8.)   *Ans.* $x = 0$.

25. If $f(x)$ is continuous, is its square continuous? Is its reciprocal?

26. Given two continuous functions, what can be said of the continuity of their sum? Their product? Their quotient?

27. Show that as x approaches zero, the function $\sin \dfrac{\pi}{x}$ oscillates between -1 and 1, without approaching any limit.

28. Discuss the behavior of $\tan \dfrac{\pi}{x}$ near the origin.

29. Show that the function $y = x \sin \dfrac{1}{x}$ is discontinuous at the origin. What type of discontinuity is present?

30. Show that the function $y = x \tan \dfrac{1}{x}$ is discontinuous at the origin.

Evaluate the limits in Exs. 31–52.

31. $\lim\limits_{x \to \infty} \dfrac{2}{x^2 - 3}$.   **32.** $\lim\limits_{x \to \infty} \dfrac{2x^2}{x^2 - 3}$.

33. $\lim\limits_{x \to -\infty} \dfrac{x^3}{4x^3 + 1}$.   *Ans.* $\frac{1}{4}$.   **34.** $\lim\limits_{x \to -\infty} \dfrac{4x^2}{3x^2 - x}$.   *Ans.* $\frac{4}{3}$.

35. $\lim\limits_{x \to \infty} \dfrac{7x^3}{x^2 + 4}$.   *Ans.* No limit (∞).

36. $\lim\limits_{x \to -\infty} \dfrac{(x + 1)^4}{(2x - 1)^3}$.   *Ans.* No limit $(-\infty)$.

37. $\lim\limits_{x \to \infty} \dfrac{(x - 2)(4x^3 + 1)}{(2x^2 + 1)^2}$.   **38.** $\lim\limits_{x \to \infty} \dfrac{(x - 1)^3}{(x^2 + 1)^2}$.

39. $\lim\limits_{x \to \infty} 2^{\frac{1}{x}}$.   *Ans.* 1.   **40.** $\lim\limits_{x \to -\infty} 2^{\frac{1}{x}}$.   *Ans.* 1.

41. $\lim\limits_{x \to 0^+} 2^{\frac{1}{x}}$.   *Ans.* No limit (∞).   **42.** $\lim\limits_{x \to 0^-} 2^{\frac{1}{x}}$.   *Ans.* 0.

43. $\lim\limits_{x \to \infty} \dfrac{1}{1 + 2^{\frac{1}{x}}}$.   *Ans.* $\frac{1}{2}$.   **44.** $\lim\limits_{x \to -\infty} \dfrac{1}{1 + 2^{\frac{1}{x}}}$.   *Ans.* $\frac{1}{2}$.

45. $\lim\limits_{x \to 0^+} \dfrac{1}{1 + 2^{\frac{1}{x}}}.$ *Ans.* 0.

46. $\lim\limits_{x \to 0^-} \dfrac{1}{1 + 2^{\frac{1}{x}}}.$ *Ans.* 1.

47. $\lim\limits_{x \to \infty} \dfrac{2}{2 + 3^{\frac{1}{x}}}.$

48. $\lim\limits_{x \to -\infty} \dfrac{3}{5 + 2^{\frac{1}{x}}}.$

49. $\lim\limits_{x \to \infty} \sin x.$ *Ans.* No limit.

50. $\lim\limits_{x \to \infty} \tan x.$ *Ans.* No limit.

51. $\lim\limits_{x \to \infty} \dfrac{\sin x}{x}.$ *Ans.* 0.

52. $\lim\limits_{x \to \infty} \dfrac{\tan x}{x}.$ *Ans.* No limit.

53. Sketch the curve $y = 2^{\frac{1}{x}}$. See Exs. 39–42.

54. Sketch the curve $y = \dfrac{1}{1 + 2^{\frac{1}{x}}}$. See Exs. 43–46.

55. In Ex. 40, page 8, graph A as a function of a with b held fixed.

77. Function with discontinuous derivative. When a function is continuous in an interval, it does not necessarily follow that the derivative is continuous.

Example (a): The function

$$y = x^{\frac{1}{3}}$$

is everywhere continuous, but the curve comes in to the origin tangent to the y-axis; thus the slope,

$$y' = \frac{1}{3x^{\frac{2}{3}}},$$

has an infinite discontinuity at that point. The graphs of y and y' are shown in Fig. 75.

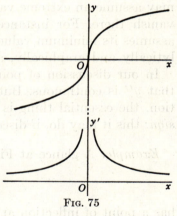

FIG. 75

Example (b): The function (§ 6)

$$y = \sqrt{x^2}$$

is everywhere continuous, but y' (slope) jumps abruptly from -1 to 1 at $x = 0$ (Fig. 76).

If a function $f(x)$ and its first derivative $f'(x)$ are both continuous, the function is said to be *smooth*, for the obvious reason that the curve is smooth in the ordinary sense.

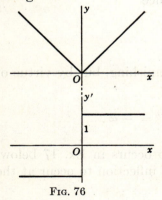

FIG. 76

A smooth function may, of course, have a discontinuous second derivative. An important instance of this occurs in highway or

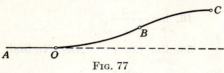

Fig. 77

railroad construction. Say that a level highway AO begins at O to climb a grade OBC. The pavement must be unbroken (y continuous) and smooth (y' continuous), but in general y''—rate of change of grade—will be discontinuous at O and B. A similar situation arises in connection with horizontal turns: the turn would usually be "eased"—y' continuous—but the rate of change of direction may jump abruptly.

78. Extremes; points of inflection. Underlying our entire theory of maxima and minima (§§ 36–41) is the vital assumption that all functions under consideration are smooth—y and y' continuous. At a point of discontinuity of either y or y', the function may assume an extreme value even though the derivative does not vanish there. For instance, the function in Example (*b*) of § 77 assumes its minimum value zero at $x = 0$, as is obvious both analytically and graphically, although the derivative is not zero.

In our discussion of points of inflection (§ 38), it was assumed that y'' is continuous. But, in order to produce a point of inflection, the essential thing is not that y'' vanish, but that it *change sign*: this it may do, if discontinuous, by jumping over the value 0.

Example: A glance at Fig. 75 shows that the curve

$$y = x^{\frac{1}{3}}$$

has a point of inflection at the origin. Since

$$y'' = \frac{-2}{9x^{\frac{5}{3}}},$$

it is clear that y'' changes sign, not by vanishing, but by virtue of an infinite discontinuity:

$$\lim_{x \to 0^-} y'' = +\infty, \qquad \lim_{x \to 0^+} y'' = -\infty.$$

An inflection effected by a finite jump occurs in Ex. 17 below. It is even possible for an extreme and an inflection to occur at the same point (Ex. 12 below).

79. Applications. In practical applications, as we have seen many times, the independent variable is usually confined, by the nature of the problem, to a limited range. Then, a function which would be continuous if x were unrestricted is discontinuous, of course, at the ends of the interval (§ 76), and in many cases assumes extreme values at those points, although as a rule the derivative does not vanish there.

Example (a): The cost of a quantity of gasoline at $0.30 per gallon is, in dollars,

$$C = 0.30Q.$$

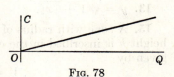

Fig. 78

The minimum cost is zero, occurring at $Q = 0$, although

$$\frac{dC}{dQ} = 0.30.$$

Example (b): The volume of a sphere is (Fig. 79)

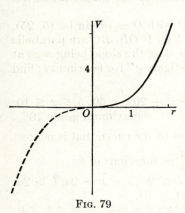

Fig. 79

$$V = \frac{4}{3}\pi r^3, \qquad \frac{dV}{dr} = 4\pi r^2.$$

The minimum volume is zero, occurring at $r = 0$. Here it is true that $\frac{dV}{dr} = 0$ when $r = 0$, but the theory of § 37 (here inapplicable of course) would show this to be not a minimum, but a point of inflection.

Similar remarks apply to most of our problems in maxima and minima (§§ 40–41, and exercises following). In any practical case the situation would almost always be just as clear as in the above examples.

EXERCISES

In Exs. 1–8, examine the curve for maxima and minima. Rationalize the equation and plot the curve; indicate the portion representing the original equation.

1. $y = x^{\frac{2}{5}}$.

2. $y = (4 - x^2)^{\frac{1}{3}}$.

3. $y = -\sqrt{1 + x}$.

4. $y = (1 + x)^{\frac{3}{2}}$.

5. $y = \sqrt{x^2 - a^2}$.

6. $y = \sqrt{2ax - x^2}$.

7. $y = \sqrt{1 - \sqrt{x}}$.

8. $y = \sqrt{1 + \sqrt{x}}$.

In Exs. 9–14, draw the graphs of y, y', and y''.

9. $y = x\sqrt{x^2}$.

10. $y = x - |x|$.

11. $y = \dfrac{|x|}{x}$.

12. $y = \sqrt{x^4 - 2x^2 + 1}$.

13. $y = \sqrt{1 + |x|}$.

14. $y = \sqrt{|x| - 1}$.

15. A cone with radius of base R, and height H, is given. A cylinder of height h is inscribed in the cone. Show that the volume of the cylinder is given by

$$V = \pi R^2 H^{-2} h (H - h)^2.$$

Draw the curve representing V as a function of h, and indicate that portion of the curve which has physical meaning in the problem.

16. A box is to be made from a rectangular piece of cardboard of dimensions 4 in. by 6 in., by cutting equal squares out of the corners, and turning them up. Graph the volume of the box as a function of the length of side of the squares cut out, and indicate the portion of the graph which has physical meaning.

17. In Fig. 77, let the coördinates of B, C with O as origin be (5, 25), (10, 50), the x-unit being 100 ft., the y-unit 1 ft. If OB, BC are parabolic arcs with equations of the form $y = ax^2 + bx + c$, the slope being zero at O and C, determine y as a function of x; investigate y'' for continuity; find the maximum grade.

Ans. $y = x^2$, $0 \leq x \leq 5$; $y = -x^2 + 20x - 50$, $5 \leq x \leq 10$;
maximum grade 10%.

In Exs. 18–21, find the abscissa of that point of the curve that is nearest the point $(k, 0)$. Draw the graphs of x and $\dfrac{dx}{dk}$ as functions of k.

18. The parabola $y^2 = 4ax$.   *Ans.* $x = 0$, $k \leq 2a$; $x = k - 2a$, $k > 2a$.

19. The hyperbola $x^2 - y^2 = a^2$. Cf. Ex. 34, p. 64.
Ans. $x = \frac{1}{2}k$, $k < -2a$; $x = -a$, $-2a \leq k < 0$;
$x = \pm a$, $k = 0$; $x = a$, $0 < k \leq 2a$; $x = \frac{1}{2}k$, $k > 2a$.

20. The ellipse $\dfrac{x^2}{a^2} + \dfrac{y^2}{b^2} = 1$.   *Ans.* $x = -a$, $k < \dfrac{b^2 - a^2}{a}$;

$x = \dfrac{a^2 k}{a^2 - b^2}$, $\dfrac{b^2 - a^2}{a} \leq k \leq \dfrac{a^2 - b^2}{a}$; $x = a$, $k > \dfrac{a^2 - b^2}{a}$.

21. The circle $x^2 + y^2 = a^2$.
Ans. $x = -a$, $k < 0$; $-a \leq x \leq a$, $k = 0$; $x = a$, $k > 0$.

22. Solve Ex. 18 by analytic geometry: write the equation of a circle of arbitrary radius with center at $(k, 0)$ and make it touch the parabola. (Eliminate y between the two equations; equate to zero the discriminant of the resulting quadratic in x.)

23. Solve Ex. 19 by the method suggested in Ex. 22.

24. Graph the difference in area between a square of side 1 and a square of side l.

25. Graph the difference in volume between a sphere of radius r and a cylinder of radius r, height 1. Discuss extremes.

26. Graph the difference in volume V between two boxes of dimensions l, 2, 2 and l, l, 2. Discuss extremes.

27. In Ex. 26, what value of l makes $V = 1$? *Ans.* 0.293, 1.707, 2.225.

28. In Ex. 40, p. 8, graph A as a function of b (with a fixed). Find the maximum attraction.

29. Sketch the curve

$$y = \sqrt{x + \sqrt{x - \tfrac{1}{4}}} + \sqrt{x - \sqrt{x - \tfrac{1}{4}}}.$$

Hint: Examine the curve for $x < \tfrac{1}{4}$, $\tfrac{1}{4} \leq x \leq \tfrac{1}{2}$, $\tfrac{1}{2} < x$; rationalize the equation.

In Exs. 30–33, a cylinder is to be cut from a sphere of diameter 1 ft. and then packed in a rectangular box. Find the volume of the largest cylinder that can be handled in this way, if the dimensions of the box are as given.

30. Box 10 × 10 × 8 in. *Ans.* $V = 96\sqrt{3}\,\pi = 166.3\pi$ cu. in.

31. Box 10 × 8 × 8 in. *Ans.* $V = 64\sqrt{5}\,\pi = 143.1\pi$ cu. in.

32. Box 12 × 12 × 6 in. *Ans.* $V = 162\pi$ cu. in.
33. Box 10 × 6 × 4 in. *Ans.* $V = 40\pi$ cu. in.

34. Express $\cos 3\theta$ as a function of $\cos \theta$ by the addition formula. Putting $x = \cos \theta$, $y = \cos 3\theta$, graph $\cos 3\theta$ as a function of $\cos \theta$; find the extremes. *Ans.* $\cos 3\theta = 4\cos^3 \theta - 3\cos \theta$; $(\pm \tfrac{1}{2}, \mp 1)$, $(\pm 1, \pm 1)$.

35. Solve Ex. 34 for the functions $\sin 3\theta$, $\sin \theta$. *Ans.* $\sin 3\theta = 3\sin \theta - 4\sin^3 \theta$; $(\pm \tfrac{1}{2}, \pm 1)$, $(\pm 1, \mp 1)$.

CHAPTER 8 TRIGONOMETRIC FUNCTIONS

80. Elementary properties. The trigonometric functions are one-valued and continuous for all values of the argument x, except that the tangent and secant become infinite when $x = \pm (n + \frac{1}{2})\pi$, the cotangent and cosecant become infinite when $x = \pm n\pi$, where n is zero or a positive integer. The sine and cosine, and their reciprocals the cosecant and secant, are periodic with the period 2π; the tangent and cotangent are periodic with the period π.

A student of calculus may save himself a great deal of time and trouble by memorizing thoroughly the fundamental facts and formulas of trigonometry. It is strongly recommended that such a review be made before proceeding further.

81. Derivative of sin x. From

$$y = \sin x,$$

it follows readily that

$$y + \Delta y = \sin (x + \Delta x),$$

(1) $$\Delta y = \sin (x + \Delta x) - \sin x.$$

Equation (1) is not yet in a form suited to our purpose, which is to divide throughout by Δx and then to let $\Delta x \to 0$. Let us rewrite (1) as

(2) $$\Delta y = \sin (x + \tfrac{1}{2} \Delta x + \tfrac{1}{2} \Delta x) - \sin (x + \tfrac{1}{2} \Delta x - \tfrac{1}{2} \Delta x).$$

By a trigonometric addition formula we know that

$$\sin (x + \tfrac{1}{2} \Delta x + \tfrac{1}{2} \Delta x)$$
$$= \sin (x + \tfrac{1}{2} \Delta x) \cos (\tfrac{1}{2} \Delta x) + \cos (x + \tfrac{1}{2} \Delta x) \sin (\tfrac{1}{2} \Delta x)$$

and

$$\sin (x + \tfrac{1}{2} \Delta x - \tfrac{1}{2} \Delta x)$$
$$= \sin (x + \tfrac{1}{2} \Delta x) \cos (\tfrac{1}{2} \Delta x) - \cos (x + \tfrac{1}{2} \Delta x) \sin (\tfrac{1}{2} \Delta x).$$

Hence equation (2) becomes

$$\Delta y = 2 \cos (x + \tfrac{1}{2} \Delta x) \sin (\tfrac{1}{2} \Delta x),$$

from which we obtain

(3) $$\frac{\Delta y}{\Delta x} = \cos (x + \tfrac{1}{2} \Delta x) \cdot \frac{\sin (\tfrac{1}{2} \Delta x)}{\tfrac{1}{2} \Delta x}.$$

In § 11 it was shown that

$$\lim_{\alpha \to 0} \frac{\sin \alpha}{\alpha} = 1,$$

which leads at once to the result

$$\lim_{\Delta x \to 0} \frac{\sin (\tfrac{1}{2} \Delta x)}{\tfrac{1}{2} \Delta x} = 1.$$

Thus, letting $\Delta x \to 0$ in both members of equation (3) yields

$$\frac{dy}{dx} = \frac{d}{dx} \sin x = \cos x.$$

If u is any function of x, it follows from (5), § 26, that

$$\frac{d}{dx} \sin u = \frac{d}{du} \sin u \cdot \frac{du}{dx},$$

or

(7) $$\frac{d}{dx} \sin u = \cos u \frac{du}{dx}.$$

Radian measure of angles is almost always used in calculus in preference to degree measure of angles. In Ex. 51, page 17, it was found that

$$\lim_{\alpha^\circ \to 0} \frac{\sin \alpha^\circ}{\alpha^\circ} = \frac{\pi}{180^\circ}.$$

With the aid of the above limit, it can be seen that, if x° is measured in degrees, then equation (3) yields

$$\frac{d}{dx^\circ} \sin x^\circ = \frac{\pi}{180^\circ} \cos x^\circ.$$

The highly undesirable factor $\left(\frac{\pi}{180^\circ}\right)$ would also appear in the derivatives of the other trigonometric functions, if degree measure were to be used. Therefore, in calculus we use radian measure whenever feasible, although in numerical studies (surveying, etc.) it is common practice to retain degree measure of angles.

82. Derivatives of cos *x*, tan *x*, etc. The derivatives of the other trigonometric functions may also be obtained directly from the definition of the derivative, but they are more easily found from (7) above.

To differentiate cos *x*, we write

$$\frac{d}{dx} \cos x = \frac{d}{dx} \sin \left(\frac{\pi}{2} - x\right) = -\cos \left(\frac{\pi}{2} - x\right)$$
$$= -\sin x.$$

If *u* is any function of *x*, we find by formula (5) of § 26

$$(8) \qquad \frac{d}{dx} \cos u = - \sin u \frac{du}{dx}.$$

The remaining trigonometric functions may be differentiated by expressing them in terms of the sine and cosine. If *u* is any function of *x*, the results are:

$$(9) \qquad \frac{d}{dx} \tan u = \sec^2 u \frac{du}{dx},$$

$$(10) \qquad \frac{d}{dx} \cot u = - \csc^2 u \frac{du}{dx},$$

$$(11) \qquad \frac{d}{dx} \sec u = \sec u \tan u \frac{du}{dx},$$

$$(12) \qquad \frac{d}{dx} \csc u = - \csc u \cot u \frac{du}{dx}.$$

Example (a): If $y = \sin 4x^2$, then

$$\frac{dy}{dx} = 8x \cos 4x^2.$$

Example (b): If $z = \tan \frac{1}{2}y$, then

$$\frac{dz}{dy} = \frac{1}{2} \sec^2 \frac{1}{2}y.$$

Example (c): If $r = (2 + 3 \cot 4\theta)^5$, then

$$\frac{dr}{d\theta} = 5(2 + 3 \cot 4\theta)^4 \cdot 3 \cdot (-4 \csc^2 4\theta)$$
$$= -60 \csc^2 4\theta(2 + 3 \cot 4\theta)^4.$$

EXERCISES

In Exs. 1–42, find the first derivative of the given function.

1. $y = \sin 4x$.   Ans. $\dfrac{dy}{dx} = 4 \cos 4x$.

2. $x = \cos 3t$.   Ans. $\dfrac{dx}{dt} = -3 \sin 3t$.

3. $x = \sec 2u$.   Ans. $\dfrac{dx}{du} = 2 \sec 2u \tan 2u$.

4. $y = -2 \csc 2t$.   Ans. $\dfrac{dy}{dt} = 4 \csc 2t \cot 2t$.

5. $t = \tan 3y$.   Ans. $\dfrac{dt}{dy} = 3 \sec^2 3y$.

6. $\theta = 4 \cot \frac{1}{2}\phi$.   Ans. $\dfrac{d\theta}{d\phi} = -2 \csc^2 \frac{1}{2}\phi$.

7. $y = \csc (3x - 1)$.   **8.** $y = \tan\left(\dfrac{\pi}{4} - \dfrac{x}{2}\right)$.

9. $r = \cos \left(\frac{1}{2}\theta^2\right)$.   **10.** $r = \sin \left(\dfrac{\pi}{3} - \dfrac{1}{2}\theta\right)$.

11. $x = \cot (1 - t^2)$.   **12.** $x = \sec \dfrac{2\pi - \theta}{3}$.

13. $u = z \sin (4z)$.   **14.** $u = \sin^2 (3z)$.

15. $y = x^2 \cos^3 x$.   **16.** $y = (1 - x)^3 \sin^2 x$.

17. $x = \sec 2t - \tan 2t$.   **18.** $x = \csc^2 (1 + 4t)$.

19. $\alpha = \sin^2 \beta \cos \beta$.   **20.** $\alpha = \sec^2 \beta \tan^2 \beta$.

21. $f(x) = \tan x - x$.   **22.** $F(x) = x + \cot x$.

23. $y = \cos^4 t - \sin^4 t$.   Ans. $\dfrac{dy}{dt} = -2 \sin 2t$.

24. $y = \sec^2 \theta - \tan^2 \theta$.   Ans. $\dfrac{dy}{d\theta} = 0$.

25. $r = \cos \theta \cot \theta$.   Ans. $\dfrac{dr}{d\theta} = -\cos \theta (1 + \csc^2 \theta)$.

26. $w = \sin^4 y \cos^4 y$.   Ans. $\dfrac{dw}{dy} = \dfrac{1}{2} \sin^3 2y \cos 2y$.

27. $x = 2 \cos^2 \dfrac{t}{2}$.   Ans. $\dfrac{dx}{dt} = -\sin t$.

28. $z = 4 \sin^2 (3u)$.   Ans. $\dfrac{dz}{du} = 12 \sin 6u$.

29. $y = \sin (\cos x)$.   Ans. $y' = -\sin x \cos (\cos x)$.

30. $y = \tan (x \sin x)$.   Ans. $y' = (x \cos x + \sin x) \sec^2 (x \sin x)$.

31. $v = (1 + \sin^4 y)^{\frac{3}{2}}$.   **32.** $v = (1 - 4 \cos 5y)^{-\frac{1}{2}}$.

33. $r = (2 \tan^3 2\theta - 1)^{\frac{1}{3}}$.   **34.** $r = \dfrac{\cos 2\theta}{1 - \sin 2\theta}$.

35. $y = \dfrac{\tan 2x}{1 - \cot 2x}$.

36. $y = \dfrac{1}{(\sec^2 3x - 4)^{\frac{1}{2}}}$.

37. $x = \dfrac{1 - \tan^2 v}{\tan^4 v}$.

38. $x = \dfrac{1}{(\cos \phi - \sin \phi)^2}$.

39. $y = \left(\dfrac{1 - \cos \theta}{1 + \cos \theta}\right)^3$.

40. $y = \dfrac{(1 + \sec x)^2}{(1 - \sec x)^3}$.

41. $u = x \csc^3 (x^2)$.

42. $v = (1 - x^2) \tan (1 - x^2)$.

43. From the equation $y = \sin (ax)$, find the first four derivatives of y with respect to x.

44. Find $y^{(4)}$ and $y^{(8)}$ from the equation $y = \cos 2x$.

45. Show that, if A, B, k, are constants, then from

$$y = A \cos kx + B \sin kx, \text{ we obtain } \frac{d^2y}{dx^2} = -k^2y.$$

46. From each of the three trigonometric formulas for $\cos 2x$, deduce by differentiation the trigonometric formula for $\sin 2x$.

47. From the trigonometric formula for $\sin (x + \alpha)$, deduce by differentiation the trigonometric formula for $\cos (x + \alpha)$.

48. From the trigonometric formula for $\tan 2x$, deduce by differentiation the trigonometric formula for $\cos 2x$.

49. Show that $\tan x$ increases as x increases, for all values of x for which $\tan x$ is defined.

50. Derive (9) from the fact that $\tan x = \dfrac{\sin x}{\cos x}$.

51. Derive (10).   **52.** Derive (11).   **53.** Derive (12).

54. Assuming that you know $\dfrac{d}{dx} \sin x = \cos x$, find $\dfrac{d}{dx} \cos x$ from the relation $\cos^2 x = 1 - \sin^2 x$.

55. Assuming that you know $\dfrac{d}{dx} \sin u = \cos u \dfrac{du}{dx}$, find $\dfrac{d}{dx} \cos x$ from the relation $\cos x = 1 - 2 \sin^2 (\tfrac{1}{2}x)$.

83. Graphs of trigonometric functions. To draw the graph of the function

$$y = \sin x,$$

we may proceed as in § 39. On account of the periodicity of the sine function, it will be sufficient to determine the appearance of the curve in the interval from $x = 0$ to $x = 2\pi$; the remainder of the curve must consist of repetitions of this portion.

1. When $x = 0$, $y = 0$; when $y = 0$, $x = 0$, π, 2π.

2. Evidently, large values of x need not be considered.

3. $y' = \cos x$: hence the critical points are $(\tfrac{1}{2}\pi, 1)$, a maximum, and $(\tfrac{3}{2}\pi, -1)$, a minimum.

4. $y'' = -\sin x$: the points of inflection are $(0, 0)$, with slope 1, $(\pi, 0)$, with slope -1, and $(2\pi, 0)$, with slope 1.

The curve consists of an infinite succession of waves along the x-axis, as shown in Fig. 80.

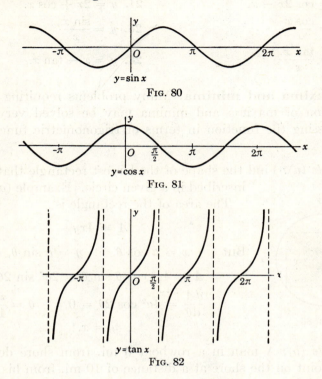

FIG. 80

FIG. 81

FIG. 82

The graphs of the cosine and tangent are shown in Figs. 81 and 82; they are obtained in a similar way, except that in the case of the tangent the points of discontinuity $x = \pm(n + \frac{1}{2})\pi$ must be specially investigated in addition to the usual discussion.

EXERCISES

Trace the curve in each exercise.

1. $y = \sec x$.
2. $y = \csc x$.
3. $y = \cot x$.
4. $y = \frac{1}{2} \cos 2x$.
5. $y = -2 \sin (\frac{1}{2}x)$.
6. $y = 3 \tan 2x$.
7. $y = 4 \cos (\frac{1}{3}x)$.
8. $y = -\frac{1}{2} \sin 4x$.
9. $x = \cos^2 t$.
10. $x = \sin^2 t$.
11. $z = \sin^2 (3x)$.
12. $z = \cos^2 (\frac{1}{2}x)$.
13. $y = \sin^3 x$.
14. $y = \cos^3 x$.
15. $y = \sin^2 x + \sin x$.
16. $y = \cos^2 x - \cos x$.
17. $u = 2 \sin v - 1$.
18. $u = 1 - 3 \cos 2v$.

19. $y = \sin 2x - 2 \cos x + 2.$　　　**20.** $y = \cos x - \frac{1}{2} \sin 2x - 1.$
21. $y = 2 \cos^3 x - 3 \sin x.$　　　**22.** $y = x - \sin x.$
23. $y = \cos 2x - x.$　　　**24.** $y = 2x + \cos x.$

25. $y = \dfrac{\cos x}{x}.$　　　　　　　**26.** $y = \dfrac{\sin x}{x}.$

27. $y = \dfrac{\tan x}{x}.$　　　　　　　**28.** $y = x - \tan x.$

84. Maxima and minima. Many problems requiring the determination of maxima and minima may be solved very neatly by expressing the function in terms of trigonometric functions of an angle.

Example (a): Find the shape of the largest rectangle that can be inscribed in a given circle. [Example (a), § 41.]

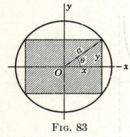

FIG. 83

The area of the rectangle is

$$A = 4xy.$$

But　　$x = a \cos \theta, \qquad y = a \sin \theta,$

$$A = 4a^2 \cos \theta \sin \theta = 2a^2 \sin 2\theta:$$

$$\frac{dA}{d\theta} = 4a^2 \cos 2\theta = 0, \qquad \theta = \frac{\pi}{4},$$

$$y = x.$$

Example (b): A man in a rowboat 6 mi. from shore desires to reach a point on the shore at a distance of 10 mi. from his present position. If he can walk 4 mi. per hr. and row 2 mi. per hr., in what direction should he row in order to reach his destination in the shortest possible time? [Example (c), § 41.]

The time required is

$$T = \frac{y}{2} + \frac{8 - x}{4}.$$

Since

$$y = 6 \sec \theta, \qquad x = 6 \tan \theta,$$

$$T = \frac{6 \sec \theta}{2} + \frac{8 - 6 \tan \theta}{4}$$

$$= 3 \sec \theta + 2 - \tfrac{3}{2} \tan \theta,$$

$$\frac{dT}{d\theta} = 3 \sec \theta \tan \theta - \tfrac{3}{2} \sec^2 \theta$$

$$= 3 \sec^2 \theta (\sin \theta - \tfrac{1}{2}) = 0,$$

$$\theta = 30°.$$

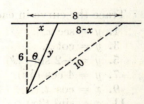

FIG. 84

EXERCISES

Solve the following exercises by making use of trigonometric functions.

1. Find the shape of the rectangle of maximum perimeter inscribed in a circle.   *Ans.* A square.

2. A cylinder is inscribed in a given sphere. Find the shape of the cylinder if its convex surface is a maximum.   *Ans.* Diameter = height.

3. Find the weight of the heaviest circular cylinder that can be cut from a 16-lb. shot.   *Ans.* 9.2 lbs.

4. The stiffness of a rectangular beam is proportional to the breadth and the cube of the depth. Find the shape of the stiffest beam that can be cut from a log of given size.   *Ans.* Depth = $\sqrt{3}$ × breadth.

5. The strength of a rectangular beam is proportional to the breadth and the square of the depth. Find the shape of the strongest beam that can be cut from a log of given size.   *Ans.* Depth = $\sqrt{2}$ × breadth.

6. A trapezoidal gutter is to be made, from a strip of metal 22 in. wide, by bending up the edges. If the base is 14 in. wide, what width across the top gives the greatest carrying capacity?   *Ans.* 16 in.

7. Solve Ex. 6, if the strip is 13 in. wide and the base width 7 in.   *Ans.* 9 in.

8. Solve Ex. 6, if the strip is 9 in. wide and the base width 3 in.   *Ans.* 6 in.

9. Solve Ex. 6, if the strip width is w and the base width b.
$$Ans.\ \tfrac{1}{2}[b + \sqrt{b^2 + 2(w - b)^2}].$$

10. Find the largest conical tent that can be constructed having a given slant height.   *Ans.* $r = \sqrt{\tfrac{2}{3}}\,s.$

11. A gutter having a triangular cross-section is to be made by bending a strip of tin in the middle. Find the angle between the sides when the carrying capacity is a maximum.   *Ans.* 90°.

12. Find the altitude of the circular cone of maximum convex surface inscribed in a sphere of radius a.   *Ans.* Altitude = $\tfrac{4}{3}a$.

13. A sphere is cut in the shape of a circular cone. How much of the material can be saved?   *Ans.* About 30%.

14. A wall 8 ft. high is 12 ft. from a house. Find the length of the shortest ladder that will reach the house, when one end rests on the ground outside the wall.   *Ans.* 28.1 ft.

15. Solve Ex. 14, if the height of the wall is b and its distance from the house is c.   *Ans.* $(b^{\frac{2}{3}} + c^{\frac{2}{3}})^{\frac{3}{2}}.$

16. Solve Ex. 53, p. 66.

17. A man in a motorboat at A receives a message at noon, calling him to B. A bus making 40 mi. per hr. leaves C, bound for B, at 1:00 P.M. If $AC = 30$ mi., what must be the speed of the boat, to enable the man to catch the bus?   *Ans.* 24 mi. per hr.

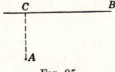

Fig. 85

18. Solve Ex. 17, if $AC = 20$ mi., and the bus makes 50 mi. per hr., leaving C at 12:18 P.M., bound for B.   *Ans.* 40 mi. per hr.

19. A pole 27 ft. long is carried horizontally along a corridor 8 ft. wide and into a second corridor at right angles to the first. How wide must the second corridor be?   *Ans.* $5\sqrt{5} = 11.18$ ft.

20. Solve Ex. 19, if the pole is of length L and the first corridor is of width C.   *Ans.* $(L^{\frac{2}{3}} - C^{\frac{2}{3}})^{\frac{3}{2}}$.

21. A sphere of radius a is dropped into a conical vessel full of water. Find the altitude of the smallest cone that will permit the sphere to be entirely submerged.   *Ans.* Altitude $= 4a$.

22. A sphere is cut in the form of a right pyramid with a square base. How much of the material can be saved?   *Ans.* 19%.

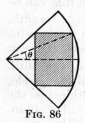

23. Find the area of the largest rectangle that can be cut from a circular quadrant as in Fig. 86.

Ans. $\theta = 22\frac{1}{2}°$; $A = (\sqrt{2} - 1)a^2 = 0.414a^2$.

24. In Ex. 23, draw the graph of A as a function of θ, indicating the portion of the curve that has a meaning.

25. A corridor 4 ft. wide opens into a room 100 ft. long and 32 ft. wide, at the middle of one side. Find the length of the longest thin rod that can be carried horizontally into the room.   *Ans.* $20\sqrt{5} = 44.72$ ft.

Fig. 86

26. Solve Ex. 25 if the room is 56 ft. long.   *Ans.* 43.86 ft.

CHAPTER *9* INVERSE TRIGONOMETRIC
FUNCTIONS

85. Inverse functions. In § 1 we have pointed out the fact that an equation connecting two variables defines either one, explicitly or implicitly, as a function of the other.

Consider now an equation solved explicitly for x,

$$(1) \qquad\qquad x = \phi(y).$$

This defines y as a function of x: say

$$(2) \qquad\qquad y = f(x).$$

When two functions $f(x)$ and $\phi(y)$ are connected in this way, each is said to be the *inverse* of the other. (It should be noted that "inverse" does *not* mean "reciprocal.")

In case $\phi(y)$ is an algebraic function, the inverse function $f(x)$ in simple cases can be explicitly expressed in algebraic symbols. In fact, nothing is new in such cases except the name "inverse function," because the situation has been familiar to us since the days of elementary algebra. For example,

(a) $\qquad\qquad$ if $\quad x = 2y + 4$, $\quad$ then $\quad y = \frac{1}{2}x - 2$;

(b) $\qquad\qquad$ if $\quad x = y^2$, $\qquad$ then $\quad y = \pm \sqrt{x}$.

86. Inverse trigonometric functions. Let y be defined as a function of x by the equation

$$\sin y = x:$$

that is, x is the sine of y, or, what is exactly the same thing, y *is an angle whose sine is* x. When this equation is solved for y, a new*

---

* New, that is, so far as this book is concerned. Inverse trigonometric functions are usually studied to some extent in trigonometry.

kind of function, neither algebraic nor trigonometric, is obtained; we must therefore devise a new symbol to denote this function.

An *angle whose sine is x* is represented by the symbol arcsin x, or $\sin^{-1} x$:

$$y = \textbf{arcsin } x \quad if \quad \sin y = x.$$

That is, the function arcsin x is the *inverse* of the sine, by the definition of § 85.

Similarly, we lay down the definitions

$$y = \textbf{arccos } x \quad if \quad \cos y = x;$$
$$y = \textbf{arctan } x \quad if \quad \tan y = x;$$

etc. The new functions here defined are called *inverse trigonometric functions*.

The graph of the inverse function

(1) $$y = \text{arcsin } x$$

is obtained by interchanging the roles of x and y in the graph (Fig. 80, p. 141) of $y = \sin x$. Thus, the graph of (1) can be found by reflecting the graph of

(2) $$y = \sin x$$

in the line $y = x$. The curve (1) consists of an infinite succession of waves along the y-axis, as shown in Fig. 87.

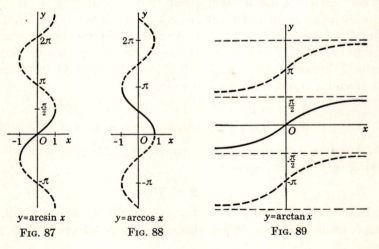

$y=$arcsin x $y=$arccos x $y=$arctan x
FIG. 87   FIG. 88   FIG. 89

The curves $y = $ arccos x, $y = $ arctan x appear in Figs. 88, 89. They are obtained, of course, by reflection of Figs. 81, 82.

87. Restriction to a single branch. When either the given or the inverse function is one-valued, it by no means follows that the other is one-valued. Both were so in Example (*a*), § 85, but in Example (*b*), the given function was one-valued, the inverse two-valued; and in fact, examples are easily found to illustrate any sort of combination.

When an angle is given, its sine, cosine, etc., are uniquely determined: that is, the trigonometric functions are one-valued. On the other hand, if the sine is given, the angle is not uniquely determined; for instance, there are infinitely many angles whose sine is $\frac{1}{2}$, viz. $\frac{\pi}{6}, \frac{5\pi}{6}$, or an angle differing from one of these by any multiple of 2π. Thus it appears that the inverse trigonometric functions are *infinitely many-valued:* corresponding to a given value of the variable there are infinitely many values of the function. Geometrically this means that a line $x = k$, if it meets the curve at all, meets it in an infinite number of points; the truth of this statement is evident from a glance at Figs. 87–89.

Following the rule of § 5, we shall in future, unless the contrary is noted, *confine our attention to a single branch* of each of these functions; the branch chosen is the one drawn full in each figure. In order to distinguish between the single-valued function and its infinitely many-valued counterpart, we use a capital letter to denote the single-valued function. Thus in our future work the three principal inverse trigonometric functions are subject to the following restrictions:

(1) $$-\frac{\pi}{2} \leqq \mathbf{Arcsin}\ x \leqq \frac{\pi}{2};$$

(2) $$0 \leqq \mathbf{Arccos}\ x \leqq \pi;$$

(3) $$-\frac{\pi}{2} \leqq \mathbf{Arctan}\ x \leqq \frac{\pi}{2}.$$

With (1) in effect, we have now, uniquely,

$$\text{Arcsin}\ \frac{1}{2} = \frac{\pi}{6}.$$

Any other angle whose sine is $\frac{1}{2}$ is readily expressed in terms of Arcsin $\frac{1}{2}$:

$$\frac{5\pi}{6} = \pi - \text{Arcsin}\ \frac{1}{2}; \qquad \frac{13\pi}{6} = 2\pi + \text{Arcsin}\ \frac{1}{2}; \text{ etc.}$$

Also,

$$\text{Arcsin} \, (-1) = -\frac{\pi}{2}, \; \text{not} \; \frac{3\pi}{2};$$

$$\text{Arccos} \frac{1}{2}\sqrt{2} = \frac{\pi}{4}, \qquad \text{Arccos} \left(-\frac{1}{2}\sqrt{2}\right) = \frac{3\pi}{4};$$

$$\text{Arctan} \, (-1) = -\frac{\pi}{4}, \; \text{not} \; \frac{3\pi}{4}.$$

The student must note these conventions carefully, since failure to observe them leads to frequent errors.*

In dealing with the other three functions, we shall restrict ourselves to *positive values of x*. The conventions are as follows:

$$0 \leqq \text{Arccot} \, x \leqq \frac{\pi}{2}, \qquad x \geqq 0;$$

$$0 \leqq \text{Arcsec} \, x \leqq \frac{\pi}{2}, \qquad x \geqq 1;$$

$$0 \leqq \text{Arccsc} \, x \leqq \frac{\pi}{2}, \qquad x \geqq 1.$$

These last three functions are distinctly troublesome when x is negative. For instance, it will appear presently that

(4) $$\text{Arccot} \, x = \frac{\pi}{2} - \text{Arctan} \, x, \qquad x > 0;$$

also that

(5) $$\text{Arccot} \, x = \text{Arctan} \frac{1}{x}, \qquad x > 0.$$

These are useful formulas to have; yet no convention can be laid down under which both formulas are true when x is negative. (For instance, try $x = -1$.) Thus our agreement to consider these functions only for positive x makes greatly for simplicity.†

This book will make very little use of the three minor functions, chiefly because of the difficulty just mentioned.

---

* It must be clearly understood that in calculus, just as surely as in trigonometry, there are infinitely many angles corresponding to a given value of the sine. We have merely agreed that the symbol Arcsin x shall denote *that one* of these angles (there will always be one and only one) that lies in the interval between $-\frac{\pi}{2}$ and $\frac{\pi}{2}$. Compare the similar discussion in § 6.

† The restriction is not serious. Of course it is possible to avoid the three minor functions completely; on the rather infrequent occasions when it seems simpler to use them, x is usually positive. If they are to be used when x is negative, great care must be exercised. Much confusion exists; many standard handbooks contain formulas that are invalid for negative x, with no warning given.

88. Elementary properties. Discovery of the elementary properties of the inverse trigonometric functions will be left largely to the student. However, since this new language may be troublesome at first, numerous examples are provided.

Example (a): Prove that

$$\text{Arcsin } (-x) = - \text{Arcsin } x.$$

This formula is nearly self-evident. Put

$$\alpha = \text{Arcsin } (-x), \quad \beta = \text{Arcsin } x,$$

so that

$$\sin \alpha = -x, \quad \sin \beta = x.$$

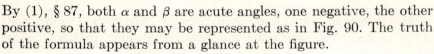

FIG. 90

By (1), § 87, both α and β are acute angles, one negative, the other positive, so that they may be represented as in Fig. 90. The truth of the formula appears from a glance at the figure.

Example (b): Prove that

$$\text{Arccot } x = \tfrac{1}{2}\pi - \text{Arctan } x.$$

Put

$$\alpha = \text{Arccot } x, \quad \beta = \text{Arctan } x.$$

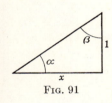

FIG. 91

By § 87, both are positive acute, and may be represented as in Fig. 91. The truth of the formula is obvious.

Example (c): Prove that

$$\sin (2 \text{ Arcsin } x) = 2x \sqrt{1 - x^2}.$$

Put

$$\alpha = \text{Arcsin } x,$$

whence

$$\sin \alpha = x.$$

By trigonometry,

$$\cos \alpha = \pm \sqrt{1 - \sin^2 \alpha} = \pm \sqrt{1 - x^2}.$$

But since (§ 87) α lies in either the first or the fourth quadrant, the cosine is positive and we have definitely

(1) $$\cos \alpha = \sqrt{1 - x^2},$$

$$\sin (2 \text{ Arcsin } x) = \sin 2\alpha = 2 \sin \alpha \cos \alpha = 2x \sqrt{1 - x^2}.$$

Example (d): Simplify the expression $(\text{Arctan } 2 + \text{Arctan } 3)$. Put

$$\alpha = \text{Arctan } 2, \quad \beta = \text{Arctan } 3,$$

whence
$$\tan \alpha = 2, \quad \tan \beta = 3,$$
and let
$$\gamma = \text{Arctan } 2 + \text{Arctan } 3 = \alpha + \beta.$$
Then

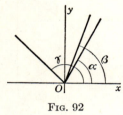

$$\tan \gamma = \tan (\alpha + \beta) = \frac{\tan \alpha + \tan \beta}{1 - \tan \alpha \tan \beta}$$

$$= \frac{2 + 3}{1 - 2 \cdot 3} = -1.$$

Since the sum of two positive acute angles must lie in either the first or the second quadrant,

FIG. 92

$$\text{Arctan } 2 + \text{Arctan } 3 = \tfrac{3}{4}\pi.$$

This example, typical of many similar situations, shows that when $\tan \gamma = -1$, we must not hastily conclude that $\gamma = -\tfrac{1}{4}\pi$.

Example (e): Simplify the equation

(2) $$\text{Arcsin } x + \text{Arcsin } y = \tfrac{1}{3}\pi.$$

Put

(3) $$\alpha = \text{Arcsin } x, \quad \beta = \text{Arcsin } y,$$

so that (2) becomes

(4) $$\alpha + \beta = \tfrac{1}{3}\pi.$$

From (3),
$$\sin \alpha = x, \quad \cos \alpha = \sqrt{1 - x^2};$$
$$\sin \beta = y, \quad \cos \beta = \sqrt{1 - y^2}.$$

It can be shown by trial (see Ex. 48 below) that in simplifying the sum of two Arcsines or two Arccosines, the best procedure is to take the cosine of the sum. (To simplify the sum of an Arcsine and an Arccosine, it is best to take the sine of the sum.) Hence, taking the cosine of both members of (4), we get

$$\sqrt{1 - x^2} \cdot \sqrt{1 - y^2} - xy = \tfrac{1}{2},$$

or, after isolating the radical, squaring, and simplifying,

(5) $$4x^2 + 4xy + 4y^2 = 3.$$

Thus, from equation (2), equation (5) follows. Therefore, every point on the curve (2) must lie on the curve (5), but by no means do all points on the locus (5) need to satisfy equation (2). Equation (2) consists of only a part of the ellipse (5). For instance, the point $(-\frac{1}{2}, -\frac{1}{2})$ is on the ellipse; it satisfies equation (5). Because of the principal value convention,

$$\text{Arcsin}\ (-\tfrac{1}{2}) = -\frac{\pi}{6},$$

so that, for $x = y = -\frac{1}{2}$, the left member of equation (2) becomes

$$-\frac{\pi}{6} - \frac{\pi}{6} = -\frac{\pi}{3} \neq \frac{\pi}{3}.$$

The point $(-\frac{1}{2}, -\frac{1}{2})$ satisfies equation (5), but not equation (2). Similar remarks apply to Exs. 42–47 below.

EXERCISES

1. Find Arcsin $(\frac{1}{2}\sqrt{3})$, Arcsin $(-\frac{1}{2}\sqrt{3})$, Arcsin $(-\frac{1}{2}\sqrt{2})$, Arcsin (1).

2. Find Arctan $(\frac{1}{3}\sqrt{3})$, Arctan $(-\frac{1}{3}\sqrt{3})$, Arctan $(-\sqrt{3})$.

3. Find Arccos (-1), Arccos (0), Arccos $(-\frac{1}{2}\sqrt{3})$, Arccos $(\frac{1}{2})$.

4. Find Arcsec $(\sqrt{2})$, Arccot $(\sqrt{3})$, Arcsec 2.

Establish the formulas in Exs. 5–22.

5. Arctan $(-x) = -$ Arctan x. **6.** Arccos $(-x) = \pi -$ Arccos x.

7. Arccos $x = \frac{1}{2}\pi -$ Arcsin x. **8.** Arctan $\dfrac{1}{x} =$ Arccot x.

9. Arcsin $\dfrac{1}{x} =$ Arccsc x. **10.** Arccos $\dfrac{1}{x} =$ Arcsec x.

11. Arcsin $\dfrac{x}{\sqrt{1 + x^2}} =$ Arctan x. **12.** Arctan $\dfrac{x}{\sqrt{1 - x^2}} =$ Arcsin x.

13. $\sin$ (Arccos x) $= \sqrt{1 - x^2}$. **14.** $\cos$ (Arctan x) $= \dfrac{1}{\sqrt{1 + x^2}}$.

15. $\tan$ (2 Arctan x) $= \dfrac{2x}{1 - x^2}$.

16. $\sin$ (2 Arccos x) $= 2x\sqrt{1 - x^2}$.

17. $\cos$ (2 Arccos x) $= 2x^2 - 1$. **18.** $\cos$ (2 Arctan x) $= \dfrac{1 - x^2}{1 + x^2}$.

19. $\sin$ (2 Arctan x) $= \dfrac{2x}{1 + x^2}$. **20.** $\cos$ (2 Arcsin x) $= 1 - 2x^2$.

21. $\tan$ (2 Arcsin x) $= \dfrac{2x\sqrt{1 - x^2}}{1 - 2x^2}$.

22. $\tan$ (2 Arccos x) $= \dfrac{2x\sqrt{1 - x^2}}{2x^2 - 1}$.

In Exs. 23–28, evaluate the given expression.

23. $\tan$ (Arctan $\frac{2}{3} -$ Arctan $\frac{1}{5}$). *Ans.* $\frac{7}{17}$.

24. $\cos$ (Arcsin $\frac{5}{13} +$ Arccos $\frac{4}{5}$). *Ans.* $\frac{33}{65}$.

25. $\cos (\text{Arctan } \tfrac{12}{5} - \text{Arcsin } \tfrac{3}{5})$. *Ans.* $\tfrac{56}{65}$.

26. $\tan (\text{Arcsin } \tfrac{4}{5} - \text{Arctan } 2)$. *Ans.* $\tfrac{-2}{11}$.

27. $\sin (\text{Arctan } \tfrac{6}{7} - \text{Arctan } \tfrac{1}{4})$. *Ans.* $\dfrac{\sqrt{5}}{5}$.

28. $\sin (\text{Arctan } \tfrac{2}{3} + \text{Arctan } \tfrac{4}{7})$. *Ans.* $\dfrac{2\sqrt{5}}{5}$.

In Exs. 29–41, simplify the given expression, in the sense of Example (*d*) above.

29. $\text{Arctan } \tfrac{3}{8} + \text{Arctan } \tfrac{8}{3}$. *Ans.* $\tfrac{1}{2}\pi$.

30. $\text{Arcsin } \tfrac{5}{13} + \text{Arcsin } \tfrac{12}{13}$. *Ans.* $\tfrac{1}{2}\pi$.

31. $\text{Arccos } \tfrac{4}{5} + \text{Arctan } \tfrac{4}{3}$. *Ans.* $\tfrac{1}{2}\pi$.

32. $\text{Arctan } \tfrac{1}{3} + \text{Arctan } \tfrac{1}{2}$. *Ans.* $\tfrac{1}{4}\pi$.

33. $\text{Arctan } \tfrac{5}{12} + \text{Arcsin } \tfrac{12}{13}$. *Ans.* $\tfrac{1}{2}\pi$.

34. $\text{Arctan } \tfrac{1}{13} + \text{Arctan } \tfrac{1}{4}$. *Ans.* $\text{Arctan } \tfrac{1}{3}$.

35. $\text{Arctan } \tfrac{1}{2} - \text{Arctan } \tfrac{1}{3}$. *Ans.* $\text{Arctan } \tfrac{1}{7}$.

36. $2 \text{ Arctan } 2 + \text{Arctan } \tfrac{4}{3}$. *Ans.* π.

37. $2 \text{ Arctan } \tfrac{1}{2} - \text{Arctan } \tfrac{4}{3}$. *Ans.* 0.

38. $2 \text{ Arctan } \tfrac{1}{2} - \text{Arctan } \tfrac{1}{7}$. *Ans.* $\tfrac{1}{4}\pi$.

39. $\text{Arctan } \tfrac{4}{3} - 2 \text{ Arctan } 3$. *Ans.* $-\tfrac{1}{2}\pi$.

40. $\text{Arctan } 2 + \text{Arctan } 4 + \text{Arctan } 13$. *Ans.* $\tfrac{5}{4}\pi$.

41. $\text{Arctan } \tfrac{1}{3} + \text{Arctan } \tfrac{4}{3} - \text{Arctan } \tfrac{1}{2}$. *Ans.* $\tfrac{1}{4}\pi$.

In Exs. 42–47, change the equation to algebraic form, with the realization that the new form may contain points not satisfying the original equation. Identify the resulting curve by name, when you can, and point out what steps in your procedure may introduce extraneous portions of the curve.

42. $\text{Arcsin } x + \text{Arcsin } y = \tfrac{1}{2}\pi$. *Ans.* $x^2 + y^2 = 1$.

43. $\text{Arctan } x + \text{Arctan } y = \tfrac{1}{4}\pi$. *Ans.* $xy + x + y = 1$.

44. $\text{Arccos } x + \text{Arcsin } y = \tfrac{1}{6}\pi$. *Ans.* $4x^2 - 4xy + 4y^2 = 3$.

45. $2 \text{ Arcsin } x + \text{Arcsin } y = \pi$. *Ans.* $y^2 = 4x^2(1 - x^2)$.

46. $\text{Arctan } x - 2 \text{ Arctan } y = \pi$. *Ans.* $xy^2 = x - 2y$.

47. $\text{Arctan } x + \text{Arctan } y = \tfrac{1}{2}\pi$. *Ans.* $xy = 1$.

48. In Example (*e*) § 88, simplify by taking the sine of both members.

89. Derivatives of the inverse trigonometric functions. To differentiate the function

$$y = \text{Arcsin } x,$$

let us pass to the form

(1) $$\sin y = x.$$

Equation (1) yields

$$\cos y \, \frac{dy}{dx} = 1,$$

$$\frac{dy}{dx} = \frac{1}{\cos y}.$$

Since $\sin y = x$, and $\dfrac{-\pi}{2} \leq y \leq \dfrac{\pi}{2}$, it follows that

$$\cos y = \sqrt{1 - \sin^2 y} = \sqrt{1 - x^2},$$

so that

$$\frac{d}{dx} \operatorname{Arcsin} x = \frac{1}{\sqrt{1 - x^2}}.$$

Differentiation of the other functions may be left to the reader. If u is any function of x, the general formulas for the three principal functions are:

$$(13) \qquad \frac{d}{dx} \operatorname{Arcsin} u = \frac{\dfrac{du}{dx}}{\sqrt{1 - u^2}};$$

$$(14) \qquad \frac{d}{dx} \operatorname{Arccos} u = -\frac{\dfrac{du}{dx}}{\sqrt{1 - u^2}};$$

$$(15) \qquad \frac{d}{dx} \operatorname{Arctan} u = \frac{\dfrac{du}{dx}}{1 + u^2}.$$

Example (a): If $\theta = \operatorname{Arctan} \tfrac{1}{3}t$,

$$\frac{d\theta}{dt} = \frac{\tfrac{1}{3}}{1 + \tfrac{1}{9}t^2} = \frac{3}{9 + t^2}.$$

Example (b): If $y = \operatorname{Arcsin} (2 \cos \theta)$,

$$\frac{dy}{d\theta} = \frac{-2 \sin \theta}{\sqrt{1 - 4 \cos^2 \theta}}.$$

Example (c): A man on a wharf 20 ft. above the water pulls in a rope, to which a boat is tied, at the rate of 4 ft. per sec. Find the rate of change of the angle θ (Fig. 93) when there is 25 ft. of rope out.

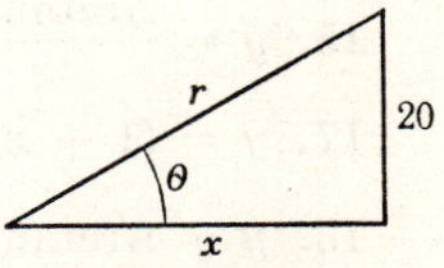

By the figure,

$$\theta = \operatorname{Arcsin} \frac{20}{r},$$

FIG. 93

$$\frac{d\theta}{dt} = \frac{-\dfrac{20}{r^2} \dfrac{dr}{dt}}{\sqrt{1 - \dfrac{400}{r^2}}} = \frac{-20 \dfrac{dr}{dt}}{r \sqrt{r^2 - 400}}.$$

We have given

$$\frac{dr}{dt} = -4,$$

so that when $r = 25$,

$$\frac{d\theta}{dt} = \frac{16}{75} \text{ rad. per sec.}$$

This example may also be solved very neatly by using the equations

$$\csc \theta = \frac{r}{20}; \quad -\csc \theta \cot \theta \frac{d\theta}{dt} = \frac{1}{20}\frac{dr}{dt}; \text{ etc.}$$

EXERCISES

In Exs. 1–28, find the first derivative of the function given.

1. $y = \text{Arcsin } 5x.$
$\quad Ans.\ y' = \dfrac{5}{\sqrt{1 - 25x^2}}.$

2. $u = \text{Arctan } \frac{1}{2}t.$
$\quad Ans.\ u' = \dfrac{2}{4 + t^2}.$

3. $\theta = \text{Arctan } a\phi.$
$\quad Ans.\ \dfrac{d\theta}{d\phi} = \dfrac{a}{1 + a^2\phi^2}.$

4. $f(y) = \text{Arcsin } (y^2).$
$\quad Ans.\ f'(y) = \dfrac{2y}{\sqrt{1 - y^4}}.$

5. $x = \text{Arcsin } (1 - 2v).$
$\quad Ans.\ \dfrac{dx}{dv} = \dfrac{-1}{\sqrt{v - v^2}}.$

6. $y = \text{Arctan } (1 + 2x).$
$\quad Ans.\ y' = \dfrac{1}{1 + 2x + 2x^2}.$

7. $x = \text{Arcsin } \sqrt{t}.$ 　　　　**8.** $\theta = \text{Arccos } 2t.$

9. $y = \text{Arctan } (t^3).$ 　　　　**10.** $y = (\text{Arctan } t)^3.$

11. $x = \text{Arccos } \sqrt{1 - y}.$ 　　**12.** $z = x \text{ Arctan } 3x.$

13. $u = x^2 \text{ Arcsin } x.$ 　　　**14.** $w = \dfrac{\text{Arcsin } \alpha}{\alpha}.$

15. $y = \dfrac{\text{Arctan } 2x}{x}.$ 　　　**16.** $y = \dfrac{\text{Arcsin } (x^2)}{x^2}.$

17. $y = (1 + x^2) \text{ Arctan } x - x.$
$\quad Ans.\ y' = 2x \text{ Arctan } x.$

18. $y = \text{Arctan}^2 (x^3).$
$\quad Ans.\ y' = \dfrac{6x^2 \text{ Arctan } (x^3)}{1 + x^6}.$

19. $y = \sqrt{\text{Arcsin } x}.$
$\quad Ans.\ \dfrac{dy}{dx} = \dfrac{1}{2\sqrt{1 - x^2} \cdot \sqrt{\text{Arcsin } x}}.$

20. $y = \text{Arcsin } \sqrt{1 + \dfrac{1}{x}}.$ (Note that x must be negative, so that in simplifying the answer we must put $\sqrt{x^2} = -x$.)
$\quad Ans.\ \dfrac{dy}{dx} = \dfrac{1}{2x\sqrt{-x - 1}}.$

21. $y = (x - 1)\sqrt{2x - x^2} + \text{Arcsin } (x - 1)$.   Ans. $y' = 2\sqrt{2x - x^2}$.

22. $y = 2 \text{ Arcsin } \sqrt{\dfrac{x}{2}}$.   Ans. $y' = \dfrac{1}{\sqrt{2x - x^2}}$.

23. $y = x \text{ Arcsin } x + \sqrt{1 - x^2}$.   Ans. $y' = \text{Arcsin } x$.

24. $y = \dfrac{x}{\sqrt{a^2 - x^2}} - \text{Arcsin } \dfrac{x}{a}$.   Ans. $\dfrac{dy}{dx} = \dfrac{x^2}{(a^2 - x^2)^{\frac{3}{2}}}$.

25. $y = a^2 \text{ Arcsin } \dfrac{x}{a} - x\sqrt{a^2 - x^2}$.   Ans. $\dfrac{dy}{dx} = \dfrac{2x^2}{\sqrt{a^2 - x^2}}$.

26. $y = \text{Arcsin } \dfrac{x}{a} + \dfrac{\sqrt{a^2 - x^2}}{x}$.   Ans. $y' = - \dfrac{\sqrt{a^2 - x^2}}{x^2}$.

27. $y = \text{Arcsin } \dfrac{a}{x}$.

Ans. $\dfrac{dy}{dx} = \dfrac{-a}{x\sqrt{x^2 - a^2}}$, $x > a$; $\dfrac{dy}{dx} = \dfrac{a}{x\sqrt{x^2 - a^2}}$, $x < -a$.

28. $y = \text{Arctan } \dfrac{a}{x}$.   Ans. $y' = \dfrac{-a}{a^2 + x^2}$.

29. Derive (15) from (13).   (Ex. 11, p. 151.)

30. Derive the formula $\dfrac{d}{dx} \text{ Arccot } u = \dfrac{-\dfrac{du}{dx}}{1 + u^2}$; $u > 0$.

31. Derive the formula $\dfrac{d}{dx} \text{ Arcsec } u = \dfrac{\dfrac{du}{dx}}{u\sqrt{u^2 - 1}}$; $u > 1$.

32. Derive the formula $\dfrac{d}{dx} \text{ Arccsc } u = \dfrac{-\dfrac{du}{dx}}{u\sqrt{u^2 - 1}}$; $u > 1$.

33. If $\tan \theta = \dfrac{y}{x}$, where x and y are functions of t, show that

$$\frac{d\theta}{dt} = \frac{x\dfrac{dy}{dt} - y\dfrac{dx}{dt}}{x^2 + y^2}.$$

34. A ladder 13 ft. long leans against a vertical wall. If the top slides down at 3 ft. per sec., how fast is the angle of elevation of the ladder decreasing, when the lower end is 9 ft. from the wall?   Ans. $\frac{1}{3}$ rad. per sec.

35. A ship, moving 8 mi. per hr., sails north for 30 min., then turns east. If a searchlight at the point of departure follows the ship, how fast is the light rotating 2 hr. after the start?   Ans. 0.2 rad. per hr.

36. A balloon, leaving the ground 80 ft. from an observer, rises 10 ft. per sec. How fast is the angle of elevation of the line of sight increasing, after 6 sec.?   Ans. $\frac{2}{25}$ rad. per sec.

37. The base of a right triangle grows 2 ft. per sec., the altitude grows 4 ft. per sec. If the base and altitude are originally 10 ft. and 6 ft., respectively, find the time-rate of change of the base angle, when that angle is 45°.   *Ans.* $\frac{1}{14}$ rad. per sec.

38. Prove that an angle is a maximum or minimum when its tangent is a maximum or minimum, and conversely. (Let $\theta = $ Arctan m, where m is a function of x; compare the conditions for extreme θ and extreme m.)

39. Prove that an acute angle is a maximum or minimum when its sine is a maximum or minimum, and conversely.

40. Prove that an acute angle is a maximum or minimum when its cosine is a minimum or maximum, and conversely.

41. A rowboat is pushed off from a beach at 8 ft. per sec. A man on shore holds a rope, tied to the boat, at a height of 4 ft. Find how fast the angle of elevation of the rope is decreasing, after 1 sec.   *Ans.* $\frac{2}{5}$ rad. per sec.

42. A kite is 60 ft. high, with 100 ft. of cord out. If the kite is moving horizontally 4 mi. per hr. directly away from the boy flying it, find the rate of change of the angle of elevation of the cord.   *Ans.* $-\frac{22}{625}$ rad. per sec.

43. A ship, moving at 8 mi. per hr., sails E. for 2 hr., then turns N. 30° W. A searchlight, placed at the starting point, follows the ship. Find how fast the light is rotating, (*a*) 3 hr. after the start; (*b*) just after the turn.

Ans. (*a*) $\frac{1}{3}\sqrt{3}$ rad. per hr.; (*b*) $\frac{1}{4}\sqrt{3}$ rad. per hr.

44. In Ex. 43, find when the light rotates most rapidly.

Ans. After 3 hr.

45. Prove that the results in Exs. 43–44 are independent of the speed of the ship.

46. A ship, moving at 10 mi. per hr., sails E. for 2 hr., then turns N. 30° E. A searchlight, placed at the starting point, follows the ship. Find how fast the light is rotating (*a*) 4 hr. after the start; (*b*) just after the turn.

Ans. (*a*) $\frac{1}{12}\sqrt{3}$ rad. per hr.; (*b*) $\frac{1}{4}\sqrt{3}$ rad. per hr.

47. Using the methods of §§ 78–79, show that in Ex. 46 the maximum rate of rotation of the light occurs at the time the ship turns.

48. Show that the answers to Exs. 46–47 are independent of the speed of the ship.

49. A car drives S. at 20 mi. per hr. Another car, starting from the same point at the same time and traveling 40 mi. per hr., goes E. for 30 min., then turns N. Find the rate of rotation of the line joining the cars (*a*) 1 hr. after the start; (*b*) at the time the second car makes its turn.

Ans. (*a*) 0.6 rad. per hr.; (*b*) 2.4 rad. per hr.

50. Prove that the results in Ex. 49 are independent of the speed of the cars, if the second car travels twice as fast as the first car.

51. Two points are moving horizontally in space at different heights above the earth. Show that the angle of elevation of the line joining them is greatest when the distance between them is least.

52. The lower edge of a picture is a ft., the upper edge b ft., above the eye of an observer. At what horizontal distance should he stand, if the vertical angle subtended by the picture is to be greatest?   *Ans.* $\sqrt{ab}$ ft.

CHAPTER 10 *EXPONENTIAL AND LOGARITHMIC FUNCTIONS*

90. The exponential function. The number $a^n(a > 0)$ is defined in algebra for all rational values of n. In calculus it becomes necessary to attach a meaning to the function

$$y = a^x \qquad (a > 0)$$

as x varies continuously.

Let x_0 be any irrational number. Then a^{x_0} is defined as the limit of a^x, where x is rational, as x approaches x_0. That the limit exists is proved in more advanced texts. The function

$$y = a^x \qquad (a > 0),$$

called the *exponential function*, thus becomes defined for all values of x. It is one-valued and continuous, and obeys the laws of exponents, viz.:

(1) $$a^x \cdot a^t = a^{x+t},$$

(2) $$(a^x)^t = a^{xt}.$$

The exponential function is evidently positive for all values of x.

91. The logarithm. The inverse of the exponential function is the *logarithm*, defined by the statement that

$$y = \log_a x \quad if \quad x = a^y \qquad (a > 1).$$

This function is one-valued and continuous for all *positive* values of x. The number a is called the *base* of the system of logarithms. The assumption $a > 1$ is introduced for simplicity; this condition is satisfied in all cases of practical importance.

The following facts concerning the function

$$y = \log_a x$$

appear at once from the definition:

(a) *Negative numbers have no (real) logarithms.*
(b) *Numbers between 0 and 1 have negative logarithms.*
(c) *Numbers greater than 1 have positive logarithms.*
(d) *As $x \to 0^+$, $y \to -\infty$.*
(e) *The logarithm of 1 is 0.*
(f) *As $x \to \infty$, $y \to \infty$.*

It is easily discovered that some of these properties would not hold if a were less than 1.

92. Fundamental properties of logarithms. Further important properties of the logarithmic function are as follows:

(1) $$\log_a xy = \log_a x + \log_a y;$$

(2) $$\log_a \frac{x}{y} = \log_a x - \log_a y;$$

(3)* $$\log_a x^n = n \log_a x;$$

(4) $$\log_a a^x = x;$$

(5) $$a^{\log_a x} = x.$$

Since (1), (2), and (3) have been met in the study of trigonometry, their proofs will be omitted. Formulas (4) and (5) are self-evident from the definition of logarithm. To prove (5) formally, set

$$a^{\log_a x} = t,$$

and take logarithms to the base a on each side:

$$\log_a x = \log_a t,$$

whence

$$t = x.$$

---

* If n is a positive or negative even integer, the function $\log_a x^n$ has a meaning even when x is negative, and this case frequently arises. With proper modification, (3) still applies:

$$\log x^n = n \log (-x) \text{ if } x < 0, n = \pm 2, \pm 4, \pm 6, \cdots.$$

93. Change of base. Given a table of logarithms to any base b, the logarithm of any number x to the base a can be found by the *formula for change of base:*

$$(1) \qquad \log_a x = \frac{\log_b x}{\log_b a}.$$

To prove this formula, let

$$m = \log_a x \quad \text{and} \quad n = \log_b x;$$

then

$$x = a^m = b^n.$$

Taking logarithms to the base b, we get

$$m \log_b a = n,$$

which gives the formula at once.

Taking $x = b$ in (1), we obtain the formula

$$(2) \qquad \log_a b = \frac{1}{\log_b a}.$$

94. The number e. It will be found, in § 97 below, that the problem of differentiating $y = \log_a x$ leads to a need for evaluation of

$$(1) \qquad \lim_{z \to \infty} \left(1 + \frac{1}{z}\right)^z.$$

The essence of one method for proving that the limit (1) exists will now be sketched. The details of the proof,[*] decently presented, take three or four pages and are omitted.

First, let z take on only positive integral values. Consider the sequence of numbers v_n (*i.e.*, $v_1, v_2, v_3, \cdots, v_n, v_{n+1}, \cdots$),

$$(2) \qquad v_n = \left(1 + \frac{1}{n}\right)^n; \qquad n \text{ integral, } n > 0.$$

We wish to show that v_n approaches a limit, as $n \to \infty$. It is easy to show that $v_n < 3$; it is elementary, but tedious, to show that $v_{n+1} > v_n$. Since v_n steadily increases, with increasing n, and never becomes as large as 3, v_n approaches a limit (not greater than 3) as $n \to \infty$. Call that limit e.

[*] See Philip Franklin, *A Treatise on Advanced Calculus*, New York, John Wiley and Sons, 1940, pp. 66–69.

Finally, for z non-integral, it can be shown that $\left(1 + \dfrac{1}{z}\right)^z$ lies between two numbers each of which approaches e as $z \to \infty$. It follows that

$$\lim_{z \to \infty} \left(1 + \frac{1}{z}\right)^z = e,$$

and it can further be shown that $e = 2.7182818285 \cdots$.

The function

(3) $$y = e^x$$

is of great importance in calculus and its applications. A table of values of e^x and its reciprocal e^{-x} will be found on pp. 509–514; with the help of the table the curve (3) is easily plotted by points. See Fig. 94.

95. Natural logarithms. Only two systems of logarithms are of actual importance in practice. Logarithms to the base 10, called *common logarithms*, possess the great advantage that the "mantissa," or fractional part of the logarithm, is independent of the position of the decimal point in the given number; common logarithms are therefore used very generally in computing. However, in the applications of calculus it is more convenient to use the base e.

Logarithms to the base e are called *natural logarithms*, and e is the *natural base*. The reason for these names will appear in § 97. Since the natural logarithm enters our work often, it is worthwhile to use a special symbol for it. We write $\ln x$ for $\log_e x$; that is,

(1) $$\ln x = \log_e x.$$

A table of common logarithms gives

$$\log_{10} e = \log_{10} 2.71828 = 0.43429.$$

This important number, called the *modulus* of the common system, will hereafter be noted by M:

$$\log_{10} e = M = 0.43429;$$
$$\ln 10 = \frac{1}{M} = 2.30259.$$

We thus derive from (1), § 93, the following formulas:

(2) $$\log_{10} x = M \ln x, \qquad \ln x = \frac{1}{M} \log_{10} x.$$

A brief table of natural logarithms will be found on pp. 507–508. For numbers beyond the range of the table, or with no table of natural logarithms at hand, any natural logarithm may evidently be found from a table of common logarithms with the help of (2).

The curve

$$y = \ln x$$

is shown in Fig. 95. It can be obtained from the curve $y = e^x$ of Fig. 94 by interchanging the roles of x and y; *i.e.*, by reflection in the line $y = x$.

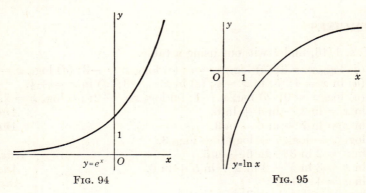

FIG. 94   FIG. 95

The following examples and exercises illustrate the use of the material so far developed in this chapter.

Example (*a*): Find x, if

$$\ln x = \ln 2 - 2 \ln 3 + \tfrac{1}{2} \ln 5.$$

By (3), § 92,

$$2 \ln 3 = \ln 9,$$

$$\tfrac{1}{2} \ln 5 = \ln \sqrt{5},$$

$$\ln x = \ln 2 - \ln 9 + \ln \sqrt{5}.$$

Hence,* by (1) and (2), § 92,

$$\ln x = \ln \frac{2\sqrt{5}}{9},$$

$$x = \frac{2\sqrt{5}}{9}.$$

* After a little practice, we shall be able to write the result almost instantly, performing all intermediate steps mentally.

Example (b): Find the inverse of the function

$$(3) \qquad\qquad y = \sin 5e^{x^3}.$$

The problem means, of course, that we are to solve the equation for x (§ 85). Pass to the inverse trigonometric form:*

$$\arcsin y = 5e^{x^3}.$$

Take the natural logarithm:

$$\ln \arcsin y = \ln 5 + \ln e^{x^3} = \ln 5 + x^3,$$
$$x = (\ln \arcsin y - \ln 5)^{\frac{1}{3}}.$$

EXERCISES

In Exs. 1–13, find x without using a table.

1. (a) $\log_{10} x = 3$; (b) $\log_{10} x = \frac{2}{3}$; (c) $\log_{10} x = -3$; (d) $\log_{10} x = -\frac{1}{2}$.

2. (a) $\ln x = 4$; (b) $\ln x = \frac{3}{2}$; (c) $\ln x = -3$; (d) $\ln x = -\frac{2}{3}$.

3. (a) $\log_a x = 0$; (b) $\log_a x = 1$; (c) $\log_a x = -2$; (d) $\log_a x = \frac{3}{2}$.

4. $\ln x = \ln 3 + \ln 4 + \ln 6$.   *Ans.* 72.

5. $\ln x = \ln 7 + \ln 6 - \ln 3$.   *Ans.* 14.

6. $\log_{10} x = \log_{10} 7 + \log_{10} 6 - \log_{10} 3$.

7. $\ln x = 2 \ln 3 - \ln 6 + \ln 5$.   *Ans.* 7.5.

8. $\ln x = 3 \ln \frac{1}{2} - 2 \ln 2 + \ln 5 + \ln 6$.   *Ans.* $\frac{15}{16}$.

9. $\ln x = 4 + \ln 7$.   *Ans.* $7e^4$.

10. $\log_{10} x = 4 + \log_{10} 7$.

11. $\ln x = \frac{1}{2} \ln 6 + \frac{3}{2} \ln 3 - 3$.   *Ans.* $9e^{-3}\sqrt{2}$.

12. $\ln x = \frac{3}{2} \ln 2 - \frac{1}{2} \ln 3 + \ln 6 - 1$.   *Ans.* $\dfrac{4\sqrt{6}}{e}$.

13. $\log_{10} x = \frac{3}{2} + \frac{1}{2} \log_{10} 5 - \frac{3}{2} \log_{10} 2$.   *Ans.* 25.

14. Show that negative numbers have no (real) logarithms.

15. Show that numbers between 0 and 1 have negative logarithms.

16. Show that numbers greater than 1 have positive logarithms.

17. Simplify: (a) $e^{\ln 5}$; (b) $e^{-\ln y}$; (c) $e^{4 \ln x}$; (d) $e^{-2 \ln 4}$; (e) $e^{2x + \ln x}$; (f) $e^{-2 + 2 \ln 3}$; (g) $e^{2 \ln 4 - 3 \ln x}$.   *Ans.* (c) x^4; (f) $9e^{-2}$; (g) $16x^{-3}$.

18. Simplify: (a) $\ln e^{3x}$; (b) $\ln (3e^{-x})$; (c) $\ln (4x^3)^{\frac{1}{2}}$; (d) $\ln (4e^{2 \cos y})$.

In Exs. 19–30, find the inverse of the given function; that is, solve the equation for x.

19. $y = e^{5x}$.   *Ans.* $x = \frac{1}{5} \ln y$.

20. $y = 3e^{-2x}$.   *Ans.* $x = -\frac{1}{2} \ln \dfrac{y}{3}$.

21. $y = 10^{x+3}$.   *Ans.* $x = -3 + \log_{10} y$.

22. $y = 10^{2x-1}$.

---

* Since, in (3), the quantity $5e^{x^3}$ may represent any angle whose sine is y — not necessarily the acute angle — what is needed here is the many-valued function arcsin y, not the single-valued function Arcsin y.

23. $y = \sin 4x$. *Ans.* $x = \frac{1}{4} \arcsin y$.

24. $y = 2 \tan (3x)$. *Ans.* $x = \frac{1}{3} \arctan (\frac{1}{2}y)$.

25. $y = \arcsin e^{-x}$. *Ans.* $x = -\ln \sin y$.

26. $y = 3 \arctan (x + 2)$. *Ans.* $x = -2 + \tan (\frac{1}{3}y)$.

27. $y = \ln (3x + 1)$. *Ans.* $x = \frac{1}{3}(e^y - 1)$.

28. $y = \frac{1}{2} \ln (4x)$. *Ans.* $x = \frac{1}{4}e^{2y}$.

29. $y = \ln \tan x$.

30. $y = 3 + \frac{1}{2} \ln \sin (4x)$.

31. Show that the function $y = \text{Arcsin } e^{x^2}$ is imaginary except at one point.

32. Show that the curve $y = \text{Arcsin } e^{\sin^2 x}$ consists of a set of isolated points.

In Exs. 33–38, break up the given expression into sums and differences of simpler logarithms.

33. $\ln \dfrac{x(2x + 1)}{x + 4}$.

34. $\ln \dfrac{x^2 - 9}{x^2(x^2 - 1)}$.

35. $\ln \dfrac{4x^2}{x^2 - 5x + 4}$.

36. $\ln \sqrt{\dfrac{x^3}{x + 4}}$.

37. $\ln \dfrac{4x^5 e^{-x}}{(x + 1)^3}$.

Ans. $2 \ln 2 + 5 \ln x - x - 3 \ln (x + 1)$.

38. $\ln \dfrac{e^{3x} - e^{-3x}}{x^4(e^{3x} + e^{-3x})}$.

Ans. $\ln (e^{3x} - e^{-3x}) - 4 \ln x - \ln (e^{3x} + e^{-3x})$.

In Exs. 39–46, solve for x by first taking logarithms of each member of the equation.

39. $3^x = 4$. *Ans.* $x = \dfrac{2 \ln 2}{\ln 3}$. **40.** $5^x = 2$. *Ans.* $x = \dfrac{\ln 2}{\ln 5}$.

41. $7 \cdot 3^{2x} = 6$. **42.** $8 \cdot 3^{-x} = 7$.

43. $2^{3x} = 3^{2x-1}$. *Ans.* $x = \dfrac{\ln 3}{\ln 9 - \ln 8}$.

44. $5^{2x} = 2^{3x+1}$.

45. $10^x = 5^{3x-2}$.

46. $a^{x^2} = (a^x)^x$, $a > 0$. *Ans.* $x = 1; x = 2$.

47. Show that, for $0 < a < x$,

$$\ln (x - \sqrt{x^2 - a^2}) = 2 \ln a - \ln (x + \sqrt{x^2 - a^2}).$$

48. Show that, for $0 < a, 0 < x$,

$$\ln (\sqrt{x + a} + \sqrt{x}) = \ln a - \ln (\sqrt{x + a} - \sqrt{x}).$$

49. Show that, for $\dfrac{-\pi}{2} < \theta < \dfrac{\pi}{2}$,

$$\ln (\sec \theta - \tan \theta) = -\ln (\sec \theta + \tan \theta).$$

96. Exponential and logarithmic equations. Equations involving exponential functions only, or logarithms only, may in simple cases be solved by applying the theory of §§ 91–92.

Example (a): Solve for x the equation

$$e^x - e^{-x} = 2.$$

Multiplying by e^x, we get

$$e^{2x} - 1 = 2e^x,$$
$$e^{2x} - 2e^x - 1 = 0.$$

This is a quadratic equation in e^x as the unknown quantity, whose solution is found by elementary algebra to be

$$e^x = 1 + \sqrt{2}.$$

(The root $e^x = 1 - \sqrt{2}$ must be rejected, since e^x is never negative.) Hence

$$x = \ln (1 + \sqrt{2}).$$

Check:

$$e^{\ln (1+\sqrt{2})} - e^{-\ln (1+\sqrt{2})} = 1 + \sqrt{2} - \frac{1}{1 + \sqrt{2}}$$

$$= 1 + \sqrt{2} - \frac{1 - \sqrt{2}}{(1 + \sqrt{2})(1 - \sqrt{2})}$$

$$= 1 + \sqrt{2} + 1 - \sqrt{2}$$

$$= 2.$$

Example (b): Solve the equation

$$\ln (2x + 7) - \ln (x - 1) = \ln 5.$$

Combining the logarithms in the left member, we get

$$\ln \frac{2x + 7}{x - 1} = \ln 5,$$

whence

(1) $$\frac{2x + 7}{x - 1} = 5,$$

and

$$x = 4.$$

Check:　$\ln 15 - \ln 3 = \ln 5.$

EXERCISES

Solve the equations in Exs. 1–18.

1. $e^x + 6e^{-x} = 5$.   *Ans.* $x = 0.693, 1.099$.
2. $e^x + 15e^{-x} = 8$.   *Ans.* $x = 1.099, 1.609$.
3. $e^x + 1 = 6e^{-x}$.   *Ans.* $x = 0.693$.
4. $2e^x + 1 = e^{-x}$.   *Ans.* $x = -0.693$.
5. $e^{2x} + 20e^{-x} = 21$.   *Ans.* $x = 0, 1.386$.
6. $1 - 3e^x = 4e^{-x}(e^{-x} + 1)$.   *Ans.* No real solutions.
7. $3^x + 8 \cdot 3^{-x} = 6$.   *Ans.* $x = 0.631, 1.262$.
8. $4^x + 2 \cdot 4^{-x} = 3$.   *Ans.* $x = 0, 0.5$.
9. $\ln (x - 1) + \ln (x - 2) = \ln 6$.   *Ans.* $x = 4$.
10. $\ln (x + 1) + \ln (x - 3) = \ln 5$.   *Ans.* $x = 4$.
11. $\ln (1 - x) + \ln (x + 7) = \ln 15$.   *Ans.* $x = -2, -4$.
12. $\ln (5 - 3x) + \ln (1 + x) = \ln 4$.   *Ans.* $x = 1, -\frac{1}{3}$.
13. $\log_{10} (2x - 5) + \log_{10} (x - 1) = \log_{10} 2$.   *Ans.* $x = 3$.
14. $\ln (x^2 - 3x + 7) + \ln (x + 3) = \ln 17$.   *Ans.* $x = -2$.
15. $\ln (x + 4) - \ln (2x - 1) + \ln (x - 3) = \ln 2$.   *Ans.* $x = 5$.
16. $\log_{10} (x + 5) - \log_{10} (x - 1) + \log_{10} 5 + \log_{10} (x + 2) = 2$.
      Ans. $x = 3, 10$.
17. $\ln (x - 3) + \ln (x + 1) - \ln (x^2 - x + 2) + \ln (2 - x) = 2 \ln 2$.
      Ans. No solutions.
18. $\ln (x^2 + 2x + 4) - \ln (x^2 + x + 2) + \ln (1 - x) = \ln 3$.
      Ans. $x = -1, -2$.

In Exs. 19–23, write the equation in a form free from logarithms. State the range of values of x and y for which the original equation is valid.

19. $\ln x + \ln y - \ln (x - y) = \ln 3$.
     Ans. $xy - 3x + 3y = 0$, for $x > y > 0$.
20. $\frac{1}{2} \ln (x - a) - \frac{1}{2} \ln (x + a) - \ln y + \ln a = 0$.
     Ans. $y^2(x + a) = a^2(x - a)$, for $x > a > 0$, $y > 0$.
21. $\ln (x^2 + 4) - 2 \ln y + 3 = 0$.   *Ans.* $y^2 = e^3(x^2 + 4)$, for $y > 0$.
22. $x + \ln y - \ln x = 0$.   *Ans.* $y = xe^{-x}$, for $x > 0$, $y > 0$.
23. $2 \ln (1 - x) - \ln (1 + x) + 3 \ln y = 2 \ln 3$.
     Ans. $y^3(1 - x)^2 = 9(1 + x)$, for $|x| < 1$, $y > 0$.

In Exs. 24–31, find the inverse of the given function.

24. $y = \frac{1}{2}(e^{3x} - e^{-3x})$.   *Ans.* $x = \frac{1}{3} \ln (y + \sqrt{y^2 + 1})$.
25. $4y = e^x - 8e^{-x}$.   *Ans.* $x = \ln (y + \sqrt{y^2 + 2}) + \ln 2$.
26. $y = \ln (x + 1) - \ln (x - 1)$.   *Ans.* $x = \dfrac{e^y + 1}{e^y - 1}$.
27. $y = \ln (x + 1) + \ln (x - 1)$.   *Ans.* $x = \sqrt{1 + e^y}$.
28. $y = 2 \ln x - \ln (x + 1)$.   *Ans.* $x = \frac{1}{2}e^y(1 + \sqrt{1 + 4e^{-y}})$.
29. $y = \ln (e^{2x} - 1)$.   *Ans.* $x = \frac{1}{2} \ln (1 + e^y)$.
30. $y = \frac{1}{2} \ln (3e^{\frac{1}{2}x} - 2)$.   *Ans.* $x = 2 \ln (e^{2y} + 2) - 2 \ln 3$.
31. $y = \ln (1 - \sqrt{4 - x^2})$. *Ans.* $x = \pm \sqrt{(1 + e^y)(3 - e^y)}$, for $y \leq 0$,

97. Derivative of the logarithm. To obtain the derivative of the logarithm we proceed by the method of § 14:

$$y = \log_a x,$$
$$y + \Delta y = \log_a (x + \Delta x),$$
$$\Delta y = \log_a (x + \Delta x) - \log_a x = \log_a \frac{x + \Delta x}{x}$$
$$= \log_a \left(1 + \frac{\Delta x}{x}\right),$$

by (2), § 92. Hence

$$\frac{\Delta y}{\Delta x} = \frac{1}{\Delta x} \log_a \left(1 + \frac{\Delta x}{x}\right).$$

Let us multiply and divide by x and then make use of (3), § 92:

$$\frac{\Delta y}{\Delta x} = \frac{1}{x} \cdot \frac{x}{\Delta x} \log_a \left(1 + \frac{\Delta x}{x}\right)$$
$$= \frac{1}{x} \log_a \left(1 + \frac{\Delta x}{x}\right)^{\frac{x}{\Delta x}}.$$

Hence

(1) $$\frac{dy}{dx} = \lim_{\Delta x \to 0} \frac{\Delta y}{\Delta x} = \frac{1}{x} \lim_{\Delta x \to 0} \log_a \left(1 + \frac{\Delta x}{x}\right)^{\frac{x}{\Delta x}}$$

(2) $$= \frac{1}{x} \log_a \left[\lim_{\Delta x \to 0} \left(1 + \frac{\Delta x}{x}\right)^{\frac{x}{\Delta x}} \right],$$

making use of the continuity of the logarithmic function.

Now, putting

$$\frac{x}{\Delta x} = z,$$

we see that the limit occurring in (2) is, if $\Delta x > 0$,

$$\lim_{z \to \infty} \left(1 + \frac{1}{z}\right)^z = e,$$

by § 94. (The argument must be slightly modified if $\Delta x < 0$.) Hence

(3) $$\frac{d}{dx} \log_a x = \frac{1}{x} \log_a e.$$

In order to remove the awkward factor $\log_a e$, choose the base a so that $\log_a e = 1$; that is, take $a = e$. Then $\log_a x$ becomes $\ln x$, $\log_a e$ becomes unity, and equation (3) simplifies to the form

$$\frac{d}{dx} \ln x = \frac{1}{x}.$$

This is the reason for the use of logarithms to the base e in calculus.*

By formula (5) of § 26, if u is any function of x,

$$\frac{d}{dx} \log_a u = \frac{\frac{du}{dx}}{u} \cdot \log_a e,$$

and as special cases,

(16)
$$\frac{d}{dx} \ln u = \frac{\frac{du}{dx}}{u},$$

(17)
$$\frac{d}{dx} \log_{10} u = \frac{M \frac{du}{dx}}{u}.$$

In differentiating the logarithm of a complicated expression, a great deal of labor may often be saved if we make judicious use of (1), (2), and (3) of § 92.

Example (a): Differentiate $y = \ln \sqrt{1 + 3x}$.

Let us write y in the form

$$y = \tfrac{1}{2} \ln (1 + 3x).$$

Then

$$y' = \frac{1}{2} \cdot \frac{3}{1 + 3x} = \frac{3}{2 + 6x}.$$

Example (b): Differentiate $x = \ln \dfrac{z^3(z^2 - 1)^2}{(z^2 + 1)^2}$.

Write

$$x = 3 \ln z + 2 \ln (z^2 - 1) - 2 \ln (z^2 + 1);$$
$$\frac{dx}{dz} = \frac{3}{z} + \frac{4z}{z^2 - 1} - \frac{4z}{z^2 + 1}$$
$$= \frac{3(z^4 - 1) + 4z^2(z^2 + 1) - 4z^2(z^2 - 1)}{z(z^4 - 1)}$$
$$= \frac{3z^4 + 8z^2 - 3}{z(z^4 - 1)}.$$

---

* Since the awkward factor $\log_a e$ has appeared in consequence of an intrinsic property of the logarithmic function, with no way of removing it except by adoption of e as base, the terms "natural base" and "natural logarithm" are seen to be justified. While it is clearly a nuisance to have to use two systems of logarithms — one for computing, the other in applications of calculus — it would be a much greater nuisance to use (3) every time a logarithm is differentiated. Compare similar remarks in § 81 concerning the use of radian measure of angles — which, in the same line of thought, might be called "natural measure."

EXERCISES

In Exs. 1–32, find the derivative of the given function. When necessary, use M to denote $\log_{10} e$.

1. $y = \ln (3 - 2x)$.

2. $y = \ln (4x + 1)$.

3. $y = \ln (cx)$.

4. $y = \ln (x^2 + 3x - 7)$.

5. $y = \ln (a^2 - x^2)^{\frac{5}{2}}$.

6. $u = \ln (2t - t^2)$.

7. $x = \ln \sec \theta$.

8. $x = \ln \sin (3v)$.

9. $y = \log_{10} \cos \dfrac{x}{a}$.

   Ans. $\dfrac{dy}{dx} = -\dfrac{M}{a} \tan \dfrac{x}{a}$.

10. $\alpha = \log_{10} (1 + 3 \tan \beta)$.

   Ans. $\dfrac{d\alpha}{d\beta} = \dfrac{3M \sec^2 \beta}{1 + 3 \tan \beta}$.

11. $x = \ln \dfrac{3t + 1}{3t - 1}$.

   Ans. $\dfrac{dx}{dt} = \dfrac{-6}{9t^2 - 1}$.

12. $w = \ln (b^2 - x^2)^{\frac{3}{2}}$.

   Ans. $\dfrac{dw}{dx} = \dfrac{-3x}{b^2 - x^2}$.

13. $y = \ln \sqrt{a^2 + x^2}$.

   Ans. $\dfrac{dy}{dx} = \dfrac{x}{a^2 + x^2}$.

14. $u = \ln \dfrac{1 - v^2}{1 + v^2}$.

   Ans. $\dfrac{du}{dv} = \dfrac{-4v}{1 - v^4}$.

15. $y = 4 \ln \sqrt{\dfrac{1 + x^3}{1 - x^3}}$.

   Ans. $\dfrac{dy}{dx} = \dfrac{12x^2}{1 - x^6}$.

16. $r = \log_{10} \sec^2 3\theta$.

   Ans. $\dfrac{dr}{d\theta} = 6M \tan 3\theta$.

17. $y = z^3 \ln z$.

18. $w = \dfrac{1}{\ln x}$.

19. $x = \ln^2 t$.

20. $y = \dfrac{\ln x}{x^2}$.

21. $u = x \ln (1 + x)$.

22. $v = x^2 \ln (1 - x)$.

23. $y = \ln \ln x$.

24. $x = \ln \ln \sin t$.

25. $r = \cos \ln \theta$.

26. $y = \csc \ln x$.

27. $y = x^3 (3 \ln x - 1)$.

   Ans. $y' = 9x^2 \ln x$.

28. $w = t^2 (\cos \ln t - \sin \ln t)$.   *Ans.* $w' = t(\cos \ln t - 3 \sin \ln t)$.

29. $u = t^3(\sin \ln t - \cos \ln t)$.   *Ans.* $u' = 2t^2(2 \sin \ln t - \cos \ln t)$.

30. $y = x \ln (a^2 + x^2) + 2a \operatorname{Arctan} \dfrac{x}{a} - 2x$.   *Ans.* $y' = \ln (a^2 + x^2)$.

31. $y = \ln \sqrt{\dfrac{1 + \sin x}{1 - \sin x}}$.

   Ans. $\dfrac{dy}{dx} = \sec x$.

32. $y = \ln \tan \left(\dfrac{\pi}{4} + \dfrac{x}{2}\right)$.

   Ans. $\dfrac{dy}{dx} = \sec x$.

In Exs. 33–36, find y'.

33. $x \ln y - y \ln x = c$.

   Ans. $y' = \dfrac{y(y - x \ln y)}{x(x - y \ln x)}$.

34. $x \ln (x^2 + y^2) - y = c$.   *Ans.* $y' = \dfrac{2x^2 + (x^2 + y^2) \ln (x^2 + y^2)}{(x - y)^2}$.

35. $4 \ln (\sec y + \tan y) - 2x - \sin 2x = c.$ *Ans.* $y' = \cos y \cos^2 x.$

36. $\ln (x^2 + y^2) + 4 \operatorname{Arctan} \dfrac{y}{x} = c.$ *Ans.* $y' = \dfrac{2y - x}{y + 2x}.$

37. For the function $y = x^2 \ln x$, find the first four derivatives.

38. For the function $y = (x^3 - 1) \ln x$, find $\dfrac{d^4y}{dx^4}$. *Ans.* $\dfrac{d^4y}{dx^4} = \dfrac{6(x^3 + 1)}{x^4}.$

39. For the curve $y = \ln x$, find the equation of a tangent line parallel to the line $2x - y = 4.$ *Ans.* $2x - y = 1 + \ln 2.$

40. For the curve $y = x \ln x$, find the equation of a tangent line perpendicular to the line $x + 2y = 7.$ *Ans.* $2x - y = e.$

41. Find the tangent to the curve $y = \ln x$ at any point (x_1, y_1). By finding the y-intercept of the tangent, derive a ruler-and-compass construction for the tangent at any point of the curve. *Ans.* $x_1 y - x = x_1 y_1 - x_1.$

Of the statements in Exs. 42–45, which ones are true, and why?

42. If $t^2 = k$, and $x^2 = k$, then $t = x.$ *Ans.* False.

43. If $\sin t = k$, and $\sin x = k$, then $t = x.$ *Ans.* False.

44. If $\log_a x = k$, and $\log_a t = k$, then $t = x.$

45. If $k = a^x$, and $k = a^t (a \neq 1)$, then $t = x.$ Take the logarithm in each equation.

46. By setting $y = x^n$, taking the logarithm, and differentiating, prove the formula $\dfrac{d}{dx} x^n = n x^{n-1}$ for all values of n.

Sketch carefully each of the curves in Exs. 47–53, locating all maximum, minimum, and inflection points.

47. $y = \ln (x - 1).$ **48.** $y = \ln (x + 1).$

49. $y = x - \ln x.$ **50.** $y = x^2 - 2 \ln x.$

51. $y = \ln \ln x.$ **52.** $y = \ln \cos x.$

53. $y = \frac{1}{2} \ln (x^2 - 1).$ Use Exs. 47–48.

98. Derivative of the exponential function. If

$$y = a^x,$$

then

$$\ln y = x \ln a.$$

Differentiating by the rule for implicit functions, we find

$$\frac{1}{y} \frac{dy}{dx} = \ln a,$$

$$\frac{dy}{dx} = y \ln a = a^x \ln a;$$

that is,

$$\frac{d}{dx} a^x = a^x \ln a.$$

If u is a function of x, this formula becomes

(18)
$$\frac{d}{dx} a^u = a^u \ln a \cdot \frac{du}{dx}.$$

For the case $a = e$, we have the important special case*

(19)
$$\frac{d}{dx} e^u = e^u \frac{du}{dx}.$$

Example (a): If $y = e^{2x^3}$,
$$y' = e^{2x^3} \cdot 6x^2 = 6x^2 e^{2x^3}.$$
Example (b): If $y = \sin^2 e^{3x}$,
$$y' = 2 \sin e^{3x} \cos e^{3x} \cdot e^{3x} \cdot 3 = 3e^{3x} \sin 2e^{3x}.$$

99. Variable with variable exponent. Let

$$y = u^v, \qquad (u > 0)$$

where both u and v are functions of x.

While it is easy to develop the general formula (Ex. 47 below) for the derivative of this function, it is usually simpler not to use the formula, but to *take the logarithm of both members* before differentiating.

Example: Differentiate $\qquad y = x^x$.
We have
$$\ln y = x \ln x,$$
$$\frac{y'}{y} = 1 + \ln x,$$
$$y' = y(1 + \ln x) = x^x(1 + \ln x).$$

EXERCISES

In Exs. 1–26, find the first derivative of the given function.

1. $y = e^{-4x}$.
2. $x = e^{-t^2}$.
3. $v = e^{\tan \theta}$.
4. $v = e^{-\sin 2\theta}$.
5. $y = xe^{3x}$.
6. $y = 4x^2 e^{-x}$.
7. $u = \ln (e^{2x} - 1)$.
8. $v = \ln (4 + e^{-2t})$.
9. $r = e^{\theta} \sin 3\theta$.
10. $z = e^{-2\theta} \sin 2\theta$.
11. $x = e^{2t}(\cos t - 2 \sin t)$.
12. $x = e^t(2 \cos 2t - \sin 2t)$.
13. $y = a \sin (e^{-\frac{x}{a}})$.
14. $y = b \operatorname{Arcsin} e^{-\frac{x}{b}}$.

* The number e has a way of appearing in many physical problems (for simple illustrations, see §§ 103, 105), frequently for reasons that are rather obscure. In this it resembles that other remarkable number, π, which turns up in a multitude of situations having no apparent connection with circles.

15. $y = 5^{2x}$.

16. $x = 10^{-3t}$.

17. $x = 10^{\tan \theta}$.

18. $w = 3^{-u^2}$.

19. $y = (4 - 3e^{2x})^{\frac{5}{2}}$.

20. $z = \tan^2(1 - e^{-u})$.

21. $w = e^{-3v}(1 - e^{3v})^{\frac{1}{2}}$.

22. $x = t^2 e^{-\frac{1}{t}}$.

23. $z = \dfrac{e^{3y}}{y^2}$.

24. $y = x + x^3 e^{-3 \ln x}$.   *Ans.* $y' = 1$.

25. $y = (1 + e^{-x})^3(1 - e^{-x})^{\frac{1}{2}}$.   **26.** $x = \dfrac{e^{2t} - e^{-2t}}{e^{2t} + e^{-2t}}$.

27. Find y' from the equation $x^2 e^y - y^2 e^x = 1$.

28. Find y' from the equation $e^{xy} - xe^y = 3$.   *Ans.* $y' = \dfrac{e^y - ye^{xy}}{x(e^{xy} - e^y)}$.

29. Find y'' from the equation $y = xe^{-x^2}$.   *Ans.* $y'' = 2xe^{-x^2}(2x^2 - 3)$.

30. Find $\dfrac{d^2x}{dt^2}$ from the equation $x = t^3 e^{-t}$.

$$\textit{Ans. } \frac{d^2x}{dt^2} = te^{-t}(t^2 - 6t + 6).$$

31. Find $y^{(n)} = \dfrac{d^n y}{dx^n}$ from the equation $y = e^{ax}$.

32. Find $y^{(n)}$ from the equation $y = xe^x$.

33. From $u = e^{-t} \sin t$, show that $\dfrac{d^2u}{dt^2} + 2\dfrac{du}{dt} + 2u = 0$.

34. From $y = e^{3x} \sin 2x$, show that $y'' - 6y' + 13y = 0$.

35. From $x = e^{-\frac{1}{2}t} \cos t$, show that $4\dfrac{d^2x}{dt^2} + 4\dfrac{dx}{dt} + 5x = 0$.

In Exs. 36–44, sketch the curve carefully.

36. $y = e^{-3x}$.   **37.** $y = 1 + e^x$.   **38.** $y = 4(e^{-x} - 1)$.

39. $y = e^x - x$.   **40.** $y = e^{-x^2}$.   **41.** $y = e^{\frac{1}{x}}$.

42. $y = e^{-x} \sin x$.   **43.** $y = \text{Arcsin } e^{-x}$.   **44.** $y = e^{\sin x}$.

45. For the curve $y = e^{-2x}$, find the tangent line parallel to the line $x + y = 4$.   *Ans.* $x + y = \frac{1}{2}(1 + \ln 2)$.

46. For the curve $y = e^{3x}$, find the tangent line perpendicular to the line $x + 6y = 7$.   *Ans.* $y - 6x = 2 - 2 \ln 2$.

47. If u and v are functions of x, find the derivative of u^v.

$$\textit{Ans. } \frac{d}{dx} u^v = vu^{v-1}\frac{du}{dx} + u^v \ln u \frac{dv}{dx}.$$

48. Differentiate $y = x^{e^x}$.   *Ans.* $y' = x^{e^x - 1}e^x(1 + x \ln x)$.

49. Differentiate $y = x^{x^2}$.   *Ans.* $y' = x^{1+x^2}(1 + 2 \ln x)$.

50. Differentiate $y = e^{x^x}$.   *Ans.* $y' = x^x e^{x^x}(1 + \ln x)$.

51. Differentiate $y = (\ln x)^x$.   *Ans.* $y' = (\ln x)^{x-1}(1 + \ln x \ln \ln x)$.
52. Differentiate $y = x^{\ln x}$.   *Ans.* $y' = 2(\ln x)x^{\ln x - 1}$.

Fundamental Differentiation Formulas

(1) $\dfrac{dc}{dx} = 0;$

(2) $\dfrac{d}{dx}(u + v) = \dfrac{du}{dx} + \dfrac{dv}{dx};$

(3) $\dfrac{d}{dx} uv = u\dfrac{dv}{dx} + v\dfrac{du}{dx};$ (3′) $\dfrac{d}{dx} cv = c\dfrac{dv}{dx};$

(4) $\dfrac{d}{dx}\dfrac{u}{v} = \dfrac{v\dfrac{du}{dx} - u\dfrac{dv}{dx}}{v^2};$ (4′) $\dfrac{d}{dx}\dfrac{c}{v} = -\dfrac{c\dfrac{dv}{dx}}{v^2};$

(5) $\dfrac{dy}{dx} = \dfrac{dy}{du}\cdot\dfrac{du}{dx};$ (5′) $\dfrac{dy}{dx} = \dfrac{\dfrac{dy}{du}}{\dfrac{dx}{du}};$ (5″) $\dfrac{dy}{dx} = \dfrac{1}{\dfrac{dx}{dy}};$

(6) $\dfrac{d}{dx} u^n = nu^{n-1}\dfrac{du}{dx};$ (6′) $\dfrac{d}{dx}\sqrt{u} = \dfrac{\dfrac{du}{dx}}{2\sqrt{u}};$

(7) $\dfrac{d}{dx}\sin u = \cos u\,\dfrac{du}{dx};$

(8) $\dfrac{d}{dx}\cos u = -\sin u\,\dfrac{du}{dx};$

(9) $\dfrac{d}{dx}\tan u = \sec^2 u\,\dfrac{du}{dx};$

(10) $\dfrac{d}{dx}\cot u = -\csc^2 u\,\dfrac{du}{dx};$

(11) $\dfrac{d}{dx}\sec u = \sec u\tan u\,\dfrac{du}{dx};$

(12) $\dfrac{d}{dx}\csc u = -\csc u\cot u\,\dfrac{du}{dx};$

(13) $\dfrac{d}{dx}\text{Arcsin } u = \dfrac{\dfrac{du}{dx}}{\sqrt{1 - u^2}},$ $-\dfrac{\pi}{2} \leqq \text{Arcsin } u \leqq \dfrac{\pi}{2};$

(14) $\dfrac{d}{dx}\text{Arccos } u = -\dfrac{\dfrac{du}{dx}}{\sqrt{1 - u^2}},$ $0 \leqq \text{Arccos } u \leqq \pi;$

(15) $\dfrac{d}{dx}\text{Arctan } u = \dfrac{\dfrac{du}{dx}}{1 + u^2},$ $-\dfrac{\pi}{2} < \text{Arctan } u < \dfrac{\pi}{2};$

$$\text{(16)} \quad \frac{d}{dx} \ln u = \frac{\frac{du}{dx}}{u};$$

$$\text{(17)} \quad \frac{d}{dx} \log_{10} u = \frac{M \frac{du}{dx}}{u};$$

$$\text{(18)} \quad \frac{d}{dx} a^u = a^u \ln a \frac{du}{dx};$$

$$\text{(19)} \quad \frac{d}{dx} e^u = e^u \frac{du}{dx}.$$

MISCELLANEOUS EXERCISES

Differentiate the following functions.

1. $u = x \operatorname{Arcsin} \dfrac{x}{3}.$

2. $u = x\sqrt{1 - 4x^2}.$

3. $y = (t^3 + 2)e^{-2t}.$

4. $y = z^2 \ln \sin z.$

5. $w = \operatorname{Arctan}(1 + v^2).$

6. $w = \dfrac{v^3}{\sqrt{1 - 6v^2}}.$

7. $y = \ln \dfrac{x^4}{(1 - x^2)^3}.$

8. $y = \cos x \cot x.$

9. $y = (a^{\frac{2}{3}} - x^{\frac{2}{3}})^{\frac{3}{2}}.$

10. $y = e^{-x} \ln x.$

11. $x = \dfrac{t^4}{(1 - t^2)^3}.$

12. $r = \ln^2 \cos \theta.$

13. $r = \ln \cos^2 \theta.$

14. $y = z^3(1 - z^2)^{\frac{1}{2}}.$

15. $t = e^{-x}(1 - e^{2x})^{-\frac{3}{2}}.$

16. $r = \dfrac{\cos^3 2\theta}{(1 + \sin 2\theta)^3}.$

17. $\alpha = \cos 2\beta \sin 3\beta.$

18. $\psi = 4^{3x}.$

19. $y = \operatorname{Arctan} \ln x.$

20. $y = \operatorname{Arcsin} e^{-5x}.$

21. $x = \sin^2\left(\dfrac{\pi}{4} - 2t\right).$

22. $z = \ln(1 - e^{-3v}).$

23. $y = \ln \ln(1 + e^x).$

24. $y = 4x^2 e^{-\frac{1}{2}x}.$

25. $x = t \ln \sqrt{1 + t}.$

26. $v = e^{e^{-x}}.$

27. $\theta = \operatorname{Arcsin}(1 - r).$

28. $r = \sqrt{\dfrac{1 - \cos \theta}{1 + \cos \theta}}.$

29. $y = \sec^4 3x.$

30. $y = \csc^2 x \cot^3 x.$

31. $v = (e^{4x} - 1)^{-\frac{1}{2}}.$

32. $v = \tan^2(1 + 3x).$

33. $u = (1 - x^2)^{\frac{1}{2}}(1 + x^2)^{-\frac{3}{2}}.$

34. $u = v^2 e^{-v^2}.$

35. $A = \dfrac{t^3}{\sqrt{2at - t^2}}.$

36. $\beta = \sqrt[3]{1 - 4 \ln \alpha}.$

37. $z = \log_{10}(9u^2 - 1).$

38. $t = \log_{10} \dfrac{4e^z - 1}{4e^z + 1}.$

39. $V = \sin 2\theta \cos^2 \theta.$

40. $W = \sin^3 2\theta \cos^4 2\theta.$

CHAPTER *11* HYPERBOLIC FUNCTIONS

100. Hyperbolic functions. Certain combinations of the functions e^x and e^{-x} are known as *hyperbolic functions*. They are denoted by the symbols sinh x (read hyperbolic sine of x), cosh x, tanh x, etc. The definitions are as follows:

$$\text{(1)} \qquad \sinh x = \frac{e^x - e^{-x}}{2},$$

$$\text{(2)} \qquad \cosh x = \frac{e^x + e^{-x}}{2},$$

$$\text{(3)} \qquad \tanh x = \frac{\sinh x}{\cosh x} = \frac{e^x - e^{-x}}{e^x + e^{-x}};$$

the reciprocals of these are csch x, sech x, coth x respectively. The importance of these particular functions is due to their frequent occurrence in engineering, physics, etc.

The use of symbols and names so similar to those of trigonometry may seem unwise. Some justification will appear in the next section where the basic formulas for these new functions are shown to bear a striking resemblance to those of ordinary trigonometry.

101. Basic formulas of hyperbolic trigonometry. From the definition of sinh x and cosh x, it follows that

$$\sinh^2 x = \tfrac{1}{4}(e^{2x} - 2 + e^{-2x})$$

and

$$\cosh^2 x = \tfrac{1}{4}(e^{2x} + 2 + e^{-2x}),$$

so that

$$\text{(1)} \qquad \cosh^2 x - \sinh^2 x = 1,$$

174

an identity similar to the identity $\cos^2 x + \sin^2 x = 1$ in circular trigonometry. Many other such relations will be found in the exercises below.

The curves $y = \cosh x$ and $y = \sinh x$ are exhibited in Fig. 96. Note the important properties:

(a) $\cosh x \geq 1$, for all real x,

(b) the only real value of x for which $\sinh x = 0$ is $x = 0$,

(c) $\cosh (-x) = \cosh x$; that is, $\cosh x$ is an even function of x,

(d) $\sinh (-x) = -\sinh x$; $\sinh x$ is an odd function of x.

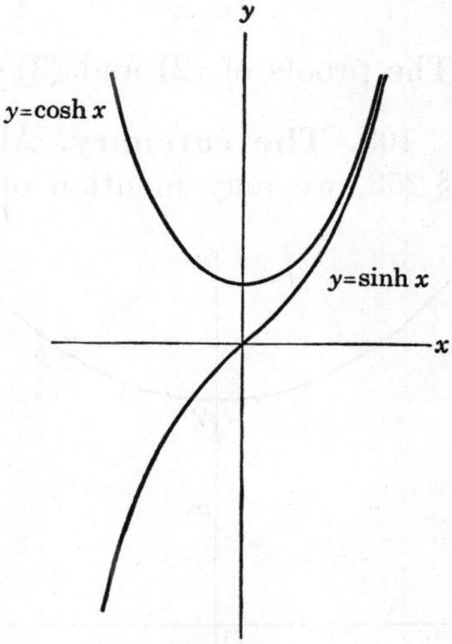

The hyperbolic functions have no real period.

Corresponding to the period 2π possessed by the circular functions, there is a period $2\pi i$ for the six hyperbolic functions.

With regard to the word hyperbolic in the name of the functions being treated here, consider the parametric equations

Fig. 96

(2) $$x = a \cosh t, \qquad y = a \sinh t,$$

with t as a parameter. From the identity (1) above, it follows that

$$x^2 - y^2 = a^2,$$

so that the equations (2) are seen to be parametric equations of an equilateral hyperbola. This is analogous to the result that $x = a \cos t$, $y = a \sin t$, are parametric equations of the circle $x^2 + y^2 = a^2$.

102. Derivatives of the hyperbolic functions. The differentiation formulas are as follows:

(1) $$\frac{d}{dx} \sinh u = \cosh u \frac{du}{dx};$$

(2) $$\frac{d}{dx} \cosh u = \sinh u \frac{du}{dx};$$

(3) $$\frac{d}{dx} \tanh u = \operatorname{sech}^2 u \frac{du}{dx}.$$

To prove (1), differentiate both members of the equation

$$\sinh u = \frac{e^u - e^{-u}}{2}:$$

$$\frac{d}{dx}\sinh u = \frac{e^u \dfrac{du}{dx} + e^{-u}\dfrac{du}{dx}}{2} = \cosh u \frac{du}{dx}.$$

The proofs of (2) and (3) are left as exercises.

103. The catenary. Although the proof must be deferred to § 253, we may mention one elementary application of hyperbolic functions.

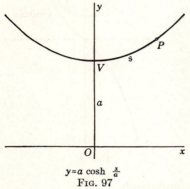

$y = a \cosh \frac{x}{a}$

FIG. 97

When a flexible, homogeneous cord or wire hangs from two of its points under its own weight (suspended cable, telephone wire, clothesline), it falls in a curve called the *catenary*. With the origin at distance a below the lowest point, the equation is

$$y = a \cosh \frac{x}{a}.$$

We know by observation, of course, that the curve has the general form shown in Fig. 97. Using the table, pp. 509–514, the student may easily plot the curve.

In Fig. 97, if s is the length of arc VP from the vertex to any point of the curve, then (Ex. 13, p. 304)

$$s = a \sinh \frac{x}{a}.$$

FIG. 98

When a catenary has been constructed, say by suspending a given length of wire or cable between two points A, B at the same height * in a vertical plane, the position of the origin is not ob-

---

* Of course the wire will hang in a catenary whether or not the points of suspension are at the same height.

vious. To find a, and thus locate the origin, we may use the formula (to be derived by the reader in Ex. 36 below)

$$(1) \qquad\qquad a = \frac{S^2 - d^2}{2d},$$

where S is the half-length of wire VA, and d is the "dip" VC. A glance at (1) shows that when d is small (tight wire), a is large; as d approaches S (slack wire), a decreases.

EXERCISES

In Exs. 1–16, prove the stated property of the hyperbolic functions. Use the definitions, the results in the text, or the properties obtained in any previous exercise.

1. $\sinh 0 = 0$; $\cosh 0 = 1$; $\tanh 0 = 0$.
2. $\sinh(-x) = -\sinh x$; $\cosh(-x) = \cosh x$; $\tanh(-x) = -\tanh x$.
3. $\operatorname{sech}^2 x = 1 - \tanh^2 x$.   **4.** $\operatorname{csch}^2 x = \coth^2 x - 1$.
5. $e^x = \cosh x + \sinh x$; $e^{-x} = \cosh x - \sinh x$.
6. $\sinh^2 y = \frac{1}{2}(\cosh 2y - 1)$.   **7.** $\cosh^2 y = \frac{1}{2}(\cosh 2y + 1)$.
8. $\cosh 2A = \cosh^2 A + \sinh^2 A = 2\cosh^2 A - 1 = 2\sinh^2 A + 1$.
9. $\sinh 2y = 2\sinh y \cosh y$.
10. $\sinh(x+y) = \sinh x \cosh y + \cosh x \sinh y$;
$\sinh(x-y) = \sinh x \cosh y - \cosh x \sinh y$.
11. $\cosh(x+y) = \cosh x \cosh y + \sinh x \sinh y$;
$\cosh(x-y) = \cosh x \cosh y - \sinh x \sinh y$.
12. $\dfrac{d}{dx}\cosh u = \sinh u \dfrac{du}{dx}$.
13. $\dfrac{d}{dx}\tanh u = \operatorname{sech}^2 u \dfrac{du}{dx}$.   **14.** $\dfrac{d}{dx}\coth u = -\operatorname{csch}^2 u \dfrac{du}{dx}$.
15. $\dfrac{d}{dx}\operatorname{sech} u = -\operatorname{sech} u \tanh u \dfrac{du}{dx}$.
16. $\dfrac{d}{dx}\operatorname{csch} u = -\operatorname{csch} u \coth u \dfrac{du}{dx}$.

In Exs. 17–28, find the first derivative.

17. $y = \sinh 3x$.   **18.** $y = \cosh(2x+1)$.
19. $y = \tanh(1-2x)$.   **20.** $y = \operatorname{sech} 3x$.
21. $x = \cosh^2 4t$.   **22.** $x = \tanh^2 t$.
23. $y = x^2 \sinh 3x$.   **24.** $y = e^{2x}\cosh x$.
25. $y = \cosh x^2$.   **26.** $y = \tanh(x-1)^2$.
27. $y = \ln \sinh 2x$.   *Ans.* $y' = 2\coth 2x$.
28. $y = \ln \tanh^2 x$.   *Ans.* $y' = 4\operatorname{csch} 2x$.
29. Sketch the curve which has for parametric equations

$$x = 3\cosh t, \qquad y = 4\sinh t.$$

30. Trace the curve $y = a \sinh \dfrac{x}{a}$. [Reflect the curve $y = ae^{\frac{x}{a}}$ in the origin to obtain $y = -ae^{-\frac{x}{a}}$; average the ordinates.]

31. Trace the curve $y = a \sinh \dfrac{x}{a}$ by the method of § 39. Also use the table, pp. 509–514.

32. Trace the curve $y = a \tanh \dfrac{x}{a}$.   **33.** Trace the curve $y = a \operatorname{sech} \dfrac{x}{a}$.

34. Prove that Arcsin tanh x = Arctan sinh x.

35. Prove that Arcsin tanh x = Arccos sech x $(x \geqq 0)$.

36. Derive (1), § 103.

104. Inverse hyperbolic functions. The *inverse hyperbolic sine*, also called *antihyperbolic sine*, is defined and denoted as follows:

$$y = \sinh^{-1} x \qquad if \qquad x = \sinh y.$$

Similarly for the other inverse functions.

Since the hyperbolic functions are exponential, the inverse functions must be logarithmic. The explicit formulas are as follows:

(1) $\sinh^{-1} x = \ln (x + \sqrt{x^2 + 1})$;

(2) $\cosh^{-1} x = \ln (x + \sqrt{x^2 - 1})$, $x \geqq 1$;

(3) $\tanh^{-1} x = \frac{1}{2} \ln \dfrac{1 + x}{1 - x}$, $|x| < 1$;

(4) $\coth^{-1} x = \frac{1}{2} \ln \dfrac{x + 1}{x - 1}$, $|x| > 1$;

(5) $\operatorname{sech}^{-1} x = \ln \dfrac{1 + \sqrt{1 - x^2}}{x}$, $0 < x \leqq 1$;

(6) $\operatorname{csch}^{-1} x = \begin{cases} \ln \dfrac{1 + \sqrt{1 + x^2}}{x}, & x > 0; \\[2ex] -\ln \dfrac{1 + \sqrt{1 + x^2}}{-x}, & x < 0. \end{cases}$

The problem of deriving these formulas is similar to Example (a), § 96. We will carry out the work for (2).

The equation

$$y = \cosh^{-1} x$$

means that

$$\cosh y = x,$$

$$\frac{e^y + e^{-y}}{2} = x, \qquad e^y + e^{-y} - 2x = 0,$$

$$e^{2y} - 2xe^y + 1 = 0.$$

Solving this quadratic in e^y, we get

$$e^y = x \pm \sqrt{x^2 - 1},$$

which gives two values of y:

$$y = \ln (x + \sqrt{x^2 - 1}),$$

$$y = \ln (x - \sqrt{x^2 - 1}).$$

By Ex. 47, p. 163, with $a = 1$,

$$\ln (x - \sqrt{x^2 - 1}) = -\ln (x + \sqrt{x^2 - 1}),$$

so that the two values of y are

$$y = \pm\ln (x + \sqrt{x^2 - 1}), \qquad x \geqq 1.$$

(It is easily seen that y is imaginary if $x < 1$.) Thus it turns out that $\cosh^{-1} x$ is two-valued: to make it one-valued (§ 5), we agree to retain only the positive value.

The other formulas above may be verified by the student. The derivatives may be found either by differentiation of (1)–(6) or by the indirect method used in § 98.

105. The tractrix. To illustrate the fact that inverse hyperbolic functions appear in comparatively elementary physical problems, we cite an example.

A man, standing at O, holds a rope of length a to which a weight is attached, initially at W_0. The man walks to the right, dragging the weight after him: when the man is at M, the weight is at

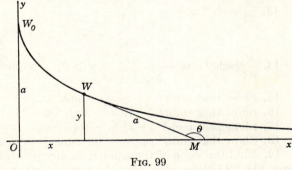

FIG. 99

W. It is intuitively obvious that the path of the weight will at least resemble the curve of Fig. 99. In § 254 it will be shown that the equation is

$$x = a \operatorname{sech}^{-1} \frac{y}{a} - \sqrt{a^2 - y^2};$$

from this we can trace the curve accurately (Ex. 21 below).

EXERCISES

1. Trace the curve $y = \sinh^{-1} x$ by reflecting, in the 45°-line, the curve $y = \sinh x$.

2. Trace the curve $y = \cosh^{-1} x$ by reflecting, in the 45°-line, the positive half of the curve $y = \cosh x$.

3. Trace the curve $y = \tanh^{-1} x$.

4. Obtain formula (1), § 104.

5. Obtain formula (3), § 104.

6. Obtain formula (4), § 104.

7. Obtain formula (5), § 104. (Of the two values that appear, only the positive is retained, by agreement.)

8. Obtain formula (6), § 104. (Of the two values that appear, one is imaginary when $x < 0$, the other when $x > 0$, so that the function is automatically one-valued.)

In Exs. 9–14, verify the given formula, if u is a function of x.

9. $\dfrac{d}{dx} \sinh^{-1} u = \dfrac{\dfrac{du}{dx}}{\sqrt{1 + u^2}}.$

10. $\dfrac{d}{dx} \tanh^{-1} u = \dfrac{\dfrac{du}{dx}}{1 - u^2}.$

11. $\dfrac{d}{dx} \cosh^{-1} u = \dfrac{\dfrac{du}{dx}}{\sqrt{u^2 - 1}}.$

12. $\dfrac{d}{dx} \coth^{-1} u = \dfrac{\dfrac{du}{dx}}{1 - u^2}.$

13. $\dfrac{d}{dx} \operatorname{sech}^{-1} u = -\dfrac{\dfrac{du}{dx}}{u\sqrt{1 - u^2}}.$

14. $\dfrac{d}{dx} \operatorname{csch}^{-1} u = -\dfrac{\dfrac{du}{dx}}{u\sqrt{1 + u^2}}, u > 0; \quad \dfrac{d}{dx} \operatorname{csch}^{-1} u = \dfrac{\dfrac{du}{dx}}{u\sqrt{1 + u^2}}, u < 0.$

15. Show that $\tanh^{-1}(-x) = -\tanh^{-1} x$.

16. Show that $\sinh^{-1}(-x) = -\sinh^{-1} x$.

17. Show that $\operatorname{csch}^{-1}(-x) = -\operatorname{csch}^{-1} x$.

18. Show that $\sinh^{-1} \tan \phi = \ln(\sec \phi + \tan \phi)$, $\sec \phi \geqq 1$.

19. Find the slope of the tractrix at any point. (Read off $\tan \theta$ directly from Fig. 99.) Hence show that the curve starts at W_0 tangent to the y-axis.

$$Ans. \quad \frac{dy}{dx} = -\frac{y}{\sqrt{a^2 - y^2}}.$$

20. Solve Ex. 19 by finding y' from the equation of the curve. [Formula (5″), p. 172.]

21. Trace the tractrix by subtracting abscissas of the circular arc $x = \sqrt{a^2 - y^2}$ from those of the curve $y = a \operatorname{sech} \dfrac{x}{a}$. (Ex. 33, p. 178.)

CHAPTER *12* CURVATURE

106. Curvature; radius of curvature. We say in ordinary language that a curve whose direction changes rapidly has great *curvature*, or is sharply curved. Thus a circular arc is said to have greater curvature when the radius is small than when it is large. This somewhat vague idea may be made precise as follows.

Consider, first, two points P, P' on a circle, and denote the arc PP' by Δs, the angle between the tangents at P, P' by $\Delta\alpha$.

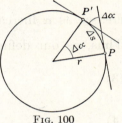

The quotient $\dfrac{\Delta\alpha}{\Delta s}$ is the *change in direction*

Fig. 100

of the curve, per unit of arc. It is evident that the central angle subtended by Δs is equal to $\Delta\alpha$; hence, by the formula

$$arc = radius \times angle,$$

we have

$$\Delta s = r\,\Delta\alpha,$$

so that the change in direction per unit of arc is

$$\frac{\Delta\alpha}{\Delta s} = \frac{1}{r}.$$

That is, in the case of the circle the quotient $\dfrac{\Delta\alpha}{\Delta s}$ is constant; it is called the *curvature* of the circle.

If now the curve in question is not a circle, the direction of the curve no longer changes uniformly, and the quotient $\dfrac{\Delta\alpha}{\Delta s}$ repre-

181

sents merely the *average curvature* of the arc Δs. But as P' (Fig. 101) approaches P along the curve, so that Δs and $\Delta \alpha$ approach zero, the quantity $\dfrac{\Delta \alpha}{\Delta s}$ in general approaches a limit $\dfrac{d\alpha}{ds}$, which is called the *curvature at the point P:*

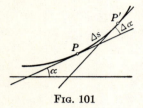

Fig. 101

(1) $$\kappa = \lim_{\Delta s \to 0} \frac{\Delta \alpha}{\Delta s} = \frac{d\alpha}{ds}.$$

The reciprocal of the curvature is called the *radius of curvature*, and is denoted by ρ:

(2) $$\rho = \frac{1}{\kappa} = \frac{ds}{d\alpha}.$$

However, it is customary to consider κ and ρ as essentially positive (just as, for a circle, the radius of the circle—equal to the radius of curvature—is always positive); and of course, if s decreases as α increases, the derivative $\dfrac{ds}{d\alpha}$ is a negative quantity. Thus, as our defining formulas, we shall replace (1) and (2) by

(3) $$\kappa = \left| \frac{d\alpha}{ds} \right|,$$

(4) $$\rho = \left| \frac{ds}{d\alpha} \right|.$$

107. Expression in Cartesian coördinates. The definitions above are independent of the particular coördinate system used; the angle α is the angle made by the tangent at P with any fixed line in the plane of the curve. When the equation of the curve is given in Cartesian coördinates, it is convenient to take α as the slope-angle of the tangent—*i.e.*, the angle between the tangent and the x-axis. The curvature κ is then easily expressed in terms of the coördinates. For,

$$\tan \alpha = \frac{dy}{dx} = y',$$

$$\alpha = \text{Arctan } y',$$

(1) $$d\alpha = \frac{dy'}{1 + (y')^2} = \frac{y'' \, dx}{1 + (y')^2}.$$

Also, by § 46,

(2) $$ds = \pm \sqrt{1 + (y')^2} \, dx.$$

Substituting (1) and (2) in the defining formulas above, we find

$$\kappa = \frac{|y''|}{[1 + (y')^2]^{\frac{3}{2}}},$$

$$\rho = \frac{[1 + (y')^2]^{\frac{3}{2}}}{|y''|}.$$

Example (*a*): Find the radius of curvature of the equilateral hyperbola

(3) $$x^2 - y^2 = a^2$$

at any point (x, y) on the curve.

We have, directly or by Example (*b*), § 30,

$$y' = \frac{x}{y}, \qquad y'' = -\frac{a^2}{y^3}.$$

Thus

(4) $$\rho = \frac{\left(1 + \dfrac{x^2}{y^2}\right)^{\frac{3}{2}}}{\dfrac{a^2}{|y^3|}} = \frac{|y^3|\left(1 + \dfrac{x^2}{y^2}\right)^{\frac{3}{2}}}{a^2} = \frac{(x^2 + y^2)^{\frac{3}{2}}}{a^2}.$$

Example (*b*): In Example (*a*), find the points of maximum curvature.*

The differentiation is somewhat simpler if instead of making κ a maximum, we make ρ a minimum. It will be convenient to express ρ in terms of y by means of (3):

$$\rho = \frac{(a^2 + 2y^2)^{\frac{3}{2}}}{a^2},$$

$$\frac{d\rho}{dy} = \frac{6y(a^2 + 2y^2)^{\frac{1}{2}}}{a^2},$$

so that $$\frac{d\rho}{dy} = 0 \text{ when } y = 0.$$

Thus the curvature is greatest at the vertices. (That we actually have maximum κ, rather than minimum or neither, is obvious, for we know that far out in the first quadrant, and again in the fourth quadrant, the curve is nearly straight.)

* This particular problem can be solved by inspection. A glance at (4) shows that ρ is least when the quantity $x^2 + y^2$ is least — *i.e.*, at that point of the curve that is nearest the origin.

We might just as easily have happened to express ρ in terms of x. If so, an interesting situation arises:

$$\rho = \frac{(2x^2 - a^2)^{\frac{3}{2}}}{a^2},$$

$$\frac{d\rho}{dx} = \frac{6x(2x^2 - a^2)^{\frac{1}{2}}}{a^2},$$

so that $\dfrac{d\rho}{dx} = 0$ when $x = 0$, or $x = \pm\frac{1}{2}\sqrt{2}\,a$.

Now all these critical values are barred, since the hyperbola does not reach so far. We are not yet fully equipped to trace the curve

$$\rho^2 = \frac{(2x^2 - a^2)^3}{a^4},$$

but it has the form shown in Fig. 116, p. 215. However, since we are limited to $|\,x\,| \geqq a$, $\rho > 0$, only the portions drawn full have a meaning. Hence ρ, as a function of x, has *endpoint minima* (§ 79) at $x = \pm a$.

108. Circle of curvature. At any point on a curve $y = f(x)$, where y' and y'' exist and $y'' \neq 0$, there is associated with the curve a circle, which is called the circle of curvature. In a sense, the circle of curvature is the circle which comes nearest (of all circles) to fitting the curve in the immediate vicinity of the point under consideration.

At a point (x, y) on $y = f(x)$, let y' and y'' exist and $y'' \neq 0$. Let a circle, with unspecified radius r and center at (a, b), pass through the point (x, y) and have, at that point, the same y' and y'' as those of the curve $y = f(x)$. The circle has the equation

(1) $$(x - a)^2 + (y - b)^2 = r^2.$$

From (1), by differentiating each member twice, we obtain

(2) $$x - a + y'(y - b) = 0,$$

(3) $$1 + y''(y - b) + (y')^2 = 0.$$

It is a simple matter to obtain the coördinates a and b, of the center of the circle (1), from equations (2) and (3). The results are

(4) $$a = x - \frac{y'[1 + (y')^2]}{y''},$$

(5) $$b = y + \frac{1 + (y')^2}{y''}.$$

Next we form the expression $(x - a)^2 + (y - b)^2$ to find the radius of the circle. From (4) and (5), we get

$$(x - a)^2 + (y - b)^2 = \frac{(y')^2[1 + (y')^2]^2}{(y'')^2} + \frac{[1 + (y')^2]^2}{(y'')^2}$$

$$= \frac{[1 + (y')^2]^3}{(y'')^2}.$$

Hence

$$r^2 = \frac{[1 + (y')^2]^3}{(y'')^2},$$

so that $r = \rho$, the radius of curvature of $y = f(x)$.

We have shown that the circle of curvature, at a point (x, y) on a curve, is the circle with *center at* (a, b) given by equations (4) and (5), and with *radius equal to the radius of curvature of the curve* at the point under consideration.

Example: Find the circle of curvature of the parabola $y^2 = 2x$ at the point $(\frac{1}{2}, 1)$, at one end of the latus rectum.

From $y = \sqrt{2}\, x^{\frac{1}{2}}$, we obtain

$$y' = \tfrac{1}{2}\sqrt{2}\, x^{-\frac{1}{2}},$$

$$y'' = -\tfrac{1}{4}\sqrt{2}\, x^{-\frac{3}{2}}.$$

Thus at the point $(\frac{1}{2}, 1)$ we have

$$y' = \tfrac{1}{2}\sqrt{2} \cdot \sqrt{2} = 1,$$

$$y'' = -\tfrac{1}{4}\sqrt{2} \cdot (\sqrt{2})^3 = -1.$$

Hence the circle of curvature has for coördinates of its center, from equations (4) and (5),

$$a = \tfrac{1}{2} - \frac{1(1 + 1)}{-1} = \tfrac{5}{2},$$

$$b = 1 + \frac{1 + 1}{-1} = -1.$$

The radius of the circle of curvature is

$$\rho = \frac{[1 + 1]^{\frac{3}{2}}}{|-1|} = +2\sqrt{2}.$$

The circle of curvature, then, is

(6) $$(x - \tfrac{5}{2})^2 + (y + 1)^2 = 8.$$

Note the check which is obtained by showing that the circle (6) passes through the given point $(\frac{1}{2}, 1)$.

EXERCISES

In Exs. 1–8, find the radius of curvature at the given point.

1. $y = x - \frac{1}{8}x^2$ at $(1, \frac{7}{8})$.   *Ans.* $\frac{125}{16}$.

2. $y = 2 + 2x - x^2$ at $(\frac{1}{2}, \frac{11}{4})$.   *Ans.* $\sqrt{2}$.

3. $y = x(x + 2)^2$ at $(0, 0)$.   *Ans.* $\dfrac{17\sqrt{17}}{8}$.

4. $y = x^2(x + 2)$ at $(0, 0)$.   *Ans.* $\frac{1}{4}$.

5. $y^2 = x - 2$ at $(3, 1)$.   *Ans.* $\dfrac{5\sqrt{5}}{2}$.

6. $y = \cos x$ at $(\pi, -1)$.   *Ans.* 1.

7. $y = a \sec \dfrac{x}{a}$ at $x = \dfrac{\pi a}{4}$.   *Ans.* $a\sqrt{\frac{3}{2}}$.

8. $y = \ln \tan \dfrac{x}{2}$ at $x = \dfrac{\pi}{4}$.   *Ans.* $2(\frac{3}{2})^{\frac{3}{2}}$.

In Exs. 9–22, find the radius of curvature at any point of the curve. In exercises involving parametric equations, reference may be made to § 32.

9. $y = \tan x$.   *Ans.* $\dfrac{(1 + \sec^4 x)^{\frac{3}{2}}}{2 \sec^2 x |\tan x|}$.

10. $y = \cos x$.

11. $y = \ln \sin x$.   *Ans.* $|\csc x|$.

12. $y = \ln \sec x$.   *Ans.* $|\sec x|$.

13. The parabola $y^2 = 4ax$.   *Ans.* $\dfrac{2(a + x)^{\frac{3}{2}}}{a^{\frac{1}{2}}}$.

14. Hyperbola $2xy = a^2$.   *Ans.* $\dfrac{(4x^4 + a^4)^{\frac{3}{2}}}{8a^2 |x^3|}$.

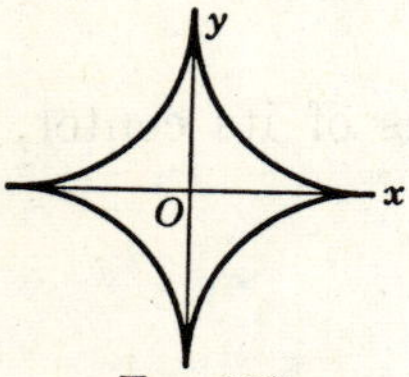

Fig. 102

15. The *four-cusped hypocycloid* $x^{\frac{2}{3}} + y^{\frac{2}{3}} = a^{\frac{2}{3}}$. (Fig. 102.)   *Ans.* $3|axy|^{\frac{1}{3}}$.

16. $x = 3t + 1$, $y = t^2$, with t as a parameter.   *Ans.* $\frac{1}{6}(9 + 4t^2)^{\frac{3}{2}}$.

17. $x = 1 - 2t$, $y = t^2 + 3$.   *Ans.* $2(1 + t^2)^{\frac{3}{2}}$.

18. $x = a \sin^3 t$, $y = a \cos^3 t$, the four-cusped hypocycloid of Ex. 15.   *Ans.* $3|a \sin t \cos t|$.

19. The ellipse $x = a \cos \phi$, $y = b \sin \phi$.   *Ans.* $\dfrac{(a^2 \sin^2 \phi + b^2 \cos^2 \phi)^{\frac{3}{2}}}{ab}$.

20. The parabola $x = a \tan^2 \phi$, $y = 2a \tan \phi$.   *Ans.* $2a|\sec^3 \phi|$.

21. $x = a \tan \phi$, $y = a \cot \phi$.   *Ans.* $\frac{1}{2}a|\tan^3 \phi|(1 + \cot^4 \phi)^{\frac{3}{2}}$.

22. $x = a \cos^4 \theta$, $y = a \sin^4 \theta$.   *Ans.* $2a(\sin^4 \theta + \cos^4 \theta)^{\frac{3}{2}}$.

In Exs. 23–33, find the points of maximum curvature.

23. $3y = x^3$.   *Ans.* $x = \pm(\frac{1}{5})^{\frac{1}{4}}$.

24. $4y = x^4$.   *Ans.* $x = \pm(\frac{2}{7})^{\frac{1}{6}}$.

25. $21y = x^{14}$.   *Ans.* $x = \pm 1$.

26. $x^2 y = a^3$.   *Ans.* $x = \pm(5)^{\frac{1}{6}}a$.

27. $y = \sin x.$

28. $y = \ln \sin x.$ *Ans.* $x = \frac{1}{2}\pi.$

29. $y = a \cosh \dfrac{x}{a}.$

30. A parabola. (Ex. 13.) *Ans.* The vertex.

31. $y = e^x.$ *Ans.* $(-\frac{1}{2}\ln 2, \frac{1}{2}\sqrt{2}).$

32. $y = \ln x.$ (Cf. Ex. 31.)

33. $y = \sinh x.$ *Ans.* $x = \pm \ln(1+\sqrt{2}).$

34. If x is given as a function of y, derive the formula (see § 26)

$$\rho = \frac{\left[\left(\dfrac{dx}{dy}\right)^2 + 1\right]^{\frac{3}{2}}}{\left|\dfrac{d^2x}{dy^2}\right|}.$$

35. Find the radius of curvature of the tractrix

$$x = a \operatorname{sech}^{-1}\frac{y}{a} - \sqrt{a^2 - y^2}.$$

Ans. (See Ex. 19, p. 180.) $-\dfrac{a}{y'}.$

36. Show that when a weight is drawn along the ground as in Fig. 99, p. 179, the path of the weight continually tends to straighten out. (Ex. 35.)

37. In Example (b), § 107, verify in two ways (§§ 36, 37) that ρ is a minimum.

38. Find the point of minimum curvature for the four-cusped hypo-cycloid. *Ans.* Midway between the cusps.

In Exs. 39–43, find the equation of the circle of curvature at the given point. Draw the figure.

39. $y = x^2$ at $(0,0)$. *Ans.* $x^2 + y^2 = y.$

40. $y = x^2$ at $(1,1)$. *Ans.* $x^2 + y^2 + 8x - 7y = 3.$

41. $y = x^3 - x^2$ at $(0,0)$. *Ans.* $x^2 + y^2 + y = 0.$

42. $y = x^3 - x^2$ at $(1,0)$. *Ans.* $x^2 + y^2 = x + y.$

43. The four-cusped hypocycloid $x^{\frac{2}{3}} + y^{\frac{2}{3}} = 2$, at the point of minimum curvature in the first quadrant. See Ex. 38.

Ans. $x^2 + y^2 = 8x + 8y - 14.$

CHAPTER *13* INDETERMINATE FORMS

109. The Law of the Mean. Let $f(x)$ be a function which is continuous, one-valued, and differentiable in the interval $x = a$ to $x = b$. At some point such as P the tangent must be parallel to the secant SQ. Now the slope of the secant is

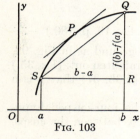

FIG. 103

$$\frac{RQ}{SR} = \frac{f(b) - f(a)}{b - a};$$

the slope of the tangent at P is $f'(x_1)$, where x_1 is the abscissa of P. Hence

$$\frac{f(b) - f(a)}{b - a} = f'(x_1),$$

or

(1) $\qquad f(b) - f(a) = (b - a) f'(x_1), \qquad a < x_1 < b.$

This formula is called the *Law of the Mean.*

110. The indeterminate forms $\dfrac{0}{0}$, $\dfrac{\infty}{\infty}$. If two functions $f(x)$, $F(x)$ both vanish at $x = a$:

$$f(a) = 0, \qquad F(a) = 0,$$

the quotient $\dfrac{f(x)}{F(x)}$ is said to * *assume the "indeterminate form"* $\dfrac{0}{0}$ at $x = a$, and is undefined at that point. Nevertheless the *limit*

---

* It should be clearly understood that the symbols $\dfrac{0}{0}$, $\dfrac{\infty}{\infty}$, etc., are never to be taken literally, since, so taken, they have no meaning whatever. In fact, the term "indeterminate form" is something of a misnomer, since the function is simply not defined at the point in question. No confusion will arise if we always remember that these symbols are nothing more than convenient shorthand to designate the various situations described.

188

of the quotient — *i.e.*, $\lim\limits_{x \to a} \dfrac{f(x)}{F(x)}$ — may exist. This fact is illustrated in the derivation of the fundamental differentiation formulas, where in each case both numerator and denominator of the difference-quotient $\dfrac{\Delta y}{\Delta x}$ approach zero, yet the derivative, which is the limit of that quotient, exists. See also Example (*b*), § 9, and Formula (1), § 11.

If the function $\dfrac{f(x)}{F(x)}$ does approach a limit, it may be possible to evaluate the limit by means of more or less obvious transformations of $\dfrac{f(x)}{F(x)}$, as was done in deriving the differentiation formulas. In many cases the limit may be obtained by a method that will now be developed.

In Formula (1) of § 109, let us take $b = x$. This gives

$$f(x) = f(a) + (x - a)f'(x_1),$$
$$F(x) = F(a) + (x - a)F'(x_2),$$

where x_1 and x_2 lie between a and x. But by hypothesis

$$f(a) = F(a) = 0.$$

Hence

$$\frac{f(x)}{F(x)} = \frac{(x - a)f'(x_1)}{(x - a)F'(x_2)} = \frac{f'(x_1)}{F'(x_2)}.$$

As x approaches a, x_1 and x_2 must do likewise, and we have, by Theorem III of § 9,

$$\lim_{x \to a} \frac{f(x)}{F(x)} = \lim_{x \to a} \frac{f'(x_1)}{F'(x_2)} = \lim_{x \to a} \frac{f'(x)}{F'(x)} = \frac{f'(a)}{F'(a)},$$

provided $f'(a)$ and $F'(a)$ exist and $F'(a) \neq 0$.

If $f(x)$ and $F(x)$ both increase indefinitely (in either direction) as x approaches a, the quotient $\dfrac{f(x)}{F(x)}$ is said to *assume the indeterminate*

form $\dfrac{\infty}{\infty}$ at $x = a$. Here again it may happen that $\lim\limits_{x \to a} \dfrac{f(x)}{F(x)}$ exists, and it can be shown that, subject to certain broad conditions that are satisfied in all ordinary cases, the same method may be applied in this case as in the one just treated.

If the function $\dfrac{f'(x)}{F'(x)}$ takes the form $\dfrac{0}{0}$ or $\dfrac{\infty}{\infty}$, we may differentiate numerator and denominator again, and repeat as many times as necessary.

THEOREM: *If the quotient* $\dfrac{f(x)}{F(x)}$ *assumes the indeterminate form* $\dfrac{0}{0}$ *or* $\dfrac{\infty}{\infty}$ *when* $x = a$, *then*

$$\lim_{x \to a} \frac{f(x)}{F(x)} = \lim_{x \to a} \frac{f'(x)}{F'(x)},$$

provided the latter limit exists.

Further, $\dfrac{f(x)}{F(x)}$ may approach the form $\dfrac{0}{0}$ or $\dfrac{\infty}{\infty}$ when x increases indefinitely. In this case the rule holds also.

Thus in all these cases we may differentiate the numerator and the denominator *separately*, and take the limit of the new quantity thus formed. It must be borne clearly in mind, however, that the theorem applies only to *quotients* in which the numerator and the denominator *both approach zero or both increase indefinitely.*

Example (a): Evaluate $\lim\limits_{x \to 0} \dfrac{\tan x}{x}$.

This takes the form $\dfrac{0}{0}$ when $x = 0$:

$$\lim_{x \to 0} \frac{\tan x}{x} = \lim_{x \to 0} \frac{\sec^2 x}{1} = 1.$$

Example (b): Evaluate $\lim\limits_{x \to 0^+} \dfrac{e^{-\frac{1}{x}}}{x}$.

Proceeding directly, we find

$$\lim_{x \to 0^+} \frac{e^{-\frac{1}{x}}}{x} = \lim_{x \to 0^+} \frac{\frac{1}{x^2}e^{-\frac{1}{x}}}{1} = \lim_{x \to 0^+} \frac{e^{-\frac{1}{x}}}{x^2}$$

$$= \lim_{x \to 0^+} \frac{\frac{1}{x^2}e^{-\frac{1}{x}}}{2x} = \lim_{x \to 0^+} \frac{e^{-\frac{1}{x}}}{2x^3}.$$

Evidently nothing is being accomplished. But, prominence of $\dfrac{1}{x}$ in the original expression suggests the substitution $z = \dfrac{1}{x}$:

$$\lim_{x \to 0^+} \frac{e^{-\frac{1}{x}}}{x} = \lim_{z \to \infty} ze^{-z} = \lim_{z \to \infty} \frac{z}{e^z} = \lim_{z \to \infty} \frac{1}{e^z} = 0.$$

Any factor (of the *whole expression*) which approaches a limit different from zero may be replaced by its limit as soon as it makes its appearance (Theorem II, § 9).

Example (c): $\displaystyle \lim_{\alpha \to 0} \frac{\sin \alpha - \alpha}{\tan^3 \alpha} = \lim_{\alpha \to 0} \frac{\cos \alpha - 1}{3 \tan^2 \alpha \sec^2 \alpha}$

$$= \lim_{\alpha \to 0} \frac{\cos \alpha - 1}{3 \tan^2 \alpha} = \lim_{\alpha \to 0} \frac{-\sin \alpha}{6 \tan \alpha \sec^2 \alpha}$$

$$= \lim_{\alpha \to 0} \frac{-\sin \alpha}{6 \tan \alpha} = \lim_{\alpha \to 0} \frac{-\cos \alpha}{6 \sec^2 \alpha} = -\frac{1}{6}.$$

Finally, to see that our method, even when applicable, does not always succeed, consider the next example.

Example (d): Evaluate $\displaystyle \lim_{x \to \infty} \frac{3^x}{2^{x^3}}$.

This is of the type $\dfrac{\infty}{\infty}$:

$$\lim_{x \to \infty} \frac{3^x}{2^{x^3}} = \lim_{x \to \infty} \frac{3^x \ln 3}{2^{x^3} \cdot 2x \ln 2}; \text{ etc.}$$

Evidently differentiation will never affect the exponential factors. But we may write

$$\lim_{x \to \infty} \frac{3^x}{2^{x^3}} = \lim_{x \to \infty} \frac{3^x}{2^{2x}} \cdot \frac{1}{2^{x^3 - 2x}}$$

$$= \lim_{x \to \infty} \left[\left(\frac{3}{4} \right)^x \cdot \frac{1}{2^{x^3 - 2x}} \right] = 0,$$

since each factor approaches zero. See also Exs. 38 and 49 below.

111. The indeterminate form $0 \cdot \infty$. Consider the product of two functions $f(x) \cdot F(x)$ such that, as x approaches a, one function approaches zero while the other increases indefinitely. The product is then said to *take the indeterminate form* $0 \cdot \infty$.

If we write

$$f(x) \cdot F(x) = \frac{f(x)}{\dfrac{1}{F(x)}},$$

it appears that the quotient last written assumes the form $\dfrac{0}{0}$ or $\dfrac{\infty}{\infty}$, and the above theorem may be applied.

Example: Evaluate $\lim_{x \to 0^+} x^2 \ln x$.

This takes the form $0 \cdot \infty$. We write

$$\lim_{x \to 0^+} x^2 \ln x = \lim_{x \to 0^+} \frac{\ln x}{\dfrac{1}{x^2}} = \lim_{x \to 0^+} \frac{\dfrac{1}{x}}{\dfrac{-2}{x^3}} = \lim_{x \to 0^+} \left(-\frac{x^2}{2} \right) = 0.$$

EXERCISES

In Exs. 1–18, evaluate the limit by the theorem of Section 110.

1. $\lim_{x \to 0} \dfrac{x + \tan x}{\sin 3x}$.   *Ans.* $\frac{2}{3}$.

2. $\lim_{x \to \frac{\pi}{2}} \dfrac{1 - \sin x}{\cos 3x}$.   *Ans.* 0.

3. $\lim_{y \to 0} \dfrac{\text{Arcsin } y}{y}$.   *Ans.* 1.

4. $\lim_{\theta \to \frac{\pi}{2}} \dfrac{1 - \sin \theta}{(\pi - 2\theta)^2}$.   *Ans.* $\frac{1}{8}$.

5. $\lim_{x \to 0} \dfrac{\ln \sec x}{x^2}$.   *Ans.* $\frac{1}{2}$.

6. $\lim_{y \to 1} \dfrac{1 + \cos \pi y}{(y - 1)^2}$.   *Ans.* $\frac{\pi^2}{2}$.

7. $\lim_{z \to \infty} \dfrac{\ln z}{z}$.   *Ans.* 0.

8. $\lim_{x \to \infty} (x^2 e^{-x})$.   *Ans.* 0.

9. $\lim_{y \to \infty} \dfrac{e^{2y}}{y^3}$.

10. $\lim_{x \to \infty} \dfrac{\ln^2 x}{x}$.

11. $\lim_{x \to \pi} \dfrac{\ln x - \ln \pi}{\sin 2x}$.

12. $\lim_{x \to 1} \dfrac{\ln x}{x^2 - 4x + 3}$.

13. $\lim_{x \to 0^+} (\text{Arcsin } x) \ln x$.

14. $\lim_{y \to 0^+} y e^{\frac{1}{y}}$.

15. $\lim_{x \to 0} \dfrac{x - \sin x}{x(1 - \cos x)}$.   *Ans.* $\frac{1}{3}$.

16. $\lim_{y \to 0} \dfrac{y - \tan y}{\sin^3 y}$.   *Ans.* $-\frac{1}{3}$.

17. $\lim_{x \to 0} \dfrac{x^2 \sin x}{x - \sin x}$.   *Ans.* 6.

18. $\lim_{x \to 0} \dfrac{x e^x - \sin x}{\sin^2 x}$.   *Ans.* 1.

In Exs. 19–28, evaluate each limit by two methods.

19. $\lim_{x \to 1} \dfrac{x^2 - 4x + 3}{2x^2 - x - 1}$.

20. $\lim_{x \to -2} \dfrac{2x^2 + 3x - 2}{x^2 + 3x + 2}$.

21. $\lim_{x \to 3} \dfrac{x^3 - x^2 - 7x + 3}{x^3 - 8x - 3}$.

22. $\lim_{x \to \infty} \dfrac{3x^4 - x + 1}{2x^4 + x^3 - 6}$.

23. $\lim_{\theta \to 0} \dfrac{\sin^2 \theta}{1 - \cos \theta}$.

24. $\lim_{\alpha \to 0} \dfrac{1 - \cos^4 \alpha}{\alpha \sin \alpha}$.

25. $\displaystyle\lim_{x\to 0} \frac{x - \tan x}{\sin x}.$

26. $\displaystyle\lim_{y\to 0} \frac{\sqrt{y+4} - 2}{y}.$

27. $\displaystyle\lim_{x\to 0} \frac{x}{\sqrt{1+x} - \sqrt{1-x}}.$

28. $\displaystyle\lim_{x\to 0} \frac{x^2}{1 - \cos x}.$

In Exs. 29–42, evaluate the limits by any available method.

29. $\displaystyle\lim_{x\to 2} \frac{x^3 - 7x + 6}{2x^3 - 5x^2 + x + 2}.$ *Ans.* 1.

30. $\displaystyle\lim_{x\to 2} \frac{x^3 - 7x + 6}{x^3 - 3x^2 + 4}.$ *Ans.* No limit.

31. $\displaystyle\lim_{\theta\to 0} \frac{\tan\theta - \theta}{\theta^2 \sin\theta}.$ *Ans.* $\frac{1}{3}$.

32. $\displaystyle\lim_{\alpha\to 0} \frac{\sec\alpha - 1}{\alpha \sin\alpha}.$ *Ans.* $\frac{1}{2}$.

33. $\displaystyle\lim_{x\to 0} \frac{2\tan x - \sin 2x}{x^3}.$ *Ans.* 2.

34. $\displaystyle\lim_{y\to 0} \frac{\tan^2 y - \sin^2 y}{y^3 \sin y}.$ *Ans.* 1.

35. $\displaystyle\lim_{x\to\infty} \frac{\cos x}{x}.$ *Ans.* 0.

36. $\displaystyle\lim_{x\to\infty} \frac{\tan x}{x}.$ *Ans.* No limit.

37. $\displaystyle\lim_{x\to\infty} \frac{x - \sin x}{x}.$ *Ans.* 1.

38. $\displaystyle\lim_{n\to\infty} \frac{e^n}{\pi^n}.$ *Ans.* 0.

39. $\displaystyle\lim_{x\to 0} \frac{2\cos x + e^{x^2} - 3}{x^2 - x \sin x}.$ *Ans.* $\frac{7}{2}$.

40. $\displaystyle\lim_{x\to 0} \frac{e^{-x} + \cos x + \sin x - 2}{x \sin^2 x}.$ *Ans.* $-\frac{1}{3}$.

41. $\displaystyle\lim_{x\to\infty} (x \sin e^{-x}).$ *Ans.* 0.

42. $\displaystyle\lim_{x\to\infty} (\sin \frac{1}{x} \csc e^{-x}).$ *Ans.* ∞.

Prove the theorems of Exs. 43–48, k being any positive number.

43. $\displaystyle\lim_{x\to\infty} \frac{x^k}{e^x} = 0.$

44. $\displaystyle\lim_{x\to\infty} \frac{\ln x}{x^k} = 0.$

45. $\displaystyle\lim_{x\to 0+} x^k \ln x = 0.$

46. $\displaystyle\lim_{x\to\infty} \frac{e^x}{x^k} = \infty.$

47. $\displaystyle\lim_{x\to\infty} \frac{x^k}{\ln x} = \infty.$

48. $\displaystyle\lim_{x\to 0+} \frac{\ln x}{x^k} = -\infty.$

49. Solve Example (d), § 110, by a second method. (Note that $3 = 2^{\log_2 3}$.)

50. If $b > 1$, $k > 1$, prove that $\displaystyle\lim_{x\to\infty} \frac{a^x}{b^{x^k}} = 0$, regardless of the magnitude of the ratio $\frac{a}{b}$. (Cf. Ex. 49.)

112. The indeterminate form $\infty - \infty$. When two functions $f(x)$, $F(x)$ both become indefinitely large and positive, or large and negative, as x approaches a, the *difference* $f(x) - F(x)$ is said to *assume the indeterminate form* $\infty - \infty$. While no general rules can be laid down for evaluating the limit (if any) of this difference, we try to find some transformation that will render the expression amenable to the theorem of § 110.

Example: Evaluate $\lim\limits_{x \to \frac{\pi^+}{2}} (\sec^3 x - \tan^3 x)$.

This takes the form $- \infty + \infty$. The transformations required are quite obvious:

$$\lim_{x \to \frac{\pi^+}{2}} (\sec^3 x - \tan^3 x) = \lim_{x \to \frac{\pi^+}{2}} \left(\frac{1}{\cos^3 x} - \frac{\sin^3 x}{\cos^3 x} \right) = \lim_{x \to \frac{\pi^+}{2}} \frac{1 - \sin^3 x}{\cos^3 x}$$

$$= \lim_{x \to \frac{\pi^+}{2}} \frac{-3 \sin^2 x \cos x}{-3 \cos^2 x \sin x} = \lim_{x \to \frac{\pi^+}{2}} \tan x = - \infty.$$

That is, the given quantity increases indefinitely in the negative direction, without approaching any limit.

113. The indeterminate forms 0^0, ∞^0, 1^∞. Consider the function

(1) $$y = [f(x)]^{F(x)}.$$

If

$$\lim_{x \to a} f(x) = 0, \qquad \lim_{x \to a} F(x) = 0,$$

or if

$$\lim_{x \to a} f(x) = \infty, \qquad \lim_{x \to a} F(x) = 0,$$

or if

$$\lim_{x \to a} f(x) = 1, \qquad \lim_{x \to a} F(x) = \infty,$$

the function (1) is said, in the respective cases, to *assume the indeterminate form* 0^0, or ∞^0, or 1^∞. To investigate any one of these limits, take the logarithm of (1):

$$\ln y = F(x) \ln f(x),$$

and in each case the right-hand member is of the type discussed in § 111.

If $\ln y$ approaches a limit k, then y itself approaches the limit e^k.

Example (a): Evaluate $\lim\limits_{x \to 0^+} x^x$.

This evidently takes the form 0^0. Put

$$y = x^x, \qquad \ln y = x \ln x,$$

$$\lim_{x \to 0^+} \ln y = \lim_{x \to 0^+} x \ln x = \lim_{x \to 0^+} \frac{\ln x}{\dfrac{1}{x}}$$

$$= \lim_{x \to 0^+} \frac{\dfrac{1}{x}}{-\dfrac{1}{x^2}} = \lim_{x \to 0^+} (-x) = 0,$$

$$\lim_{x \to 0^+} y = \lim_{x \to 0^+} x^x = 1.$$

Example (b): Evaluate $\lim\limits_{x \to \infty} (1 + e^{-x})^{e^x}$.

First method:

$$y = (1 + e^{-x})^{e^x}, \qquad \ln y = e^x \ln (1 + e^{-x}),$$

$$\lim_{x \to \infty} e^x \ln (1 + e^{-x}) = \lim_{x \to \infty} \frac{\ln (1 + e^{-x})}{e^{-x}} = \lim_{x \to \infty} \frac{\dfrac{-e^{-x}}{1 + e^{-x}}}{-e^{-x}} = 1,$$

$$\lim_{x \to \infty} \ln y = 1, \qquad \lim_{x \to \infty} (1 + e^{-x})^{e^x} = e.$$

Second method: Put $z = e^x$, so that

$$\lim_{x \to \infty} (1 + e^{-x})^{e^x} = \lim_{z \to \infty} \left(1 + \frac{1}{z}\right)^z = e,$$

directly by * § 94.

EXERCISES

In Exs. 1–18, evaluate the limits by first converting the problem to a proper form to enable you to use the theorem of § 110.

1. $\lim\limits_{\alpha \to 0} \left(\dfrac{1}{\sin^2 \alpha} - \dfrac{1}{\alpha^2}\right)$.　　　　　　　　　*Ans.* $\frac{1}{3}$.

2. $\lim\limits_{x \to 0} \left(\csc x - \dfrac{1}{e^x - 1}\right)$.　　　　　　　　　*Ans.* $\frac{1}{2}$.

3. $\lim\limits_{\theta \to \frac{\pi}{2}} (\sec \theta - \tan \theta)$.　　　　　　　　　*Ans.* 0.

* As a matter of fact, in the first method we may be said to be "lifting ourselves by our bootstraps." For, since this is merely the fundamental limit e (even though in slightly disguised form), we cannot differentiate any exponential function until this limit has been evaluated. However, it illustrates the process as well as any other example.

4. $\lim\limits_{x \to 1} \left(\dfrac{x}{x-1} - \dfrac{1}{\ln x} \right).$ *Ans.* $\frac{1}{2}.$

5. $\lim\limits_{y \to 0} \left(\dfrac{e^{-y^2}}{y^2} - \dfrac{\sec y}{y^2} \right).$ *Ans.* $-\frac{3}{2}.$

6. $\lim\limits_{x \to 0} \left(\dfrac{1}{\sin^2 x} - \dfrac{\sin x}{x^3} \right).$ *Ans.* $\frac{1}{2}.$

7. $\lim\limits_{x \to 1} x^{\csc \pi x}.$ *Ans.* $e^{\frac{-1}{\pi}}.$ **8.** $\lim\limits_{y \to 0} (y+1)^{\cot 2y}.$ *Ans.* $e^{\frac{1}{2}}.$

9. $\lim\limits_{\alpha \to 0} (\cos \alpha - \sin \alpha)^{\frac{1}{\alpha}}.$ *Ans.* $e^{-1}.$

10. $\lim\limits_{x \to 0} (1 + x^2)^{\frac{1}{x}}.$ *Ans.* $1.$ **11.** $\lim\limits_{\alpha \to 0^+} (\sin \alpha)^{\tan \alpha}.$ *Ans.* $1.$

12. $\lim\limits_{x \to 0} (1 + \sin^2 x)^{\frac{1}{x^2}}.$ *Ans.* $e.$ **13.** $\lim\limits_{x \to 0} (e^x + 3x)^{\frac{1}{x}}.$ *Ans.* $e^4.$

14. $\lim\limits_{\alpha \to 0^+} (\csc \alpha)^{\sin \alpha}.$ *Ans.* $1.$ **15.** $\lim\limits_{x \to \frac{\pi}{2}} (\tan x)^{\cos x}.$ *Ans.* $1.$

16. $\lim\limits_{\alpha \to 0} (\sec \alpha + \tan \alpha)^{\csc \alpha}.$ *Ans.* $e.$

17. $\lim\limits_{x \to 0} (\cos x)^{\frac{1}{x^2}}.$ *Ans.* $e^{-\frac{1}{2}}.$ **18.** $\lim\limits_{x \to 0} \left(\dfrac{\sin x}{x} \right)^{\frac{1}{x^2}}.$ *Ans.* $e^{-\frac{1}{6}}.$

In Exs. 19–32, evaluate the limit by any available method.

19. $\lim\limits_{x \to \infty} (e^x - x).$ *Ans.* $+\infty.$

20. $\lim\limits_{x \to 0^+} (x + \ln x).$ *Ans.* $-\infty.$

21. $\lim\limits_{x \to \infty} (x - \ln x).$ *Ans.* $+\infty.$

22. $\lim\limits_{\alpha \to \pi^+} (\csc^3 \alpha - \cot^3 \alpha).$ *Ans.* $-\infty.$

23. $\lim\limits_{\alpha \to \pi^-} (\csc^3 \alpha - \cot^3 \alpha).$ *Ans.* $+\infty.$

24. $\lim\limits_{\alpha \to \pi} (\csc^3 \alpha - \cot^3 \alpha).$ *Ans.* No limit.

25. $\lim\limits_{x \to 0} (\csc^3 x - \cot^3 x).$ *Ans.* No limit.

26. $\lim\limits_{x \to 0} (x \csc^3 x - x \cot^3 x).$ *Ans.* $\frac{3}{2}.$

27. $\lim\limits_{x \to \infty} (1 + x^2 e^x)^{\frac{1}{x}}.$ *Ans.* $e.$

28. $\lim\limits_{x \to \infty} (1 + e^{2x})^{\frac{1}{\ln (1+e^x)}}.$ *Ans.* $e^2.$

29. $\lim\limits_{x \to 0^+} (1 + e^{\frac{4}{x}})^x.$ *Ans.* $e^4.$

30. $\lim\limits_{x \to 0^-} (1 + e^{\frac{4}{x}})^x.$ *Ans.* $1.$

31. $\lim\limits_{x \to \infty} (1 + x e^{3x^2})^{\frac{1}{x^2}}.$ *Ans.* $e^3.$

32. $\lim\limits_{\beta \to \infty} (1 + \beta \ln \beta)^{\frac{1}{\ln (1+\beta)}}$.   *Ans. e.*

In Exs. 33–36, evaluate the limit without resorting to differentiation.

33. $\lim\limits_{x \to 0+} (1 + \tan x)^{\cot x}$. Put $\cot x = v$.

34. $\lim\limits_{x \to 0} (\sec x)^{2 \cot^2 x}$.   *Ans. e.*

35. $\lim\limits_{x \to \frac{\pi}{2}} (\sec^2 x - \tan^2 x)^{\sec x}$.   *Ans. 1.*

36. $\lim\limits_{x \to 0+} (\cot x)^{x^3 - e^3 \ln x}$.   *Ans. 1.*

37. Evaluate $\lim\limits_{x \to 0} \left(\dfrac{\pi x - 1}{2x^2} + \dfrac{\pi}{x(e^{2\pi x} - 1)} \right)$.   *Ans.* $\dfrac{\pi^2}{6}$.

38. What limiting form is approached, in the first quadrant, by the curve $x^n + y^n = a^n$ as n increases through positive integral values? [Consider intersections with lines through O. Putting $y = mx$, find $x = \dfrac{a}{(1 + m^n)^{\frac{1}{n}}}$; investigate $\lim\limits_{n \to \infty} x$ for $m < 1$ and $m > 1$.]   *Ans.* One quadrant of the square $x = \pm a, y = \pm a$; if n is even, the entire curve approaches the entire square.

39. Find the points of intersection of the curves $x^{100} + y^{100} = 1$, $y = x$. (Cf. Ex. 38.)   *Ans.* $(\pm 0.993, \pm 0.993)$.

40. From the fact (Ex. 38) that $\lim\limits_{n \to \infty} (1 + m^n)^{\frac{1}{n}} = 1$, $m < 1$, deduce without differentiation the fact that $\lim\limits_{n \to \infty} (1 + m^n)^{\frac{1}{n}} = m$, $m > 1$. [Note first that $(1 + m^n)^{\frac{1}{n}} = m(1 + m^{-n})^{\frac{1}{n}}$.]

41. Draw the curve $y = \lim\limits_{n \to \infty} (1 + x^n)^{\frac{1}{n}}$, $x > 0$. (Ex. 40.)

CHAPTER *14* CURVE TRACING

114. Introduction. In this chapter we shall make a systematic attack upon the problem of curve tracing. Factorable equations (so-called "degenerate" curves) are excluded.

In §§ 114–124 only algebraic curves are under consideration. We shall for simplicity confine our attention chiefly to cases in which either y or y^2 is a rational function of x:

$$(1) \qquad y = \frac{P(x)}{Q(x)},$$

or

$$(2) \qquad y^2 = \frac{P(x)}{Q(x)},$$

where $P(x)$, $Q(x)$ are polynomials. Since *cubics* (curves of third degree) and *quartics* (curves of fourth degree) are the curves most commonly occurring, most of our work will be with these types.

It will be assumed that $P(x)$ and $Q(x)$ contain no common factor. Hence (§ 75) the only kind of discontinuity that can occur is the infinite discontinuity.

115. Asymptotes. As the point of contact of a tangent to a curve recedes indefinitely from the origin, the tangent may or may not approach a limiting position. If it does, the line approached is called an *asymptote*.* Thus an asymptote is sometimes said to be "a tangent whose point of contact lies at infinity"; but of course it is not a tangent in the strict sense.

---

* According to some writers, an asymptote is a line that is approached more and more closely by the *curve*, even though the tangent does not approach a limiting position. For algebraic curves, the two definitions are equivalent. But see Exs. 31–32, p. 217.

For example, the hyperbola

$$\frac{x^2}{a^2} - \frac{y^2}{b^2} = 1$$

has the lines

$$y = \pm \frac{b}{a}x$$

as asymptotes. On the other hand, the parabola has no asymptotes, since as the point of tangency recedes the tangent does not approach any limiting position. Many higher plane curves have one or more asymptotes, and they play an important part in the study of those curves.

For algebraic curves, asymptotes parallel to the axes can be determined (cf. §§ 73–74) by the following rule.

RULE: *If y becomes infinite as x approaches a definite limit a, the line $x = a$ is an asymptote; if y approaches b as x becomes infinite, the line $y = b$ is an asymptote.*

Example (a): Examine the curve

$$y = \frac{ax^2}{(x - a)(x - 3a)}$$

for horizontal and vertical asymptotes.

Equating the denominator to zero, we find the vertical asymptotes $x = a$, $x = 3a$. As x increases (in either direction), y approaches a (by § 110, or by direct inspection): thus the line $y = a$ is a horizontal asymptote. See Fig. 104, p. 202.

It can be shown that a curve of the n-th degree *may intersect an asymptote in, at most, $n - 2$ points.* Although we shall not prove this theorem, it may be made plausible as follows. We know from analytic geometry that a curve of n-th degree may intersect a straight line in not more than n points. Since a tangent is the limiting position of a secant when two points of intersection come to coincidence, the point of tangency counts as two intersections, so that a tangent may intersect the curve in not more than $n - 2$ other points. While an asymptote is not a tangent in the literal sense, it is the limiting position of a tangent and partakes of the nature of a tangent; hence it is to be expected that the same result will hold.

No curve of types (1)–(2) of § 114 can intersect a vertical asymptote, since, if $Q(x) = 0$, then y does not exist. These curves may, however, intersect a horizontal asymptote, and such intersections should always be looked for.

Example (b): In the equation of Example (a), viz.

$$y = \frac{ax^2}{(x - a)(x - 3a)},$$

put $y = a$:

$$a(x^2 - 4ax + 3a^2) = ax^2, \qquad x = \tfrac{3}{4}a:$$

thus the curve crosses its horizontal asymptote at $(\tfrac{3}{4}a, a)$. (Fig. 104, p. 202.)

116. Restriction to definite regions. It is frequently possible to show that the curve is confined to certain definite portions of the plane, and a result of this kind is of great value in tracing the curve. While no general directions can be given, in case the equation is, or can be, *solved for y* (or some power of y), it is highly instructive to note the *changes of sign* of the right member. The process will be explained by examples as need arises.

117. Summary. The method of curve tracing outlined in § 39 may now be greatly strengthened, as follows:

1. *Test for symmetry with respect to axes and origin.*
2. *Find the points of intersection with the axes.*
3. *Determine the behavior of y for large values of x. Find the horizontal asymptotes.*
4. *Find the vertical asymptotes.*
5. *Determine as closely as possible those regions of the plane in which the curve lies.*
6. *Find and classify the critical points.*

The above is only a general outline of the process to be followed; other steps will often suggest themselves. In some cases the points of inflection may be found and the inflectional tangents drawn, but this is not worth while if the second derivative is complicated. In fact, any step that leads to serious algebraic difficulty should be omitted if adequate information is obtainable otherwise. The elementary method of point-plotting is not usually worth using extensively, but it is often advisable to plot a few points as a check on the analysis.

118. Rational fractions. Consider the function

(1) $$y = \frac{P(x)}{Q(x)},$$

where
$$P(x) = a_0 x^p + a_1 x^{p-1} + \cdots + a_p,$$
$$Q(x) = b_0 x^q + b_1 x^{q-1} + \cdots + b_q \qquad (q \geqq 1).$$

If $q = 0$ (denominator a constant), y is a polynomial: little can be added at this time to the discussion of § 39. If $q = 1$, $p \leqq 2$, the curve is a hyperbola. These cases will therefore be excluded.

Before considering special examples, it will be well to apply our analysis to the rational fraction in general, thus deducing certain results applicable to all curves of this class. The proofs are left to the student.

1. There is no symmetry with respect to Ox.
2. The x-intercepts are the real zeros of P.
3. As x increases in either direction:

(a) If P is of higher degree than $Q(p > q)$, y becomes large, though not necessarily of the same sign as x.

(b) If P and Q are of the same degree, y approaches $\frac{a_0}{b_0}$: the line $y = \frac{a_0}{b_0}$ is an asymptote.

(c) If P is of lower degree than Q, the x-axis is an asymptote.

4. y increases indefinitely as Q approaches zero. Thus we find the real zeros (if any) of the denominator, say r_1, r_2, $\cdots$; the lines $x = r_1$, $x = r_2$, $\cdots$ are asymptotes.

5. The fraction *changes sign* when either P or Q does so. Thus we list the zeros of P and Q (already found in steps 2 and 4), *casting out those of even order*, and note for each of the others a change of sign of y and a passage of the curve across the x-axis: by intersection where $P = 0$, by jumping where $Q = 0$.

6. There may be as many as $p + q - 1$ critical points.

Example: Trace the curve (Examples, § 115)

$$y = \frac{ax^2}{(x - a)(x - 3a)}.$$

1. No symmetry.
2. $(0, 0)$.

3. The line $y = a$ is an asymptote, intersecting the curve at $(\frac{3}{4}a, a)$.

4. The lines $x = a$, $x = 3a$ are asymptotes.

5. The numerator vanishes at $x = 0$, but does not change sign because of the even exponent; the denominator, and hence the fraction, changes sign as x goes through a, $3a$. For large positive x, $x^2 > (x - a)(x - 3a)$ and $y > a$; for large negative x, $y < a$. This limits the curve to the unshaded regions.

6. $y' = \dfrac{2a^2x(3a - 2x)}{(x - a)^2(x - 3a)^2}$. Thus the critical points are $(0, 0)$, $(\frac{3}{2}a, -3a)$.

Figure 104 shows the curve, necessarily somewhat distorted because of the small space available.

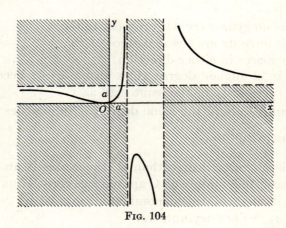

FIG. 104

EXERCISES

In Exs. 1–30, trace the curve.

1. $y = \dfrac{x - 5}{x^2 - 16}$.

2. $y = \dfrac{x - 3}{x^2 - 16}$.

3. $y = \dfrac{x - 1}{x^2 + 1}$.

4. $y = \dfrac{a^3}{x^2 + a^2}$.

5. $y = \dfrac{2x}{1 - x^2}$.

6. $y = \dfrac{2x}{x^2 + 1}$.

7. $y = \dfrac{1 - x^2}{1 + x^2}$.

8. $y = \dfrac{1 + x^2}{1 - x^2}$.

9. $y = \dfrac{x}{(x - 1)(x + 2)}$.

10. $y = \dfrac{1}{x^3 + 2x^2 - 15x}$.

11. $y = \dfrac{x^3}{1 - x^2}.$

12. $y = \dfrac{x^3}{1 - x^4}.$

13. $y = \dfrac{x^3}{1 - x^3}.$

14. $y = \dfrac{x}{x^4 + 1}.$

15. $y = \dfrac{2x - 2}{x^2 - 2x + 5}.$

16. $y = \dfrac{ax^3}{(a - x)^3}.$

17. $y = \dfrac{a^2 x}{(x - a)^2}.$

18. $y = \dfrac{(x^2 - 1)^2}{x}.$

19. $y = \dfrac{x^2 + x + 1}{x^2 - 1}.$

20. $y = \dfrac{(2a - x)^3}{ax}.$

21. $y = \dfrac{(x - a)(x - 3a)^2}{ax}.$

22. $y = \dfrac{x^3 + x^2 - 2}{x^3}.$

23. $y = \dfrac{x^2 - 6}{x(x^2 - 4)}.$

24. $y = \dfrac{(x^2 - 2)^2}{x^2(x + 3)^2}.$

25. $y = \dfrac{(x^2 - 4)^2}{x - 4}.$

26. $y = \dfrac{2x^3 - 10}{x^3 - 3x^2 + 2x}.$

27. $y^3 = \dfrac{x}{x^2 - 1}.$

28. $y^3 = \dfrac{x}{x^2 + 1}.$

29. $y = \dfrac{2(x^2 - 4x + 3)}{x^2}.$

30. $y = \dfrac{x + 1}{x^2(x + 9)}.$

31. Draw a curve from which $\tan 2\theta$ may be read if $\tan \theta$ is given. (Ex. 5.)

32. Draw a curve from which $\sin 2\theta$ may be read if $\tan \theta$ is given. (Ex. 6.)

33. Draw a curve from which $\cos 2\theta$ may be read if $\tan \theta$ is given. (Ex. 7.)

34. Draw a curve from which $\sec 2\theta$ may be read if $\tan \theta$ is given. (Ex. 8.)

35. Draw a curve from which $\sec 2\theta$ may be read if $\cos \theta$ is given.

36. A circular cone is circumscribed about a sphere of radius a. Express the volume of the cone as a function of its radius. Draw the graph,

taking $a = 1$. *Ans.* $V = \dfrac{2}{3}\pi a \cdot \dfrac{r^4}{r^2 - a^2}.$

37. In Ex. 36, graph the altitude as a function of the radius.

Ans. $h = \dfrac{2ar^2}{r^2 - a^2}.$

119. Two-valued functions. Consider now the curve

(1) $$y^2 = \frac{P(x)}{Q(x)},$$

where

$$P(x) = a_0 x^p + a_1 x^{p-1} + \cdots + a_p,$$
$$Q(x) = b_0 x^q + b_1 x^{q-1} + \cdots + b_q.$$

We exclude the case $q = 0$, $p \leq 2$, since then the curve is a conic. By way of general analysis, the following remarks may be made.

1. All curves of this class are symmetric to Ox.
2. The x-intercepts are the real zeros of $P(x)$.

3. For large x (in either direction), y may be imaginary. If not:

(a) If $p < q$, the x-axis is an asymptote.

(b) If $p = q$, there are two horizontal asymptotes.

4. A vertical asymptote falling in a region where y is imaginary may of course be disregarded.

5. y^2 changes from positive to negative, y from real (positive and negative) to imaginary, or vice versa, as x passes through a zero *of odd order* of either $P(x)$ or $Q(x)$.

6. Critical points where y is imaginary are disregarded.

Example: Trace the curve $y^2 = \dfrac{(x+1)(x+2)}{x}$.

1. Symmetric to Ox.

2. $(-1, 0)$, $(-2, 0)$.

3. For large positive x, y is real; for large negative x, y is imaginary.

4. $x = 0$.

5. The fraction changes sign as x goes through -2, -1, 0. At the extreme left $y^2 < 0$; thus the curve is absent when $x < -2$, present when $-2 < x < -1$, absent when $-1 < x < 0$, present when $x > 0$.

6. $2yy' = \dfrac{x^2 - 2}{x^2}$, $y' = \dfrac{x^2 - 2}{2x^2 y}$.

Thus the critical points are at $x = \sqrt{2}$, $y = \pm(\sqrt{2} + 1)$ and $x = -\sqrt{2}$, $y = \pm(\sqrt{2} - 1)$. The tangent is vertical at $(-2, 0)$, $(-1, 0)$. (See Fig. 105.)

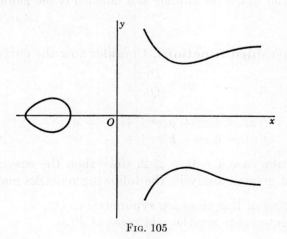

Fig. 105

EXERCISES

In Exs. 1–19, trace the curve.

1. $y^2 = x(x^2 - 9)$.   **2.** $y^2 = (x - 1)^2(x - 4)$.

3. $y^2 = x(4 - x^2)$.   **4.** $y^2 = x^4 - 10x^2 + 9$.

5. $y^2 = \dfrac{x}{1 + x}$.   **6.** $y^2 = \dfrac{x}{1 - x}$.

7. $y^2 = \dfrac{1 - x}{3 + x^2}$.   **8.** $y^2 = \dfrac{x - 2}{x^2 - 3}$.

9. $y^2 = \dfrac{x + 5}{x^2 - 16}$.   **10.** $y^2 = \dfrac{a^3x}{x^2 - a^2}$.

11. $y^2 = \dfrac{x^3}{1 - x^2}$.   **12.** $y^2 = \dfrac{x}{(x + 1)(x - 2)}$.

13. $y^2 = \dfrac{x^2 - x}{x^2 - 4}$.   **14.** $y^2 = \dfrac{(x^2 - 1)(x^2 - 9)}{x(x^2 - 4)}$.

15. $y^2 = \dfrac{(x^2 - 1)(x^2 - 4)}{x^2(x^2 - 9)}$.   **16.** $y^2 = \dfrac{x^2(x - 3)}{(x - 1)(x + 4)^4}$.

17. $y^2 = \dfrac{x(x - 1)(x - 4)}{(x - 2)^3}$.   **18.** $y^2 = \dfrac{x(x + 1)}{(x - 1)^2(x - 2)}$.

19. $y^2 = \dfrac{(x - 1)^2(x - 2)}{x(x + 1)}$.

20. Graph the eccentricity of the conic $cx^2 + y^2 = c$ in terms of c.

21. In Ex. 20, graph the distance from focus to directrix.

22. Draw a curve from which $\cos \theta$ can be measured if $\tan \theta$ is given.

23. Draw the graph of $\sin \theta$ as a function of $\sec \theta$.

24. Draw on the same axes the curves $y^2 = 1 - x^n$ for $n = 1, 2, 3, 4, 5$.

25. Draw on the same axes the curves $x^n + y^n = 1$ for $n = 1, 2, 3, 4,$ 100. (Cf. Exs. 38–39, p. 197.)

120. Oblique and curvilinear asymptotes. Asymptotes parallel to the axes are not the only ones which enter the study of simple algebraic curves. On this topic we confine our attention to an illustrative example and a few exercises.

Example: Sketch the curve

$$(1) \qquad\qquad y = \frac{x^3}{x - 2}.$$

First, proceed as in the earlier portions of this chapter, thus determining that the curve (1) has the following properties:

(a) $y = 0$ only at $x = 0$;

(b) Minimum point at $(3, 27)$;

(c) Inflection point with horizontal tangent at $(0, 0)$;

(*d*) Vertical asymptote $x = 2$;

(*e*) As $x \to \infty$, $y \to \infty$, and as $x \to -\infty$, $y \to \infty$.

The one new tool to be introduced now is based upon carrying out the division of x^3 by $(x - 2)$ on the right in equation (1). That procedure shows that (1) can be rewritten in the form

(2) $y = x^2 + 2x + 4 + \dfrac{8}{x - 2}.$

As $|x| \to \infty$, equation (2) is well approximated by

(3) $y = x^2 + 2x + 4,$

because $\dfrac{8}{x - 2} \to 0$, as $|x| \to \infty$.

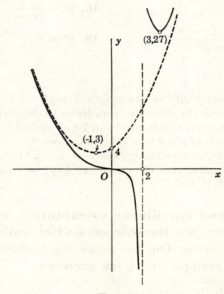

FIG. 106

Let the y of the cubic (2) be denoted by y_1, the y of the parabola (3) by y_2. Then, from

$$y_1 = x^2 + 2x + 4 + \frac{8}{x - 2}$$

and

$$y_2 = x^2 + 2x + 4,$$

we obtain

$$(4) \qquad y_1 - y_2 = \frac{8}{x - 2}.$$

Differentiation of equation (4) yields

$$y'_1 - y'_2 = -\frac{8}{(x - 2)^2}.$$

It is now easy to see that, as $|x| \to \infty$, $(y_1 - y_2) \to 0$ and also $(y'_1 - y'_2) \to 0$. Then we call the parabola (3) a *curvilinear asymptote* to the cubic (1). See Fig. 106.

EXERCISES

In each exercise find and sketch the curvilinear or rectilinear asymptote, and trace the curve whose equation is given.

1. $y = \dfrac{x^3 + 16}{x}$.

2. $y = \dfrac{2 + x - x^3}{x}$.

3. $y = \dfrac{x^2}{x - 3}$.

4. $y = \dfrac{2x^2}{x + 1}$.

5. $y = \dfrac{x^3}{x + 4}$.

6. $y = \dfrac{x^3}{x^2 + 4}$.

7. $y = \dfrac{x^3 + x^2 - 2}{x^2 + 1}$.

8. $y = \dfrac{x^4}{x^2 - 1}$.

9. $y^2 = \dfrac{4x^2 - 1}{x}$.

10. $y^2 = \dfrac{2x^2}{x + 1}$.

11. $y^2 = \dfrac{x^2 - 16}{x - 5}$.

12. $y^2 = \dfrac{x^2 - 16}{x - 3}$.

13. $y^2 = \dfrac{x^2(x^2 - 8)}{(x + 2)^2}$.

14. $y^2 = \dfrac{x^6}{x^3 - 1}$.

15. Ex. 11, p. 203. 16. Ex. 18, p. 203. 17. Ex. 25, p. 203.
18. Ex. 36, p. 203. 19. Ex. 11, p. 205. 20. Ex. 19, p. 205.

121. Singular points. If y is defined implicitly as a function of x by the equation

$$F(x, y) = 0,$$

the derivative in general takes the form of a fraction whose numerator and denominator are functions of x and y: say

$$y' = \frac{N(x, y)}{D(x, y)}.$$

(See, for instance, the examples and exercises under § 30.)

If $N(x, y)$ and $D(x, y)$ both vanish at a point (x, y) on the curve, the slope at that point assumes the indeterminate form $\frac{0}{0}$. A point at which the derivative takes this form is called a *singular point*.

To find the singular points of a curve we must therefore find the values of x and y that satisfy the three equations

(1) $$F(x, y) = 0, \quad N(x, y) = 0, \quad D(x, y) = 0.$$

As we have but two unknowns x and y to satisfy three equations, it appears that a curve will have singular points only if these three equations happen to have one or more common solutions.

For the moment, we consider only curves having a singular point at the origin.* Singularities occurring elsewhere will be discussed in § 124.

122. Determination of tangents by inspection. Let the equation of the curve be written in the form

(1) $$a_0 + b_0x + b_1y + c_0x^2 + c_1xy + c_2y^2 + d_0x^3 + \cdots + g_ny^n = 0:$$

that is, we arrange the left member in ascending powers of x and y.

Differentiating, we find

$$b_0 + b_1y' + 2c_0x + c_1xy' + c_1y + 2c_2yy' + \cdots = 0,$$

$$y' = -\frac{b_0 + 2c_0x + c_1y + \cdots}{b_1 + c_1x + 2c_2y + \cdots}.$$

The origin is on the curve only if $a_0 = 0$. In that case the equation of the tangent at $(0, 0)$ is found by the usual methods to be

$$b_0x + b_1y = 0,$$

provided b_0 and b_1 are not both zero; *i.e.*, the equation of the tangent at the origin may be found by equating to zero the group of terms of the first degree.

If a_0, b_0, and b_1 are all zero, the origin is on the curve and the derivative is indeterminate at that point; hence the origin is a singular point. In this case, since the method of § 33 fails, we proceed as follows.

For convenience let us put

$$c_0x^2 + c_1xy + c_2y^2 \equiv c_2(y - m_1x)(y - m_2x).$$

---

* When a curve has one and only one singular point, that point is usually taken as origin, since this almost always gives the equation of the curve in simplest form.

(The argument needs only slight modification when $c_2 = 0$.) Then (1) becomes

$$c_2(y - m_1x)(y - m_2x) + d_0x^3 + \cdots = 0.$$

The abscissas of the points of intersection of the line

$$y = mx$$

with this curve are given by the equation

(2) $$c_2x^2(m - m_1)(m - m_2) + x^3(d_0 + \cdots) + \cdots = 0.$$

Two roots of this equation are zero: every line $y = mx$ intersects the curve in two coincident points at the origin. But (2) also shows that if we let m approach either m_1 or m_2, the coefficient of x^2 approaches zero; *i.e.*, a third point of intersection of the curve with the line $y = mx$ approaches the origin, and the lines

$$y = m_1x, \quad y = m_2x$$

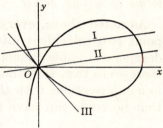

FIG. 107

are both tangent to the curve at the singular point. These lines may of course be real and distinct, real and coincident, or imaginary.

To interpret all this geometrically, let us examine Fig. 107, which exhibits a typical situation—that in which the curve crosses itself. The random line I intersects the curve in three distinct points. As it moves toward position II, two points approach each other and finally coincide—every line through the singular point intersects the curve twice there. Now as the line rotates to position III, the third point approaches, and ultimately, in the position of tangency, attains coincidence with the other two. Evidently in this figure there are two positions of tangency.

Since

$$c_2(y - m_1x)(y - m_2x) \equiv c_0x^2 + c_1xy + c_2y^2,$$

we see that the equations of the two tangents are obtained by *equating the group of terms of second degree to zero*, and factoring the resulting equation.

The argument we have used can be extended to show that if $F(x, y)$ has no terms of degree lower than the k-th, any line through the origin meets the curve there in k points, and the k tangents to the curve at the origin are obtained by *equating the group of terms of lowest degree to zero.*

A point at which there are two tangents (whether distinct, co-incident, or imaginary) is called a *double point;* one at which there are three tangents is a *triple point;* etc. In most cases that arise in practice, a curve having only one singular point, and that a triple or higher-ordered singularity, is much more easily traced from its polar than from its Cartesian equation. Partly for this reason, and partly because they occur much more often, we shall study chiefly curves whose only singularities are double points.

THEOREM: *If the equation $F(x, y) = 0$ contains terms of the second, but none of lower degree, the origin is a double point; the tangents at that point are found by equating to zero, and factoring, the group of terms of second degree.*

As noted above, every line through a double point has at that point two coincident intersections with the curve. Hence a (non-degenerate) cubic cannot have more than one double point; for if there were two, the straight line through those points would have four intersections with the curve. By similar argument, it appears that no cubic can have a triple point.

123. Classification of double points. If the tangents at a double point are real and different, the point is called a *node:* two branches of the curve cross each other, as in Fig. 108.

If the tangents are imaginary, the point is an *isolated point,* or *conjugate point:* there is no other portion of the curve in its vicinity. Such a point is P in Fig. 109.

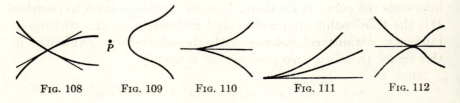

FIG. 108   FIG. 109   FIG. 110   FIG. 111   FIG. 112

If the tangents are real and coincident, the point is either a *cusp* (Figs. 110–111) or a *double cusp* (Fig. 112), or in some instances an isolated point. If the two branches of a cusp lie on opposite sides of the cuspidal tangent, as in Fig. 110, the point is a *cusp of the first kind;* if on the same side, as in Fig. 111, a *cusp of the second kind.*

Example (a): Trace the curve $y^2 = 4x^2(1 - x)$.

1. The curve is symmetric with respect to Ox.

2. The curve intersects the axes at $(0, 0)$, $(1, 0)$.

3. When x is large positive, y is imaginary; x large negative, y large positive and negative.

4. No vertical asymptotes.

5. y is imaginary when $x > 1$.

6. $2yy' = 4(2x - 3x^2)$, $\quad y' = \dfrac{2(2x - 3x^2)}{y}$. Equating the numerator to zero, we appear to find the critical values $x = 0$, $x = \frac{2}{3}$. But by the equation of the curve, when $x = 0$, $y = 0$, so that y' takes the form $\frac{0}{0}$, and the origin is a singular point. The only critical points are $(\frac{2}{3}, \pm\frac{4}{9}\sqrt{3})$.

7. Since the equation contains no terms of degree lower than the second, the origin is a singular point (as also discovered above). Equating to zero the terms of lowest degree, *i.e.*, $y^2 - 4x^2 = 0$, we find the two real distinct tangents $y = \pm 2x$: thus the origin is a node.

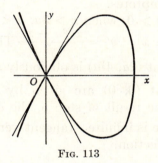

Fig. 113

Example (b): Trace the curve $y^2 = x^4(1 - x^2)$.

1. The curve is symmetric with respect to both axes.

2. The curve crosses the axes at $(0, 0)$, $(\pm 1, 0)$.

3. When x is large, y is imaginary.

4. There are no vertical asymptotes.

5. y is imaginary outside the interval $-1 < x < 1$.

6. $2yy' = 4x^3 - 6x^5$, $\quad y' = \dfrac{x^3(2 - 3x^2)}{y}$. At $(0, 0)$ the derivative is indeterminate, so that the origin is a singular point; the only critical values are $x = \pm\sqrt{\frac{2}{3}}$.

7. The tangents at the origin are the coincident lines $y^2 = 0$ (the x-axis counted twice). Thus the point is either a cusp or a double cusp; by symmetry, it must be the latter.

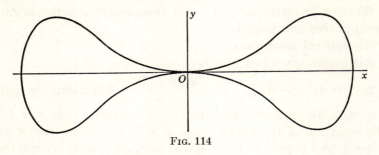

FIG. 114

Example (c): Trace the curve $y^3 = x^2(3a - x)$.

1. There is no symmetry.

2. $(0, 0)$, $(3a, 0)$.

3. When x is large positive or negative, y is large negative or positive.

4. No vertical asymptotes.

5. When $x < 3a$, $y > 0$; when $x > 3a$, $y < 0$.

6. $3y^2y' = 3x(2a - x)$, $\quad y' = \dfrac{x(2a - x)}{y^2}$. The slope is indeterminate at $(0, 0)$; the point $(2a, 4^{\frac{1}{3}}a)$ is obviously a maximum.

7. The tangents at $(0, 0)$ are given by $3ax^2 = 0$: the y-axis counted twice. By the result of step 5, the origin is a cusp.

Evidently the slope is infinite—tangent vertical—at $(3a, 0)$; this is also a point of inflection.

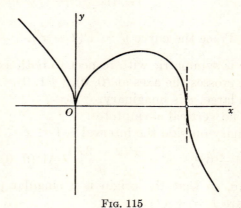

FIG. 115

EXERCISES

In Exs. 1–32, trace the curve.

1. $y^2 = 10x^2 - 7x^3 + x^4$.

2. $a^3y^2 = x^5$.

3. $y^2 = 4x^3 - 3x^4$.

4. $y^2 = 35x^2 + 2x^3 - x^4$.

5. $a^2y^2 = x^2(a^2 - x^2)$.

6. $a^2y^2 = x^2(x^2 - a^2)$.

7. $y^2 = x^2(x + 3)$.

8. $y^2 = x^3(x + 3)$.

9. $y^2 = \dfrac{a^2x^2}{x^2 + a^2}$.

10. $y^2 = \dfrac{a^2x^2}{x^2 - a^2}$.

11. $y^2 = \dfrac{x^4}{1 - x^2}$.

12. $y^2 = \dfrac{x^3}{1 - x^2}$.

13. $y^2 = \dfrac{x^2}{x - 1}$.

14. $y^2 = \dfrac{x^2}{(1 - x)^3}$.

15. $y^2 = \dfrac{x^2}{x^2 + 3x - 4}$.

16. $y^2 = \dfrac{x^2}{(x - 1)^2(x + 4)}$.

17. $y^2 = \dfrac{x^2}{(x - 1)(x - 2)}$.

18. $y^2 = \dfrac{x^2}{(x - 1)^2(x - 2)}$.

19. $y^2 = x^6 - 4x^4 + 3x^2$.

20. $y^2 = 20x^2 - x^5$.

21. $y^2 = \dfrac{x^3}{a - x}$, the cissoid.

22. $y^2 = \dfrac{x^2(3a - x)}{a + x}$, the trisectrix of Maclaurin.

23. $y^2 = \dfrac{x^2(x - 1)}{x - 2}$.

24. $y^2 = \dfrac{x^2(1 - x)}{x - 2}$.

25. $y^2 = \dfrac{x^2(x + 1)}{x - 2}$.

26. $y^2 = \dfrac{x^2(x + 1)}{2 - x}$.

27. $y^3 = x^2(8 - x^2)$.

28. $y^3 = 4x^5 - 5x^4$.

29. $y^3 = \dfrac{a^3x^2}{(x - a)^2}$.

30. $y^3 = \dfrac{x^2}{1 - x^2}$.

31. $y^4 = \dfrac{x^4}{x^2 - 7x + 10}$.

32. $y^2 = \dfrac{x^2(x^2 + 4ax + 3a^2)}{(x - a)^2}$.

In Exs. 33–42, transform the equation to one in polar coördinates. Sketch the curve.

33. $(x^2 + y^2)^2 = 2a^2xy$. *Ans.* $r^2 = a^2 \sin 2\theta$.

34. $(x^2 + y^2)^3 = 4a^2x^2y^2$. *Ans.* $r = a \sin 2\theta$.

35. $(x^2 + y^2)^3 = a^4x^2$. *Ans.* $r^2 = a^2 \cos \theta$.

36. $(x^2 + y^2 + ax)^2 = a^2(x^2 + y^2)$. *Ans.* $r = a(1 - \cos \theta)$.

37. $(x^2 + y^2)(x^2 + y^2 - a^2)^2 = a^4y^2$. *Ans.* $r^2 = a^2(1 + \sin \theta)$.

38. $(x^2 + y^2 - 2ax)^2 = a^2(x^2 + y^2)$. *Ans.* $r = a(1 + 2 \cos \theta)$.

39. $(x^2 + y^2)^3 = 4a^2xy(x^2 - y^2)$. *Ans.* $r^2 = a^2 \sin 4\theta$.

40. $(x^2 + y^2)^5 = 16a^2x^2y^2(x^2 - y^2)^2$. *Ans.* $r = a \sin 4\theta$.

41. $y^4 - 2axy^2 = x^4$. *Ans.* $r = a \sin \theta \tan 2\theta$.

42. $y^4 + 2a^2xy = x^4$. *Ans.* $r^2 = a^2 \tan 2\theta$.

Prove the theorems in Exs. 43–47.

43. The graph of a one-valued algebraic function $y = f(x)$ cannot have a singular point.

44. A line tangent to a cubic at a double point cannot intersect the curve elsewhere.

45. If a quartic curve has a triple point, it can have no other singularity.

46. A quartic cannot have more than three double points. (Assume four; then consider the conic through these four points and a fifth point of the curve.)

47. A straight line through two double points of a quartic cannot intersect the curve elsewhere.

124. Singular points not at the origin. To locate singular points not at the origin, we must look for values of x and y satisfying the three equations (1) of § 121. Of course no rules can be given; we try to solve the simplest-looking pair, then substitute the coördinates of the points thus found in the other equation. The algebra may conceivably be very difficult. But when a curve has only one singularity, if that point is not taken as origin, it is at least, in most cases, placed on a coördinate axis; if there are two, the line joining them is likely to be taken as one of the axes. Thus as a rule the problem of finding singular points is actually rather simple.

THEOREM: *Given the curve*

$$(1) \qquad\qquad y^k = \frac{P(x)}{Q(x)}, \qquad (k \geqq 2)$$

where $P(x)$, $Q(x)$ are polynomials, if $(x - c)^r (r \geqq 2)$ is a factor of $P(x)$, the point $(c, 0)$ is a singular point of the curve.

Further, if $k = 2$, $r = 2$, the point is a node or isolated point; if $k = 2$, $r \geqq 3$, or if $k \geqq 3$, $r = 2$, the point is a cusp with horizontal or vertical tangent respectively, or an isolated point.

To prove the theorem, merely write $P(x)$ in the form

$$P(x) = (x - c)^r R(x),$$

and find y' from (1). Translation of the origin to $(c, 0)$ easily proves the succeeding statements.

Example: Graph the radius of curvature of the hyperbola

$$(2) \qquad\qquad x^2 - y^2 = a^2$$

as a function of x.

In Example (b), § 107 (p. 184), we found

(3)
$$\rho = \frac{(2x^2 - a^2)^{\frac{3}{2}}}{a^2}.$$

First rationalize the equation:

$$a^4\rho^2 = (2x^2 - a^2)^3.$$

1. Symmetric to both axes.
2. $\rho = 0$, $x = \pm\frac{1}{2}\sqrt{2}\, a$.
3. x large positive or negative, ρ large positive and negative.
5. ρ is imaginary for $|x| < \frac{1}{2}\sqrt{2}\, a$.
6. $2a^4\rho\rho' = 12x(2x^2 - a^2)^2$, $\rho' = \dfrac{6x(2x^2 - a^2)^2}{a^4\rho}$. There are no

critical points, since ρ' is indeterminate for $x = \pm\frac{1}{2}\sqrt{2}\, a$, and ρ is imaginary for $x = 0$.

7. By the theorem above, and remarks following, the points $(\pm\frac{1}{2}\sqrt{2}\, a, 0)$ are cusps with the x-axis as cuspidal tangent.

Since we must have $|x| \geqq a$, by (2), and ρ is limited to positive values, the graph of (3) is the part of the curve drawn full.

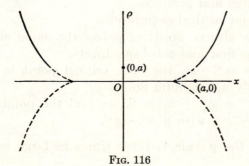

FIG. 116

EXERCISES

In Exs. 1–16, trace the curve.

1. $y^2 = x(x - 4)^2$.
2. $y^2 = x(x + 2)^2$.
3. $y^2 = x^3(x - 1)^2$.
4. $y^2 = x^3(x + 2)^2$.
5. $y^2 = x(x - 1)^3$.
6. $a^3y^2 = x(a^2 - x^2)^2$.
7. $ay^4 = x(a^2 - x^2)^2$.
8. $ay^3 = (x^2 - a^2)^2$.
9. $y^2 = \dfrac{(x - 4)^2}{x}$.
10. $y^2 = \dfrac{(x - 4)^2}{x^3}$.
11. $y^2 = \dfrac{(x^2 - 4a^2)^2}{x^2 - a^2}$.
12. $y^2 = \dfrac{a^4(x^2 - 4a^2)^2}{(x^2 - a^2)^3}$.

13. $y^2 = \dfrac{a^3(x^2 - a^2)^2}{x^5}.$

14. $y^2 = \dfrac{x(x + 1)^2}{(x^2 + 1)^2}.$

15. $y^2 = \dfrac{x^3(x - 1)^2}{(x^2 + 1)^4}.$

16. $y^2 = \dfrac{a^4(x^2 - a^2)}{(x^2 - 4a^2)^2}.$

17. Graph the curvature of the parabola $y^2 = 4ax$ as a function of x.

18. Rationalize the equation $x^{\frac{2}{3}} + y^{\frac{2}{3}} = a^{\frac{2}{3}}$, and trace the curve.

Ans. $(x^2 + y^2 - a^2)^3 + 27a^2x^2y^2 = 0.$

125. Transcendental curves. We have already had from time to time considerable practice in tracing the graphs of transcendental functions; but many curves were excluded by the fact that, at one or more points, the function or its derivative takes an "indeterminate" form. A few simple cases of this sort will now be studied.

Example (a): Trace the curve $y = xe^x$. The curve is shown in Fig. 117 below.

1. There is no symmetry.

2. The curve crosses the axes at $(0, 0)$.

3. As x becomes large and negative, y approaches zero (§ 111); hence the negative x-axis is an asymptote. When x is large and positive, y is large and positive.

4. There are no vertical asymptotes.

5. Since e^x is always positive, y has the same sign as x: the curve lies in the first and third quadrants.

6. Since $y' = xe^x + e^x$, the only critical point is $(-1, \ -e^{-1})$. This is obviously a minimum point.

7. Putting $y'' = xe^x + 2e^x = 0$, we find the point of inflection $x = -2$, $y = -2e^{-2}$, with $y' = -e^{-2}$.

In Fig. 117, the y-scale is three times as large as the x-scale.

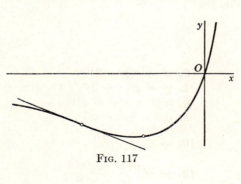

Fig. 117

Example (b): Trace the curve $y = x^2 \ln x$.

1. No symmetry.

2. As $x \to 0^+$, $y \to 0^-$. When $y = 0$, $x = 1$.

3. As $x \to \infty$, $y \to \infty$.

4. There are no asymptotes.

5. For $x > 1$, $y > 0$; for $0 < x < 1$, $y < 0$; for $x < 0$, y is imaginary.

6. $y' = 2x \ln x + x = x(1 + 2 \ln x)$. Because y does not exist for $x = 0$, the only critical value is $x = e^{-\frac{1}{2}}$. Since $x < 0$ leads to imaginary y, the curve starts near the origin. But, $\lim_{x \to 0^+} y' = 0$, so the slope is small for small positive x. The curve drops to a minimum at $(e^{-\frac{1}{2}}, -\frac{1}{2}e^{-1})$, then rises as shown in Fig. 118. The y-scale in the figure is twice the x-scale.

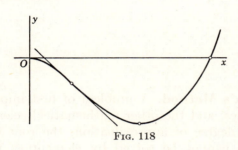

Fig. 118

EXERCISES

In Exs. 1–30, trace the curve.

1. $y = x \ln x$.

2. $y = x^2 e^{-x}$.

3. $y = e^{-x^2}$.

4. $y = xe^{-x^2}$.

5. $y = \dfrac{\ln x}{x}$.

6. $y = xe^{-x}$.

7. $y = \dfrac{e^{-x}}{x}$.

8. $y = \dfrac{1 - \ln x}{x}$.

9. $y = \dfrac{1 + \ln x}{x}$.

10. $y = \dfrac{x}{\ln x}$.

11. $y = x \ln^2 x$.

12. $y = \dfrac{\ln x}{x^3}$.

13. $y = \dfrac{\ln^2 x}{x^2}$.

14. $y = \dfrac{x}{\ln^2 x}$.

15. $y = \dfrac{e^x}{x^2 - 3}$.

16. $y = \dfrac{e^x}{x^2}$.

17. $y = \dfrac{1 + \sin x}{\cos x}$.

18. $y = e^{-x} \sin x$.

19. $y = \dfrac{1 + \tan x}{\cos 2x}$.

20. $y^2 = xe^{-x}$.

21. $y^2 = -xe^{-x}$.

22. $y^2 = e^{-x}(8 - x^2)$.

23. $y^2 = x \ln x$.

24. $y^2 = \ln x$.

25. $y = e^{-\frac{1}{x}}$.

26. $y = e^{\frac{1}{4 - x^2}}$.

27. $y = e^{\frac{1}{x^2 - 4}}$.

28. $y = \dfrac{1}{1 + e^{-\frac{1}{x}}}$.

29. $y = \dfrac{1}{4 - e^{\frac{1}{x}}}$.

30. $y = \dfrac{1}{1 + e^{\frac{1}{x^2 - 1}}}$.

31. For the curve $y = \dfrac{\sin x^2}{x}$, show that $\lim_{x \to \infty} y = 0$, but that $\lim_{x \to \infty} y'$ does not exist; hence that the x-axis is not an asymptote.

32. For the curve $y = e^{-x} \sin e^x$, investigate $\lim_{x \to \infty} y$, $\lim_{x \to \infty} y'$.

33. Sketch $y^2 = -\ln x$.

CHAPTER *15* SOLUTION OF EQUATIONS: NEWTON'S METHOD

126. Newton's Method. A problem of first importance in engineering, physics, and the other mathematical sciences is to find, to any desired degree of approximation, the root or roots of an equation which cannot be solved by elementary methods. This problem can be solved by *Newton's Method*, which we shall now develop.

The method exhibited in this chapter is useful in obtaining approximations to complex roots, as well as real roots, of equations. Only approximations to real roots are treated here.

Let the equation whose root is desired be

$$(1) \qquad\qquad f(x) = 0.$$

Consider the curve

$$(2) \qquad\qquad y = f(x).$$

A root of equation (1) is the x-coördinate of a point at which the curve (2) crosses the x-axis.

For the moment, suppose that a first approximation to the desired root has been obtained by some device, such as one of those to be discussed soon. Newton's Method is essentially one for improving an approximation already obtained. With skilled application, it can be made to yield a root to any desired degree of accuracy.

Let the first approximation to the root be $x = x_1$, as shown in Fig. 119. The point B, where the ordinate AB intersects the curve, has the coördinates $x = x_1$, $y = f(x_1)$. The tangent line at B will intersect the x-axis at C, whose coördinate x_2 may be a better approximation to the desired root than is x_1.

To find x_2, knowing x_1, note that $\overline{BA} = f(x_1)$, $\overline{CA} = x_1 - x_2$, and

$\dfrac{\overline{BA}}{\overline{CA}} = f'(x_1)$. Thus

$$\frac{f(x_1)}{x_1 - x_2} = f'(x_1),$$

which yields

(3) $$x_2 = x_1 - \frac{f(x_1)}{f'(x_1)}.$$

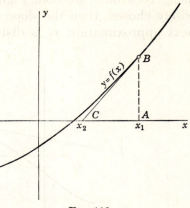

Fig. 119

If we have one approximation x_1, to a root of $f(x) = 0$, equation (3) gives us another approximation x_2, to that root. From x_2 still another approximation x_3 is obtained in the same way by using

$$x_3 = x_2 - \frac{f(x_2)}{f'(x_2)},$$

and the process can be repeated as many times as we wish.

The term $\left[-\dfrac{f(x_1)}{f'(x_1)} \right]$ in equation (3) may be called the correction; it is the difference between the successive approximations x_1 and x_2. Newton's Method is to iterate this process until the correction has vanished to the number of decimal places required in the root.

Examples of the use of the method will follow after a short discussion of the difficulties to be avoided, and some common procedures for obtaining a first approximation to get the wheels of Newton's Method rolling.

127. Difficulties present in Newton's Method. In the basic formula

$$x_2 = x_1 - \frac{f(x_1)}{f'(x_1)}$$

of Newton's Method, the correction term will usually be large if its denominator $f'(x_1)$ is small. Since $f'(x)$ will vanish at a critical point of $y = f(x)$, it is highly desirable to avoid such a point in using Newton's Method. Figure 120 emphasizes that, if x_1 is un-wisely chosen, then the slope of the tangent line is small, and the next approximation x_2 is distressingly far from the desired root.

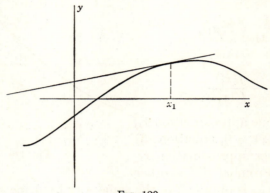

F IG. 120

When two roots of the equation $f(x) = 0$ are close together, it can become quite a problem to avoid the nearby critical point. When the root is a repeated root, both $f(x)$ and $f'(x)$ vanish there. In theory, no difficulty arises because $\dfrac{f(x)}{f'(x)} \to 0$ as x approaches the desired root; in practice, plenty of difficulty arises because we lose significant figures rapidly in computing the small values of $f(x)$ and $f'(x)$ near the root. The cure is usually effected by solving $f'(x) = 0$ for a double root, or $f''(x) = 0$ for a triple root, etc.

Since the solution of equations is a minor, not a major, portion of this course, the difficulties discussed here will be avoided by careful selection of problems to be solved.

128. The first approximation. Three simple methods for ob-taining a first approximation will now be explained.

First method: Plot points on the curve $y = f(x)$ until the root is pinned in between two values of x, one yielding a positive y, the other a negative y. Then approximate the root by interpolation, call that approximation x_1, and proceed with Newton's Method. See Example (a) in the next section.

Second method: If the equation $f(x) = 0$ can be written, by trans-ferring terms from one side to the other, as $g(x) = h(x)$, where

$g(x)$ and $h(x)$ are simple functions, then plot $y_1 = g(x)$ and $y_2 = h(x)$. The x-coördinate of a point of intersection of these curves is a root of the equation $f(x) = 0$.

Example: The equation $x^2 - \sin x = 0$ can be written $x^2 = \sin x$. By sketching $y_1 = x^2$ and $y_2 = \sin x$ on the same figure (Fig. 121), we obtain a first rough approximation, $x_1 = 0.9$.

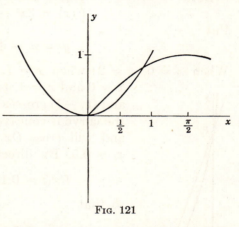

FIG. 121

Third method: If the equation is so simple that its component parts can be obtained readily from a single table, then a first approximation may be obtained from that table by inspection. For example, to start on the solution of the equation $e^{-x} = x$, we may well consult a table of exponentials, pp. 509–514, and look down the appropriate columns until we find where e^{-x} and x are about equal. Thus we soon find that $x_1 = 0.57$ is a good first approximation.

In summary, any of the three methods may be employed or combinations of them can be particularly useful. The first method has many advantages in that the more we know about the curve $y = f(x)$, the more effective will be our use of Newton's Method.

129. Solution of equations. In applying the technique described in this chapter, it should be kept in mind that any approximation x_n is considered exact, once chosen, and that $f(x_n)$ and $f'(x_n)$ are computed on that basis. If tables are used, the precision of the result is restrained by the limited accuracy of the tables. The root can then be approximated more closely only by computing the functions $f(x_n)$ and $f'(x_n)$ to a greater degree of accuracy than that present in the tables.

For a smooth curve, Newton's Method yields the root as closely as desired; it "converges" to the correct value of x. In practice, once we get fairly close to the root, the method converges quite rapidly. Often two or three additional significant figures are picked up in a single step.

Example (a): Find to four decimal places the smaller positive root of the equation

(1)
$$x^3 - 4x + 2 = 0.$$

Here
$$f(x) = x^3 - 4x + 2,$$
$$f'(x) = 3x^2 - 4.$$

Put
$$y = x^3 - 4x + 2.$$

When $x = 0$, $y = 2$; when $x = 1$, $y = -1$. A root lies between $x = 0$ and $x = 1$, Fig. 122. The chord joining $(0, 2)$ and $(1, -1)$ crosses Ox at $x = \frac{2}{3}$; but since $y'' = 6x$, the curve is concave upward (§ 37) in this interval, and will cross Ox to the left of the chord: try $x_1 = 0.5$. By direct substitution, we find

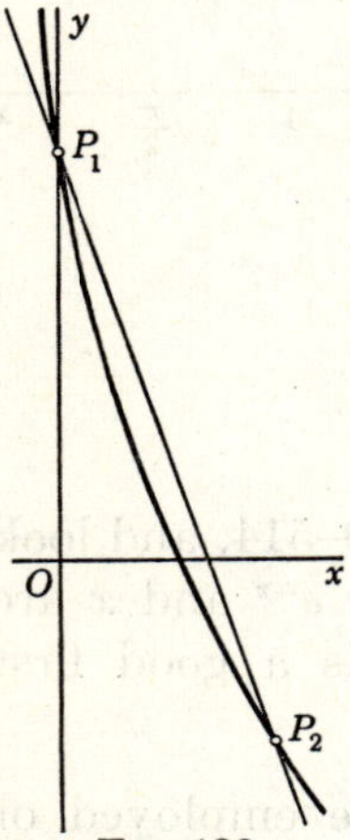

$$f(x_1) = 0.125, \qquad f'(x_1) = -3.25,$$

so that

$$x_2 = 0.5 - \frac{0.125}{-3.25} = 0.5 + 0.04,$$

$$x_2 = 0.54.$$

Next we use x_2 in a similar manner to find

$$f(x_2) = -0.0025, \qquad f'(x_2) = -3.13,$$

and

$$x_3 = 0.54 - \frac{-0.0025}{-3.13} = 0.54 - 0.0008,$$
$$= 0.5392.$$

Finally, from x_3 we obtain

$$x_4 = 0.5392 - \frac{-0.00003}{-3.13} = 0.5392 - 0.00001,$$
$$= 0.5392,$$

so that the desired root, to four decimal places, is $x = 0.5392$.

The work is conveniently arranged in tabular form. Let $y_n = f(x_n)$, $y_n' = f'(x_n)$.

n	x_n	y_n	y_n'	$-y_n/y_n'$
1	0.5	0.125	-3.25	0.04
2	0.54	-0.0025	-3.13	-0.0008
3	0.5392	-0.00003	-3.13	-0.00001

FIG. 122

Example (b): Solve to four places the equation

$$\cos x = x.$$

A first approximation might be found graphically: draw the curves $y = \cos x$, $y = x$ fairly accurately, and measure the abscissa of the point of intersection. This gives, as at least a fair guess, $x_1 = 0.75$. However, if we turn to the table, pp. 515–519, and merely hunt for the place where "Radian" and "Cosine" are nearly equal, we get a much closer approximation: $x_1 = 0.7389$.

Put

$$y = x - \cos x, \qquad y' = 1 + \sin x.$$

Then, by the table,

$$y_1 = -0.0003,$$
$$y_1' = 1 + 0.6734 = 1.67,$$

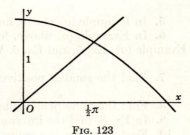

FIG. 123

so that

$$-\frac{y_1}{y_1'} = 0.0002, \qquad x_2 = 0.7391.$$

By interpolation in the table,

$$y_2 = 0.00003, \qquad y_2' = 1.67, \qquad -\frac{y_2}{y_2'} = -0.00002,$$

and the root to four places is

$$x = 0.7391.$$

n	x_n	y_n	y_n'	$-y_n/y_n'$
1	0.7389	−0.0003	1.67	0.0002
2	0.7391	0.00003	1.67	−0.00002

Sometimes the value of x that we have to work with is inconvenient—for example, it may fall within a range where our table functions imperfectly. The difficulty may frequently be removed by one of the following substitutions.

1. $x = -z$. (*Reflection.*) This changes the sign of the roots (employed when the root is negative).

2. $x = z + n$. (*Translation.*) This diminishes the roots by n.

3. $x = \dfrac{z}{n}$. (*Expansion.*) This multiplies the roots by n.

4. $x = nz$. (*Contraction.*) This divides the roots by n.

It is hardly necessary to say that other transformations, including combinations of the above, are allowable and sometimes useful. See, particularly, Exs. 40–42 below.

EXERCISES

1. Find the cube root of 6, without using tables. (Solve $x^3 = 6$.)

Ans. 1.817.

2. Find the cube root of 3, without tables. *Ans.* 1.442.

3. Find the cube root of 441, without tables. *Ans.* 7.61.

4. Find, to three decimal places, the real root of $x^3 + 3x - 2 = 0$.

Ans. 0.596.

5. In Example (*a*) above, find the larger positive root. *Ans.* 1.675.

6. In Example (*a*) above, find the negative root. Add the answers to Example (*a*), Ex. 5, and Ex. 6. What should be the sum, and why?

Ans. $x = -2.214$.

7. Find the smaller positive root of $x^3 - x^2 - 2x + 1 = 0$.

Ans. 0.445.

8. Find the numerically smallest root of $x^3 + 9x^2 + 23x + 14 = 0$.

9. In Ex. 8, find the intermediate root.

10. Find, in inches, the radius of a sphere of volume $\frac{1}{8}$ cu. ft. *Ans.* 3.72.

11. Find, in inches, the radius of a sphere of volume 1 cu. ft. *Ans.* 7.44.

12. The base of a box is a square; the height is 1 ft. less than the side of the base. If the volume is 5 cu. ft., find the dimensions.

Ans. One side = 2.12 ft.

13. A hollow sphere of outer radius 10 in. weighs $\frac{1}{5}$ as much as a solid sphere of the same size and material. Find the inner radius. *Ans.* 9.28 in.

14. Find the edge of a cube, if the volume is tripled when the edge is increased 1 in. *Ans.* 2.26 in.

15. Find the radius of a sphere, if the volume is halved when the radius is decreased by 2 in.

16. A metal sphere of radius 2 in. is recast in the form of a cone of height 2 in. surmounted by a hemisphere of the same radius as the cone. Find the radius of the cone.

Ans. 2.23 in.

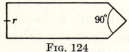

Fig. 124

17. A torpedo has the longitudinal section shown. When submerged it displaces a volume of water equal to a sphere of radius 1 ft. Find r in inches.

18. A cylinder is inscribed in a sphere of radius a. Find the half-altitude of the cylinder, if the volume of the cylinder is half that of the sphere.

Ans. $0.395a$, $0.742a$.

19. A cylinder is inscribed in a cone whose diameter and height are equal. Find the radius of the cylinder, if its volume is $\frac{3}{20}$ that of the cone. (Two answers.)

20. A metal hemisphere of radius 2 is recast as a circular cylinder of base radius r and height 8, surmounted by a hemisphere of radius r. Find r.

Ans. 0.791.

In Exs. 21–38, solve the given equation.

21. $\sin \alpha = \frac{1}{3}\alpha^2$.   **22.** $x^2e^x = 1$.   **23.** $\sin \theta = 1 - \theta$.

24. $\tan x = e^x, 0 \leq x \leq \frac{1}{2}\pi$.   **25.** $x + \ln x = 0$.

26. $e^x \cos x = 1, 0 \leq x \leq \frac{1}{2}\pi$.   **27.** $\tan \theta = 2\theta, 0 \leq \theta \leq \frac{1}{2}\pi$.

28. $x + e^x = 0$.   **29.** $e^x = 3x$.

30. $e^x \sin x = 1, 0 \leq x \leq \frac{1}{2}\pi$.   **31.** $(x + 2)e^{-x} = 1$.

32. $2 \tan \theta = \theta$, the smallest positive root.

33. $\cosh x = 3x$.   **34.** $\sinh x = 2x$.

35. $\cos \alpha = \alpha^2$.   **36.** $\sinh x = \cos x$.

37. $2 \cos \theta + \sqrt{\theta} = 0$.   *Ans.* 141° 53′.

38. $4 \sin \theta + \sqrt{\theta} = 0$.   *Ans.* 208° 29′.

39. A piece of wire 18 in. long is bent in the form of a circular arc, with the ends 1 ft. apart. Find the angle subtended at the center.   *Ans.* 171.5°.

40. Solve Ex. 25 by first passing to the exponential form.

41. Solve Ex. 22 by first passing to the logarithmic form.

42. Solve Ex. 31 by first passing to the logarithmic form.

43. The triangular frame ABC is to be strengthened by braces BD perpendicular to AC and DE perpendicular to AB. If AE must equal DC, find θ.   *Ans.* 40° 59′.

Fig. 125

44. Solve Ex. 43 if AE is to equal BC.   *Ans.* 34° 18.5′.

45. From the corners of a piece of tin 16×10 in. equal squares are cut out and the flaps bent up to form an open box, as in Example (*a*), § 40. If the box is to contain 100 cu. in., find the size of the squares. (Two answers.)

46. Find the eccentricity of an ellipse if the latus rectum is one-fourth the distance between the directrices. (Two answers.)

47. A circular cone is inscribed in a sphere in such a manner that the volume of the cone is one-eighth the volume of the sphere. Find the altitude of the cone.

48. A top, consisting of a cone of radius a and height a surmounted by a hemisphere of the same radius, is whittled down to a cylinder with axis coinciding with that of the top. How much of the material can be saved?   *Ans.* 51.5%.

49. A rope 22 ft. long is tied at the same height to posts 20 ft. apart. Find the "dip" (§ 103).

50. A rope, tied at the same height to posts 20 ft. apart, sags 2 ft. in the middle. Find the length of the rope. Note that $d = a\left(\cosh \dfrac{10}{a} - 1\right)$. (§ 103.)

51. A suspended rope 20 ft. long sags 4 ft. in the middle. If the points of support are at the same height, find the distance between them. (§ 103.)

CHAPTER 16 FUNDAMENTAL INTEGRATION FORMULAS

130. Standard formulas. In this chapter we shall learn how to apply the following basic formulas:

(1) $\displaystyle\int u^n \, du = \frac{u^{n+1}}{n+1} + C, \qquad (n \neq -1)$

(2) $\displaystyle\int \frac{du}{u} = \ln u + C,$

(3) $\displaystyle\int e^u \, du = e^u + C, \qquad$ (3') $\displaystyle\int a^u \, du = \frac{a^u}{\ln a} + C,$

(4) $\displaystyle\int \cos u \, du = \sin u + C,$

(5) $\displaystyle\int \sin u \, du = -\cos u + C,$

(6) $\displaystyle\int \sec^2 u \, du = \tan u + C,$

(7) $\displaystyle\int \csc^2 u \, du = -\cot u + C,$

(8) $\displaystyle\int \sec u \tan u \, du = \sec u + C,$

(9) $\displaystyle\int \csc u \cot u \, du = -\csc u + C,$

(10) $\displaystyle\int \frac{du}{\sqrt{a^2 - u^2}} = \operatorname{Arcsin} \frac{u}{a} + C, \qquad (a > 0)$

(11) $\displaystyle\int \frac{du}{a^2 + u^2} = \frac{1}{a} \operatorname{Arctan} \frac{u}{a} + C,$

(12) $\displaystyle\int u \, dv = uv - \int v \, du.$

It is strongly recommended that each of the formulas be written out by the student in words, and memorized in that form.

The test of the correctness of an integral is that its derivative must be the given integrand. The above formulas are easily verified by differentiation.

131. Formula (1): Powers. Although the power formula was studied in § 50 (which should be thoroughly reviewed), our attention there was necessarily confined to algebraic integrands, so that further work with this formula is needed.

Example: Evaluate $\int \sqrt{\cos 2\theta} \, \sin 2\theta \, d\theta$.

Since
$$d(\cos 2\theta) = -2 \sin 2\theta \, d\theta,$$

we insert the factor -2 and apply (1) with $u = \cos 2\theta$:

$$\int \sqrt{\cos 2\theta} \, \sin 2\theta \, d\theta = -\tfrac{1}{2} \int (\cos 2\theta)^{\frac{1}{2}} (-2 \sin 2\theta) \, d\theta$$

$$= -\frac{1}{2} \cdot \frac{(\cos 2\theta)^{\frac{3}{2}}}{\frac{3}{2}} + C$$

$$= -\tfrac{1}{3}(\cos 2\theta)^{\frac{3}{2}} + C.$$

EXERCISES

Evaluate the following integrals; check by differentiation.

1. $\int \sin^4 y \cos y \, dy.$

2. $\int \cos^3 \theta \sin \theta \, d\theta.$

3. $\int \frac{\sin x}{\cos^3 x} \, dx.$

4. $\int \frac{\cos x \, dx}{(1 + 3 \sin x)^{\frac{3}{2}}}.$

5. $\int \sin 3x \cos 3x \, dx.$ Solve in two ways.

6. $\int \sin \frac{u}{4} \cos \frac{u}{4} \, du.$ Solve in two ways.

7. $\int \sin 3x \sqrt{1 + 4 \cos 3x} \, dx.$

8. $\int (3 - 2 \sin 7\beta)^4 \cos 7\beta \, d\beta.$

9. $\int \tan y \sec^2 y \, dy.$ Solve in two ways.

10. $\int \cot z \csc^2 z \, dz$. Solve in two ways.

11. $\int \csc^2 x(1 + 4 \cot x)^2 \, dx$.

12. $\int \sqrt{1 - 3 \tan \phi} \, \sec^2 \phi \, d\phi$.   **13.** $\int \tan^4 2x \sec^2 2x \, dx$.

14. $\int \dfrac{\csc^2 3x \, dx}{(4 + \cot 3x)^3}$. $Ans. \ \dfrac{1}{6(4 + \cot 3x)^2} + C.$

15. $\int \sec^3 \alpha \tan \alpha \, d\alpha$.

16. $\int (1 - \sec^3 y)^{\frac{3}{2}} \sec^3 y \tan y \, dy$.   **17.** $\int (4 + 3e^x)^2 e^x \, dx$.

18. $\int e^t(1 - 4e^t)^{\frac{1}{2}} \, dt$. $Ans. \ -\frac{1}{6}(1 - 4e^t)^{\frac{3}{2}} + C.$

19. $\int \dfrac{e^{3t} \, dt}{(1 + e^{3t})^2}$.

20. $\int \sin^3 (e^{2x}) \cos (e^{2x}) e^{2x} dx$.   **21.** $\int t^2 \cos^2 (t^3) \sin (t^3) \, dt$.

22. $\int \dfrac{\ln x}{x} \, dx$.   **23.** $\int (1 + \ln x)^3 \, \dfrac{dx}{x}$.

24. $\int \dfrac{du}{u \ln^3 u}$.

25. $\int \dfrac{y \ln (1 + y^2)}{1 + y^2} \, dy$. $Ans. \ \frac{1}{4} \ln^2 (1 + y^2) + C.$

26. $\int \tan^2 (2x + 1) \sec^2 (2x + 1) \, dx$.

27. $\int \dfrac{\cos \left(y - \dfrac{\pi}{4}\right) dy}{\left[1 + 5 \sin \left(y - \dfrac{\pi}{4}\right)\right]^3}$

28. $\int \cot x \ln \sin x \, dx$. $Ans. \ \frac{1}{2} \ln^2 \sin x + C.$

29. $\int \tan \phi \ln \cos \phi \, d\phi$.   **30.** $\int \sqrt{2 - \ln \sec \phi} \, \tan \phi \, d\phi$.

31. $\int \dfrac{(x - 3) \, dx}{(x - 1)^2(x - 5)^2}$. $Ans. \ \dfrac{-1}{2(x^2 - 6x + 5)} + C.$

32. $\int \frac{\sqrt{x+1}}{x^{\frac{5}{2}}}\, dx.$ *Ans.* $-\frac{2}{3}\Big(1+\frac{1}{x}\Big)^{\frac{3}{2}} + C.$

33. $\int \cosh^2 x \sinh x\, dx.$

34. $\int \sinh^3 (1 - 2x) \cosh (1 - 2x)\, dx.$

35. $\int \frac{\cosh t\, dt}{(1 + 2 \sinh t)^4}.$ **36.** $\int \frac{\sinh 3u\, du}{(1 - 2 \cosh 3u)^3}.$

132. Formula (2): Logarithms.

Example (a): Evaluate $\int \frac{x\, dx}{1 - x^2}.$

Formula (2) says, in words: The integral of any quotient *whose numerator is the differential of the denominator* is the logarithm of the denominator. Therefore, we insert the factor -2:

$$\int \frac{x\, dx}{1 - x^2} = -\frac{1}{2}\int \frac{-2x\, dx}{1 - x^2} = -\frac{1}{2}\ln (1 - x^2) + C.$$

The integral in this example can equally well be evaluated in the following manner:

$$\int \frac{x\, dx}{1 - x^2} = -\int \frac{x\, dx}{x^2 - 1} = -\frac{1}{2}\int \frac{2x\, dx}{x^2 - 1}$$

$$= -\tfrac{1}{2}\ln (x^2 - 1) + C_1.$$

Example (b): Evaluate $\int \frac{x^2 - x}{x + 1}\, dx.$

By division we find

$$\frac{x^2 - x}{x + 1} = x - 2 + \frac{2}{x + 1}.$$

Whence

$$\int \frac{x^2 - x}{x + 1}\, dx = \int \Big(x - 2 + \frac{2}{x + 1}\Big)\, dx$$

$$= \tfrac{1}{2}x^2 - 2x + 2 \ln (x + 1) + C.$$

RULE: *As the first step toward integrating a rational fraction, carry out the indicated division until the numerator is of lower degree than the denominator.*

EXERCISES

Evaluate each integral; check by differentiation.

1. $\displaystyle\int \frac{3\,dt}{4t+1}.$

2. $\displaystyle\int \frac{5\,dx}{1-2x}.$

3. $\displaystyle\int \frac{v\,dv}{3v^2-4}.$

4. $\displaystyle\int \frac{y^2\,dy}{y^3-1}.$

5. $\displaystyle\int \frac{(2x+1)\,dx}{x^2+x+1}.$

6. $\displaystyle\int \frac{(3y^2+2)\,dy}{y^3+2y-7}.$

7. $\displaystyle\int \frac{(1+x)^2}{x}\,dx.$

8. $\displaystyle\int \frac{(t^2-1)^2}{t^3}\,dt.$

9. $\displaystyle\int \frac{y\,dy}{(1+y^2)^3}.$

10. $\displaystyle\int \frac{x^2\,dx}{(x^3+8)^2}.$

11. $\displaystyle\int \frac{u+2}{u-1}\,du.$

12. $\displaystyle\int \frac{x(x^2+1)}{x^2-1}\,dx.$

13. $\displaystyle\int \tan x\,dx.$

14. $\displaystyle\int \cot y\,dy.$

15. $\displaystyle\int \frac{\sin\theta\,d\theta}{3+2\cos\theta}.$

16. $\displaystyle\int \frac{\cos 2t\,dt}{4-3\sin 2t}.$

17. $\displaystyle\int \frac{\sec^2 x\,dx}{\tan x+1}.$

18. $\displaystyle\int \frac{\csc^2 2x\,dx}{\sqrt{2+\cot 2x}}.$

19. $\displaystyle\int \frac{(t^2+4)\,dt}{t^3+12t+2}.$

20. $\displaystyle\int \frac{dy}{(1+y)^{\frac{3}{2}}}.$

21. $\displaystyle\int \frac{x^3}{x+1}\,dx.$

22. $\displaystyle\int \frac{x^3+x-4}{x-1}\,dx.$

23. $\displaystyle\int \frac{\sec\theta\tan\theta\,d\theta}{2+3\sec\theta}.$

24. $\displaystyle\int \frac{\csc x\cot x\,dx}{1+\csc x}.$

25. $\displaystyle\int \frac{e^x\,dx}{1+e^x}.$

26. $\displaystyle\int \frac{e^{2t}\,dt}{e^{2t}-4}.$

27. $\displaystyle\int \frac{e^{2x}\,dx}{1+e^x}.$

28. $\displaystyle\int \frac{e^{2v}-e^{-2v}}{e^{2v}+e^{-2v}}\,dy.$

29. $\displaystyle\int \frac{dv}{v\ln v}.$

30. $\displaystyle\int \frac{dt}{t(1+\ln t)}.$

31. $\displaystyle\int \frac{\sin 2\theta\,d\theta}{1+\sin^2\theta}.$

32. $\displaystyle\int \frac{\sec^2 x\tan x\,dx}{4+\tan^2 x}.$

33. $\int \dfrac{(x+6)\,dx}{(x+2)^2}$. $\qquad$ *Hint:* $\dfrac{x+6}{(x+2)^2} = \dfrac{(x+2)+4}{(x+2)^2}$.

34. $\int \dfrac{dx}{\sqrt{x}(1+\sqrt{x})}$. $\qquad$ *Ans.* $2\ln(1+\sqrt{x}) + C$.

35. $\int \dfrac{dx}{x(1+x^2)}\left[\dfrac{1}{x(1+x^2)} = \dfrac{(1+x^2)-x^2}{x(1+x^2)}\right]$ *Ans.* $\tfrac{1}{2}\ln\dfrac{x^2}{1+x^2} + C$.

36. $\int \sec\theta\,d\theta$. (Multiply and divide by $\sec\theta + \tan\theta$.)
$\qquad$ *Ans.* $\ln(\sec\theta + \tan\theta) + C$.

37. Ex. 36 by a second method. (Multiply and divide by $\sec\theta - \tan\theta$.)

38. $\int \csc\theta\,d\theta$ by two methods. (Cf. Exs. 36–37.)
$\qquad$ *Ans.* $\ln(\csc\theta - \cot\theta) + C$.

39. $\int \dfrac{d\phi}{\cos 5\phi}$. $\qquad\qquad$ **40.** $\int \dfrac{dx}{\sin 3x}$.

41. $\int \dfrac{1-\cos t}{\cos t}\,dt$. $\qquad$ **42.** $\int \dfrac{4+\sin 3x}{\sin 3x}\,dx$.

43. $\int \dfrac{\sin x - \cot x}{\sin^2 x}\,dx$. $\qquad$ **44.** $\int \dfrac{\cos y + \tan y}{\cos^2 y}\,dy$.

45. $\int \tanh 3x\,dx$. $\qquad\qquad$ **46.** $\int \coth \tfrac{1}{4}x\,dx$.

133. Formulas (3)–(3′): Exponential functions.

Example (a): Evaluate $\int \sin 2x\, e^{\cos 2x}\,dx$.

If we insert the factor -2, this can be evaluated by (3), with $u = \cos 2x$, $du = -2\sin 2x\,dx$:

$$\int \sin 2x\, e^{\cos 2x}\,dx = -\tfrac{1}{2}\int e^{\cos 2x}\,(-2\sin 2x)\,dx = -\tfrac{1}{2}e^{\cos 2x} + C.$$

Example (b): Evaluate $\int \dfrac{dx}{3^{2x}}$.

Since
$$\frac{d}{dx}\,a^u = a^u(\ln a)\frac{du}{dx},$$

we proceed as follows:

$$\int \frac{dx}{3^{2x}} = \int 3^{-2x}\,dx = -\frac{1}{2}\frac{3^{-2x}}{\ln 3} + C.$$

EXERCISES

Evaluate the following integrals.

1. $\displaystyle\int e^{-2t}\,dt.$
2. $\displaystyle\int e^{4x}\,dx.$
3. $\displaystyle\int \frac{dy}{e^y}.$

4. $\displaystyle\int xe^{-x^2}\,dx.$
5. $\displaystyle\int 2^x\,dx.$
6. $\displaystyle\int 10^{-2x}\,dx.$

7. $\displaystyle\int (e^x + e^{-x})^2\,dx.$
8. $\displaystyle\int e^{3y}(1 + e^{3y})^4\,dy.$

9. $\displaystyle\int t^2 e^{2t^3}\,dt.$
10. $\displaystyle\int ue^{4u^2+3}\,du.$

11. $\displaystyle\int \frac{e^\theta\,d\theta}{(4e^\theta + 3)^2}.$
12. $\displaystyle\int e^{2x}\sqrt{1 - e^{2x}}\,dx.$

13. $\displaystyle\int \frac{(e^v - 1)^2}{e^v}\,dy.$
14. $\displaystyle\int \frac{e^{2t}\,dt}{1 + 4e^{2t} + 4e^{4t}}.$

15. $\displaystyle\int \cos 3x\; e^{\sin 3x}\,dx.$
16. $\displaystyle\int (1 + e^{\tan x})\sec^2 x\,dx.$

17. $\displaystyle\int \frac{e^{\cot\theta}\,d\theta}{\sin^2\theta}.$
18. $\displaystyle\int \frac{e^{-\frac{1}{x}}}{x^2}\,dx.$

19. $\displaystyle\int 3e^{2\ln x}\,dx.$ $Ans.\ x^3 + C.$

20. $\displaystyle\int \ln e^{2x}\,dx.$ $Ans.\ x^2 + C.$

21. $\displaystyle\int \sinh u\,du = \cosh u + C.$
22. $\displaystyle\int \cosh u\,du = \sinh u + C.$

23. $\displaystyle\int 4\sinh 3y\,dy.$
24. $\displaystyle\int 3\cosh 2t\,dt.$

25. $\displaystyle\int \tanh u\,du.$
26. $\displaystyle\int e^{-x}\cosh x\,dx.$

27. $\displaystyle\int t\cosh (3t^2)\,dt.$
28. $\displaystyle\int \coth v\,dv.$

29. $\displaystyle\int (\cosh^2 t - \sinh^2 t)\,dt.$
30. $\displaystyle\int (\cosh^2 t + \sinh^2 t)\,dt.$

134. Formulas (4)–(9): Trigonometric functions.

Example (a): $\displaystyle\int x\sin x^2\,dx = \tfrac{1}{2}\int \sin x^2 \cdot 2x\,dx$

$$= -\tfrac{1}{2}\cos x^2 + C.$$

Example (b): $\displaystyle\int \tan^2\theta\,d\theta = \int (\sec^2\theta - 1)\,d\theta = \tan\theta - \theta + C.$

EXERCISES

Evaluate the integrals below.

1. $\displaystyle\int \cos 3\beta \, d\beta.$

2. $\displaystyle\int \sin \tfrac{1}{2}t \, dt.$

3. $\displaystyle\int \csc^2 4x \, dx.$

4. $\displaystyle\int \sec^2 3x \, dx.$

5. $\displaystyle\int \sec 2y \tan 2y \, dy.$

6. $\displaystyle\int \csc 4x \cot 4x \, dx.$

7. $\displaystyle\int \frac{\cos 4x \, dx}{3 - 2 \sin 4x}.$

8. $\displaystyle\int \frac{\sin t \cos t \, dt}{1 + 3 \cos 2t}.$

9. $\displaystyle\int \tan 2u \sec^2 2u \, du.$

10. $\displaystyle\int \frac{\cos \phi \, d\phi}{\sin^4 \phi}.$

11. $\displaystyle\int \frac{\sin \ln x}{x} \, dx.$

12. $\displaystyle\int \frac{dy}{e^y \cos^2 (e^{-y})}.$

13. $\displaystyle\int \tan \left(\theta - \frac{\pi}{6}\right) d\theta.$

14. $\displaystyle\int \cot \left(\phi - \frac{\pi}{4}\right) d\phi.$

15. $\displaystyle\int \cot^2 z \, dz.$

16. $\displaystyle\int \tan^2 ky \, dy.$

17. $\displaystyle\int (1 - \tan \theta)^2 \, d\theta.$

18. $\displaystyle\int (1 + \cot x)^2 \, dx.$

19. $\displaystyle\int \frac{\sin t + \cos t}{\sin t} \, dt.$

20. $\displaystyle\int \frac{y \cos (y^2) \, dy}{\sin (y^2)}.$

21. $\displaystyle\int \sec^2 \beta \tan^2 \beta \, d\beta.$

22. $\displaystyle\int \frac{\sin^2 x \, dx}{1 - \cos x}.$

23. $\displaystyle\int \frac{\cos^2 \alpha}{1 + \sin \alpha} \, d\alpha.$

24. $\displaystyle\int \frac{\cos^3 \theta}{1 + \sin \theta} \, d\theta.$

25. $\displaystyle\int \frac{\sin^3 u}{1 - \cos u} \, du.$

26. $\displaystyle\int \frac{\cos^2 x \, dx}{\sin^4 x}.$

27. $\displaystyle\int \sin 3y \sin 6y \, dy.$

28. $\displaystyle\int (\cos^4 t - \sin^4 t) \, dt.$

29. $\displaystyle\int \frac{\sec^2 3u \, du}{1 - \tan 3u}.$

30. $\displaystyle\int \frac{\csc^2 x \, dx}{\cot x - 1}.$

Use the "double angle" formulas of Trigonometry in Exs. 31–34.

31. $\displaystyle\int \frac{1 + \cos 2y}{1 - \cos 2y} \, dy.$

32. $\displaystyle\int \frac{\tan w}{1 - \tan^2 w} \, dw.$

33. $\displaystyle\int \sin \beta \, (1 + \cos 2\beta)^3 \, d\beta.$

34. $\displaystyle\int \frac{(1 - \cos 4x) \, dx}{(1 + \cos 4x)^2}.$

135. Transformation by trigonometric formulas. Many trigonometric integrals can be evaluated after transformations of the integrand, requiring only the most familiar trigonometric formulas. If instead of memorizing the types listed below, the student will observe the character of the transformations employed, he can easily pick the requisite method in any given case.

Type I: $\int \sin^m x \cos^n x\, dx$, *where either m or n is a positive odd integer.*

For definiteness, let n be a positive odd integer. Writing the integral in the form $\int \sin^m x \cos^{n-1} x \cdot \cos x\, dx$, and putting

$$\cos^2 x = 1 - \sin^2 x,$$

we obtain a series of powers of $\sin x$ each multiplied by $\cos x\, dx$. Similarly when m is positive odd.

Example (a):

$$
\begin{aligned}
\int \sin^2 x \cos^3 x\, dx &= \int \sin^2 x \cos^2 x \cdot \cos x\, dx \\
&= \int \sin^2 x (1 - \sin^2 x) \cos x\, dx \\
&= \int \sin^2 x \cos x\, dx - \int \sin^4 x \cos x\, dx \\
&= \tfrac{1}{3} \sin^3 x - \tfrac{1}{5} \sin^5 x + C.
\end{aligned}
$$

Type II: $\int \tan^n x\, dx$, *or* $\int \cot^n x\, dx$, *where n is an integer.*

By use of the formulas

$$\tan^2 x = \sec^2 x - 1, \qquad \cot^2 x = \csc^2 x - 1,$$

these integrals reduce to forms that can be evaluated.

Example (b):

$$
\begin{aligned}
\int \tan^4 x\, dx &= \int \tan^2 x (\sec^2 x - 1)\, dx \\
&= \int \tan^2 x \sec^2 x\, dx - \int \tan^2 x\, dx \\
&= \tfrac{1}{3} \tan^3 x - \int (\sec^2 x - 1)\, dx \\
&= \tfrac{1}{3} \tan^3 x - \tan x + x + C.
\end{aligned}
$$

Type III: $\int \tan^m x \sec^n x \, dx$, *or* $\int \cot^m x \csc^n x \, dx$, *where n is a positive even integer.*

Example (c):

$$\int \tan^2 x \sec^4 x \, dx = \int \tan^2 x \sec^2 x (1 + \tan^2 x) \, dx$$

$$= \int \tan^2 x \sec^2 x \, dx + \int \tan^4 x \sec^2 x \, dx$$

$$= \tfrac{1}{3} \tan^3 x + \tfrac{1}{5} \tan^5 x + C.$$

Type IV: $\int \sin^m x \cos^n x \, dx$, *where both m and n are positive even integers.*

When m and n are *both even*, it is easily seen that the method used for Type I is useless. Instead, we use the formulas

$$\sin^2 x = \tfrac{1}{2}(1 - \cos 2x), \qquad \cos^2 x = \tfrac{1}{2}(1 + \cos 2x),$$
$$\sin x \cos x = \tfrac{1}{2} \sin 2x,$$

repeatedly if necessary.

Example (d):

$$\int \sin^4 \theta \cos^2 \theta \, d\theta = \int (\sin^2 \theta \cos^2 \theta) \sin^2 \theta \, d\theta$$

$$= \tfrac{1}{8} \int \sin^2 2\theta \, (1 - \cos 2\theta) \, d\theta$$

$$= \tfrac{1}{8} \int \sin^2 2\theta \, d\theta - \tfrac{1}{8} \int \sin^2 2\theta \cos 2\theta \, d\theta$$

$$= \tfrac{1}{16} \int (1 - \cos 4\theta) \, d\theta - \tfrac{1}{48} \sin^3 2\theta$$

$$= \tfrac{1}{16}\theta - \tfrac{1}{64} \sin 4\theta - \tfrac{1}{48} \sin^3 2\theta + C.$$

EXERCISES

Evaluate each of the following integrals. •

1. $\int \sin^3 x \, dx.$

Ans. $\tfrac{1}{3} \cos^3 x - \cos x + C.$

2. $\int \cos^3 x \, dx.$

Ans. $\sin x - \tfrac{1}{3} \sin^3 x + C.$

3. $\int \cos^3 y \sin^3 y \, dy.$

Ans. $\tfrac{1}{4} \sin^4 y - \tfrac{1}{6} \sin^6 y + C_1,$
or $\tfrac{1}{6} \cos^6 y - \tfrac{1}{4} \cos^4 y + C_2.$

4. Do Ex. 3 with the aid of the formula: $\sin y \cos y = \frac{1}{2} \sin 2y$.

$\qquad$ *Ans.* $\frac{1}{48} \cos^3 2y - \frac{1}{16} \cos 2y + C_3$.

5. $\displaystyle\int \cos^2 t \sin^5 t \, dt.$ $\qquad$ *Ans.* $-\frac{1}{3} \cos^3 t + \frac{2}{5} \cos^5 t - \frac{1}{7} \cos^7 t + C.$

6. $\displaystyle\int \sin^2 u \cos^5 u \, du.$ $\qquad$ *Ans.* $\frac{1}{3} \sin^3 u - \frac{2}{5} \sin^5 u + \frac{1}{7} \sin^7 u + C.$

7. $\displaystyle\int \cos^5 2\theta \, d\theta.$ $\qquad$ *Ans.* $\frac{1}{2} \sin 2\theta - \frac{1}{3} \sin^3 2\theta + \frac{1}{10} \sin^5 2\theta + C.$

8. $\displaystyle\int \sin^5 3\theta \, d\theta.$ $\qquad$ *Ans.* $-\frac{1}{3} \cos 3\theta + \frac{2}{9} \cos^3 3\theta - \frac{1}{15} \cos^5 3\theta + C.$

9. $\displaystyle\int \frac{\sin^3 v \, dv}{\cos^2 v}.$ $\qquad\qquad$ **10.** $\displaystyle\int \frac{\cos^3 v \, dv}{\sin^4 v}.$

11. $\displaystyle\int \frac{\sin^5 2y \, dy}{\cos^2 2y}.$ $\qquad\qquad$ **12.** $\displaystyle\int \frac{\cos^5 t \, dt}{\sin^2 t}.$

13. $\displaystyle\int \sin^7 x \, dx.$ $\qquad\qquad$ **14.** $\displaystyle\int \cos x (1 - \sin x)^4 \, dx.$

15. $\displaystyle\int \sin^2 x \, dx.$ $\qquad\qquad$ *Ans.* $\frac{1}{2} x - \frac{1}{4} \sin 2x + C.$

16. $\displaystyle\int \cos^2 y \, dy.$ $\qquad\qquad$ *Ans.* $\frac{1}{2} y + \frac{1}{4} \sin 2y + C.$

17. $\displaystyle\int \sin^2 \beta \cos^2 \beta \, d\beta.$ (See Ex. 4.) $\qquad$ *Ans.* $\frac{1}{8} \beta - \frac{1}{32} \sin 4\beta + C.$

18. $\displaystyle\int \cos^4 2\theta \, d\theta.$ $\qquad\qquad$ *Ans.* $\frac{3}{8} \theta + \frac{1}{8} \sin 4\theta + \frac{1}{64} \sin 8\theta + C.$

19. $\displaystyle\int \sin x \sqrt{1 + 4 \cos x} \, dx.$

20. $\displaystyle\int \frac{\cos^3 \theta \, d\theta}{\sin \theta}.$ $\qquad\qquad$ **21.** $\displaystyle\int \frac{t \sin^3 (t^2) \, dt}{\cos (t^2)}.$

22. $\displaystyle\int \sin^2 z \sin^3 2z \, dz.$ $\qquad\qquad$ **23.** $\displaystyle\int \cos^3 y \sin^3 2y \, dy.$

24. $\displaystyle\int \sin^5 u \cos^5 u \, du.$ $\qquad\qquad$ **25.** $\displaystyle\int \sin^4 x \cos^4 x \, dx.$

26. $\displaystyle\int \sin^6 \phi \cos^6 \phi \, d\phi.$ $\qquad\qquad$ **27.** $\displaystyle\int \sin^2 \theta \cos^4 \theta \, d\theta.$

28. $\displaystyle\int \frac{\sin^2 y}{\cot y} \, dy.$

29. $\displaystyle\int \tan^3 \theta \, d\theta.$ $\qquad$ *Ans.* $\frac{1}{2} \sec^2 \theta - \ln \sec \theta + C_1$

$\qquad\qquad\qquad\qquad\qquad = \frac{1}{2} \tan^2 \theta - \ln \sec \theta + C_2$

$\qquad\qquad\qquad\qquad\qquad = \frac{1}{2} \sec^2 \theta + \ln \cos \theta + C_3,$ etc.

30. $\int \cot^4 y \, dy.$ *Ans.* $-\frac{1}{3} \cot^3 y + \cot y + y + C.$

31. $\int \tan^2 4x \, dx.$ **32.** $\int \cot^3 y \, dy.$

33. $\int \tan^5 x \, dx.$ *Ans.* $\frac{1}{4} \tan^4 x - \frac{1}{2} \tan^2 x - \ln \cos x + C.$

34. $\int \tan^6 x \, dx.$ *Ans.* $\frac{1}{5} \tan^5 x - \frac{1}{3} \tan^3 x + \tan x - x + C.$

35. $\int \sec^4 \alpha \, d\alpha.$ **36.** $\int \csc^4 \alpha \, d\alpha.$

37. $\int \tan^4 z \sec^2 z \, dz.$ **38.** $\int \cot^3 z \csc^2 z \, dz.$

39. $\int \sec^4 y \tan^4 y \, dy.$ **40.** $\int \csc^6 u \, du.$

136. Formulas (10)–(11): Inverse trigonometric functions.

Example (a): $\displaystyle \int \frac{dx}{\sqrt{9 - 4x^2}} = \frac{1}{2} \int \frac{2 \, dx}{\sqrt{9 - (2x)^2}}$

$$= \frac{1}{2} \operatorname{Arcsin} \frac{2x}{3} + C.$$

Example (b): $\displaystyle \int \frac{dx}{x^2 + 2x + 5} = \int \frac{dx}{(x + 1)^2 + 4}$

$$= \frac{1}{2} \operatorname{Arctan} \frac{x + 1}{2} + C.$$

Example (c): $\displaystyle \int \frac{dx}{x\sqrt{1 - 4 \ln^2 x}} = \int \frac{\dfrac{dx}{x}}{\sqrt{1 - 4 \ln^2 x}}$

$$= \frac{1}{2} \int \frac{2\dfrac{dx}{x}}{\sqrt{1 - 4 \ln^2 x}}$$

$$= \frac{1}{2} \operatorname{Arcsin} (2 \ln x) + C.$$

EXERCISES

1. $\displaystyle \int \frac{dx}{9 + x^2}.$ **2.** $\displaystyle \int \frac{dy}{\sqrt{16 - y^2}}.$ **3.** $\displaystyle \int \frac{dv}{4 + 9v^2}.$

4. $\displaystyle \int \frac{dt}{\sqrt{3 - 4t^2}}.$ **5.** $\displaystyle \int \frac{y \, dy}{4 + y^2}.$ **6.** $\displaystyle \int \frac{x \, dx}{\sqrt{16 - 25x^2}}.$

7. $\displaystyle\int \frac{y\,dy}{4 + y^4}.$ **8.** $\displaystyle\int \frac{x\,dx}{\sqrt{16 - 25x^4}}.$ **9.** $\displaystyle\int \frac{dx}{x^2 + 2x + 10}.$

10. $\displaystyle\int \frac{dt}{4t^2 + 4t + 5}.$ **11.** $\displaystyle\int \frac{dy}{\sqrt{3 + 4y - 4y^2}}.$ **12.** $\displaystyle\int \frac{dy}{4y - 25 - 4y^2}.$

13. $\displaystyle\int \frac{x + 4}{x^2 + 9}\,dx.$ **14.** $\displaystyle\int \frac{(2\beta - 1)\,d\beta}{16\beta^2 + 8\beta + 37}.$ **15.** $\displaystyle\int \frac{\cos\phi\,d\phi}{3 + \sin^2\phi}.$

16. $\displaystyle\int \frac{e^{2x}\,dx}{\sqrt{7 - e^{4x}}}.$ **17.** $\displaystyle\int \frac{x^2 - 3}{x^2 + 1}\,dx.$ **18.** $\displaystyle\int \frac{y^3\,dy}{4 + y^2}.$

19. $\displaystyle\int \frac{\sec^2\theta\,d\theta}{\sqrt{5 - \sec^2\theta}}.$ *Ans.* Arcsin $(\tfrac{1}{2}\tan\theta) + C.$

20. $\displaystyle\int \frac{du}{\sqrt{9e^{-2u} - 1}}.$ *Ans.* Arcsin $(\tfrac{1}{3}e^u) + C.$

21. $\displaystyle\int \sin(\text{Arctan } x)\,dx.$ *Ans.* $\sqrt{1 + x^2} + C.$

22. $\displaystyle\int \frac{\csc^2\phi\cot\phi\,d\phi}{4 - \csc^2\phi}.$

23. $\displaystyle\int \frac{(3x - 2)\,dx}{x^2 + 2x + 17}.$ Write as $\displaystyle\int \frac{3(x + 1) - 5}{(x + 1)^2 + 16}\,dx.$

Ans. $\tfrac{3}{2}\ln(x^2 + 2x + 17) - \tfrac{5}{4}$ Arctan $\dfrac{x + 1}{4} + C.$

24. $\displaystyle\int \frac{(4x - 15)\,dx}{x^2 - 4x + 13}.$ See Ex. 23.

25. $\displaystyle\int \frac{(10y + 11)\,dy}{4y^2 - 4y + 5}.$ **26.** $\displaystyle\int \frac{x\,dx}{\sqrt{-7 - 8x - x^2}}.$

27. $\displaystyle\int \frac{u(u^2 + 4)\,du}{u^4 + 9}.$ **28.** $\displaystyle\int \frac{\sin\theta\,(\cos\theta + 4)\,d\theta}{1 + \cos^2\theta}.$

29. $\displaystyle\int \frac{x^4\,dx}{x^2 + 1}.$ **30.** $\displaystyle\int \frac{x^3\,dx}{x^2 + 1}.$

31. $\displaystyle\int \frac{e^{4x}\,dx}{\sqrt{9 - e^{4x}}}.$ **32.** $\displaystyle\int \frac{e^{2t}\,dt}{9 + 25e^{4t}}.$

33. $\displaystyle\int \frac{(3\sin\theta - 7)\cos\theta\,d\theta}{4\sin^2\theta + 9}.$ **34.** $\displaystyle\int \frac{(1 + \tan x)\,dx}{\cos^2 x\,\sqrt{5 - 3\tan^2 x}}.$

35. $\displaystyle\int \frac{dt}{t\,\sqrt{t^2 - a^2}}.$ *Ans.* $-\dfrac{1}{a}$ Arcsin $\dfrac{a}{t} + C.$

36. $\displaystyle\int \frac{\tan\theta\,d\theta}{\sec\theta + 4\cos\theta}.$

137. Formula (12): Integration by parts. From the formula for the differential of a product,

$$d(uv) = u\,dv + v\,du,$$

we find, integrating both sides,

$$uv = \int u\,dv + \int v\,du.$$

Transposing, we obtain formula (**12**):

$$\int u\,dv = uv - \int v\,du.$$

Integration by this formula is called *integration by parts*.

Example (a): Evaluate $\int x \sin 2x\,dx$.

Let

$$u = x, \qquad dv = \sin 2x\,dx,$$

$$du = dx, \qquad v = \int \sin 2x\,dx = -\tfrac{1}{2}\cos 2x.$$

(It is a fact, which should be verified by the student, that in evaluating $\int dv = v$ the constant of integration may be omitted, since the final result is the same with or without it.) Hence

$$\int x \sin 2x\,dx = -\tfrac{1}{2}x \cos 2x + \tfrac{1}{2}\int \cos 2x\,dx$$

$$= -\tfrac{1}{2}x \cos 2x + \tfrac{1}{4}\sin 2x + C.$$

Only by experience and practice can one develop skill in telling when integration by parts is indicated. Further, when it has been decided to try the method, no rules can be laid down telling how to choose u and dv (except that, obviously, dv must be so chosen that $\int dv$ can be evaluated). However, in integrating a product, this method gives us a chance to differentiate one of the factors. In Example (*a*), differentiating x, we replace it by 1; differentiating $\sin x$, we replace it by $\cos x$. The former change, being more drastic, seems more promising. By looking ahead a bit in this way, we can usually make the right choice in the first instance.

Example (b): Evaluate $\int \sec^3 \theta\,d\theta$.

Take

$$u = \sec \theta, \qquad dv = \sec^2 \theta\,d\theta,$$

$$du = \sec \theta \tan \theta\,d\theta, \qquad v = \tan \theta:$$

$$\int \sec^3 \theta \, d\theta = \sec \theta \tan \theta - \int \sec \theta \tan^2 \theta \, d\theta$$

$$= \sec \theta \tan \theta - \int \sec^3 \theta \, d\theta + \int \sec \theta \, d\theta.$$

Evaluate the last integral (Ex. 36, p. 231) and transpose the next-to-last to the other side:

$$2 \int \sec^3 \theta \, d\theta = \sec \theta \tan \theta + \ln (\sec \theta + \tan \theta) + C,$$

$$\int \sec^3 \boldsymbol{\theta} \, \boldsymbol{d\theta} = \tfrac{1}{2} \sec \boldsymbol{\theta} \tan \boldsymbol{\theta} + \tfrac{1}{2} \ln (\sec \boldsymbol{\theta} + \tan \boldsymbol{\theta}) + C_1.$$

Example (c): Evaluate $\int e^x \sin 2x \, dx.$

Take

$$u = e^x, \qquad\qquad dv = \sin 2x \, dx,$$
$$du = e^x \, dx, \qquad\quad v = -\tfrac{1}{2} \cos 2x:$$

(1) $\qquad \int e^x \sin 2x \, dx = - \tfrac{1}{2} e^x \cos 2x + \tfrac{1}{2} \int e^x \cos 2x \, dx.$

Since this new integral is no simpler than the original, let us return to the given integral and take

$$u = \sin 2x, \qquad\qquad dv = e^x \, dx,$$
$$du = 2 \cos 2x \, dx, \qquad\quad v = e^x:$$

(2) $\qquad \int e^x \sin 2x \, dx = e^x \sin 2x - 2 \int e^x \cos 2x \, dx.$

Here again we have failed temporarily, but since the troublesome integral is exactly the same one that appeared in (1), it may be *eliminated from the two equations:* multiplying (1) by 4 and adding to (2), we find

$$5 \int e^x \sin 2x \, dx = -2e^x \cos 2x + e^x \sin 2x + C,$$

$$\int e^x \sin 2x \, dx = - \tfrac{2}{5} e^x \cos 2x + \tfrac{1}{5} e^x \sin 2x + C_1.$$

EXERCISES

1. $\int x e^{-x} \, dx.$

2. $\int y e^{3y} \, dy.$

3. $\int \ln u \, du.$

4. $\int x \ln x \, dx.$

5. $\int x \cos 3x \, dx.$

6. $\int x \sin 2x \, dx.$

7. $\int t^2 \sin t \, dt.$

8. $\int v^2 \cos 2v \, dv.$

9. $\int t^2 \sin (t^3) \, dt.$

10. $\int v \sin (v^2) \, dv.$ 11. $\int x^2 e^{3x} \, dx.$ 12. $\int y^2 e^{-y} \, dy.$

13. $\int \text{Arctan } u \, du.$ 14. $\int u \text{ Arctan } u \, du.$ 15. $\int x(3x + 1)^7 \, dx,$
    by parts.

16. $\int x(3x + 1)^7 \, dx,$ by using $x = \frac{1}{3}(3x + 1) - \frac{1}{3}.$

17. $\int \frac{\theta \, d\theta}{(\theta + 1)^3},$ in two ways. See Exs. 15, 16.

18. $\int x\sqrt{x - 2} \, dx,$ in two ways. See Exs. 15, 16.

19. $\int x^3 e^{-x^2} \, dx.$ 20. $\int x e^{-x^2} \, dx.$

21. $\int x^3(a^2 + x^2)^{\frac{1}{2}} \, dx.$ 22. $\int y^3(a^2 - y^2)^{\frac{1}{2}} \, dy.$

23. $\int v \sin 3v \cos 3v \, dv.$ 24. $\int x \cos^2 x \, dx.$

25. $\int \phi \csc^2 \phi \, d\phi.$ 26. $\int \phi \sec^2 \phi \tan \phi \, d\phi.$

27. $\int x \cosh \frac{x}{a} \, dx.$ 28. $\int y \sinh \frac{y}{a} \, dy.$

29. $\int y \cos y \sin^2 y \, dy.$ Ans. $\frac{1}{3}y \sin^3 y + \frac{1}{3} \cos y - \frac{1}{9} \cos^3 y + C.$

30. $\int x \cos^3 x \, dx.$ Ans. $x \sin x - \frac{1}{3}x \sin^3 x + \frac{2}{3} \cos x + \frac{1}{9} \cos^3 x + C.$

In Exs. 31–36, employ integration by parts twice to evaluate the indicated integral.

31. $\int \sin x \sin 4x \, dx.$ Ans. $\frac{1}{15}(\cos x \sin 4x - 4 \sin x \cos 4x) + C.$

32. $\int \cos 2x \sin 3x \, dx.$
    Ans. $-\frac{1}{5}(3 \cos 2x \cos 3x + 2 \sin 2x \sin 3x) + C.$

33. $\int e^{ax} \cos mx \, dx.$ Ans. $\frac{e^{ax}(a \cos mx + m \sin mx)}{a^2 + m^2} + C.$

34. $\int e^{ax} \sin mx \, dx.$ Ans. $\frac{e^{ax}(a \sin mx - m \cos mx)}{a^2 + m^2} + C.$

35. $\int \ln^2 x \, dx.$ Ans. $x \ln^2 x - 2x \ln x + 2x + C.$

36. $\int \cos (\ln x)\, dx.$ *Ans.* $\frac{1}{2}x[\cos (\ln x) + \sin (\ln x)] + C.$

In Exs. 37–38, combine integration by parts with other appropriate devices, as in Example (*b*) above, to evaluate the indicated integral.

37. $\int \csc^3 y\, dy.$ *Ans.* $-\frac{1}{2} \csc y \cot y + \frac{1}{2} \ln (\csc y - \cot y) + C.$

38. $\int \sqrt{a^2 - x^2}\, dx.$ *Ans.* $\frac{1}{2}x \sqrt{a^2 - x^2} + \frac{1}{2}a^2 \operatorname{Arcsin} \dfrac{x}{a} + C.$

MISCELLANEOUS EXERCISES

Evaluate the integrals in Exs. 1–60.

1. $\int \tan 3\theta\, d\theta.$

2. $\int z e^z\, dz.$

3. $\int x \ln (x + 1)\, dx.$

4. $\int \csc^2 5\phi\, d\phi.$

5. $\int x(1 + x^2)^3\, dx.$

6. $\int x^2(1 + x^2)^3\, dx.$

7. $\int e^{-2x} \cos 5x\, dx.$

8. $\int e^{3x} \sin 4x\, dx.$

9. $\int \dfrac{2(y + 6)\, dy}{y^2 + 9}.$

10. $\int \dfrac{3(y - 8)\, dy}{4y^2 + 1}.$

11. $\int \sec^2 2\theta \tan^2 2\theta\, d\theta.$

12. $\int \sec^2 2\theta \tan 2\theta\, d\theta.$

13. $\int \dfrac{dx}{e^{3x} + 4}.$

14. $\int \dfrac{\tan \theta\, d\theta}{2 + \sec \theta}.$

15. $\int \cos \theta \sin 3\theta\, d\theta.$

16. $\int \cos 2\theta \sin 4\theta\, d\theta.$

17. $\int \dfrac{y^3\, dy}{y^4 - 1}.$

18. $\int \dfrac{y^3\, dy}{y^2 - 1}.$

19. $\int \dfrac{(3t - 2)\, dt}{t^2 - 4t + 5}.$

20. $\int \dfrac{(t - 2)\, dt}{t^2 - 4t + 5}.$

21. $\int \cos^7 \alpha\, d\alpha.$

22. $\int \sin^4 y \cos^3 y\, dy.$

23. $\int \cos^2 6\theta\, d\theta.$

24. $\int \tan^2 3y\, dy.$

25. $\int \text{Arcsin } x \, dx.$

26. $\int \sin (\ln u) \, du.$

27. $\int x \cos 7x \, dx.$

28. $\int \sec^3 2z \tan 2z \, dz.$

29. $\int \frac{(x-1)^2 \, dx}{x+3}.$

30. $\int \frac{e^{3y} \, dy}{e^{2y} + 9}.$

31. $\int \cos^4 \frac{x}{2} \, dx.$

32. $\int \frac{dy}{\sqrt{2ay - y^2}}.$

33. $\int \frac{y \, dy}{\sqrt{2ay - y^2}}.$

34. $\int \frac{(2t^3 - 5t) \, dt}{9t^4 + 4}.$

35. $\int \csc^3 4\beta \cot 4\beta \, d\beta.$

36. $\int \csc^6 (2\phi) \, d\phi.$

37. $\int \sin^2 x \csc^2 2x \, dx.$

38. $\int x^3 \ln x \, dx.$

39. $\int \frac{dz}{(2z-1)^4}.$

40. $\int \frac{dv}{\sqrt{3 - 4v^2}}.$

41. $\int y \ln (3y + 1) \, dy.$

42. $\int \cosh^3 \frac{x}{a} \sinh \frac{x}{a} \, dx.$

43. $\int \sin^2 \tfrac{1}{4}x \cos^2 \tfrac{1}{4}x \, dx.$

44. $\int \frac{y^3 \, dy}{(y-1)^2}.$

45. $\int t^2 \cos \tfrac{1}{2}t \, dt.$

46. $\int \frac{u \ln (u^2 + 4)}{u^2 + 4} \, du.$

47. $\int \frac{d\phi}{\sqrt{\phi} \sqrt{1 - \phi}}.$

48. $\int (10)^{-3x} \, dx.$

49. $\int x(10)^{-3x} \, dx.$

50. $\int \sec^4 3\phi \, d\phi.$

51. $\int \beta \tan^3 (\beta^2) \, d\beta.$

52. $\int \frac{\sin^3 2x}{\cos^5 2x} \, dx.$

53. $\int \frac{(6v + 1) \, dv}{v^2 - v + 1}.$

54. $\int (x + 1)e^{2 \ln x} \, dx.$

55. $\int (\sin^4 2z - \cos^4 2z) \, dz.$

56. $\int \sec^4 u \tan^3 u \, du.$

57. $\int \frac{(1 + x)^5}{x^7} \, dx.$

58. $\int \frac{dx}{x \ln \sqrt{x}}.$

59. $\int (x^2 + 2x - 3)(x - 1)^2\, dx.$

60. $\int \dfrac{dx}{\sin x \cos x}.$ Solve in two ways: (a) by using $\sin x \cos x = \frac{1}{2} \sin 2x$; and (b) by first dividing numerator and denominator by $\sin^2 x$.

Exs. 61-69 concern the motion of a particle in a straight line; the distance x from a specified origin is dependent upon the time t. For the given acceleration a, and the given "boundary conditions," determine in each instance the velocity v, and the distance x, in terms of t.

61. $a = 3 \sin 2t$; when $t = 0$, then $x = 4$ and $v = 0$.

$\qquad\qquad\qquad\qquad\qquad$ *Ans.* $x = 4 + \frac{3}{2}t - \frac{3}{4} \sin 2t.$

62. $a = 4e^{-2t} - e^{-t}$; when $t = 0$, then $x = 2$ and $v = -1$.

63. $a = (t - 2)e^{-t}$; when $t = 0$, then $x = 0$ and $v = 1$.

64. $a = -3 \cos 3t$; when $t = 0$, then $x = 0$ and $v = 0$.

65. $a = 4(e^{-2t} - 2e^{-4t})$; when $t = 0$, then $x = \frac{1}{2}$ and $v = 0$.

66. $a = 4(t + 2)e^{-2t}$; when $t = 0$, then $x = 3$ and $v = -7$.

$\qquad\qquad\qquad\qquad\qquad$ *Ans.* $x = (t + 3)e^{-2t} - 2t.$

67. $a = -32$; when $t = 0$, then $x = 100$, and when $t = 2$, then $x = 30$.

68. $a = -\frac{3}{4}(2 \cos \frac{1}{2}t + \sin \frac{1}{2}t)$; when $t = 0$, then $x = -6$, and $v = 1.5$.

69. $a = 8 \sin 4t$; when $t = 0$, then $x = 0$, and when $t = \dfrac{4\pi}{3}$, then $v = 0$.

CHAPTER *17* INTEGRATION BY

SUBSTITUTION

138. Integration by substitution. Many integrals may be evaluated by introducing a new variable of integration, say z, in place of the original variable x, the two variables being connected by some suitable formula. The change of variable is usually brought about by means of an explicit substitution

$$x = \phi(z), \qquad dx = \phi'(z)\, dz.$$

This process, called *integration by substitution*, is highly important. It is to be remembered that *not merely x, but dx as well*, must be replaced by the proper value in terms of the new variable.

As a rule, the nature of the substitution to be made—*i.e.*, the formula connecting x and z—must be determined by inspection of the given integrand. No general directions can be given; skill in the use of substitutions comes only with practice. In many cases, several different substitutions may be found, any one of which will succeed.

Example (a): Evaluate $\displaystyle\int \frac{\sqrt{x}\, dx}{1+x}$.

Let $\qquad \sqrt{x} = z, \qquad x = z^2, \qquad dx = 2z\, dz:$

$$\int \frac{\sqrt{x}\, dx}{1+x} = 2 \int \frac{z^2\, dz}{1+z^2} = 2 \int \left(1 - \frac{1}{1+z^2}\right) dz$$

$$= 2z - 2 \operatorname{Arctan} z + C$$

$$= 2\sqrt{x} - 2 \operatorname{Arctan} \sqrt{x} + C.$$

Example (b): Evaluate $\int \dfrac{x^3\, dx}{\sqrt{x^2 - a^2}}$.

Let
$$x^2 - a^2 = z^2, \qquad x^2 = z^2 + a^2, \qquad x\, dx = z\, dz:$$

$$\int \frac{x^3\, dx}{\sqrt{x^2 - a^2}} = \int \frac{x^2 \cdot x\, dx}{\sqrt{x^2 - a^2}} = \int \frac{(z^2 + a^2)z\, dz}{z}$$

$$= \tfrac{1}{3}z^3 + a^2 z + C$$

$$= \tfrac{1}{3}(x^2 - a^2)^{\frac{3}{2}} + a^2(x^2 - a^2)^{\frac{1}{2}} + C.$$

Example (c): Evaluate $\int \dfrac{(e^x - 1)e^x\, dx}{e^x + 1}$.

Let
$$e^x + 1 = z, \qquad e^x\, dx = dz:$$

$$\int \frac{(e^x - 1)e^x\, dx}{e^x + 1} = \int \frac{(z - 2)\, dz}{z}$$

$$= z - 2 \ln z + C$$

$$= e^x - 2 \ln (e^x + 1) + C_1.$$

Integrals involving $\sqrt{a^2 - x^2}$, $\sqrt{a^2 + x^2}$, $\sqrt{x^2 - a^2}$ occur very often. It should be noted that substitution of a new variable for the radical, as in Example (b), is indicated whenever the integrand contains, as a factor, an *odd* positive or negative integral power of x; but if not, the radical will reappear after the substitution.

It will be found that some of the integrals in this chapter can be solved directly by the methods of Chapter 16. Although substitutions are frequently necessary, the student should be alert for opportunities to avoid them by exercise of a little ingenuity.

EXERCISES

Evaluate the integrals in Exs. 1–30.

1. $\int \dfrac{(6x - 1)\, dx}{\sqrt{3x + 1}}$.   *Ans.* $\tfrac{4}{9}(3x + 1)^{\frac{3}{2}} - 2(3x + 1)^{\frac{1}{2}} + C.$

2. $\int \dfrac{dx}{1 - \sqrt{x}}$.   *Ans.* $2(1 - \sqrt{x}) - 2 \ln (1 - \sqrt{x}) + C.$

3. $\int (2v - 1)\sqrt{v + 3}\, dv$.   *Ans.* $\tfrac{4}{5}(v + 3)^{\frac{5}{2}} - \tfrac{14}{3}(v + 3)^{\frac{3}{2}} + C.$

4. $\int \dfrac{2(x-7)\,dx}{(2x+1)^{\frac{3}{2}}}$. *Ans.* $(2x+1)^{\frac{1}{2}} + 15(2x+1)^{-\frac{1}{2}} + C$.

5. $\int \cos \sqrt{t}\; dt$. *Ans.* $2(\sqrt{t}\,\sin\sqrt{t} + \cos\sqrt{t}) + C$.

6. $\int \dfrac{dx}{\sqrt{x+2}-4}$.

Ans. $2(\sqrt{x+2}-4) + 8\ln(\sqrt{x+2}-4) + C$
$= 2\sqrt{x+2} + 8\ln(\sqrt{x+2}-4) + C_1$.

7. $\int \dfrac{u\,du}{\sqrt{u}-1}$.

Ans. $\frac{2}{3}(\sqrt{u}-1)^3 + 3(\sqrt{u}-1)^2 + 6(\sqrt{u}-1) + 2\ln(\sqrt{u}-1) + C$.

8. $\int (x+2)\sqrt{3x-1}\;dx$. *Ans.* $\frac{2}{45}(3x-1)^{\frac{5}{2}} + \frac{14}{27}(3x-1)^{\frac{3}{2}} + C$.

9. $\int \dfrac{x^3}{\sqrt{x^2-a^2}}\;dx$. *Ans.* $\frac{1}{3}(x^2-a^2)^{\frac{3}{2}} + a^2(x^2-a^2)^{\frac{1}{2}} + C$.

10. $\int x^3\sqrt{a^2+x^2}\;dx$. *Ans.* $\frac{1}{5}(a^2+x^2)^{\frac{5}{2}} - \dfrac{a^2}{3}(a^2+x^2)^{\frac{3}{2}} + C$.

11. $\int \dfrac{x^3}{(4-x^2)^2}\;dx$. *Ans.* $\dfrac{2}{4-x^2} + \frac{1}{2}\ln(4-x^2) + C$.

12. $\int \dfrac{\sqrt{y^5-1}}{y}\;dy$. *Ans.* $\frac{2}{5}\sqrt{y^5-1} - \frac{2}{5}\operatorname{Arctan}\sqrt{y^5-1} + C$.

13. $\int \dfrac{\sqrt{x^2-a^2}}{x}\;dx$. *Ans.* $\sqrt{x^2-a^2} + a\operatorname{Arcsin}\dfrac{a}{x} + C$.

14. $\int \sqrt{1-\sqrt{x}}\;dx$. **15.** $\int \dfrac{x\,dx}{(x^2-a^2)^{\frac{5}{2}}}$.

16. $\int y^2(1+y^3)^4\;dy$. **17.** $\int \dfrac{e^{3v}\,dv}{\sqrt{e^v-1}}$.

18. $\int \sqrt{e^y-4}\;dy$. **19.** $\int \dfrac{\cos\theta\,\sin^2\theta\,d\theta}{\sqrt{1+\sin\theta}}$.

20. $\int \sec^2\theta\,\tan\theta\,(1+3\tan\theta)^{\frac{1}{2}}\,d\theta$.

21. $\int \dfrac{dx}{1-x^{\frac{1}{5}}}$. **22.** $\int \dfrac{(x^3+4x)\,dx}{\sqrt{1-x^4}}$.

23. $\int \dfrac{dt}{\sqrt{1+t^{\frac{1}{3}}}}$. **24.** $\int \dfrac{dy}{y^{\frac{1}{2}}+y^{\frac{1}{3}}}$.

25. $\int \dfrac{z^5\,dz}{(z^2-a^2)^2}$. **26.** $\int \dfrac{dt}{(1-\sqrt{t})^{\frac{5}{2}}}$.

27. $\int \dfrac{(x^2-1)^{\frac{3}{2}}\,dx}{x}$.

28. $\int \dfrac{(x^2-1)^{\frac{5}{2}}\,dx}{x}$.

29. $\int \dfrac{(1+\ln x)\,dx}{x^2}$.

30. $\int \ln(\sqrt{x}+4)\,dx$.

In Exs. 31–39, evaluate by using the reciprocal substitution $x = \dfrac{a^2}{v}$.

31. $\int \dfrac{x^3\,dx}{(x^2+a^2)^3}$.

Ans. $\dfrac{x^4}{4a^2(x^2+a^2)^2}+C$.

32. $\int \dfrac{dx}{x^2\sqrt{a^2-x^2}}$.

Ans. $-\dfrac{\sqrt{a^2-x^2}}{a^2x}+C$.

33. $\int \dfrac{\sqrt{a^2+x^2}\,dx}{x^4}$.

Ans. $\dfrac{-(a^2+x^2)^{\frac{3}{2}}}{3a^2x^3}+C$.

34. $\int \dfrac{dx}{x^2(a^2+x^2)}$.

Ans. $-\dfrac{1}{a^2x}+\dfrac{1}{a^3}\text{Arctan}\dfrac{a}{x}+C$.

35. $\int \dfrac{x^3\,dx}{(x^2-a^2)^3}$.

36. $\int \dfrac{dx}{(a^2-x^2)^{\frac{3}{2}}}$.

37. $\int \dfrac{dx}{x(x^2-a^2)}$.

38. $\int \dfrac{dx}{(a^2+x^2)^{\frac{3}{2}}}$.

39. $\int \dfrac{\sqrt{a^2-x^2}\,dx}{x^2}$.

Ans. $-\dfrac{\sqrt{a^2-x^2}}{x}-\text{Arcsin}\dfrac{x}{a}+C$.

40. Evaluate the integral of Ex. 31 by first writing

$$\int \frac{x^3\,dx}{(x^2+a^2)^3}=\int\frac{x(x^2+a^2-a^2)\,dx}{(x^2+a^2)^3}=\int\frac{x\,dx}{(x^2+a^2)^2}-\int\frac{a^2x\,dx}{(x^2+a^2)^3}.$$
Ans. $-\frac{1}{2}(x^2+a^2)^{-1}+\frac{1}{4}a^2(x^2+a^2)^{-2}+C_1$.

41. Compare the answers to Exs. 31 and 40 and show that $C_1 = C + \dfrac{1}{4a^2}$.

42. Evaluate the integral in Ex. 34 by first writing

$$\int \frac{dx}{x^2(a^2+x^2)}=\frac{1}{a^2}\int\frac{(x^2+a^2)-x^2}{x^2(a^2+x^2)}\,dx.$$

43. Evaluate the integral of Ex. 35 by the technique used in Exs. 40 and 42.

44. Evaluate the integral of Ex. 37 by the technique used in Exs. 40 and 42.

45. Evaluate $\int x^3(a^2+x^2)^k\,dx$, $(k\neq -1)$.

46. Evaluate $\int x^3(a^2+x^2)^{-1}\,dx$.

139. Trigonometric substitutions. Many integrals can be evaluated by substituting a trigonometric function for x. The following substitutions are especially promising:

When the integrand involves $a^2 - x^2$, try $x = a \sin \theta$.
When the integrand involves $a^2 + x^2$, try $x = a \tan \theta$.
When the integrand involves $x^2 - a^2$, try $x = a \sec \theta$.

However, it will be found that these combinations by no means exhaust the usefulness of trigonometric substitutions.

Example (a): Evaluate $\displaystyle\int \frac{dx}{(a^2 - x^2)^{\frac{3}{2}}}$.

Putting $x = a \sin \theta$, $dx = a \cos \theta \, d\theta$, we get

$$\int \frac{a \cos \theta \, d\theta}{(a^2 - a^2 \sin^2 \theta)^{\frac{3}{2}}} = \frac{1}{a^2}\int \frac{\cos \theta \, d\theta}{(1 - \sin^2 \theta)^{\frac{3}{2}}} = \frac{1}{a^2}\int \frac{\cos \theta \, d\theta}{\cos^3 \theta}$$

$$= \frac{1}{a^2}\int \sec^2 \theta \, d\theta = \frac{1}{a^2} \tan \theta + C.$$

From the triangle,

$$\tan \theta = \frac{x}{\sqrt{a^2 - x^2}},$$

whence

$$\int \frac{dx}{(a^2 - x^2)^{\frac{3}{2}}} = \frac{x}{a^2 \sqrt{a^2 - x^2}} + C.$$

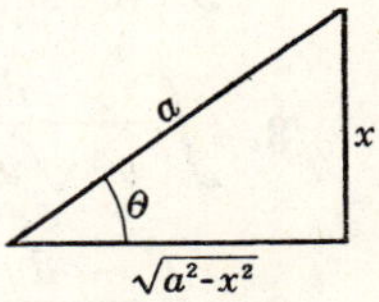

FIG. 126

Example (b): Evaluate $\displaystyle\int \frac{\sqrt{x - a}}{x^{\frac{5}{2}}} \, dx$.

Putting $x = a \sec^2 \theta$, $dx = 2a \sec^2 \theta \tan \theta \, d\theta$ gives

$$\int \frac{\sqrt{x - a}}{x^{\frac{5}{2}}} \, dx = \int \frac{\sqrt{a \sec^2 \theta - a} \cdot 2a \sec^2 \theta \tan \theta \, d\theta}{a^{\frac{5}{2}} \sec^5 \theta}$$

$$= \frac{2}{a}\int \frac{\sqrt{\sec^2 \theta - 1} \cdot \tan \theta \, d\theta}{\sec^3 \theta}$$

$$= \frac{2}{a}\int \tan^2 \theta \cos^3 \theta \, d\theta$$

$$= \frac{2}{a}\int \sin^2 \theta \cos \theta \, d\theta$$

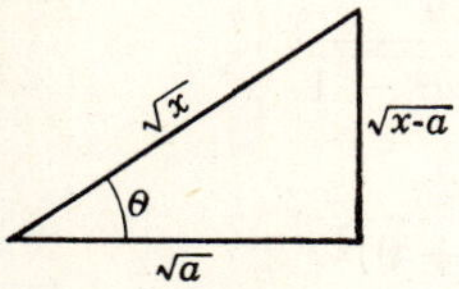

FIG. 127

$$= \frac{2}{3a} \sin^3 \theta + C = \frac{2}{3a}\frac{(x - a)^{\frac{3}{2}}}{x^{\frac{3}{2}}} + C.$$

EXERCISES

Evaluate the integrals in Exs. 1–36, making use of trigonometric substitutions.

1. $\displaystyle\int \frac{dx}{(a^2 + x^2)^{\frac{3}{2}}}$.   Ans. $\dfrac{x}{a^2\sqrt{a^2 + x^2}} + C.$

2. $\displaystyle\int \frac{dx}{(a^2 + x^2)^{\frac{5}{2}}}$.   Ans. $\dfrac{x(3a^2 + 2x^2)}{3a^4(a^2 + x^2)^{\frac{3}{2}}} + C.$

3. $\displaystyle\int \frac{dx}{x^2\sqrt{a^2 - x^2}}$.   Ans. $\dfrac{-\sqrt{a^2 - x^2}}{a^2 x} + C.$

4. $\displaystyle\int \sqrt{a^2 - x^2}\, dx.$ Ans. $\frac{1}{2}x\sqrt{a^2 - x^2} + \frac{1}{2}a^2 \operatorname{Arcsin} \dfrac{x}{a} + C.$

5. $\displaystyle\int \frac{\sqrt{a^2 - x^2}}{x^2}\, dx.$ Ans. $\dfrac{-\sqrt{a^2 - x^2}}{x} - \operatorname{Arcsin} \dfrac{x}{a} + C.$

6. $\displaystyle\int \frac{dx}{(x^2 - a^2)^{\frac{3}{2}}}$.   Ans. $\dfrac{-x}{a^2\sqrt{x^2 - a^2}} + C.$

7. $\displaystyle\int \frac{v^2\, dv}{(a^2 - v^2)^{\frac{3}{2}}}$.   Ans. $\dfrac{v}{\sqrt{a^2 - v^2}} - \operatorname{Arcsin} \dfrac{v}{a} + C.$

8. $\displaystyle\int \frac{dw}{w^2\sqrt{w^2 + a^2}}$.   Ans. $\dfrac{-\sqrt{w^2 + a^2}}{a^2 w} + C.$

9. $\displaystyle\int \frac{dy}{\sqrt{y^2 + a^2}}$.   Ans. $\ln\left(y + \sqrt{y^2 + a^2}\right) + C.$

10. $\displaystyle\int \frac{du}{(u^2 + a^2)^2}$.   Ans. $\dfrac{1}{2a^3}\left(\dfrac{au}{u^2 + a^2} + \operatorname{Arctan} \dfrac{u}{a}\right) + C.$

11. $\displaystyle\int \frac{\sqrt{9x^2 - 4}}{x}\, dx.$

12. $\displaystyle\int \frac{\sqrt{16 - x^2}}{x}\, dx.$

13. $\displaystyle\int \frac{dy}{y(y^2 + 1)}$.

14. $\displaystyle\int \frac{dy}{y^3(y^2 + 1)}$.

15. $\displaystyle\int \frac{du}{u^2\sqrt{4u^2 - 1}}$.

16. $\displaystyle\int \frac{du}{u^4\sqrt{4u^2 - 1}}$.

17. $\displaystyle\int \frac{dx}{x^4\sqrt{9 - x^2}}$.

18. $\displaystyle\int \frac{y^2\, dy}{(16y^2 + 9)^{\frac{3}{2}}}$.

19. $\displaystyle\int \frac{\sqrt{x}\, dx}{(1 + x)^2}$.

20. $\displaystyle\int \frac{\sqrt{x}\, dx}{(1 + x)^3}$.

21. $\int (a^2 - x^2)^{\frac{3}{2}} dx.$

$Ans.\ \dfrac{x}{4}(a^2 - x^2)^{\frac{3}{2}} + \dfrac{3a^2x}{8}(a^2 - x^2)^{\frac{1}{2}} + \dfrac{3a^4}{8} \text{Arcsin} \dfrac{x}{a} + C.$

22. $\int \sqrt{a^2 + x^2}\, dx.$ $Ans.\ \dfrac{x}{2}\sqrt{a^2 + x^2} + \dfrac{a^2}{2} \ln\left(x + \sqrt{a^2 + x^2}\right) + C.$

23. $\int \dfrac{x^2\, dx}{\sqrt{a^2 + x^2}}.$ $Ans.\ \dfrac{x}{2}\sqrt{a^2 + x^2} - \dfrac{a^2}{2} \ln\left(x + \sqrt{a^2 + x^2}\right) + C.$

24. $\int \dfrac{dx}{(a^2 - x^2)^{\frac{5}{2}}}.$ $Ans.\ \dfrac{x(3a^2 - 2x^2)}{3a^4(a^2 - x^2)^{\frac{3}{2}}} + C.$

25. $\int \dfrac{\sqrt{a - y}}{\sqrt{y}}\, dy.$ **26.** $\int \dfrac{\sqrt{y}}{\sqrt{a - y}}\, dy.$

27. $\int \dfrac{dx}{\sqrt{1 + \sqrt{x}}}.$ **28.** $\int \sqrt{1 - \sqrt{x}}\, dx.$

29. $\int \dfrac{\cos\phi \sin\phi\, d\phi}{(1 - \cos\phi)^2}.$ **30.** $\int \dfrac{\cos\beta\, d\beta}{(1 + \sin^2\beta)^{\frac{3}{2}}}.$

31. $\int \dfrac{dx}{x\sqrt{2ax - x^2}}.$ (Put $x = 2a \sin^2\theta$.) $Ans.\ -\dfrac{\sqrt{2ax - x^2}}{ax} + C.$

32. $\int \dfrac{dx}{x\sqrt{2ax + x^2}}.$ (Put $x = 2a \tan^2\theta$.) $Ans.\ -\dfrac{\sqrt{2ax + x^2}}{ax} + C.$

33. $\int \dfrac{dx}{x\sqrt{x^2 - 2ax}}.$ (Put $x = 2a \sec^2\theta$.) $Ans.\ \dfrac{\sqrt{x^2 - 2ax}}{ax} + C.$

34. Solve Ex. 31 by a second method. Put $x - a = a \sin\theta$.
35. Solve Ex. 32 by a second method.
36. Solve Ex. 33 by a second method.

37. Evaluate $\int \dfrac{dx}{x(x^4 - 1)}$ in several ways.

In Exs. 38–48, evaluate the integral with, or without, the aid of trigonometric substitutions, using whatever method seems best adapted to the problem.

38. $\int \dfrac{dy}{1 - e^y}.$ **39.** $\int \dfrac{du}{e^{2u} + 1}.$ **40.** $\int \dfrac{dx}{\sqrt{4 - 9x^2}}.$

41. $\int \dfrac{d\phi}{16\phi^2 + 1}.$ **42.** $\int \dfrac{dx}{x(x + a)}.$ **43.** $\int \dfrac{dy}{y(y - 9)}.$

44. $\displaystyle\int \frac{dy}{y(y-4)^2}.$ **45.** $\displaystyle\int \frac{x^2\,dx}{(x^2+a^2)^2}.$ **46.** $\displaystyle\int \frac{y^3\,dy}{(y^2+a^2)^3}.$

47. $\displaystyle\int \frac{dx}{x(x+k)^2}.$ **48.** $\displaystyle\int \frac{dx}{\sqrt{4e^{2x}-9}}.$

140. Limitations on certain formulas. To verify (**10**), p. 226, the work is as follows:

$$\frac{d}{du}\,\text{Arcsin}\,\frac{u}{a} = \frac{\dfrac{1}{a}}{\sqrt{1-\dfrac{u^2}{a^2}}} = \frac{1}{a}\cdot\frac{1}{\sqrt{\dfrac{a^2-u^2}{a^2}}} = \frac{1}{a}\cdot\frac{\sqrt{a^2}}{\sqrt{a^2-u^2}}.$$

This proves the formula for the case $a > 0$; but if $a < 0$, then $\sqrt{a^2} = -a$, and *the formula must be changed* to read

(1) $$\int \frac{du}{\sqrt{a^2-u^2}} = -\text{Arcsin}\,\frac{u}{a} + C \qquad (a < 0).$$

The above is typical of a phenomenon that occurs many times in integration. A formula, valid within certain ranges, is incorrect in other ranges, even though all the functions occurring are well-defined there. The commonest region of failure is for negative values of the variable of integration x, or of some constant.

With the limitation $a > 0$ on (**10**), the standard formulas (p. 226) are valid wherever the functions are defined. But the exercises of this and the previous chapter contain a number of formulas to which the above remarks apply.

Example: Find the area in the second quadrant bounded by the curve $y^2 = \dfrac{x^2-1}{x^2}$, the x-axis, and the line $x = -2$.

In the second quadrant

$$y = -\frac{\sqrt{x^2-1}}{x},$$

(2) $$A = \int_{-2}^{-1} y\,dx = -\int_{-2}^{-1} \frac{\sqrt{x^2-1}\,dx}{x}.$$

An attempt to evaluate the above integral by using the result of Ex. 13, p. 247,

(3) $$\int \frac{\sqrt{x^2-a^2}}{x}\,dx = \sqrt{x^2-a^2} + a\,\text{Arcsin}\,\frac{a}{x} + C,$$

is doomed to failure, because (3) is based on the assumption that x is positive. [In the derivation of (3), $\sqrt{x^2}$ is replaced by x.] Indeed,

$$-\left[\sqrt{x^2 - 1} + \text{Arcsin}\, \frac{1}{x}\right]_{-2}^{-1}$$

$$= -\text{Arcsin}\,(-1) - \left[-\sqrt{3} - \text{Arcsin}\,(-\tfrac{1}{2})\right]$$

$$= \sqrt{3} + \frac{\pi}{3} = 1.73 + 1.05 = 2.78.$$

But the area A, shaded in Fig. 128, is less than $\frac{1}{2}\sqrt{3} = 0.87$.

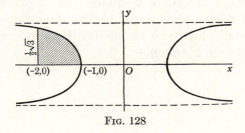

FIG. 128

Evaluation of the integral in (3) for negative x, replacing $\sqrt{x^2}$ by $(-x)$ in the derivation, yields

$$(4) \quad \int \frac{\sqrt{x^2 - a^2}}{x}\, dx = \sqrt{x^2 - a^2} - a\, \text{Arcsin}\, \frac{a}{x} + C; \; x \leq -a < 0.$$

The integral in (2) may now be evaluated with the aid of (4), which produces the correct answer,

$$A = \sqrt{3} - \frac{\pi}{3} = 0.68.$$

The whole difficulty is even more easily circumvented by employing a reasonable substitution in treating the integral in (2). Put $v = \sqrt{x^2 - 1}$. Then from (2), changing limits with the change of variable, (See §148 below.)

$$A = -\int_{-2}^{-1} \frac{\sqrt{x^2 - 1}}{x}\, dx = -\int_{\sqrt{3}}^{0} \frac{v \cdot v\, dv}{v^2 + 1}$$

$$= \int_{0}^{\sqrt{3}} \left[1 - \frac{1}{v^2 + 1}\right] dv$$

$$= \left[v - \text{Arctan}\, v\right]_{0}^{\sqrt{3}} = \sqrt{3} - \frac{\pi}{3} = 0.68,$$

as desired.

Although of course such situations are not the most usual thing, they occur far too often to be considered freakish. But it would be wearisome and time-consuming to keep constant track of such matters in our daily work; thus we have perforce ignored them and must continue to do so. We leave the subject with the following injunction (applying not so much to the work of this course, where these difficulties will be largely avoided, as to activities in applied mathematics in which the student may now or subsequently be interested):

In an integration involving a square root or other many-valued function, particularly when some of the quantities are negative, watch every detail closely to make sure that in each transformation the right branch is taken.

CHAPTER *18* INTEGRATION OF
RATIONAL FRACTIONS

141. Standard cases. We take up next the problem of integrating a *rational algebraic fraction—i.e.*, the quotient of two polynomials.

As noted in § 132, the first step in dealing with an integral of this type is to *carry out the indicated division until the numerator is of lower degree than the denominator.* In developing our theory, we shall suppose always that this preliminary step has been taken.

In this chapter, whenever the quantity $ax^2 + bx + c$ occurs, it will be assumed that $b^2 - 4ac < 0$. If $b^2 - 4ac \geqq 0$, the quantity $ax^2 + bx + c$ can be factored into real linear factors.

By methods already familiar, we can immediately integrate fractions of the forms $\dfrac{A}{(ax + b)^n}$, $\dfrac{A(2ax + b)}{(ax^2 + bx + c)^n}$, $\dfrac{A}{ax^2 + bx + c}$. The first two lead to powers, if $n > 1$, to logarithms, if $n = 1$; the third leads to an arctangent. We can also integrate $\dfrac{A}{(ax^2 + bx + c)^n}$, $n > 1$, by a trigonometric substitution (§ 139).

142. Partial fractions. It is shown in algebra that every rational fraction whose numerator is of lower degree than the denominator can be broken up into so-called *partial fractions* of the exact forms listed above. It follows that *every rational fraction can be integrated in elementary terms.* In the next few pages we show how to effect the break-up into partial fractions.

In order to apply the results, it is necessary that the operator actually be able to find the linear and quadratic factors of the denominator—conceivably a formidable task. Fortunately, most cases that arise are relatively simple.

143. Distinct linear factors. The simplest case is that in which the denominator can be broken up into real linear factors, none of which are repeated. In this case we may always rewrite the given fraction (provided the numerator is of lower degree than the denominator) as a sum of fractions whose numerators are constants and whose respective denominators are the factors of the original denominator.

Example (a): Evaluate $\int \dfrac{x^3 + 2}{x^3 - x}\, dx$.

By division,

$$\frac{x^3 + 2}{x^3 - x} = 1 + \frac{x + 2}{x^3 - x}.$$

The factors of the denominator are x, $x + 1$, $x - 1$. Assume

$$\frac{x + 2}{x^3 - x} = \frac{A}{x} + \frac{B}{x + 1} + \frac{C}{x - 1},$$

where A, B, C are constants to be determined. Clearing of fractions, we find

$$x + 2 = A(x^2 - 1) + Bx(x - 1) + Cx(x + 1).$$

This relation must hold for *all values* of x. Hence, assigning to x any three values whatever, we must obtain three simultaneous equations to determine A, B, C. But obviously the most convenient values to use are 0, -1, 1 (the zeros of the original denominator), for each of these causes two terms to drop out:

$$x = 0, \qquad A = -2;$$
$$x = -1, \qquad B = \tfrac{1}{2};$$
$$x = 1, \qquad C = \tfrac{3}{2}.$$

Thus

$$\int \frac{x^3 + 2}{x(x^2 - 1)}\, dx = \int \left(1 - \frac{2}{x} + \frac{1}{2} \cdot \frac{1}{x + 1} + \frac{3}{2} \cdot \frac{1}{x - 1} \right) dx$$
$$= x - 2 \ln x + \tfrac{1}{2} \ln (x + 1) + \tfrac{3}{2} \ln (x - 1) + C.$$

The student is urgently warned not to forget the preliminary division (when necessary). Without that, the above process will determine values of A, B, C; but the sum of partial fractions thus found will be equal to the given fraction for no values of x except the three that were assigned.

Careful scrutiny of the method used in Example (a) shows that the expansion is easily obtained mentally. Let us develop the idea in detail.

Consider any rational fraction with numerator of lower degree than the denominator, and with denominator consisting of distinct linear factors only. Let $(x - a)$ be a representative factor of the denominator. Then the fraction may be written $\dfrac{f(x)}{(x - a)g(x)}$, where $g(a) \neq 0$. The theory of rational fractions shows that

(1) $$\frac{f(x)}{(x - a)g(x)} = \frac{A}{x - a} + \phi(x),$$

where $\phi(x)$ is the sum of the other terms in the desired expansion into rational fractions. Multiply each term of (1) by $(x - a)$, thus getting

$$\frac{f(x)}{g(x)} = A + (x - a)\,\phi(x),$$

from which

$$A = \frac{f(a)}{g(a)}.$$

Thus the numerator of the representative term $\dfrac{A}{x - a}$ can be obtained from the original fraction by (mentally) removing the factor $(x - a)$ and evaluating what remains at $x = a$.

Example (b): Expand $\dfrac{x^2 + 1}{(x - 2)(x - 1)(2x + 1)}$ into rational fractions.

We know that

$$\frac{x^2 + 1}{(x - 2)(x - 1)(2x + 1)} = \frac{A}{x - 2} + \frac{B}{x - 1} + \frac{C}{2x + 1},$$

from which

$$A = \left[\frac{x^2 + 1}{(x - 1)(2x + 1)}\right]_{x=2} = \frac{5}{(1)(5)} = 1,$$

$$B = \left[\frac{x^2 + 1}{(x - 2)(2x + 1)}\right]_{x=1} = \frac{2}{(-1)(3)} = -\tfrac{2}{3},$$

$$C = \left[\frac{x^2 + 1}{(x - 2)(x - 1)}\right]_{x=-\frac{1}{2}} = \frac{\frac{5}{4}}{(-\frac{5}{2})(-\frac{3}{2})} = \tfrac{1}{3}.$$

Therefore,

$$\frac{x^2 + 1}{(x - 2)(x - 1)(2x + 1)} = \frac{1}{x - 2} + \frac{-\frac{2}{3}}{x - 1} + \frac{\frac{1}{3}}{2x + 1},$$

all of which should be accomplished mentally.

144. An important logarithmic formula. Under the heading of § 143, one particular integral occurs so often that it is worth listing for reference.

To evaluate $\int \dfrac{dx}{a^2 - x^2}$, assume

$$\frac{1}{a^2 - x^2} = \frac{A}{a + x} + \frac{B}{a - x},$$

$$1 = A(a - x) + B(a + x).$$

$$x = -a, \qquad A = \frac{1}{2a};$$

$$x = a, \qquad B = \frac{1}{2a};$$

$$\int \frac{dx}{a^2 - x^2} = \frac{1}{2a} \int \frac{dx}{a + x} + \frac{1}{2a} \int \frac{dx}{a - x}$$

$$= \frac{1}{2a} \ln (a + x) - \frac{1}{2a} \ln (a - x) + C,$$

or

$$\int \frac{dx}{a^2 - x^2} = \frac{1}{2a} \ln \frac{a + x}{a - x} + C = \frac{1}{2a} \ln \frac{x + a}{x - a} + C'.$$

As a corollary, by changing signs we get

$$\int \frac{dx}{x^2 - a^2} = \frac{1}{2a} \ln \frac{a - x}{a + x} + C_1 = \frac{1}{2a} \ln \frac{x - a}{x + a} + C_1'.$$

EXERCISES

Evaluate each of the following integrals.

1. $\int \dfrac{(3x + 7)\, dx}{x^2 - 2x - 3}.$ *Ans.* $4 \ln (x - 3) - \ln (x + 1) + C.$

2. $\int \dfrac{(x + 2)\, dx}{x^2 - 6x + 8}.$ *Ans.* $3 \ln (x - 4) - 2 \ln (x - 2) + C.$

3. $\int \dfrac{dx}{x^2 + ax}.$ *Ans.* $\dfrac{1}{a} \ln \dfrac{x}{x + a} + C.$

4. Do Ex. 3 by using the reciprocal substitution, $x = \dfrac{a^2}{v}.$

5. $\int \dfrac{(2x^2 + 5x - 4)\, dx}{x^3 + x^2 - 2x}.$

   Ans. $2 \ln x + \ln (x - 1) - \ln (x + 2) + C.$

6. $\int \dfrac{(2x^2 + 5x + 5)\, dx}{x^3 + 7x^2 + 10x}.$

   Ans. $\frac{1}{2} \ln x + 2 \ln (x + 5) - \frac{1}{2} \ln (x + 2) + C.$

7. $\int \dfrac{(7x+1)\,dx}{x^3+2x^2-5x-6}.$

8. $\int \dfrac{(x+1)\,dx}{x^3-7x^2+14x-8}.$

9. $\int \dfrac{(2x^2+x-5)\,dx}{x^2+x-2}.$

10. $\int \dfrac{5x^2\,dx}{x^2-x-6}.$

11. $\int \dfrac{(x+12)\,dx}{x(x+2)(x-3)}.$

12. $\int \dfrac{dx}{(x-1)(x+2)(x-4)}.$

13. $\int \dfrac{(x^2-16x-12)\,dx}{x(x-4)(x+1)}.$

14. $\int \dfrac{x^2\,dx}{(x-1)(x-2)(x-3)}.$

15. $\int \dfrac{x^3\,dx}{x^2-4}.$

16. $\int \dfrac{x^3\,dx}{x^4-16}.$

17. $\int \dfrac{15y^4\,dy}{y^{10}-4y^5-5}.$

18. $\int \dfrac{(2\sin\theta-1)\cos\theta\,d\theta}{\sin^2\theta+3\sin\theta-10}.$

19. $\int \dfrac{3t^2\,dt}{t^4+5t^2-14}.$

20. $\int \dfrac{(3u^3-u)\,du}{u^4+16}.$

21. $\int \dfrac{e^{3v}\,dy}{e^{2v}-4}.$

22. $\int \dfrac{dz}{(4-z)\sqrt{z}}.$

23. $\int \dfrac{d\theta}{\theta(\theta^3+2)}.$

24. $\int \dfrac{dx}{x(1-x^5)}.$

25. $\int \dfrac{dv}{\sqrt{4e^v+1}}.$

26. $\int \dfrac{dy}{\sqrt{1-e^{2y}}}.$

27. $\int \dfrac{4\,dx}{e^x+4}.$ Use the substitution $e^x+4=v.$

28. $\int \dfrac{4\,dx}{e^x+4}.$ Use the fact that $\dfrac{4}{e^x+4}=\dfrac{4e^{-x}}{1+4e^{-x}}.$

29. $\int \dfrac{4\,dx}{e^x+4}.$ Use the substitution $e^x=4\tan^2\phi.$

30. $\int \dfrac{4\,dx}{e^x+4}.$ Use the fact that $\dfrac{4}{e^x+4}=1-\dfrac{e^x}{e^x+4}.$

31. $\int \dfrac{dx}{e^x-1}.$ See the suggestions in Exs. 27–30.

32. $\int \dfrac{dx}{x\sqrt{a^2+x^2}}.$ (Put $a^2+x^2=v^2$.)   *Ans.* $-\dfrac{1}{a}\ln\dfrac{a+\sqrt{a^2+x^2}}{x}+C.$

33. $\int \dfrac{dx}{x\sqrt{a^2-x^2}}.$ (Put $a^2-x^2=y^2$.)   *Ans.* $-\dfrac{1}{a}\ln\dfrac{a+\sqrt{a^2-x^2}}{x}+C.$

34. $\int \dfrac{\sqrt{a^2-x^2}}{x}\,dx.$ (Put $a^2-x^2=y^2$.)

145. Repeated linear factors. If the denominator contains a factor $(x - \alpha)^r$, the above method fails, since there would be r partial fractions with denominator $x - \alpha$, and these could be combined into a single fraction with denominator $x - \alpha$. In this case, corresponding to the factor $(x - \alpha)^r$, we *assume r partial fractions of the form*

$$\frac{A}{x - \alpha} + \frac{B}{(x - \alpha)^2} + \cdots + \frac{D}{(x - \alpha)^r}.$$

Example: Evaluate $\displaystyle\int \frac{x^3 - 1}{x(x + 1)^3} \, dx.$

Assume

(1) $$\frac{x^3 - 1}{x(x + 1)^3} = \frac{A}{x} + \frac{B}{x + 1} + \frac{C}{(x + 1)^2} + \frac{D}{(x + 1)^3},$$

(2) $$x^3 - 1 = A(x+1)^3 + Bx(x + 1)^2 + Cx(x + 1) + Dx.$$

To get the necessary four equations for the determination of A, B, C, D, two methods are at once available. Specific values of x can be used in the identity (2), or the coefficients of like powers of x in the two members of (2) can be equated.

We naturally employ whatever combination of these methods yields simple equations to be solved for the unknowns A, B, etc.

From (2) we obtain equations as follows:

$$x = 0: \qquad -1 = A,$$
$$x = -1: \quad -2 = -D,$$
$$\text{Coefficients of } x^3: \quad 1 = A + B,$$
$$\text{Coefficients of } x^2: \quad 0 = 3A + 2B + C.$$

These equations yield $A = -1$, $B = 2$, $C = -1$, $D = 2$, whence

$$\int \frac{(x^3 - 1)\, dx}{x(x + 1)^3} = \int \left(-\frac{1}{x} + \frac{2}{x + 1} - \frac{1}{(x + 1)^2} + \frac{2}{(x + 1)^3} \right) dx$$

$$= -\ln x + 2\ln(x + 1) + \frac{1}{x + 1} - \frac{1}{(x + 1)^2} + C.$$

The algebra may be checked by obtaining an additional equation from the identity (2). For instance,

$$x = 1: \quad 0 = 8A + 4B + 2C + D,$$

which must also be satisfied by the A, B, C, D, if they are correct.

EXERCISES

Evaluate each of the following integrals.

1. $\displaystyle\int \frac{dx}{x^3 - x^2}.$ *Ans.* $\displaystyle\frac{1}{x} - \ln x + \ln (x - 1) + C.$

2. $\displaystyle\int \frac{(5u + 2)\, du}{u^3 + 2u^2}.$ *Ans.* $\displaystyle\frac{-1}{u} + 2 \ln u - 2 \ln (u + 2) + C.$

3. $\displaystyle\int \frac{(7x - 4)\, dx}{x^3 - 3x + 2}.$ *Ans.* $2 \ln (x - 1) - 2 \ln (x + 2) - \displaystyle\frac{1}{x - 1} + C.$

4. $\displaystyle\int \frac{(5x - 1)\, dx}{x^3 - 3x - 2}.$ *Ans.* $\ln (x - 2) - \ln (x + 1) - \displaystyle\frac{2}{x + 1} + C.$

5. $\displaystyle\int \frac{(2x^3 - 1)\, dx}{x^4 + 2x^3 + x^2}.$ *Ans.* $2 \ln x + \displaystyle\frac{1}{x} + \frac{3}{x + 1} + C.$

6. $\displaystyle\int \frac{dy}{y^2(y + 2)^2}.$ *Ans.* $\tfrac{1}{4} \ln \displaystyle\frac{y + 2}{y} - \frac{y + 1}{2y(y + 2)} + C.$

7. $\displaystyle\int \frac{(9v^2 + 4v - 12)\, dv}{v^2(v^2 - 4)}.$

Ans. $2 \ln (v - 2) - \ln v - \ln (v + 2) - \displaystyle\frac{3}{v} + C.$

8. $\displaystyle\int \frac{(11u - 14)\, du}{u^4 + u^3 - 2u^2}.$

Ans. $3 \ln (u + 2) - 2 \ln u - \ln (u - 1) - \displaystyle\frac{7}{u} + C.$

9. $\displaystyle\int \frac{(3x^4 - 2x^2 + 2)\, dx}{x^3(x - 1)}.$ *Ans.* $3x + \displaystyle\frac{2}{x} + \frac{1}{x^2} + 3 \ln (x - 1) + C.$

10. $\displaystyle\int \frac{(3x^2 - 2x - 4)\, dx}{x^3(x + 2)}.$ *Ans.* $\displaystyle\frac{1}{x^2} + \tfrac{3}{2} \ln \frac{x}{x + 2} + C.$

11. $\displaystyle\int \frac{(13x - 12)\, dx}{x^3 - 3x^2}.$ **12.** $\displaystyle\int \frac{(2y^2 + 1)\, dy}{y^3 + 2y^2 + y}.$

13. $\displaystyle\int \frac{dv}{(4 + v)^3}.$ **14.** $\displaystyle\int \frac{v\, dv}{(4 + v)^3}.$

15. $\displaystyle\int \frac{z\, dz}{(z^2 - 1)^2}.$ **16.** $\displaystyle\int \frac{(y^4 + 1)\, dy}{y^2(y - 1)^2}.$

17. $\displaystyle\int \frac{d\theta}{\sin \theta \cos^2 \theta}.$ Introduce a new variable, $\alpha = \cos \theta.$

18. $\displaystyle\int \frac{dx}{(a^2 - x^2)^2}.$ *Ans.* $\displaystyle\frac{x}{2a^2(a^2 - x^2)} + \frac{1}{4a^3} \ln \frac{a + x}{a - x} + C.$

19. $\int \sec^3 \theta \, d\theta.$ $\left[\sec^3 \theta = \dfrac{1}{\cos^3 \theta} = \dfrac{\cos \theta}{\cos^4 \theta} = \dfrac{\cos \theta}{(1 - \sin^2 \theta)^2}; \text{ Ex. 18.} \right]$

20. $\int \csc^3 \theta \, d\theta.$ (Cf. Ex. 19.)   *Ans.* $-\dfrac{\cos \theta}{2 \sin^2 \theta} + \tfrac{1}{4} \ln \dfrac{1 - \cos \theta}{1 + \cos \theta} + C.$

21. $\int \dfrac{dx}{x(x^2 - 1)^2}.$ *Ans.* $\dfrac{1}{2(1 - x^2)} + \tfrac{1}{2} \ln \dfrac{x^2}{x^2 - 1} + C.$

22. Do Ex. 21 in another way.

23. $\int \dfrac{dx}{e^x(e^x + 1)}.$ Use $v = e^x$.   *Ans.* $\ln (1 + e^x) - x - e^{-x} + C.$

24. Do Ex. 23 in two other ways.

25. $\int \dfrac{dx}{(1 - e^x)^2}.$ Use $e^x = \beta$.

26. Do Ex. 25, using $e^{-x} = v$.
27. Do Ex. 25, using $e^x = \sin^2 \phi$.

28. $\int \dfrac{dx}{x(1 - \sqrt{x})^2}.$ *Ans.* $\dfrac{2}{1 - \sqrt{x}} + \ln \dfrac{x}{(1 - \sqrt{x})^2} + C.$

146. Quadratic factors. Corresponding to a factor in the denominator of the form $ax^2 + bx + c$ with $b^2 - 4ac < 0$, we assume the partial fraction * $\dfrac{A(2ax + b) + B}{ax^2 + bx + c}$, where A and B are to be determined.

Example (a): Evaluate $\int \dfrac{x^2 + 4x + 10}{x^3 + 2x^2 + 5x} \, dx.$

Assume

$$\frac{x^2 + 4x + 10}{x^3 + 2x^2 + 5x} = \frac{A}{x} + \frac{B(2x + 2)}{x^2 + 2x + 5} + \frac{C}{x^2 + 2x + 5},$$

$$x^2 + 4x + 10 = A(x^2 + 2x + 5) + Bx(2x + 2) + Cx.$$

Put $x = 0$: $5A = 10, A = 2.$
Equate coefficients of x^2: $A + 2B = 1, B = -\tfrac{1}{2}.$
Equate coefficients of x: $2A + 2B + C = 4, C = 1.$

---

* This form rather than the equivalent form $\dfrac{Ax + B}{ax^2 + bx + c}$, in order that the new integrals shall be in form to evaluate at once.

Whence

$$\int \frac{x^2 + 4x + 10}{x^3 + 2x^2 + 5x} dx$$

$$= \int \left(\frac{2}{x} - \frac{1}{2} \cdot \frac{2x + 2}{x^2 + 2x + 5} + \frac{1}{x^2 + 2x + 5} \right) dx$$

$$= 2 \ln x - \frac{1}{2} \ln (x^2 + 2x + 5) + \frac{1}{2} \text{Arctan} \frac{x + 1}{2} + C.$$

The case of repeated quadratic factors occurs less often, and may be dismissed very briefly. Corresponding to a factor $(ax^2 + bx + c)^r$, we assume r partial fractions with linear numerators as above, and successive denominators building up step-by-step just as in § 145.

Example (b): Evaluate $\int \dfrac{x^2 \, dx}{(x^2 + 4x + 5)^2}$.

Assume

$$\frac{x^2}{(x^2 + 4x + 5)^2} = \frac{A(2x + 4) + B}{(x^2 + 4x + 5)} + \frac{C(2x + 4) + D}{(x^2 + 4x + 5)^2};$$

etc. The last integral may be evaluated as suggested in § 141.

EXERCISES

Evaluate the following integrals.

1. $\int \dfrac{(4x - 7) \, dx}{x^2 - 6x + 13}$.

   Ans. $2 \ln (x^2 - 6x + 13) + \dfrac{5}{2} \text{Arctan} \dfrac{x - 3}{2} + C.$

2. $\int \dfrac{(6x + 1) \, dx}{x^2 + 4x + 20}$.

   Ans. $3 \ln (x^2 + 4x + 20) - \dfrac{11}{4} \text{Arctan} \dfrac{x + 2}{4} + C.$

3. $\int \dfrac{dx}{x^3 + 2x^2 + 5x}$.

   Ans. $\dfrac{1}{5} \ln x - \dfrac{1}{10} \ln (x^2 + 2x + 5) - \dfrac{1}{10} \text{Arctan} \dfrac{x + 1}{2} + C.$

4. $\int \dfrac{(7x - 58) \, dx}{x^3 - 4x^2 + 29x}$.

   Ans. $\ln (x^2 - 4x + 29) - 2 \ln x + \dfrac{3}{5} \text{Arctan} \dfrac{x - 2}{5} + C.$

5. $\int \dfrac{dy}{(y - 1)(y^2 + 1)}$.

6. $\int \dfrac{(9y + 14) \, dy}{(y - 2)(y^2 + 4)}$.

7. $\int \dfrac{u \, du}{9u^4 + 1}$.

8. $\int \dfrac{dv}{v^3(1 + v^2)}$.

9. $\int \dfrac{dy}{y(9 + y^2)^2}.$

10. $\int \dfrac{y\,dy}{(4 + y^2)^3}.$

11. $\int \dfrac{\cos \phi \, d\phi}{\sin^3 \phi + 9 \sin \phi}.$

Ans. $\dfrac{1}{18} \ln \dfrac{\sin^2 \phi}{9 + \sin^2 \phi} + C.$

12. $\int \dfrac{\sec^2 \theta \, d\theta}{4 \tan^3 \theta + \tan \theta}.$

Ans. $\dfrac{1}{2} \ln \dfrac{\tan^2 \theta}{4 \tan^2 \theta + 1} + C.$

13. $\int \dfrac{(x^3 - 4) \, dx}{x^3 + 2x^2 + 2x}.$

Ans. $x - 2 \ln x + 2 \operatorname{Arctan} (x + 1) + C.$

14. $\int \dfrac{(x^3 + 10) \, dx}{x^3 - 2x^2 + 5x}.$

Ans. $x + 2 \ln x - \dfrac{1}{2} \operatorname{Arctan} \dfrac{x - 1}{2} + C.$

15. $\int \dfrac{v \ln v \, dv}{(1 + v^2)^2}.$

Ans. $\dfrac{1}{2} \ln v - \dfrac{1}{4} \ln (1 + v^2) - \dfrac{1}{2} \dfrac{\ln v}{1 + v^2} + C.$

16. $\int \dfrac{\operatorname{Arctan} y \, dy}{y^3}.$

Ans. $-\dfrac{1}{2y} - \dfrac{1 + y^2}{2y^2} \operatorname{Arctan} y + C.$

17. $\int \dfrac{dx}{x^3 - 2x^2 + 9x - 18}.$

Ans. $\dfrac{1}{13} \ln (x - 2) - \dfrac{1}{26} \ln (x^2 + 9) - \dfrac{2}{39} \operatorname{Arctan} \dfrac{x}{3} + C.$

18. $\int \dfrac{(2x + 7) \, dx}{x^3 + x^2 + 4x + 4}.$

Ans. $\ln (x + 1) - \dfrac{1}{2} \ln (x^2 + 4) + \dfrac{3}{2} \operatorname{Arctan} \dfrac{x}{2} + C.$

19. $\int \dfrac{(\theta + 65) \, d\theta}{\theta^3 + \theta^2 + \theta - 39}.$

Ans. $2 \ln (\theta - 3) - \ln (\theta^2 + 4\theta + 13) - 3 \operatorname{Arctan} \dfrac{\theta + 2}{3} + C.$

20. $\int \dfrac{(y - 1)(y - 5) \, dy}{y^3 - y^2 + 3y + 5}.$

Ans. $\dfrac{3}{2} \ln (y + 1) - \dfrac{1}{4} \ln (y^2 - 2y + 5) - \dfrac{3}{2} \operatorname{Arctan} \dfrac{y - 1}{2} + C.$

21. $\int \dfrac{dx}{(x^2 + 2x + 10)^2}.$

Ans. $\dfrac{x + 1}{18(x^2 + 2x + 10)} + \dfrac{1}{54} \operatorname{Arctan} \dfrac{x + 1}{3} + C.$

22. $\int \dfrac{(x^3 - 2x^2 + 1) \, dx}{(x^2 - 2x + 5)^2}.$

Ans. $\dfrac{1}{2} \ln (x^2 - 2x + 5) + \dfrac{1}{4} \operatorname{Arctan} \dfrac{x - 1}{2} - \dfrac{x - 6}{2(x^2 - 2x + 5)} + C.$

CHAPTER *19* DEFINITE INTEGRALS.
WALLIS' FORMULA

147. Definite integrals. Now that we have acquired some facility in integration, it is feasible to start seriously on the many applications of the definite integral. Before taking up the applications, let us review the technique of definite integration and, in Section 149, add one more tool to our kit.

Example (a): Evaluate $\int_0^{\frac{\pi}{3}} x \sin x \, dx.$

We employ integration by parts to obtain

$$\int_0^{\frac{\pi}{3}} x \sin x \, dx = \left[-x \cos x \right]_0^{\frac{\pi}{3}} + \int_0^{\frac{\pi}{3}} \cos x \, dx$$

$$= -\frac{\pi}{3} \cos \frac{\pi}{3} + 0 + \left[\sin x \right]_0^{\frac{\pi}{3}}$$

$$= -\frac{\pi}{6} + \sin \frac{\pi}{3} - 0$$

$$= \frac{\sqrt{3}}{2} - \frac{\pi}{6} = 0.342.$$

Example (b): Evaluate $\int_0^1 \frac{dy}{3 + 4y^2}.$

One of our standard formulas yields

$$\int_0^1 \frac{dy}{3 + 4y^2} = \frac{1}{2} \int_0^1 \frac{2 \, dy}{3 + 4y^2} = \frac{1}{2\sqrt{3}} \left[\text{Arctan} \frac{2y}{\sqrt{3}} \right]_0^1$$

$$= \frac{1}{2\sqrt{3}} \text{Arctan} \frac{2}{\sqrt{3}} = 0.289 \, \text{Arctan} \, (1.155)$$

$$= (0.289)(0.86) = 0.25.$$

148. Change of variable with change of limits. In the definite integral $\int_a^b f(x)\ dx$ it is always implied that a and b are *the limiting values of the variable of integration* x. If we change the variable by a substitution

(1) $$x = \phi(z),$$

we must either return to the original variable before substituting the limits, or *change the limits to correspond with the change of variable.* The latter method is usually preferable. The new limits are found, of course, from the equation of substitution (1).

Example: Evaluate $\int_0^a \dfrac{x^3\ dx}{(a^2 + x^2)^{\frac{5}{2}}}$.

Put $x = a \tan \phi$. Then $dx = a \sec^2 \phi\ d\phi$; when $x = 0$, $\phi = 0$, and when $x = a$, $\phi = \frac{1}{4}\pi$. Thus we proceed as follows:

$$\int_0^a \frac{x^3\ dx}{(a^2 + x^2)^{\frac{5}{2}}} = \int_0^{\frac{\pi}{4}} \frac{a^3 \tan^3 \phi\ a \sec^2 \phi\ d\phi}{(a^2 \sec^2 \phi)^{\frac{5}{2}}}$$

$$= \frac{1}{a} \int_0^{\frac{\pi}{4}} \frac{\tan^3 \phi\ d\phi}{\sec^3 \phi} = \frac{1}{a} \int_0^{\frac{\pi}{4}} \sin^3 \phi\ d\phi$$

$$= \frac{1}{a} \int_0^{\frac{\pi}{4}} \sin \phi\ (1 - \cos^2 \phi)\ d\phi$$

$$= \frac{1}{a} \left[-\cos \phi + \frac{\cos^3 \phi}{3} \right]_0^{\frac{\pi}{4}}$$

$$= \frac{1}{a} \left[-\frac{1}{\sqrt{2}} + \frac{1}{6\sqrt{2}} - \left(-1 + \frac{1}{3} \right) \right]$$

$$= \frac{1}{a} \left[\frac{2}{3} - \frac{5}{6\sqrt{2}} \right] = \frac{4\sqrt{2} - 5}{6a\sqrt{2}}.$$

149. Wallis' Formula. The integral

(1) $$\int_0^{\frac{\pi}{2}} \sin^m x \cos^n x\ dx,$$

in which m and n are integers ≥ 0, arises over and over again in elementary applications. Fortunately, the integral (1) can be evaluated simply, with a formula which is easy to remember in words, though bulky looking in symbols.

We prove in the next section that, if m and n are integers > 1, [For exponents 0 and 1, see the rule following Example (c) below.] then

$$(2) \qquad \int_0^{\frac{\pi}{2}} \sin^m x \cos^n x \, dx =$$

$$\frac{\left[(m-1)(m-3)\cdots \begin{array}{c} 2 \\ \text{or} \\ 1 \end{array}\right]\left[(n-1)(n-3)\cdots \begin{array}{c} 2 \\ \text{or} \\ 1 \end{array}\right]}{(m+n)(m+n-2)\cdots \begin{array}{c} 2 \\ \text{or} \\ 1 \end{array}} \cdot \alpha,$$

in which

$$\alpha = \frac{\pi}{2}, \text{ if } m \text{ and } n \text{ are both even,}$$

$$\alpha = 1, \text{ otherwise.}$$

In words, the value of the integral (1) is $\dfrac{A \cdot B}{C} \cdot \alpha$, in which

A = the product, starting with one less than the exponent m, going down 2 at a time, until 2 or 1 is reached,

B = a similar product, starting with one less than the other exponent,

C = a similar product, starting with the sum of the exponents,

$\alpha = \dfrac{\pi}{2}$, if m and n are both even,

$\alpha = 1$, otherwise.

Example (a): Evaluate $\displaystyle\int_0^{\frac{\pi}{2}} \sin^8 x \cos^4 x \, dx$.

By Wallis' Formula, we obtain

$$\int_0^{\frac{\pi}{2}} \sin^8 x \cos^4 x \, dx = \frac{(7 \cdot 5 \cdot 3 \cdot 1)(3 \cdot 1)}{12 \cdot 10 \cdot 8 \cdot 6 \cdot 4 \cdot 2} \cdot \frac{\pi}{2} = \frac{7\pi}{2^{11}} = \frac{7\pi}{2048}.$$

Example (b): Evaluate $\displaystyle\int_0^{\frac{\pi}{2}} \sin^5 \beta \cos^6 \beta \, d\beta$.

By Wallis' Formula,

$$\int_0^{\frac{\pi}{2}} \sin^5 \beta \cos^6 \beta \, d\beta = \frac{(4 \cdot 2)(5 \cdot 3 \cdot 1)}{11 \cdot 9 \cdot 7 \cdot 5 \cdot 3 \cdot 1} \cdot 1 = \frac{2^3}{11 \cdot 9 \cdot 7} = \frac{8}{693}.$$

Example (c): Evaluate $\displaystyle\int_0^{\frac{\pi}{2}} \cos^3 \phi \sin^5 \phi \, d\phi$.

At once,

$$\int_0^{\frac{\pi}{2}} \cos^3 \phi \sin^5 \phi \, d\phi = \frac{(2)(4 \cdot 2)}{8 \cdot 6 \cdot 4 \cdot 2} \cdot 1 = \frac{1}{8 \cdot 3} = \frac{1}{24}.$$

If either m or n is unity, the integral (1) can be evaluated at once by the power formula. If either m or n is zero, the result is not so simple, but one added device permits us to include that result in the formula (2).

RULE: *If the first factor in any of the products to be formed in applying Wallis' Formula, for m, $n \geqq 0$, is less than one, replace that product by unity.*

Example (d): Evaluate $\displaystyle\int_0^{\frac{\pi}{2}} \cos^7 \phi \sin \phi \, d\phi$.

Here, in forming the product associated with the **exponent of** the sine, we would normally start with one less than one, namely with zero. Hence, by the rule above, we replace that product by unity, and write

$$\int_0^{\frac{\pi}{2}} \cos^7 \phi \sin \phi \, d\phi = \frac{(6 \cdot 4 \cdot 2)(1)}{8 \cdot 6 \cdot 4 \cdot 2} = \frac{1}{8},$$

a result readily verified by direct integration.

Example (e): Evaluate $\displaystyle\int_0^{\frac{\pi}{2}} \sin^6 y \, dy$.

Here one exponent is zero. Now $6 + 0 = 6$, to start the denominator product. Also, 6 and 0 are both even. Hence,

$$\int_0^{\frac{\pi}{2}} \sin^6 y \, dy = \frac{(5 \cdot 3 \cdot 1)(1)}{6 \cdot 4 \cdot 2} \cdot \frac{\pi}{2} = \frac{5\pi}{2^5} = \frac{5\pi}{32}.$$

150. Derivation of Wallis' Formula. First, consider the integral

$$(1) \qquad\qquad T = \int_0^{\frac{\pi}{2}} \cos^n x \, dx.$$

Use integration by parts, with $u = \cos^{n-1} x$, $dv = \cos x \, dx$, to obtain

$$T = \left[\cos^{n-1} x \sin x \right]_0^{\frac{\pi}{2}} + (n-1) \int_0^{\frac{\pi}{2}} \cos^{n-2} x \sin^2 x \, dx$$

$$= 0 + (n-1) \int_0^{\frac{\pi}{2}} \cos^{n-2} x \, (1 - \cos^2 x) \, dx$$

$$= (n-1) \int_0^{\frac{\pi}{2}} \cos^{n-2} x \, dx - (n-1)T,$$

from which

$$(2) \qquad T = \frac{n-1}{n} \int_0^{\frac{\pi}{2}} \cos^{n-2} x \, dx.$$

In a like manner, replacing n by $(n-2)$ in (2) we find that

$$\int_0^{\frac{\pi}{2}} \cos^{n-2} x \, dx = \frac{n-3}{n-2} \int_0^{\frac{\pi}{2}} \cos^{n-4} x \, dx,$$

and the process can be iterated, beating down the exponent of the cosine two at a time, until the exponent is one or zero.

Thus, if n is even,

$$T = \frac{n-1}{n} \cdot \frac{n-3}{n-2} \cdots \frac{3}{4} \cdot \frac{1}{2} \int_0^{\frac{\pi}{2}} \cos^0 x \, dx$$

$$= \frac{(n-1)(n-3) \cdots 3 \cdot 1}{n(n-2) \cdots 4 \cdot 2} \cdot \frac{\pi}{2},$$

as described in the rule of the preceding section.

If n is odd, iteration of (2) yields

$$T = \frac{n-1}{n} \cdot \frac{n-3}{n-2} \cdots \frac{4}{5} \cdot \frac{2}{3} \int_0^{\frac{\pi}{2}} \cos x \, dx$$

$$= \frac{(n-1)(n-3) \cdots 4 \cdot 2}{n(n-2) \cdots 5 \cdot 3} \cdot 1,$$

also as described in the rule of the preceding section.

In order to evaluate $\int_0^{\frac{\pi}{2}} \sin^n x \, dx$, put $x = \frac{1}{2}\pi - y$, and thus obtain

$$\int_0^{\frac{\pi}{2}} \sin^n x \, dx = -\int_{\frac{\pi}{2}}^0 \cos^n y \, dy = \int_0^{\frac{\pi}{2}} \cos^n y \, dy,$$

the integral already treated above.

Finally, consider

(3)
$$W = \int_0^{\frac{\pi}{2}} \sin^m x \cos^n x \, dx.$$

Use integration by parts, with $u = \sin^{m-1} x$, $dv = \cos^n x \sin x \, dx$, to find that

$$W = \frac{-1}{n+1}\left[\sin^{m-1} x \cos^{n+1} x \right]_0^{\frac{\pi}{2}} + \frac{m-1}{n+1}\int_0^{\frac{\pi}{2}} \sin^{m-2} x \cos^{n+2} x \, dx$$

$$= 0 + \frac{m-1}{n+1}\int_0^{\frac{\pi}{2}} \sin^{m-2} x \cos^n x (1 - \sin^2 x) \, dx,$$

or

$$W = \frac{m-1}{n+1}\int_0^{\frac{\pi}{2}} \sin^{m-2} x \cos^n x \, dx - \frac{m-1}{n+1} W.$$

This last equation is easily solved for W, yielding

(4)
$$W = \frac{m-1}{m+n}\int_0^{\frac{\pi}{2}} \sin^{m-2} x \cos^n x \, dx.$$

Formula (4) can be used to reduce the exponent on the sine two at a time, until that exponent is one or zero.

If m is odd in (3), then iteration of (4) gives

$$W = \frac{(m-1)(m-3)\cdots 4 \cdot 2}{(m+n)(m+n-2)\cdots(n+5)(n+3)}\int_0^{\frac{\pi}{2}} \sin x \cos^n x \, dx$$

$$= \frac{(m-1)(m-3)\cdots 4 \cdot 2}{(m+n)(m+n-2)\cdots(n+5)(n+3)(n+1)},$$

from which the result stated in Wallis' Formula follows by inserting

the factors $\left[(n-1)(n-3)\cdots \begin{array}{c} 2 \\ \text{or} \\ 1 \end{array} \right]$ in numerator and denominator.

If m is even in (3), then iteration of (4) gives

$$W = \frac{(m-1)(m-3)\cdots 3 \cdot 1}{(m+n)(m+n-2)\cdots(n+4)(n+2)}\int_0^{\frac{\pi}{2}} \cos^n x \, dx.$$

As the last step in obtaining the desired expression for W, we insert the value of the integral T, of equation (1), as determined at the beginning of this section, and we thus arrive at the formula

$$W = \frac{\left[(m-1)(m-3)\cdots 3\cdot 1 \right]\left[(n-1)(n-3)\cdots \begin{smallmatrix} 2 \\ \text{or} \\ 1 \end{smallmatrix} \right]}{\left[(m+n)(m+n-2)\cdots(n+4)(n+2) \right]\left[n(n-2)\cdots \begin{smallmatrix} 2 \\ \text{or} \\ 1 \end{smallmatrix} \right]} \cdot \alpha,$$

which is the result stated in Wallis' Formula.

EXERCISES

In Exs. 1–18, use Wallis' Formula.

1. $\displaystyle\int_0^{\frac{\pi}{2}} \sin^2 x\, dx.$ *Ans.* $\dfrac{\pi}{4}.$ **2.** $\displaystyle\int_0^{\frac{\pi}{2}} \cos^2 x\, dx.$ *Ans.* $\dfrac{\pi}{4}.$

3. $\displaystyle\int_0^{\frac{\pi}{2}} \cos^5 y\, dy.$ *Ans.* $\tfrac{8}{15}.$ **4.** $\displaystyle\int_0^{\frac{\pi}{2}} \sin^7 y\, dy.$ *Ans.* $\tfrac{16}{35}.$

5. $\displaystyle\int_0^{\frac{\pi}{2}} \cos^3 \phi \sin^4 \phi\, d\phi.$ *Ans.* $\tfrac{2}{35}.$

6. $\displaystyle\int_0^{\frac{\pi}{2}} \sin^6 \phi \cos^4 \phi\, d\phi.$ *Ans.* $\dfrac{3\pi}{512}.$

7. $\displaystyle\int_0^{\frac{\pi}{2}} \sin^2 \alpha \cos^2 \alpha\, d\alpha.$ **8.** $\displaystyle\int_0^{\frac{\pi}{2}} \sin^4 x \cos^5 x\, dx.$

9. $\displaystyle\int_0^{\frac{\pi}{2}} \cos^6 y \sin^7 y\, dy.$ **10.** $\displaystyle\int_0^{\frac{\pi}{2}} \cos^{10} \theta \sin \theta\, d\theta.$

11. $\displaystyle\int_0^{\frac{\pi}{2}} \sin^8 \theta\, d\theta.$ **12.** $\displaystyle\int_0^{\frac{\pi}{2}} \sin^5 \theta \cos^5 \theta\, d\theta.$

13. $\displaystyle\int_0^1 (1-x^2)^{\frac{5}{2}}\, dx.$ Put $x = \sin \phi.$ *Ans.* $\dfrac{5\pi}{32}.$

14. $\displaystyle\int_0^a x^2(a^2-x^2)^{\frac{3}{2}}\, dx.$ Put $x = a\sin \phi.$ *Ans.* $\dfrac{\pi a^6}{32}.$

15. $\displaystyle\int_0^a x^5(a^2-x^2)^6\, dx.$ **16.** $\displaystyle\int_0^1 x^4\sqrt{1-x^2}\, dx.$

17. $\displaystyle\int_0^{\frac{\pi}{6}} \cos^8 3\theta\, d\theta.$ Put $3\theta = x.$ *Ans.* $\dfrac{35\pi}{768}.$

18. $\displaystyle\int_0^{\pi} \sin^3 \tfrac{1}{2}y \cos^4 \tfrac{1}{2}y\, dy.$ Put $y = 2\phi.$ *Ans.* $\tfrac{4}{35}.$

In Exs. 19–44, evaluate the given definite integral by any available device.

19. $\int_0^1 \dfrac{dx}{\sqrt{1+8x}}$.   *Ans.* $\tfrac{1}{2}$.

20. $\int_{-1}^0 \dfrac{x^2\,dx}{(1-x^3)^{\frac{3}{2}}}$.   *Ans.* $\dfrac{2-\sqrt{2}}{3}$.

21. $\int_0^{\frac{\pi}{3}} \sin^3 y\,dy$.   *Ans.* $\tfrac{5}{24}$.

22. $\int_0^{\frac{\pi}{2}} \sin^3 y\,dy$.   *Ans.* $\tfrac{2}{3}$.

23. $\int_0^{\frac{\pi}{3}} \sin^2 x\,dx$.   *Ans.* $\dfrac{4\pi-3\sqrt{3}}{24}$.

24. $\int_0^{\ln 2} xe^{-x}\,dx$.   *Ans.* $\tfrac{1}{2}(1-\ln 2)$.

25. $\int_1^2 \dfrac{x\,dx}{x+1}$.   *Ans.* $1-\ln\tfrac{3}{2}$.

26. $\int_0^{\frac{1}{2}} \dfrac{(5-x)\,dx}{4x^2+1}$.   *Ans.* $\dfrac{5\pi-\ln 2}{8}$.

27. $\int_1^{\sqrt{3}} \text{Arctan}\,x\,dx$.   *Ans.* $-\dfrac{1}{2}\ln 2+\dfrac{\pi}{12}(4\sqrt{3}-3)$.

28. $\int_0^1 \dfrac{y\,dy}{(1+y)^4}$.   *Ans.* $\tfrac{1}{12}$.

29. $\int_0^1 x\sin(2x^2)\,dx$.   *Ans.* $\tfrac{1}{4}(1-\cos 2)$.

30. $\int_2^3 \dfrac{x^3-2x}{x-1}\,dx$.   *Ans.* $\tfrac{47}{6}-\ln 2$.

31. $\int_3^4 \dfrac{dv}{(2-v)^3}$.   *Ans.* $-\tfrac{3}{8}$.

32. $\int_{-2}^2 \dfrac{dv}{v^2+4}$.   *Ans.* $\dfrac{\pi}{4}$.

33. $\int_{\frac{\pi}{3}}^{\frac{2\pi}{3}} \csc x\cot x\,dx$.   *Ans.* 0.

34. $\int_0^a \dfrac{x^2\,dx}{(a^2+x^2)^2}$.   *Ans.* $\dfrac{\pi-2}{8a}$.

35. $\int_0^1 \dfrac{x^3\,dx}{(1+x^2)^3}$.   *Ans.* $\tfrac{1}{16}$.

36. $\int_{-1}^{1} \dfrac{dz}{\sqrt{4 - z^2}}$.   *Ans.* $\dfrac{\pi}{3}$.   **37.** $\int_{0}^{\frac{\pi}{6}} \tan 2\theta \, d\theta$.   *Ans.* 0.347.

38. $\int_{0}^{\ln 2} \dfrac{e^x \, dx}{2e^x - 1}$.   *Ans.* 0.549.   **39.** $\int_{2}^{3} \dfrac{dx}{x^2 - 6x + 10}$.   *Ans.* $\dfrac{\pi}{4}$.

40. $\int_{0}^{\frac{\pi}{2}} \alpha \sin 3\alpha \, d\alpha$.   *Ans.* $-\frac{1}{9}$.   **41.** $\int_{1}^{2} \dfrac{\ln x}{x} \, dx$.   *Ans.* 0.240.

42. $\int_{0}^{1} ye^{-v^2} dy$. *Ans.* $\frac{1}{2}(1 - e^{-1})$.   ~~squared; int (y)2~~   **43.** $\int_{0}^{2} \dfrac{u \, du}{u^4 + 1}$.   *Ans.* 0.663.

44. $\int_{0}^{1} \sqrt{1 - \sqrt{u}} \, du$. Put $u = \sin^4 x$.   *Ans.* $\frac{8}{15}$.

CHAPTER *20* PLANE AREAS.
IMPROPER INTEGRALS

151. Plane areas. In our first attack on the problem of plane area, we were greatly handicapped by limited facility in integration. We therefore return briefly to this topic.

Example: Find the area of the loop of the curve

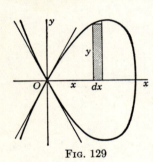

FIG. 129

$$y^2 = 4x^2(1 - x).$$

We have

$$A = 2\int_0^1 y \, dx = 4\int_0^1 x\sqrt{1 - x} \, dx.$$

Integrate by parts, with $u = x$:

$$A = -\tfrac{8}{3}\left[x(1 - x)^{\frac{3}{2}}\right]_0^1 + \tfrac{8}{3}\int_0^1 (1 - x)^{\frac{3}{2}} \, dx$$

$$= 0 - \tfrac{16}{15}\left[(1 - x)^{\frac{5}{2}}\right]_0^1 = \tfrac{16}{15}.$$

An even neater evaluation of the integral is accomplished by using the substitution $x = \sin^2 \phi$, after which Wallis' Formula becomes applicable. Thus, we write

$$A = 4\int_0^1 x\sqrt{1 - x} \, dx = 4\int_0^{\frac{\pi}{2}} \sin^2 \phi \cdot \cos \phi \cdot 2 \sin \phi \cos \phi \, d\phi$$

$$= 8\int_0^{\frac{\pi}{2}} \sin^3 \phi \cos^2 \phi \, d\phi$$

$$= 8\frac{2 \cdot 1}{5 \cdot 3 \cdot 1} = \frac{16}{15},$$

in verification of our earlier evaluation.

274

152. Substitution suggested by the problem. In Chapter 6, when finding plane areas by the formula

(1) $$A = \int_a^b y \, dx,$$

we invariably substituted for y. But it is equally proper, and frequently more convenient, to *substitute for dx and change to y-limits*. That is, we take, as the substitution-formula, *the equation of the curve itself*.

Of course similar remarks will apply in all the other applications that we shall take up.

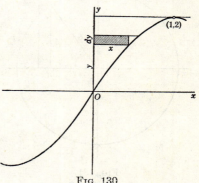

FIG. 130

Example: Find, in two ways, the area in the first quadrant bounded by the cubic $y = 3x - x^3$, and the lines $x = 0$, $y = 2$. The curve is shown in Fig. 130.

First method: Using a vertical element (not shown) and the technique of Chapter 6, we find that

$$A = \int_0^1 (2 - y) \, dx = \int_0^1 (2 - 3x + x^3) \, dx$$

$$= \left[2x - \frac{3x^2}{2} + \frac{x^4}{4} \right]_0^1$$

$$= 2 - \frac{3}{2} + \frac{1}{4} = \frac{3}{4}.$$

Second method: As a check, we find the same area using the horizontal element shown in Fig. 130:

$$A = \int_0^2 x \, dy.$$

It is not feasible to substitute for x, but we may easily substitute for dy and change limits:

$$dy = (3 - 3x^2) \, dx; \qquad x = 0 \text{ when } y = 0, \ x = 1 \text{ when } y = 2;$$

$$A = \int_0^2 x \, dy = 3 \int_0^1 (x - x^3) \, dx$$

$$= \left[\tfrac{3}{2}x^2 - \tfrac{3}{4}x^4 \right]_0^1 = \tfrac{3}{4}.$$

To evaluate an integral such as (1) when x and y are given in terms of a parameter, we *substitute for both y and dx*, taking as new limits the values of the parameter corresponding to the given limits.

Example (b): Find the area of the circle (Fig. 131)

$$x = a \cos \theta, \qquad y = a \sin \theta.$$

We have

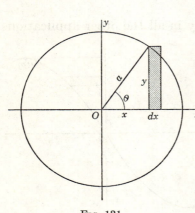

$$A = 4 \int_0^a y \, dx.$$

When $x = 0$, $\theta = \frac{1}{2}\pi$; when $x = a$, $\theta = 0$:

$$A = 4 \int_{\frac{\pi}{2}}^0 (a \sin \theta)(-a \sin \theta) \, d\theta$$

$$= -4a^2 \int_{\frac{\pi}{2}}^0 \sin^2 \theta \, d\theta$$

$$= 4a^2 \int_0^{\frac{\pi}{2}} \sin^2 \theta \, d\theta$$

$$= 4a^2 \cdot \tfrac{1}{2} \cdot \frac{\pi}{2} = a^2\pi.$$

Fig. 131

The transformations suggested in this and the preceding section are intuitively reasonable. Rigorous justification of them belongs to a course in advanced calculus.

EXERCISES

1. Find the area under one arch of the curve $y = \sin \frac{1}{2} x$.   *Ans.* 4.

2. Find the area under one arch of the curve $y = a \cos \dfrac{x}{a}$.   *Ans.* $2a^2$.

3. Find the area bounded by the curve $y = \ln x$ and the lines $y = 0$ and $x = e$. Solve in two ways.   *Ans.* 1.

4. Find the area bounded by the curve $y^2 = \dfrac{1}{(1 - x)^3}$ and the lines $x = -1$, $x = 0$.   *Ans.* 1.17.

5. Find the area of an ellipse, using the equations $x = a \cos \phi$, $y = b \sin \phi$.   *Ans.* πab.

6. Find the area bounded by the hyperbola $xy = a^2$ and the lines $y = 0$, $x = a$, $x = 2a$.   *Ans.* $a^2 \ln 2$.

7. Solve Ex. 6, using the equations $x = a \sec \phi$, $y = a \cos \phi$.

8. Find the area bounded by the curve $y = (1 - x^2)^2$ and the x-axis.   *Ans.* $\frac{16}{15}$.

9. Solve Ex. 8, using the horizontal element. Evaluate the integral in two ways.

10. Find the area bounded by the curve $y = \dfrac{\ln x}{x}$, the x-axis, and the maximum ordinate.   *Ans.* $\frac{1}{2}$.

11. Find the area bounded by the curve $y = \dfrac{\ln x - 1}{x}$, the x-axis, and the maximum ordinate.   *Ans.* $\frac{1}{2}$.

12. Find the area under the catenary $y = a \cosh \dfrac{x}{a}$ from $x = -a$ to $x = a$.   *Ans.* $2.35a^2$.

13. Find the area bounded by the curve $y = xe^{-x^2}$, the x-axis, and the maximum ordinate.   *Ans.* $\frac{1}{2}(1 - e^{-\frac{1}{2}})$.

14. Find the area bounded by the curve $y = \dfrac{x}{(x^2 + 3)^2}$, the x-axis, and the extreme ordinates.   *Ans.* $\frac{1}{12}$.

15. Find the area of the first arch of the curve $y = x \sin x$.

16. Find the area of the first arch of the curve $y = e^{-x} \sin x$.
                    Ans. $\frac{1}{2}(1 + e^{-\pi})$.

17. Find the area of one arch of the cycloid (Fig. 132)
$$x = a(\theta - \sin \theta), \quad y = a(1 - \cos \theta).$$
                    Ans. $3\pi a^2$.

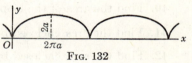

Fig. 132

18. Find the area of a circular sector of radius r and angle α.   *Ans.* $\frac{1}{2}r^2\alpha$.

19. Find the area of the four-cusped hypocycloid $x^{\frac{2}{3}} + y^{\frac{2}{3}} = a^{\frac{2}{3}}$. (Fig. 102, p. 186.)   *Ans.* $\frac{3}{8}\pi a^2$.

20. Solve Ex. 19, using the parametric equations $x = a \cos^3 t$, $y = a \sin^3 t$.

21. Find the area bounded by the curve $y = \dfrac{1 + x^2}{2x^2}$ and the lines $y = 0$, $y = x$, $x = 2$.   *Ans.* $\frac{5}{4}$.

22. Find the area bounded by the curve $y^3 = x^3 + x^4$ and the x-axis.
                    Ans. $\frac{9}{28}$.

23. Find the area bounded by the curve $y = \dfrac{2x - 3}{x^2 + 4}$, the axes, and the minimum ordinate.   *Ans.* 0.92.

24. Find the area in the first quadrant under the curve $y^2 = \dfrac{x^2}{x - 1}$ between the minimum ordinate and the line $x = 3$.   *Ans.* 2.05.

25. Find the area bounded by the curve $2y^2 + 2y - x - 2 = 0$ and the line $x = 2y$.   *Ans.* $\frac{8}{3}$.

26. Find the area bounded by the parabolas $y^2 = 4x$ and $y^2 + 12x = 36$.
                    Ans. 12.

27. Find the area of the loop of the curve $y^2 = x(1 - x^2)^2$.   *Ans.* $\frac{16}{21}$.
28. Find the area of the loop of the curve $y^2 = x^3(1 - x^2)^2$.   *Ans.* $\frac{16}{45}$.

29. Find the area of the loop of the curve $a^7y^2 = x^5(a^2 - x^2)^2$.

Ans. $\frac{16}{77}a^2$.

30. Find the area enclosed by the curve $a^2y^2 = x^2(a^2 - x^2)$.

Ans. $\frac{4}{3}a^2$.

In solving Exs. 31–41, it will be found that Wallis' Formula is particularly useful.

31. Find the area enclosed by the curve $y^2 = x^4(1 - x^2)$.   *Ans.* $\frac{1}{4}\pi$.

32. Find the area enclosed by the curve $y^2 = x^6(1 - x^2)^3$.   *Ans.* $\frac{8}{35}$.

33. Find the area enclosed by the curve $y^2 = x^3(1 - x)$.   *Ans.* $\dfrac{\pi}{8}$.

34. Find the area enclosed by the curve $y^2 = x(1 - x)^5$.   *Ans.* $\dfrac{5\pi}{64}$.

35. Find the area enclosed by the curve $a^6y^2 = x^5(a - x)^3$.   *Ans.* $\dfrac{3\pi}{128}a^2$.

36. Find the area of the loop of the curve $y^2 = x^2(1 - x)$.   *Ans.* $\frac{8}{15}$.

37. Find the area of the loop of the curve $a^3y^2 = x^2(a - x)^3$.

Ans. $\frac{8}{35}a^2$.

38. Find the area of the loop of the curve $y^2 = x^4(1 - x)^3$.   *Ans.* $\frac{32}{315}$.

39. Find the area of the loop of the curve $y^2 = x^3(1 - x)^2$.   *Ans.* $\frac{8}{35}$.

40. Find the area of the loop of the curve $y^2 = x(1 - x)^6$.   *Ans.* $\frac{64}{315}$.

41. Find the area enclosed by the curve $y^2 = (1 - x^2)^9$.   *Ans.* $\dfrac{63\pi}{128}$.

42. Find the area enclosed by the curve $y^2 = (x + 1)^2(4 - x^2)$.

Ans. $6\sqrt{3} + \frac{4}{3}\pi$.

153. Plane areas in polar coördinates. Given the equation

$$r = f(\theta)$$

of a plane curve in polar coördinates, let us try to find the area bounded by the curve and two fixed radius vectors $\theta = \alpha$, $\theta = \beta$.

Inscribe in the area n *circular sectors* of radius r_i and angle $\Delta\theta$. By elementary geometry (or Ex. 18, p. 277), the area of each sector is $\frac{1}{2}r_i^2\,\Delta\theta$. Now add up the areas of all the sectors: $\sum_{i=1}^{n}\frac{1}{2}r_i^2\,\Delta\theta$. As n increases and the sectors become narrower and narrower, this sum *approaches as its limit the area under the curve.* Hence, by the Fundamental Theorem (§ 65),

$$A = \lim_{n \to \infty} \sum_{i=1}^{n} \tfrac{1}{2}r_i^2\,\Delta\theta = \tfrac{1}{2}\int_{\alpha}^{\beta} r^2\,d\theta.$$

For the present, we must rely upon geometric intuition to assure us that the limit of this sum (*i.e.*, the area) is the same as the one appearing in the definition (§ 65). From a formulation to be set up in § 233, this fact will appear clearly.

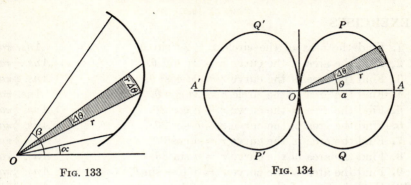

FIG. 133   FIG. 134

Example: Find the area within the curve $r^2 = a^2 \cos \theta$.

As θ varies from 0 to $\frac{1}{2}\pi$, we get positive and negative values of r, giving rise to the arcs APO, $A'P'O$. For $\frac{1}{2}\pi < \theta < \frac{3}{2}\pi$, r is imaginary. For $\frac{3}{2}\pi < \theta < 2\pi$, we get the arcs OQA, $OQ'A'$. Integrate through the first quadrant and multiply by * 4:

$$A = 4 \cdot \frac{1}{2} \int_0^{\frac{1}{2}\pi} r^2 \, d\theta = 2a^2 \int_0^{\frac{1}{2}\pi} \cos \theta \, d\theta = 2a^2 \Big[\sin \theta \Big]_0^{\frac{1}{2}\pi} = 2a^2.$$

In this example, since the curve is symmetric in all four quadrants, it might seem that we could equally well have integrated from 0 to 2π. Trying this, we find

$$\frac{1}{2} \int_0^{2\pi} r^2 \, d\theta = \frac{1}{2}a^2 \int_0^{2\pi} \cos \theta \, d\theta = \frac{1}{2}a^2 \Big[\sin \theta \Big]_0^{2\pi} = 0.$$

This result, puzzling at first, is due to a peculiarity of the polar coördinate system. While the curve appears in the second and third quadrants, these arcs, as noted above, correspond not to values of θ in those quadrants, but to values of θ in the first and fourth quadrants with negative r: when $\frac{1}{2}\pi < \theta < \frac{3}{2}\pi$, r^2 becomes negative and r imaginary. When we integrate across a region in which this occurs, each of the elements $\frac{1}{2}r^2 \, d\theta$ is negative, and the same is true of the limit of their sum. This illustrates the fact that in polar coördinates *it is not safe to choose the limits merely from the appearance of the curve.* Here even more than in Cartesian coördinates, it is best to *keep the limits of integration as narrow as possible* by using considerations of symmetry to the fullest extent.

---

* The answer may be checked by comparing the area of the curve with that of a rectangle of sides $2a$, a with center at O. Cf. the second paragraph of § 67.

EXERCISES

1. Find the area of the circle $r = 2a \sin \theta$.   *Ans.* πa^2.
2. Find the area of the curve $r = 2a \sin^2 \theta$.   *Ans.* $\frac{3}{2}\pi a^2$.
3. Find the area of the curve $r = 2a \cos^2 \theta$.   *Ans.* $\frac{3}{2}\pi a^2$.
4. Find the area of the circle $r = 2a \cos \theta$.   *Ans.* πa^2.
5. Find the area of the curve $r = a \cos 2\theta$.   *Ans.* $\frac{1}{2}\pi a^2$.
6. Find the area of the curve $r = a \sin 2\theta$.   *Ans.* $\frac{1}{2}\pi a^2$.
7. Find the area of the curve $r = a \cos 3\theta$.   *Ans.* $\frac{1}{4}\pi a^2$.
8. Find the area of the curve $r = a \sin 3\theta$.   *Ans.* $\frac{1}{4}\pi a^2$.
9. Find the area of the curve $r = a(1 - \sin \theta)$.   *Ans.* $\frac{3}{2}\pi a^2$.
10. Find the area of the curve $r = a(2 + \cos \theta)$.   *Ans.* $\frac{9}{2}\pi a^2$.
11. Find the area of the curve $r = a(3 - 2 \sin \theta)$.   *Ans.* $11\pi a^2$.
12. Find the area of the curve $r^2 = a^2 \sin 2\theta$.   *Ans.* a^2.
13. Find the area of the curve $r^2 = a^2 \cos 2\theta$.   *Ans.* a^2.
14. Find the area of the curve $r^2 = a^2(2 \cos \theta - 1)$.   *Ans.* $1.37a^2$.
15. Find the area of the curve $r = a(1 + \cos \theta)$.   *Ans.* $\frac{3}{2}\pi a^2$.
16. Find the area of the curve $r^2 = a^2 \cos \theta(1 - \cos \theta)$.   *Ans.* $0.43a^2$.
17. Find the area of the curve $r^2 = a^2 \sin \theta(1 + \sin \theta)$.   *Ans.* $3.57a^2$.
18. Find the area of the curve $r^2 = a^2 \sin \theta(1 - 2 \sin \theta)$.   *Ans.* $0.09a^2$.
19. Find the area of the curve $r^2 = a^2(\sin \theta + \cos \theta)$.   *Ans.* $2\sqrt{2}a^2$.
20. Find the area of the inner loop of the curve $r = a(1 + 2 \cos \theta)$.
                                                                                    Ans. $0.54a^2$.
21. Find the area between the inner and outer ovals of the curve $r^2 = a^2(1 + \sin \theta)$.   *Ans.* $4a^2$.
22. Find the area between the ovals of the curve $r^2 = a^2(2 - \cos \theta)$.
                                                                                    Ans. $4a^2$.
23. Find the area of the curve $r^2 = a^2 \sin \theta(1 - \cos \theta)$.   *Ans.* $2a^2$.

24. Find the area of the curve $r^2 = a^2 \cos \theta \,(2 - \cos^2 \theta)$.   *Ans.* $\dfrac{8a^2}{3}$.

25. Find the area of the curve $r^2 = a^2 \cos \theta \cos 2\theta$.
                                    Ans. $\frac{1}{3}(4\sqrt{2} - 2)a^2 = 1.22a^2$.

26. Find the area inside the *spiral of Archimedes* $r = a\theta$, from $\theta = 0$ to $\theta = 2\pi$.   *Ans.* $\frac{4}{3}\pi^3 a^2$.
27. Find the area inside the *logarithmic spiral* $r = ae^{k\theta}$, from $\theta = 0$ to $\theta = 2\pi$.

                                    Ans. $\dfrac{a^2}{4k}(e^{4k\pi} - 1)$.

Solve Exs. 28–35 in polar coördinates.
28. Find the area cut off from the parabola $y^2 = 4ax$ by a chord through the vertex making an angle α with the axis.   *Ans.* $\frac{8}{3}a^2 \cot^3 \alpha$.
29. A chord of a circle makes an angle α with the tangents at its ends. Find the area of the segment cut off.   *Ans.* $(\alpha - \sin \alpha \cos \alpha)a^2$.
30. Find the area in the first quadrant bounded by the curves $y = x^3$, $y = 2x$.

31. Find the area bounded by the curves $y^2 = 4ax$, $y = 2x$, $y = 4x$.
$$Ans. \; \tfrac{7}{24}a^2.$$

32. Find the area of the loop of the folium $x^3 + y^3 = 3axy$. $Ans. \; \tfrac{3}{2}a^2.$

33. Find the area in the first quadrant bounded by the straight line $y = x$ and the curve $(x^2 + a^2)y^2 = 4a^2x^2$. $Ans. \; \tfrac{1}{2}a^2.$

34. Find the area between the curve $(a^2 - x^2)y^2 = x^4$ and its asymptotes. $Ans. \; \pi a^2.$

35. Find the area of the loop of the curve $(y^2 - x^2)^2 = x^5$. $Ans. \; \tfrac{128}{315}.$

36. Solve Ex. 33 in Cartesian coördinates.

37. Solve Ex. 35 in Cartesian coördinates.

154. Integrable functions. A function $f(x)$ is said to be *integrable* in the interval $a \leqq x \leqq b$ if the definite integral

$$A = \int_a^b f(x) \; dx$$

has a meaning.

We have spoken from time to time of being "able to evaluate" an integral, meaning by this, able to express it in terms of elementary functions. But we know (§ 65) that the area "under" any continuous curve *exists; hence every continuous function is integrable.* Whether or not we can express the integral in elementary terms is immaterial: if not, it will still be possible by more advanced methods to evaluate it in the strict sense of the term—*i.e.*, to find its value, to any degree of approximation, for given values of a and b.

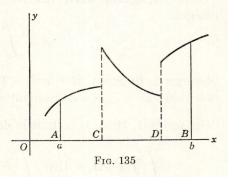

Fᴉɢ. 135

Furthermore, if the function has a finite number of finite discontinuities in the interval, as in Fig. 135, the area still exists, and the function is integrable.

Dᴇғɪɴɪᴛɪᴏɴ: *If $f(x)$ has a finite discontinuity at $x = b$, then*

$$\int_a^b f(x) \; dx = \lim_{b' \to b-} \int_a^{b'} f(x) \; dx;$$

if there is a finite discontinuity at $x = a$, then

$$\int_a^b f(x) \; dx = \lim_{a' \to a+} \int_{a'}^b f(x) \; dx.$$

Applying this definition, repeatedly if necessary, we integrate over the separate segments and add the results. In this connection, missing-point discontinuities (§ 71) may be ignored, since the value of the function, or lack of any value, at a single point cannot affect the value of the area.

We proceed to extend the list of integrable functions still further.

155. Improper integrals. In certain cases, a meaning may be assigned to the function

$$A = \int_a^b f(x)\, dx$$

under either or both of the following circumstances:

(*a*) Either a or b, or both, increase numerically without limit; or
(*b*) The integrand $f(x)$ has an infinite discontinuity at an endpoint or one or more interior points of the interval.

In either case, the integral is called an *improper integral*.

156. Integrals with infinite limits. If we keep a fixed, the integral

$$A = \int_a^b f(x)\, dx$$

becomes a function of b only (Theorem (3), § 62). It may happen that, as b increases indefinitely, the function A approaches a definite limit. If so, this limit is denoted by the symbol $\int_a^{\infty} f(x)\, dx$:

$$\int_a^{\infty} f(x)\, dx = \lim_{b \to \infty} \int_a^b f(x)\, dx.$$

Similarly,

$$\int_{-\infty}^b f(x)\, dx = \lim_{a \to -\infty} \int_a^b f(x)\, dx;$$

$$(1) \qquad \int_{-\infty}^{\infty} f(x)\, dx = \lim_{a \to -\infty} \int_a^c f(x)\, dx + \lim_{b \to \infty} \int_c^b f(x)\, dx,$$

where c may have any fixed value. If the limits occurring in the right members do not exist, the integrals have no meaning.

It should be noted that $\int_{-\infty}^{\infty} f(x)\,dx$ does not mean $\lim\limits_{b \to \infty} \int_{-b}^{b} f(x)\,dx$. If the former exists, then the latter also exists, and the two limits are equal; but the latter may exist when the former does not. For example,

$$\lim_{b \to \infty} \int_{-b}^{b} x\,dx = \lim_{b \to \infty} \left[\frac{x^2}{2}\right]_{-b}^{b} = \lim_{b \to \infty} \left(\frac{b^2}{2} - \frac{b^2}{2}\right) = 0;$$

but $\int_{-\infty}^{\infty} x\,dx$ has no meaning, since neither limit in (1) exists.

Example (a): $\int_{1}^{\infty} \frac{dx}{x^2} = \lim\limits_{b \to \infty} \int_{1}^{b} \frac{dx}{x^2} = \lim\limits_{b \to \infty} \left[-\frac{1}{x}\right]_{1}^{b} = 1.$

The curve $y = \dfrac{1}{x^2}$ is shown in Fig. 136. Geometrically, the above integral evidently means the limit of the shaded area as b becomes infinite. This limit we *define* as the "area bounded by" the curve, the x-axis, and the line $x = 1$, although it is not properly a bounded area in the literal sense. It is evident that similar argument holds in general: an integral with an infinite limit may be interpreted as the area under a curve which approaches the x-axis, usually without ever reaching it: in ordinary cases, the x-axis is an

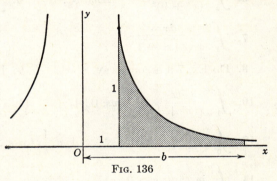

FIG. 136

asymptote of the curve. However, even though the curve is asymptotic to Ox, the integral does not necessarily have a meaning (see, for example, Exs. 24–25 below).

Example (b): Find the area between the curve $y = \dfrac{x^2 - 1}{x^2 + 1}$ and its asymptote.

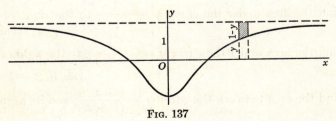

FIG. 137

Since the curve is symmetric with respect to Oy, we may write

$$A = 2\int_0^\infty \left(1 - \frac{x^2 - 1}{x^2 + 1}\right) dx.$$

Reduce the integrand to a common denominator:

$$A = 4\int_0^\infty \frac{dx}{1 + x^2} = \lim_{b\to\infty} 4\int_0^b \frac{dx}{1 + x^2} = \lim_{b\to\infty}\left[4 \operatorname{Arctan} x\right]_0^b = 2\pi.$$

EXERCISES

Evaluate the integrals in Exs. 1–13.

1. $\int_1^\infty \frac{dx}{x^4}.$ *Ans.* $\frac{1}{3}.$ **2.** $\int_0^\infty e^{-4y}\, dy.$ *Ans.* $\frac{1}{4}.$

3. $\int_{-\infty}^0 e^{3x}\, dx.$ *Ans.* $\frac{1}{3}.$ **4.** $\int_0^\infty xe^{-x^2}\, dx.$ *Ans.* $\frac{1}{2}.$

5. $\int_0^\infty \frac{x\, dx}{(x^2 + 9)^2}.$ *Ans.* $\frac{1}{18}.$ **6.** $\int_{-\infty}^\infty \frac{x\, dx}{(x^2 + 9)^2}.$ *Ans.* $0.$

7. $\int_1^\infty \frac{dx}{x\sqrt{4x^2 - 1}}.$ *Ans.* $\frac{\pi}{6}.$

8. Do Ex. **7** a second way.   **9.** Do Ex. **7** a third way.

10. $\int_1^\infty \frac{dx}{x(x^2 + 1)}.$ *Ans.* $0.347.$ **11.** $\int_1^\infty \frac{dx}{x\sqrt{x^2 + 1}}.$ *Ans.* $0.881.$

12. $\int_0^\infty e^{-st}\, dt;\ s$ real.   *Ans.* $\frac{1}{s},$ for $s > 0$; meaningless, for $s \leq 0.$

13. $\int_0^\infty te^{-st}\, dt;\ s > 0.$ *Ans.* $\frac{1}{s^2}.$

14. Find the area between the curve $y = xe^{-\frac{1}{2}x^2}$ and its asymptote.   *Ans.* 2.

15. Find the area bounded by the curve $y = xe^x$ and its asymptote.   *Ans.* 1.

16. Find the area between the curve $y = \frac{a^3}{x^2 + a^2}$ and its asymptote.   *Ans.* $\pi a^2.$

17. Find the area under the curve $y = \frac{1}{x^2 - 1}$ to the right of the line $x = 2.$ *Ans.* $\frac{1}{2}\ln 3.$

18. Find the area under the curve $y = \frac{1}{x(x + 1)^2}$ to the right of the line $x = 1.$ *Ans.* $\ln 2 - \frac{1}{2} = 0.193.$

19. Find the area between the curve $y = \frac{x}{(1 + x^2)^2}$ and its asymptote.   *Ans.* 1.

20. Find the area bounded by the curve $y^2 = \dfrac{a^8}{(a^2 + x^2)^3}$ and the lines $x = \pm\frac{1}{3}\sqrt{3}\,a$.   *Ans.* $2a^2$.

21. Find the entire area inclosed by the curve $y^2 = \dfrac{a^8}{(a^2 + x^2)^3}$.   *Ans.* $4a^2$.

22. Solve Ex. 21 by another method.

23. Find the area bounded by the curve $y = \dfrac{1}{(x^2 + 4)^2}$ and its asymptote.

Ans. $\dfrac{\pi}{16}$.

24. Find the area under the hyperbola $xy = a^2$ to the right of the line $x = a$.   *Ans.* Meaningless.

25. Find the area under the curve $y = \dfrac{1}{x \ln x}$ to the right of the line $x = e$.

Ans. Meaningless.

26. In § 105, find the area bounded by the path of the man, the path of the weight, and the original position of the rope. (Set up the integral with vertical element; see Ex. 19, p. 180.)   *Ans.* $\frac{1}{4}\pi a^2$.

157. Infinite discontinuities of the integrand. Consider now the second class of improper integrals discussed in § 155—viz. those in which the limits are finite, but the integrand has an infinite discontinuity at an endpoint or an interior point of the interval.

DEFINITIONS: *If $f(x)$ increases numerically without limit as $x \to b^-$,*

$$\int_a^b f(x)\ dx = \lim_{c \to b-} \int_a^c f(x)\ dx;$$

if $f(x)$ increases numerically without limit as $x \to a^+$,

$$\int_a^b f(x)\ dx = \lim_{c \to a+} \int_c^b f(x)\ dx.$$

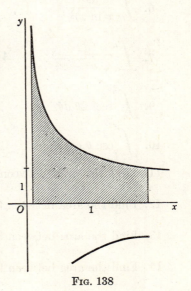

Example (a): Find the area bounded by the curve $xy^2 = 1$, the axes, and the line $x = 1$.

We write

$$A = \int_0^1 y\ dx = \lim_{c \to 0^+} \int_c^1 \frac{dx}{\sqrt{x}}$$

$$= \lim_{c \to 0^+} \left[2\sqrt{x}\right]_c^1 = \lim_{c \to 0^+} (2 - 2\sqrt{c})$$

$$= 2.$$

When the integrand $f(x)$ has an infinite discontinuity at an interior point of the interval—say at $x = c$, where $a < c < b$—we merely subdivide the interval.

FIG. 138

Example (b): Find the area under the curve $x^2y = 1$ from $x = -1$ to $x = 1$.

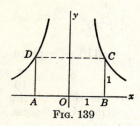
FIG. 139

Since y becomes infinite at the interior point $x = 0$, we write

$$A = \int_{-1}^{1} y \, dx = \lim_{c_1 \to 0-} \int_{-1}^{c_1} \frac{dx}{x^2} + \lim_{c_2 \to 0+} \int_{c_2}^{1} \frac{dx}{x^2}$$

$$= \lim_{c_1 \to 0-} \left[-\frac{1}{x} \right]_{-1}^{c_1} + \lim_{c_2 \to 0+} \left[-\frac{1}{x} \right]_{c_2}^{1}.$$

Since these limits do not exist, the integral has no meaning.

EXERCISES

Evaluate the integrals in Exs. 1–10.

1. $\int_{0}^{1} \frac{dx}{x^{\frac{1}{3}}}$.   *Ans.* $\frac{3}{2}$.   **2.** $\int_{0}^{1} \frac{dx}{x^{\frac{4}{3}}}$.   *Ans.* Meaningless.

3. $\int_{-1}^{1} \frac{dx}{x^{\frac{4}{3}}}$.   *Ans.* 0.   **4.** $\int_{-1}^{1} \frac{dy}{y^{\frac{5}{3}}}$.   *Ans.* Meaningless.

5. $\int_{-1}^{3} \frac{du}{u+1}$.   *Ans.* Meaningless.

6. $\int_{\frac{1}{e}}^{e} \frac{dx}{x(\ln x)^{\frac{1}{3}}}$.   *Ans.* 0.

7. $\int_{-a}^{a} \frac{dx}{\sqrt{a^2 - x^2}}$.   *Ans.* π.   **8.** $\int_{-a}^{a} \frac{x^4 \, dx}{\sqrt{a^2 - x^2}}$.   *Ans.* $\frac{3\pi a^4}{8}$.

9. $\int_{0}^{\frac{\pi}{2}} \sec^2 2\theta \, d\theta$.   *Ans.* Meaningless.

10. $\int_{-\frac{\pi}{4}}^{\frac{\pi}{4}} \csc \theta \cot \theta \, d\theta$.   *Ans.* Meaningless.

11. Find the area between the curve $xy^2 = (x - 1)^2$ and the y-axis.
    Ans. $\frac{8}{3}$.

12. Find the area between the curve $y^2 = \dfrac{1}{x(4 - x)}$ and its asymptotes.
    Ans. 2π.

13. Find the area between the curve $y^2 = \dfrac{x^4}{a^2 - x^2}$ and its asymptotes.
    Ans. πa^2.

14. Find the area between the curve $y^2 = \dfrac{1}{x(1 + x)^2}$ and the y-axis.
    Ans. 2π.

15. Find the area in the fourth quadrant bounded by $y = \ln x$ and the axes. Solve in two ways.

16. Find the area between the curve $xy^2 = 1 - x$ and its asymptote. Solve in two ways.   *Ans.* π.

17. Find the area in the second quadrant under the curve $x^2 y = e^{\frac{1}{x}}$.
                                                              Ans. 1.

18. Find the area between the curves $y = \dfrac{1}{x}$, $y = \dfrac{1}{x + x^2}$, from $x = 0$ to $x = 2$.   *Ans.* $\ln 3 = 1.099$.

19. Find the area between the curves $y = \csc x$, $y = \cot x$, from $x = -\dfrac{\pi}{2}$ to $x = \dfrac{\pi}{2}$.   *Ans.* $2 \ln 2 = 1.386$.

20. Find the area between the cissoid $y^2 = \dfrac{x^3}{2a - x}$ and its asymptote.
                                                              Ans. $3\pi a^2$.

21. Find the area between the curve $y = \dfrac{1}{x(1 + x^2)}$ and the x-axis.
                                                              Ans. Meaningless.

22. Find the area under the curve $y = \dfrac{1}{x^2 - 1}$.   *Ans.* Meaningless.

$f(x) = x \ln x + C$

$f'(x) = x \cdot \dfrac{1}{x} + \ln x \cdot 1$

$f(x) = (x + 8) \ln (x + 8) - (x + 8) + C$

$f'(x) = x + 8 \cdot \dfrac{1}{(x + 8)} + \ln (x + 8) \cdot 1 - 1$

$ = 1 + \ln (x + 8) - 1$

$ = \ln (x + 8)$

$f'(x) = 24 \ln (x$

CHAPTER *21* APPLICATIONS OF
INTEGRATION

158. The general method. From the mode of development of the Fundamental Theorem (§ 65), it might be thought that the theorem applies only in the computation of plane areas. But *any function of one variable may be represented graphically as a plane curve*. It follows that the Fundamental Theorem may be used to evaluate the limit of a sum of infinitesimal elements—*i.e.*, $\lim\limits_{\Delta x \to 0} \sum\limits_{i=1}^{n} f(x_i)\, \Delta x$ — regardless of the physical meaning of the function $f(x)$. For if the graph of the function were to be drawn (it is not necessary actually to do this), we can see that the quantity $f(x_i)\, \Delta x$ would represent a rectangular element of area, so that the theorem becomes applicable at once.

In this and succeeding chapters we shall develop a considerable variety of applications of integral calculus. In every case, the quantity to be computed will appear in the first instance as the limit of a sum of infinitesimal elements; this limit will then be evaluated by application of the Fundamental Theorem—*i.e.*, by a definite integration. This general method is one of the most important and far-reaching in the whole field of science, since it solves, directly or indirectly, a large proportion of the mathematical problems arising in engineering, physics, chemistry, astronomy, biology.

159. Solids of revolution: circular disks. Let a solid be generated by rotating the area OAB about the x-axis (the figure shows one quadrant of the solid). Imagine this solid cut into thin slices by *planes perpendicular to the axis of revolution* (a typical slice being formed by rotation of the area $PQRS$). Trim off the irregular outer edge (generated by revolving the area $S'RS$), to leave a thin *circular disk* (generated by revolving the rectangle $PQRS'$). The radius of this element is y_i, the thickness Δx, the volume $\pi y_i^2 \, \Delta x$. Now as the disks are taken thinner and thinner, the aggregate volume of trimmings approaches zero, and the sum of all the elementary volumes $\pi y_i^2 \, \Delta x$ approaches as its limit *the volume of the solid:*

$$V = \lim_{n \to \infty} \sum_{i=1}^{n} \pi y_i^2 \, \Delta x = \pi \int_a^b y^2 \, dx.$$

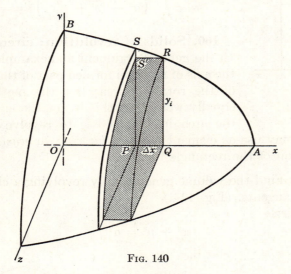

Fig. 140

This formula may be viewed as a *definition.*

The student is strongly advised not to memorize this or any similar formulas, but to make sure that he fully understands the argument. Then, only the simplest elementary geometry is required to make up the correct integral in any given case.

Example (a): The area bounded by a parabola, its axis, and its latus rectum revolves about the axis. Find the volume generated.

Let the equation of the parabola be $y^2 = 4ax$. Dividing the area into elements as in Fig. 141, we see that each rectangle generates a cylindrical volume-element of radius y, altitude dx, and volume $\pi y^2 \, dx$. Hence

$$V = \pi \int_0^a y^2 \, dx = 4\pi a \int_0^a x \, dx = 2\pi a^3.$$

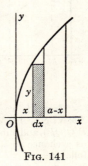

Fig. 141

Example (b): The above area rotates about the latus rectum. Find the volume generated.

If we divide the area into elements as in Fig. 142, each element generates a circular disk of radius $a - x$, thickness dy, volume $\pi(a - x)^2 \, dy$. Hence

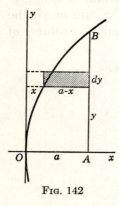

$$V = \pi \int_0^{2a} (a - x)^2 \, dy = \pi \int_0^{2a} \left(a - \frac{y^2}{4a} \right)^2 dy$$

$$= \pi \int_0^{2a} \left(a^2 - \frac{y^2}{2} + \frac{y^4}{16a^2} \right) dy = \frac{16}{15} \, \pi a^3.$$

Fig. 142

160. Solids of revolution: circular rings. In the general argument and examples of § 159, the axis of rotation formed part of the boundary of the rotating area; but the method works equally well when this is not the case. If, say, the area in Fig. 143 is to revolve about the x-axis, we may use as element the *circular ring*, or *washer*, formed by revolution of the rectangle* *PQRS*.

Example: Find the volume generated by revolving a circle about one of its tangents. (Fig. 144.)

Let the circle

$$x^2 + y^2 = a^2$$

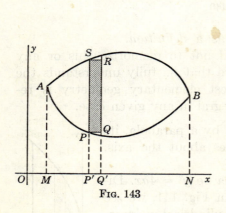

Fig. 143

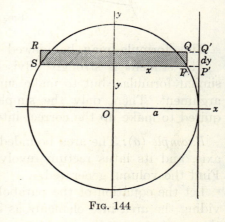

Fig. 144

---

*Instead, we might find separately the volumes generated by rotating the areas *AMNBSA*, *AMNBPA* (using as elements the disks generated by the rectangles *P'Q'RS*, *P'Q'QP*), and subtract the latter from the former. But the method of circular rings gives us a chance to *simplify before integrating*, as is beautifully illustrated by the example following.

revolve about the line $x = a$. The volume-element is a circular ring of outer radius $SP' = a + x$, inner radius $PP' = a - x$, thickness dy:

$$V = \pi \int_{-a}^{a} [(a + x)^2 - (a - x)^2] \, dy,$$

which reduces to

$$V = 8\pi a \int_{0}^{a} x \, dy.$$

Since this integral obviously represents the area of the circular quadrant, we know its value:

$$V = 8\pi a \cdot \tfrac{1}{4}\pi a^2 = 2\pi^2 a^3.$$

EXERCISES

1. The area bounded by the curve $y = e^{-x}$, the axes, and the line $x = 1$ is revolved about the x-axis. Find the volume generated.
   Ans. $\tfrac{1}{2}\pi(1 - e^{-2})$.

2. The area bounded by the parabola $ay = x^2$, the x-axis, and the line $x = b$, is revolved about the x-axis. Find the volume generated.

   Ans. $\dfrac{\pi b^5}{5a^2}$.

3. The area of Ex. 2 is revolved about the y-axis. Find the volume generated.   Ans. $\dfrac{\pi b^4}{2a}$.

4. The area bounded by the parabola $ay = x^2$ and the line $y = b$ is revolved about the x-axis. Find the volume generated.

   Ans. $\tfrac{8}{5}\pi b^2 \sqrt{ab}$.

5. The area bounded by the curve $a^2 y = x^3$, the x-axis, and the line $x = a$ revolves about Ox. Find the volume generated.   Ans. $\tfrac{1}{7}\pi a^3$.

6. The area bounded by the hyperbola $x^2 - y^2 = a^2$, the x-axis, and the line $x = 2a$ revolves about Ox. Find the volume.   Ans. $\tfrac{4}{3}\pi a^3$.

7. Find the volume generated by revolving about Ox the area in the second quadrant under the curve $y = e^x$.   Ans. $\tfrac{1}{2}\pi$.

8. Find the volume of a sphere.   Ans. $\tfrac{4}{3}\pi a^3$.

9. Find the volume of a circular cone.   Ans. $\tfrac{1}{3}\pi a^2 h$.

10. Find the volume of a prolate spheroid.   Ans. $\tfrac{4}{3}\pi ab^2$.

11. Find the volume of an oblate spheroid, using the equations $x = a \cos \phi$, $y = b \sin \phi$.   Ans. $\tfrac{4}{3}\pi a^2 b$.

12. The area enclosed by the loop of the curve $y^2 = x(x - 2)^2$ is revolved about the x-axis. Find the volume generated.   Ans. $\dfrac{4\pi}{3}$.

13. Find the volume formed by revolving about the y-axis the area bounded by the parabola $x^2 = 4ay$, the line $x = a$ and the x-axis.

   Ans. $\dfrac{\pi a^3}{8}$.

14. Find the volume formed by revolving the area of Ex. 13 about the line $x = a$. *Ans.* $\dfrac{\pi a^3}{24}$.

15. Find the volume generated by revolving about Ox the area bounded by the hyperbola $xy = a^2$, the line $x = a$, and the x-axis. *Ans.* πa^3.

16. Solve Ex. 15, using for the hyperbola the equations $x = a \cot \phi$, $y = a \tan \phi$.

17. Solve Ex. 15, using the equations $x = a \sec \psi$, $y = a \cos \psi$.

18. Find the volume generated by revolving about the y-axis the area bounded by the curve $x^2 = 4(x - y)$, the y-axis, and the line $y = 1$. *Ans.* $\frac{2}{3}\pi$.

19. Find the volume formed by revolving the area of Ex. 18 about the line $y = 1$. *Ans.* $\frac{2}{5}\pi$.

20. The area under one arch of the sine-curve revolves about the x-axis. Find the volume generated. *Ans.* $\frac{1}{2}\pi^2$.

21. The area bounded by the curve $y = (x^2 - 4)^2$ and the x-axis revolves about the y-axis. Find the volume. *Ans.* $\frac{64}{3}\pi$.

22. Find the volume generated by revolving one arch of the cycloid $x = a(\theta - \sin \theta)$, $y = a(1 - \cos \theta)$ (Fig. 132, p. 277) about Ox. *Ans.* $5\pi^2 a^3$.

23. The area bounded by the curve $y = 3 - 2x + x^2$ and the line $y = 3$ is revolved about the line $y = 3$. Find the volume generated. *Ans.* $\dfrac{16\pi}{15}$.

24. Find the volume formed by revolving about the line $y = 4$ the area of Ex. 23. *Ans.* $\dfrac{56\pi}{15}$.

25. Find the volume generated by revolving about the line $x = 2a$ the area bounded by that line, the x-axis, and the curve $a^2 y = x^3$. *Ans.* $\frac{16}{5}\pi a^3$.

26. The area bounded by the parabola $y^2 = 4ax$, the y-axis, and the line $y = 2a$ revolves about the line $y = 2a$. Find the volume obtained. *Ans.* $\frac{2}{3}\pi a^3$.

27. The area bounded by the parabola $x^2 - 2x + y = 3$, the y-axis, and the line $y = 4$ revolves about the line $y = 4$. Find the volume generated. *Ans.* $\frac{1}{5}\pi$.

28. The area of Ex. 27 revolves about the line $x = 2$. Find the volume.

29. Find the volume formed by revolving the ellipse $\dfrac{x^2}{a^2} + \dfrac{y^2}{b^2} = 1$ about the line $y = b$. *Ans.* $2\pi^2 ab^2$.

30. Find the volume formed by revolving about the line $x = 1$ the area bounded by the curve $y = (x^2 - 1)^2$ and the x-axis. *Ans.* $\frac{32}{15}\pi$.

31. Find the volume generated by revolving about Oy the area in the fourth quadrant bounded by the curve $y = \ln x$. *Ans.* $\frac{1}{2}\pi$.

32. The area in the first quadrant between the curve $y(1 + x) = x$ and its horizontal asymptote revolves about the asymptote. Find the volume. *Ans.* π.

33. Find the volume of a spherical segment of height h.
$$\text{Ans. } \tfrac{1}{3}\pi h^2 (3a - h).$$

34. Find the volume generated by revolving about the y-axis the area bounded by the curve $y = \dfrac{\sin x}{x}$ and the coördinate axes. $\qquad$ *Ans.* 4π.

35. Find the volume generated by revolving about Ox the area under the curve $xy = e^{\frac{1}{x}}$, to the right of $x = 1$. $\qquad$ *Ans.* $\tfrac{1}{2}\pi(e^2 - 1)$.

36. In Ex. 35, find the volume generated by revolving the area in the third quadrant about Ox. $\qquad$ *Ans.* $\tfrac{1}{2}\pi$.

37. Find the volume of the torus formed by revolving the circle $x^2 + y^2 = a^2$ about the line $x = b$ ($b > a$). $\qquad$ *Ans.* $2\pi^2 a^2 b$.

38. Solve Ex. 37, using the equations $x = a \sin \theta,\ y = a \cos \theta$.

39. Find the volume formed by revolving the area enclosed by the curve $y^2 = (x + 1)^2(4 - x^2)$ about Ox. $\qquad$ *Ans.* $\tfrac{96}{5}\pi$.

40. Find the volume formed by revolving about the x-axis the area enclosed by the four-cusped hypocycloid $x^{\frac{2}{3}} + y^{\frac{2}{3}} = a^{\frac{2}{3}}$. $\qquad$ *Ans.* $\dfrac{32\pi a^3}{105}$.

41. Solve Ex. 40, using the parametric equations $x = a \sin^3 \theta$, $y = a \cos^3 \theta$.

42. Find the volume formed by revolving about the y-axis the area bounded by the curve $y^2 = 4(x - y - 1)$ and the line $x = 1$.
$$\text{Ans. } \dfrac{16\pi}{5}.$$

In Exs. 43–46, transform to Cartesian coördinates.

43. Find the volume generated by revolving the curve $r^2 = a^2 \sin \theta$ about Oy. $\qquad$ *Ans.* $\tfrac{8}{15}\pi a^3$.

44. Find the volume generated by revolving the curve $r = a \sin^2 \theta$ about Oy. $\qquad$ *Ans.* $\tfrac{4}{21}\pi a^3$.

45. Find the volume generated by revolving the curve $r = a \cos^3 \theta$ about Ox.

46. Find the volume generated by rotating the curve $r^2 = a^2 \cos^3 \theta$ about Ox. $\qquad$ *Ans.* $\tfrac{8}{33}\pi a^3$.

161. Solids of revolution: cylindrical shells. The following method for computing volume of a solid of revolution frequently works out more simply than those of §§ 159–160; also, when two methods are feasible, solution both ways gives a valuable check.

Let a solid be formed by revolving the area OAB about Ox (Fig. 145 exhibits one quadrant). Divide the solid into thin shells, each with its axis in the axis of revolution: a typical shell is formed by rotation of the strip $PQRS$. Trim the outer end, leaving the *cylindrical shell* formed by rotation of the rectangle $PQRS'$. The inner radius is y_i, outer radius $y_i + \Delta y$, height x_i, volume

(1) $\qquad \Delta V_i = \pi(y_i + \Delta y)^2 x_i - \pi y_i^2 x_i = 2\pi y_i x_i \Delta y + \pi x_i \overline{\Delta y}^2.$

Hence the volume of the solid is

$$V = \lim_{\Delta y \to 0} \sum_{i=1}^{n} (2\pi y_i x_i \, \Delta y + \pi x_i \, \overline{\Delta y^2})$$

$$= \lim_{\Delta y \to 0} \sum_{i=1}^{n} 2\pi y_i x_i \, \Delta y + \lim_{\Delta y \to 0} \sum_{i=1}^{n} \pi x_i \, \overline{\Delta y^2}.$$

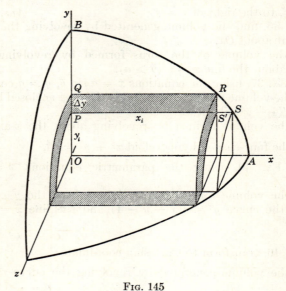

F‍IG. 145

Now, in regard to the second summation, we may write*

$$\lim_{\Delta y \to 0} \sum_{i=1}^{n} \pi x_i \, \overline{\Delta y^2} = \pi \lim_{\Delta y \to 0} \sum_{i=1}^{n} x_i \, \Delta y \cdot \lim_{\Delta y \to 0} \Delta y = 0,$$

since

$$\lim_{\Delta y \to 0} \sum_{i=1}^{n} x_i \, \Delta y = A,$$

where A is the rotating area. It follows that, in the expression for the volume-element, we may *discard the infinitesimal of higher order*, and write

$$V = \lim_{\Delta y \to 0} \sum_{i=1}^{n} 2\pi y_i x_i \, \Delta y = 2\pi \int_a^b yx \, dy.$$

In § 229 we shall lay down a definition for volume in general, and show that both the present formula and that of § 159 fall out as special cases when the solid is one of revolution.

---

* This particular method of proof requires that all the Δy's be taken equal. The result is true, however, without this restriction.

Formula (1) evidently says that, apart from infinitesimals of higher order, *the volume of a thin cylindrical shell is equal to the circumference times the height times the thickness.* This is the only formula to be remembered in connection with the present method.

Example (a): The area bounded by a parabola, its axis, and the latus rectum rotates about the latus rectum. Find the volume generated. (Fig. 146.)

With the shell as element,

$$V = 2\pi \int_0^a (a - x)y\,dx = 4\pi \sqrt{a} \int_0^a (ax^{\frac{1}{2}} - x^{\frac{3}{2}})\,dx$$

$$= 4\pi \sqrt{a} \left[\tfrac{2}{3}ax^{\frac{3}{2}} - \tfrac{2}{5}x^{\frac{5}{2}} \right]_0^a = \tfrac{16}{15}\pi a^3.$$

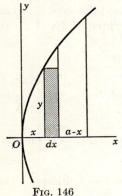

Fig. 146

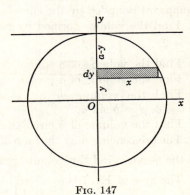

Fig. 147

Example (b): Find the volume generated by revolving a circle about one of its tangents. (Fig. 147.)

Let the circle

$$x^2 + y^2 = a^2$$

rotate around the line $y = a$. The volume, with the shell as element, is

$$V = 2 \cdot 2\pi \int_{-a}^a (a - y)x\,dy$$

(1)
$$= 4\pi a \int_{-a}^a x\,dy - 4\pi \int_{-a}^a yx\,dy.$$

The first integral in (1) represents the area of the semi-circle; the second, being the integral of an odd function between limits equally spaced from the origin, vanishes. Hence

$$V = 4\pi a \cdot \tfrac{1}{2}\pi a^2 = 2\pi^2 a^3.$$

162.   Infinitesimals of higher order. Many times as we proceed, it will be necessary to evaluate the limit of a sum of infinitesimal elements in which the formula for the element involves infinitesimals of higher order. Although we shall not usually attempt to prove the fact, it will be true in each case arising (as it was in § 161), that *infinitesimals of higher order may be neglected* without affecting the result—*i.e.*, the infinitesimal occurring under the summation sign *may be replaced by its principal part.**

EXERCISES

In Exs. 1–26, solve by the method of cylindrical shells.

1. Find the volume generated by revolving about Oy the area in the first quadrant bounded by the curve $y = 4 - x^2$ and the axes.   *Ans.* 8π.

2. Find the volume formed by revolving the area of Ex. 1 about the line $x = 2$.   *Ans.* $\dfrac{40\pi}{3}$.

3. Find the volume of a sphere.

4. Find the volume of a prolate spheroid.   *Ans.* $\frac{4}{3}\pi ab^2$.

5. Find the volume of an oblate spheroid, using the equations $x = a \cos \phi, y = b \sin \phi$.   *Ans.* $\frac{4}{3}\pi a^2 b$.

6. Find the volume of a circular cone.

7. The area enclosed by the loop of the curve $y^2 = x(1 - x)^2$ is revolved about the y-axis. Find the volume generated.   *Ans.* $\dfrac{16\pi}{35}$.

8. The area of Ex. 7 is revolved about the line $x = 1$. Find the volume formed.   *Ans.* $\dfrac{64\pi}{105}$.

9. Find the volume generated by revolving about the line $x = 2a$ the area bounded by that line, the x-axis, and the curve $a^2 y = x^3$.   *Ans.* $\frac{16}{5}\pi a^3$.

10. Find the volume formed by revolving about the line $y = 2a$ the area bounded by that line, the y-axis, and the parabola $y^2 = 4ax$.   *Ans.* $\frac{2}{3}\pi a^3$.

11. The area bounded by the parabola $x^2 - 2x + y = 3$, the y-axis, and the line $y = 4$ revolves about the line $y = 4$. Find the volume.   *Ans.* $\frac{1}{5}\pi$.

12. The area bounded by the parabola $y^2 + x - 2y = 1$, the x-axis, and the line $x = 2$ revolves about Ox. Find the volume.

13. The area of Ex. 12 revolves about the line $x = 2$. Find the volume.   *Ans.* $\frac{1}{5}\pi$.

---

* A full discussion of this whole matter belongs to a course in advanced calculus. It is in most cases easy to make the result plausible by an appeal to intuition. For instance, in § 161, imagine the shell cut lengthwise and unrolled. The result is a thin slab of thickness Δy, width x_i, length on one face $2\pi y_i$, on the other face $2\pi(y_i + \Delta y)$: that is, an ordinary rectangular plate except that it flares a trifle at the ends. Trimming off a thin slab at each end, we have left the principal part $2\pi y_i x_i \Delta y$.

14. The area in the first quadrant between the curve $y(1 + x) = x$ and its horizontal asymptote revolves about the asymptote. Find the volume.
Ans. π.

15. Find the volume of a spherical segment of height h.
Ans. $\frac{1}{3}\pi h^2(3a - h)$.

16. The area enclosed by the hypocycloid of four cusps, $x^{\frac{2}{3}} + y^{\frac{2}{3}} = a^{\frac{2}{3}}$, is revolved about Oy. Use the parametric equations $x = a \sin^3 \phi$, $y = a \cos^3 \phi$, in finding the volume formed. *Ans.* $\dfrac{32\pi a^3}{105}$.

17. Find the volume generated by revolving about Oy the area under that arch of the curve $y = \sin x$ for which x varies from 0 to π. *Ans.* $2\pi^2$.

18. Find the volume generated by revolving about Oy the left-hand half of the area of Ex. 17. *Ans.* 2π.

19. Find the volume formed by revolving about Oy the area in the first quadrant bounded by $y = \cos x$ and the two axes. *Ans.* $\pi(\pi - 2)$.

20. Find the volume formed by revolving about the line $x = 1$ the area bounded by $x = 1$, $y = e^{-x}$, and the axes. *Ans.* $\dfrac{2\pi}{e}$.

21. Find the volume generated by revolving about the y-axis the area enclosed by the curve $a^2y^2 = x^2(a^2 - x^2)$. *Ans.* $\frac{1}{4}\pi^2 a^3$.

22. The area bounded by the curve $y = (x^2 - 4)^2$ and the x-axis revolves about the y-axis. Find the volume. *Ans.* $\frac{64}{3}\pi$.

23. A round hole of radius a is bored through the center of a sphere of radius $2a$. Find the volume cut out. *Ans.* $\frac{4}{3}\pi(8 - 3\sqrt{3})a^3$.

24. Find the volume of the torus formed by revolving the circle $x^2 + y^2 = a^2$ about the line $x = b$. *Ans.* $2\pi^2 a^2 b$.

25. Solve Ex. 24, using the equations $x = a \sin \theta$, $y = a \cos \theta$.

26. Find the volume formed by revolving about Oy the area bounded by the curve $y = \dfrac{\sin x}{x}$ and the coördinate axes. *Ans.* 4π.

In Exs. 27–46, use any legitimate method.

27. Find the volume generated by revolving the area under the curve $y = e^x$, from $x = 0$ to $x = 1$, about the line $x = 1$. *Ans.* $2\pi(e - 2)$.

28. Find the volume generated by revolving about Oy the area in the second quadrant under the curve $y = e^x$. *Ans.* 2π.

29. The area bounded by the parabola $y^2 = 4ax$ and its latus rectum revolves about the directrix. Find the volume generated. *Ans.* $\frac{128}{15}\pi a^3$.

30. The area enclosed by $y^2 = x^4(1 - x^2)$ is revolved about the x-axis. Find the volume generated. *Ans.* $\dfrac{4\pi}{35}$.

31. The area of Ex. 30 is revolved about Oy. Find the volume formed. *Ans.* $\dfrac{8\pi}{15}$.

32. The area under the curve $y = \ln x$ from $x = 1$ to $x = e$ is revolved about the y-axis. Find the volume generated. *Ans.* $\frac{1}{2}\pi(1 + e^2)$.

33. Find the volume formed by revolving about Ox the area in the first quadrant bounded by the curves $y = 3x - x^3$, $x = 0$, $y = 2$.   *Ans.* $\frac{72}{35}\pi$.

34. Find the volume formed by revolving about Ox the area between the curves $x^2 = 2ay$, $x^2 = 4ay - a^2$.   *Ans.* $\frac{2}{15}\pi a^3$.

35. Find the volume formed by revolving the area of Ex. 34 about Oy.   *Ans.* $\frac{1}{8}\pi a^3$.

36. Find the volume generated by revolving the first arch of the cycloid $x = a(\theta - \sin\theta)$, $y = a(1 - \cos\theta)$ about Oy. (Fig. 132, p. 277.)   *Ans.* $6\pi^3 a^3$.

37. Find the volume formed by revolving one arch of the cycloid (Ex. 36) about the tangent at the vertex.   *Ans.* $\pi^2 a^3$.

38. Find the volume formed by revolving about Oy the area bounded by the curve $x^2 y^2 = a^2(a^2 - x^2)$.   *Ans.* $\pi^2 a^3$.

39. Find the volume obtained by revolving about Ox the area under the curve $x^3 y = a^4$ to the right of the line $x = a$.   *Ans.* $\frac{1}{5}\pi a^3$.

40. Find the volume generated by revolving about Oy the area bounded by the curve $ay^3 = (x^2 - a^2)^2$ and the x-axis.   *Ans.* $\frac{3}{5}\pi a^3$.

41. Find the volume bounded by the cylinder $x^2 + y^2 = 2a^2$ and the hyperboloid $x^2 + y^2 - z^2 = a^2$.   *Ans.* $\frac{4}{3}\pi a^3$.

42. Find the volume bounded by the surfaces $x^2 + y^2 = 4az$, $x^2 + y^2 = z^2$.   *Ans.* $\frac{32}{3}\pi a^3$.

43. Find the volume bounded by the hyperboloid $x^2 + y^2 - z^2 = a^2$ and the cone $x^2 + y^2 = 2z^2$.   *Ans.* $\frac{4}{3}\pi a^3$.

44. Find the volume inclosed by the surfaces $x^2 + y^2 - z^2 + 2a^2 = 0$, $x^2 + y^2 = az$.   *Ans.* $\frac{2}{3}\pi a^3(5 - 2\sqrt{2})$.

45. Find the volume common to the sphere $x^2 + y^2 + z^2 = a^2$ and the cone $x^2 + y^2 = z^2$.   *Ans.* $\frac{4}{3}\pi a^3(1 - \frac{1}{2}\sqrt{2})$.

46. Find the volume inside the cone $x^2 + y^2 = z^2$ and the paraboloid $x^2 + y^2 + az = 2a^2$.   *Ans.* $\frac{5}{6}\pi a^3$.

47. Find the volume formed by revolving about Ox the area under the tractrix. See § 105, and particularly Ex. 19, p. 180.   *Ans.* $\dfrac{\pi a^3}{3}$.

163. Miscellaneous solids. The volume of any solid can be expressed as a definite integral, provided we know the *area of every plane section parallel to some fixed plane*. We divide the solid into thin slices by means of n planes parallel to the fixed plane, trim off the outer edge exactly as in § 159 (which is merely a special case of the present problem), and take as element the slab remaining: the volume of this slab, of course, is the thickness times the area of the face, which by hypothesis is known.

The only plane figures whose area we are supposed to know offhand are the rectangle, the triangle, the trapezoid, the circle, the circular sector ($\frac{1}{2}r^2\alpha$), and the ellipse (πab). Thus the only solids whose volumes we can find at this time are those that can be divided into parallel slices of one of these shapes. More complicated volumes are found by double integration (Chapter 30).

Example (a): A woodsman chops halfway through a tree of diameter $2a$, one face of the cut being horizontal, the other inclined at 45°. Find the volume of wood cut out.

Figure 148 shows one-half of the required solid. If we pass cutting planes parallel to the yz-plane, the element is a *triangular plate* of width y, altitude z, and thickness dx. Hence

$$V = 2 \int_0^a \tfrac{1}{2} yz \, dx.$$

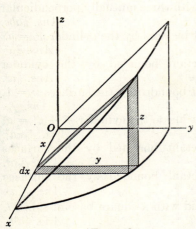

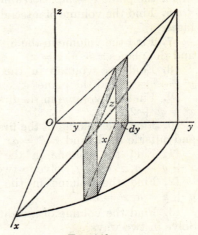

FIG. 148   FIG. 149

But $z = y$, and $y^2 = a^2 - x^2$, so that

$$V = \int_0^a (a^2 - x^2) \, dx = \tfrac{2}{3} a^3.$$

Example (b): Solve Example (a) by another method.

Planes parallel to the zx-plane cut the solid into *rectangular plates* of length x, height z, thickness dy (Fig. 149). Hence

$$V = 2 \int_0^a xz \, dy.$$

But $z = y$, $x^2 + y^2 = a^2$, $y \, dy = -x \, dx$, $x = a$ when $y = 0$, $x = 0$ when $y = a$, so that

$$V = 2 \int_0^a xy \, dy = -2 \int_a^0 x^2 \, dx = \tfrac{2}{3} a^3.$$

EXERCISES

1. Find the volume in the first octant under the plane $z = y$ and inside the cylinder $y^2 = 4 - x$. Solve in two ways.   *Ans.* 4.

2. Find the volume cut from the paraboloid $\dfrac{x^2}{a^2} + \dfrac{y^2}{b^2} = \dfrac{4z}{c}$ by the plane $z = c$.   *Ans.* $2\pi abc$.

3. Find the volume of an ellipsoid.   *Ans.* $\frac{4}{3}\pi abc$.

4. Find the volume of an elliptic cone bounded by a right section.   *Ans.* $\frac{1}{3}\pi abh$.

5. Find the volume in the first octant inside the cylinder $\dfrac{x^2}{a^2} + \dfrac{y^2}{b^2} = 1$, under the plane $z = mx$. Solve in two ways.   *Ans.* $\frac{1}{3}ma^2b$.

6. Find the volume of a tetrahedron with three mutually perpendicular faces.   *Ans.* $\frac{1}{6}abc$.

7. Find the volume in the first octant inclosed by the cylinder $y^2 = ax$ and the planes $x = a$, $z = x$.   *Ans.* $\frac{2}{5}a^3$.

8. Find the volume in the first octant bounded by the cylinder $y^2 - x^2 = a^2$ and the planes $x = a$, $z = y$.   *Ans.* $\frac{2}{3}a^3$.

9. Find the volume in the first octant bounded by the surfaces $x = 1$, $x^2 = y + 2z$.   *Ans.* $\frac{1}{20}$.

10. Find the volume in the first octant inside the cylinder $y^2 + z^2 = a^2$ and outside the cylinder $y^2 = ax$.   *Ans.* $\frac{1}{16}\pi a^3$.

11. Find the volume in the first octant bounded by the surfaces $x + y = a$, $z^2 = 4ay$. Solve in two ways.   *Ans.* $\frac{8}{15}a^3$.

12. Find the volume in the first octant bounded by the surfaces $y + z = a$, $z^2 = ax$.   *Ans.* $\frac{1}{12}a^3$.

13. Find the volume of a right pyramid with a square base of side $2a$. Solve in two ways.   *Ans.* $\frac{4}{3}a^2h$.

14. Find the volume of a wedge cut from a circular cone by two planes through the axis.   *Ans.* $\frac{1}{6}\alpha a^2h$.

15. Find the volume of a spherical wedge.   *Ans.* $\frac{2}{3}\alpha a^3$.

16. By two methods, find the volume common to two equal cylinders of revolution whose axes intersect at right angles.   *Ans.* $\frac{16}{3}a^3$.

17. Find the volume in the first octant bounded by the surfaces $az = xy$, $y^2 + ax = 4a^2$. Solve in two ways.   *Ans.* $\frac{16}{3}a^3$.

18. Find the volume in the first octant under the surface $az = xy$, bounded by the cylinder $y^2 = ax$ and the plane $x = a$.   *Ans.* $\frac{1}{6}a^3$.

19. A carpenter chisels a square hole of side 2 in. through a round post of radius 2 in., the axis of the hole intersecting that of the post at right angles. Find the volume of wood cut out.

Ans. $4\sqrt{3} + \frac{8}{3}\pi = 15.3$ cu. in.

20. A hyperbolic paraboloid is generated by a line moving parallel to the zx-plane intersecting the lines $x = a$, $z = 0$ and $z = y$, $x = 0$. Find the volume inclosed by this surface, the coördinate planes, and the plane $y = b$.   *Ans.* $\frac{1}{4}ab^2$.

21. A hyperbolic paraboloid is generated by a line moving parallel to the zx-plane and intersecting the lines $x = y = z$ and $x = a$, $z = 0$. Find the volume bounded by this surface, the xy-plane, and the plane $y = x$.

Ans. $\frac{1}{12}a^3$.

22. A surface is generated by a line parallel to the xy-plane intersecting the parabolas $z^2 = ax$, $y = 0$ and $y^2 = a^2 - az$, $x = 0$. Find the volume in the first octant bounded by this surface and the planes $x = 0$, $y = 0$.

Ans. $\frac{8}{105}a^3$.

23. A surface is generated by a line parallel to the zx-plane intersecting the parabola $y^2 = 4ax$, $z = 0$ and the line $z = b$, $x = 0$. Find the volume in the first octant bounded by this surface and the plane $y = a$.

Ans. $\frac{1}{24}a^2b$.

24. Find the volume in the first octant bounded by the hyperbolic paraboloid generated by a straight line moving always parallel to the xy-plane and passing through the lines $y + z = a$ in the yz-plane and $x = b$ in the xz-plane.

Ans. $\frac{1}{4}a^2b$.

25. In Ex. 24, derive the equation of the paraboloid; then find the volume by a second method.	*Ans.* $xz - ax - by - bz + ab = 0$.

26. Find the volume in the first octant bounded by the surfaces $y + z = a$, $x^2 + ay = a^2$. Solve in two ways.	*Ans.* $\frac{2}{5}a^3$.

27. Find the volume bounded by the cylinder $x^2 + y^2 = 2a^2$ and the planes $z = 0$, $x = 0$, $y = x$, $y = z$.	*Ans.* $\frac{2}{3}a^3$.

28. Find the volume bounded by the cylinder $x^2 = ay$ and the planes $z = 0$, $y = x$, $y = z$.	*Ans.* $\frac{1}{15}a^3$.

29. A circular conoid is generated by a straight line which moves always parallel to the xy-plane and passes through the line $y = h$ in the yz-plane and the circle $x^2 + z^2 = a^2$ in the xz-plane. Find the volume of the conoid.

Ans. $\frac{1}{2}\pi a^2 h$.

30. In Ex. 29, derive the equation of the conoid; then find the volume by a second method.	*Ans.* $h^2x^2 = (a^2 - z^2)(h - y)^2$.

31. Solve Ex. 29 if the line $y = h$ is replaced by the line $y + z = h$ ($h > a$).	*Ans.* $\frac{1}{2}\pi a^2 h$.

32. A cylinder is generated by a line moving always parallel to the line $y + z = a$, $x = 0$ and following the circle $x^2 + y^2 = a^2$, $z = 0$. Find the volume in the first octant inside the cylinder.	*Ans.* $\frac{1}{3}a^3$.

33. A cylinder is generated by a line moving always parallel to the line $x + z = a$, $y = 0$, and following the curve $y^2 + az = a^2$, $x = 0$. Find the volume in the first octant inside the cylinder.	*Ans.* $\frac{4}{15}a^3$.

34. Find the volume in the first octant bounded by the surfaces $yz = z - x$, $z = 1$. Solve in two ways.	*Ans.* $\frac{1}{4}$.

35. Find the volume in the first octant bounded by the surfaces $yz = z^2 - x$, $z = 1$.	*Ans.* $\frac{1}{8}$.

36. Find the volume in the first octant bounded by the surfaces $z = y - xy$, $x + y = 1$. Solve in two ways.	*Ans.* $\frac{1}{8}$.

37. The vertex of a cone is at $(a, 0, 0)$; the base is the curve $y^2 + z^2 = 2by$, $x = 0$. Find the volume of the cone.	*Ans.* $\frac{1}{3}\pi ab^2$.

164. Length of a curve. To find the length of the arc of a plane curve C between two given points K, L, or, as the process is often called, to *rectify* the curve, let us divide the horizontal projection MN into n equal divisions Δx and erect the ordinates, thus dividing the curve (Fig. 150) into elementary arcs Δs_i. Draw the chords

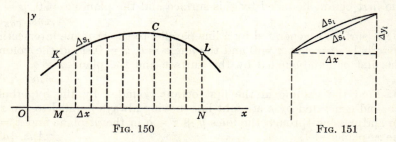

FIG. 150　　　FIG. 151

$\Delta s_i{}'$ (enlargement, Fig. 151). The sum of the lengths of the chords is the length of the inscribed broken line; as n increases, the length of the broken line approaches as its limit the *length of the curve*. (This statement evidently extends to curves in general the elementary-geometric definition of length of a circular arc.)

This limit is denoted by the symbol $\int_C ds$:

$$s = \lim_{n \to \infty} \sum_{i=1}^{n} \Delta s_i{}' = \int_C ds.$$

Now (Fig. 151)

$$\Delta s_i{}' = \sqrt{\overline{\Delta x^2} + \overline{\Delta y_i{}^2}} = \sqrt{1 + \left(\frac{\Delta y_i}{\Delta x}\right)^2}\, \Delta x,$$

so that we have to evaluate $\displaystyle\lim_{\Delta x \to 0} \sum_{i=1}^{n} \sqrt{1 + \left(\frac{\Delta y_i}{\Delta x}\right)^2}\, \Delta x$. This may be done by the Fundamental Theorem,* to give

$$s = \int_C ds = \int_a^b \sqrt{1 + \left(\frac{dy}{dx}\right)^2}\, dx,$$

---

* A temporary difficulty arises. In the Theorem, the "summand" $f(x_i)$ is supposed to be a function of x_i only, whereas here, $\sqrt{1 + \left(\frac{\Delta y_i}{\Delta x}\right)^2}$ is a function of both x_i and Δx. But the principal part of $\sqrt{1 + \left(\frac{\Delta y_i}{\Delta x}\right)^2}\, \Delta x$ is $\sqrt{1 + \left(\frac{dy_i}{dx}\right)^2}\, \Delta x$, since the limit of their ratio is 1. $\left[\text{In the notation of § 43, } \alpha = \Delta x, \beta = \sqrt{1 + \left(\frac{\Delta y_i}{\Delta x}\right)^2}\, \Delta x, k = \sqrt{1 + \left(\frac{dy_i}{dx}\right)^2}.\right]$ Thus the latter may be substituted for the former, by § 162, and the Theorem applies.

where a and b are the abscissas of the endpoints of C, and where $\dfrac{dy}{dx}$ must be replaced by its value in terms of x from the equation of the curve.

If it is more convenient to integrate with respect to y, we put

$$s = \int_c^d \sqrt{\left(\frac{dx}{dy}\right)^2 + 1}\ dy.$$

If x and y are given in terms of a parameter t,

$$s = \int_{t_1}^{t_2} \sqrt{\left(\frac{dx}{dt}\right)^2 + \left(\frac{dy}{dt}\right)^2}\ dt.$$

It is merely for convenience that the segments Δx are taken equal: the division may be made in any manner provided as n increases every segment approaches zero. Also, it is assumed that no parallel to the y-axis can meet C in more than one point. If this condition is not satisfied, C must consist of several portions for each of which the condition holds, and each portion may be considered separately.

Example (a): Find the length of the curve $y = \ln \sin x$ from $x = \frac{1}{4}\pi$ to $x = \frac{1}{2}\pi$.

From $y = \ln \sin x$, we obtain $y' = \cot x$, so that the desired length is given by

$$s = \int_{\frac{1}{4}\pi}^{\frac{1}{2}\pi} \sqrt{1 + \cot^2 x}\ dx$$

$$= \int_{\frac{1}{4}\pi}^{\frac{1}{2}\pi} \csc x\ dx = \Big[\ln(\csc x - \cot x)\Big]_{\frac{1}{4}\pi}^{\frac{1}{2}\pi}$$

$$= \ln(1 - 0) - \ln(\sqrt{2} - 1) = -\ln(\sqrt{2} - 1)$$

$$= -\ln \frac{2 - 1}{\sqrt{2} + 1} = \ln(1 + \sqrt{2}).$$

Example (b): Find the length of one arch of the cycloid $x = a(\theta - \sin \theta)$, $y = a(1 - \cos \theta)$, (Fig. 132, p. 277).

From $dx = a(1 - \cos \theta)\ d\theta$ and $dy = a \sin \theta\ d\theta$, we obtain

$$ds = \sqrt{a^2(1 - \cos \theta)^2 + a^2 \sin^2 \theta}\ d\theta.$$

Because of symmetry, we can integrate from $x = 0$ to $x = \pi a$ (from $\theta = 0$ to $\theta = \pi$) and double the result. Hence,

$$s = 2 \int_0^\pi a\sqrt{1 - 2\cos\theta + \cos^2\theta + \sin^2\theta}\, d\theta$$

$$= 2a \int_0^\pi \sqrt{2 - 2\cos\theta}\, d\theta.$$

Now $1 - \cos\theta = 2\sin^2\tfrac{1}{2}\theta$, so

$$s = 2a \int_0^\pi \sqrt{4\sin^2\tfrac{1}{2}\theta}\, d\theta = 4a \int_0^\pi \sin\tfrac{1}{2}\theta\, d\theta$$

$$= -8a \left[\cos\tfrac{1}{2}\theta\right]_0^\pi = 8a.$$

EXERCISES

In Exs. 1–22, find the length of the curve over the given interval.

1. One branch of the curve $9y^2 = 4x^3$ from $x = 0$ to $x = 3$. Ans. $\tfrac{14}{3}$.

2. The curve $y = \ln x$ from $x = \sqrt{3}$ to $x = 2\sqrt{2}$. Ans. $1 + \tfrac{1}{2}\ln\tfrac{3}{2}$.

3. The curve $y = \ln\cos x$ from $x = 0$ to $x = \tfrac{1}{4}\pi$. Use x as the variable of integration. Ans. $\ln(1 + \sqrt{2})$.

4. Solve Ex. 3, using y as the variable of integration.

5. One branch of the curve $ay^2 = x^3$ from $x = 0$ to $x = 5a$. Ans. $\tfrac{335}{27}a$.

6. Solve Ex. 5, using the parametric equations $x = at^2$, $y = at^3$.

7. The four-cusped hypocycloid $x^{\frac{2}{3}} + y^{\frac{2}{3}} = a^{\frac{2}{3}}$. Ans. $6a$.

8. Solve Ex. 7, using the parametric equations $x = a\sin^3 t$, $y = a\cos^3 t$.

9. One branch of the parabola $y^2 = 4ax$ from the vertex to the end of the latus rectum, integrating with respect to x. Ans. $2.295a$.

10. Solve Ex. 9, using y as the variable of integration.

11. Solve Ex. 9, using the equations $x = a\tan^2\psi$, $y = 2a\tan\psi$.

12. The curve $y = e^x$ from $x = 0$ to $x = 1$, using x as the variable of integration.

13. The catenary $y = a\cosh\dfrac{x}{a}$ from $x = 0$ to $x = x_1$. Ans. $a\sinh\dfrac{x_1}{a}$.

14. The curve $y = \tfrac{4}{5}x^{\frac{5}{4}}$, from $x = 0$ to $x = 9$. Evaluate the integral in two ways. Ans. $\tfrac{232}{15}$.

15. One branch of the curve $9y^2 = 4(1 + x^2)^3$, from $x = 0$ to $x = 2$. Ans. $\tfrac{22}{3}$.

16. The curve $y = \text{Arcsin } e^{-x}$, from $x = 0$ to $x = \ln\tfrac{5}{4}$. Ans. $\ln 2$.

17. The curve $y = (e^{2x} - 1)^{\frac{1}{2}} + \text{Arcsin } e^{-x}$, from $x = 0$ to $x = 1$. Ans. $e - 1$.

18. The curve $y = (1 - x^2)^{\frac{1}{2}} + \ln\dfrac{x}{1 + (1 - x^2)^{\frac{1}{2}}}$, from $x = \tfrac{3}{5}$ to $x = \tfrac{4}{5}$. Ans. $\ln\tfrac{4}{3}$.

19. One branch of the curve $25y^2 = (x + 2)^2 (2x - 1)^3$, from $x = \tfrac{1}{2}$ to $x = 3$. Ans. $\tfrac{58}{5}$.

20. The curve $y = \tfrac{1}{2}x(x^2 - 1)^{\frac{1}{2}} - \tfrac{1}{2}\ln(x + \sqrt{x^2 - 1})$, from $x = 1$ to $x = \tfrac{5}{4}$. Ans. $\tfrac{9}{32}$.

21. One branch of the curve $3y^2 = (2x + 3)^3$, from $x = -1$ to $x = 1$.

Ans. $\frac{56}{9}$.

22. The curve $y = e^x$ from $x = 0$ to $x = 1$, using y as the variable of integration.

23. The curve $6xy = x^4 + 3$ from the minimum point to $x = 2$.

Ans. $\frac{17}{12}$.

24. Find the perimeter of the loop of the curve $9ay^2 = x(x - 3a)^2$.

Ans. $4\sqrt{3}\,a$.

25. Find the perimeter of the loop of the curve $9y^2 = x^2(2x + 3)$.

Ans. $2\sqrt{3}$.

26. Find the length of the tractrix (§ 105) from the starting point to $y = h$. (See Ex. 19, p. 180.)

Ans. $a \ln \dfrac{a}{h}$.

27. A point moves in a plane curve according to the law $x = 1 - \cos 2t$, $y = 2 \cos t$. Find the length of the path.

Ans. $2\sqrt{5} + \ln(2 + \sqrt{5}) = 5.92$ ft.

28. A point moves according to the law $x = e^{-3t}$, $y = e^{-2t}$. Find the entire distance traveled ($t > 0$).   *Ans.* $\frac{1}{27}(13^{\frac{3}{2}} - 8) = 1.44$ ft.

29. A point moves according to the law $x = e^{-t}$, $y = e^{-t} - e^{-2t}$. Find the length of its path ($t > 0$).   *Ans.* 1.15 ft.

30. Find the length of the cycloid $x = a(\theta - \sin \theta)$, $y = a(1 - \cos \theta)$ from $(0, 0)$ to any point (x_1, y_1) on the curve ($0 \leqq \theta \leqq \pi$). Check the answer against Example (*b*).   *Ans.* $4a - \sqrt{4a^2 - 2ay_1}$.

165. Surfaces of revolution. The problem of this section is to find the area of the surface generated by rotating a plane curve C about a line in its plane—say for definiteness about the x-axis.

To do this, inscribe in C a broken line of n segments $\Delta s_i{}'$ exactly as in § 164. In the rotation, each segment $\Delta s_i{}'$ generates the frustum of a circular cone, the radii of whose bases are y_i, $y_i + \Delta y_i$. By elementary geometry, the surface area of this conical frustum is *the circumference of the middle section multiplied by the slant height*, or $2\pi(y_i + \frac{1}{2}\Delta y_i)\,\Delta s_i{}'$. Discarding higher-order infinitesimals as usual, we have

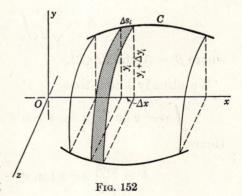

Fig. 152

$$A = \lim_{n \to \infty} \sum_{i=1}^{n} 2\pi y_i\,\Delta s_i{}' = 2\pi \int_C y\,ds.$$

Example: Find the surface area generated by revolving about the *y*-axis the hyperbola

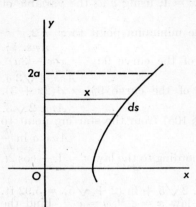

FIG. 153

$$x^2 - y^2 = a^2$$

from $y = 0$ to $y = 2a$.

At once

$$A = 2\pi \int_{y=0}^{y=2a} x \, ds.$$

From the equation $x^2 - y^2 = a^2$, we obtain $x \, dx - y \, dy = 0$, so that

$$ds = \sqrt{1 + \left(\frac{dx}{dy}\right)^2} \, dy$$

$$= \sqrt{1 + \frac{y^2}{x^2}} \, dy.$$

Thus we have

$$A = 2\pi \int_0^{2a} x \sqrt{1 + \frac{y^2}{x^2}} \, dy$$

$$= 2\pi \int_0^{2a} \sqrt{x^2 + y^2} \, dy$$

$$= 2\pi \int_0^{2a} \sqrt{a^2 + 2y^2} \, dy.$$

Put $\sqrt{2}\, y = a \tan \theta$, which yields

$$A = \frac{2\pi a^2}{\sqrt{2}} \int_0^\beta \sec^3 \theta \, d\theta,$$

where $\beta = \text{Arctan } 2\sqrt{2}$.

We already know that

$$\int \sec^3 \theta \, d\theta = \tfrac{1}{2}\left[\sec \theta \tan \theta + \ln (\sec \theta + \tan \theta)\right] + c.$$

Hence

$$A = \frac{\pi a^2}{\sqrt{2}}\left[\sec \theta \tan \theta + \ln (\sec \theta + \tan \theta)\right]_0^\beta.$$

But $\tan \beta = 2\sqrt{2}$, $\sec \beta = 3$, $\tan 0 = 0$, and $\sec 0 = 1$. Therefore,

$$A = \frac{\pi a^2}{\sqrt{2}}[6\sqrt{2} + \ln (3 + 2\sqrt{2})].$$

EXERCISES

1. Find the surface area of a sphere of radius a.   *Ans.* $4\pi a^2$.

2. Solve Ex. 1, using the equations $x = a \cos \theta$, $y = a \sin \theta$.

3. Find the surface area generated by revolving the curve $a^2 y = x^3$ about Ox, from $x = 0$ to $x = a$.   *Ans.* $\frac{1}{27}\pi a^2 (10\sqrt{10} - 1)$.

4. Find the surface area generated by revolving one arch of the cosine curve about Ox.   *Ans.* $2\pi[\sqrt{2} + \ln(1 + \sqrt{2})]$.

5. Find the surface area formed by revolving the catenary $y = a \cosh \dfrac{x}{a}$ about Oy, from $x = 0$ to $x = a$.   *Ans.* $2\pi a^2 (1 - e^{-1})$.

6. Find the surface area generated by revolving the arc of Ex. 5 about the tangent at the vertex.   *Ans.* $\pi a^2 (1 + \frac{1}{2}\sinh 2 - 2\sinh 1)$.

7. Find the surface area generated by revolving the arc of Ex. 5 about Ox.   *Ans.* $\pi a^2 (1 + \frac{1}{2}\sinh 2)$.

8. Find the surface area formed by revolving the four-cusped hypocycloid $x^{\frac{2}{3}} + y^{\frac{2}{3}} = a^{\frac{2}{3}}$ about Ox.   *Ans.* $\frac{12}{5}\pi a^2$.

9. Solve Ex. 8, using the parametric equations $x = a \sin^3 t$, $y = a \cos^3 t$.

10. Find the surface area of a torus.   *Ans.* $4\pi^2 ab$.

11. Find the surface area generated by revolving an arch of the cycloid $x = a(\theta - \sin \theta)$, $y = a(1 - \cos \theta)$ about its base.   *Ans.* $\frac{64}{3}\pi a^2$.

12. Find the surface area of a zone cut from a sphere by two parallel planes at a distance h apart.   *Ans.* $2\pi ah$.

13. Find the surface area cut from a sphere by a circular cone of half-angle α with its vertex at the center of the sphere. (Use $x = a \cos \theta$, $y = a \sin \theta$.)   *Ans.* $2\pi a^2 (1 - \cos \alpha)$.

14. Find the surface area generated by revolving about Oy that part of the curve $y = \ln x$ lying in the fourth quadrant, using x as the variable of integration.   *Ans.* $\pi[\sqrt{2} + \ln(1 + \sqrt{2})]$.

15. Solve Ex. 14, using y as the variable of integration.

16. Find the surface area generated by revolving about Ox the arc of the curve $6xy = x^4 + 3$, from the minimum point to $x = 2$.   *Ans.* $\frac{47}{16}\pi$.

17. In Ex. 16, revolve the arc about Oy.   *Ans.* $(\frac{15}{4} + \ln 2)\pi$.

18. Find the surface area generated by revolving about Ox the curve $8a^2 y^2 = x^2(a^2 - x^2)$.   *Ans.* $\frac{1}{2}\pi a^2$.

19. Find the area cut off from the paraboloid $x^2 + y^2 = 4az$ by the plane $z = a$, using z as the variable of integration.   *Ans.* $\frac{8}{3}\pi a^2 (2\sqrt{2} - 1)$.

20. Solve Ex. 19, using x or y as the variable.

21. Solve Ex. 19, using the equations $x = 2a \cot \psi$, $z = a \cot^2 \psi$.

22. Find the surface area generated by revolving about the y-axis that arc of the curve $a^2 y = x^3$ from $x = 0$ to $x = a$.

$$\textit{Ans.}\ \frac{\pi a^2}{12}[3\sqrt{10} + \ln(3 + \sqrt{10})].$$

CHAPTER 22 CENTROIDS

166. Density. A mass is said to be *homogeneous* if the masses contained in any two equal volumes are equal. In all other cases the mass is *heterogeneous*. In the present chapter we confine our attention to homogeneous masses.

The *density* of a homogeneous mass is the ratio of the mass M to the volume V that it occupies. That is, the density is the mass per unit volume.

A *mass-point* may be imagined as the limiting form approached by a body whose dimensions approach zero, while the density increases in such a way that the mass remains finite. Similarly we may think of masses of one dimension and of two dimensions—*i.e.*, of material curves and surfaces. Such masses are represented approximately, for example, by slender wires and thin sheets of metal. In these cases we define the density as "linear density," or mass per unit length, and "surface density," or mass per unit area.

167. Moment of mass. The product of a mass m, concentrated at a point P, by the distance l of P from a given point, line, or plane, is called the *mass-moment* of m with respect to the point, line, or plane (also called *simple moment*, or *moment of first order*). Denoting this moment by G, we have

$$G = ml.$$

If a system of points $P_1, P_2, \cdots, P_n$, having masses $m_1, m_2, \cdots, m_n$ respectively, be referred to Cartesian coördinate axes, the moments of the system with respect to the three coördinate planes are

(1) $$G_{yz} = \sum_{i=1}^{n} m_i x_i, \quad G_{zx} = \sum_{i=1}^{n} m_i y_i, \quad G_{xy} = \sum_{i=1}^{n} m_i z_i.$$

If the particles all lie in one of the coördinate planes, the moments with respect to coördinate planes reduce to moments with respect to coördinate axes.

The idea of mass-moment may be extended to the case of a continuous mass by thinking of the body as composed of an indefinitely large number of particles. (A definition will be laid down in § 244.) The actual computation of such a moment is usually effected by means of definite integrals; we return to this question presently.

168. Centroid. Given any mass M, let G_{yz}, G_{zx}, G_{xy} denote the moments of the mass with respect to the coördinate planes. The point C whose coördinates $\bar{x}$, $\bar{y}$, $\bar{z}$ are given by the formulas

$$(1) \qquad M\bar{x} = G_{yz}, \quad M\bar{y} = G_{zx}, \quad M\bar{z} = G_{xy}$$

clearly has the property that the moment of the mass with respect to each coördinate plane is the same as if the whole mass were concentrated at that point. For, the moments for a particle of mass M at the point C are $M\bar{x}$, $M\bar{y}$, $M\bar{z}$; and by (1), these are equal to the moments for the original distribution.

It can be shown that this property holds for moments with respect to any other plane. For a system of mass-particles the proof is as follows. Let

$$(2) \qquad x \cos \alpha + y \cos \beta + z \cos \gamma = p$$

be the equation of any plane in the normal form; let $\bar{p}$, p_1, $\cdots$, p_n be the distances of the points C, P_1, $\cdots$, P_n from this plane. Then

$$p_1 = x_1 \cos \alpha + y_1 \cos \beta + z_1 \cos \gamma - p,$$
$$\vdots \qquad\qquad\qquad \vdots$$
$$p_n = x_n \cos \alpha + y_n \cos \beta + z_n \cos \gamma - p,$$

so that by simple addition

$$\sum_{i=1}^{n} m_i p_i = \left(\sum_{i=1}^{n} m_i x_i\right) \cos \alpha + \left(\sum_{i=1}^{n} m_i y_i\right) \cos \beta + \left(\sum_{i=1}^{n} m_i z_i\right) \cos \gamma - \left(\sum_{i=1}^{n} m_i\right) p$$

$$= M\bar{x} \cos \alpha + M\bar{y} \cos \beta + M\bar{z} \cos \gamma - Mp$$

$$= M (\bar{x} \cos \alpha + \bar{y} \cos \beta + \bar{z} \cos \gamma - p) = M\bar{p}.$$

The point C is called the *centroid* (also called *center of mass*, or *center of gravity*). Hence:

The centroid of a mass is a point such that the moment of the mass with respect to any plane is the same as if the whole mass were concentrated at that point.

The moment of a mass with respect to any plane through the centroid is zero.

In the determination of centroids, the following considerations are often useful (the first two apply only to homogeneous masses):

(a) *If the body has a geometrical center, that point is the centroid.*
(b) *Any plane or line of symmetry must contain the centroid.*
(c) *If the body consists of several portions for each of which the centroid can be found, each portion may be imagined concentrated at its centroid.*

In many applications, we are concerned with centroids of purely geometric figures (volumes, areas, lines), *no idea of mass being involved*. However, it is unnecessary to write out a separate theory for such cases; the above discussion applies to plane areas, for instance, if we merely replace the word "mass" throughout by "area." To see this, note that for a homogeneous body of given size and shape, both the mass and its moment with respect to any plane are proportional to the density δ. Hence, in the formulas for $\bar{x}$, $\bar{y}$, $\bar{z}$, the factor δ cancels out from both members, leaving the coördinates of the centroid independent of the density. We may therefore take $\delta = 1$, so that the "mass" is numerically equal to the area.

169. Centroid of a system of particles. Combining (1), § 167, with (1), § 168, we see that the coördinates of the centroid of a *system of particles* are given by the formulas

$$M\bar{x} = \sum_{i=1}^{n} m_i x_i, \quad M\bar{y} = \sum_{i=1}^{n} m_i y_i, \quad M\bar{z} = \sum_{i=1}^{n} m_i z_i.$$

By use of (c), § 168, problems involving distributed masses may frequently be reduced to consideration of a set of particles, as in the following examples.

Example (a): Find the centroid of a metal plate having the shape shown in Fig. 154 (or, what amounts to the same thing, the centroid of the area itself).

Dividing the area into rectangles by the dotted lines, we have 16 units at P: $(4, 1)$, 8 units at Q: $(1, 4)$, and 24 units at R: $(3, 8)$. Hence

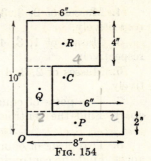

$$M\bar{x} = 16 \cdot 4 + 8 \cdot 1 + 24 \cdot 3 = 144,$$
$$\bar{x} = \tfrac{144}{48} = 3,$$

$$M\bar{y} = 16 \cdot 1 + 8 \cdot 4 + 24 \cdot 8 = 240,$$
$$\bar{y} = \tfrac{240}{48} = 5.$$

FIG. 154

In problems of this type, mistakes are easy to make. The danger is greatly reduced if we draw the figure to scale on coördinate paper. In most cases, the centroid can be fairly accurately located by estimate. A very valuable rough check is obtained if in each problem we *compare our answer with the estimate;* if a mistake of any great magnitude has been made, it will certainly be evident.

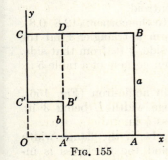

FIG. 155

It is frequently convenient to adopt the fiction of *negative mass.* That this is allowable is clear; for our theory nowhere requires that M be positive.

Example (b): Find the centroid of a square plate with a square cut out of one corner.

Place the axes as shown. We might consider the figure as composed of two rectangles $C'B'DC$, $A'ABD$; but the algebra is much simpler if we consider it as a square plate $OABC$, together with a plate $OA'B'C'$ of numerically equal but negative density:

$$M\bar{x} = M\bar{y} = a^2 \cdot \tfrac{1}{2}a - b^2 \cdot \tfrac{1}{2}b,$$
$$\bar{x} = \bar{y} = \frac{a^3 - b^3}{2(a^2 - b^2)} = \frac{a^2 + ab + b^2}{2(a + b)}.$$

EXERCISES

In Exs. 1–6, find the centroid of the given system.

1. Equal masses at $(3, 0)$, $(1, 2)$, $(4, 1)$, $(-3, -3)$.   *Ans.* $(\tfrac{5}{4}, 0)$.
2. Equal masses at $(0, 0)$, $(0, 3)$, $(2, 1)$, $(-4, -5)$.   *Ans.* $(-\tfrac{1}{2}, -\tfrac{1}{4})$.
3. Masses of 1, 2, 4, 5 units at $(-3, 2)$, $(2, 0)$, $(2, 4)$, $(-1, -2)$ respectively.   *Ans.* $(\tfrac{1}{3}, \tfrac{2}{3})$.

4. Masses of 2, 3, 3, 4 units at $(2, -1)$, $(-1, 1)$, $(3, -3)$, $(-1, 5)$ respectively.   *Ans.* $(\frac{1}{2}, 1)$.

5. Masses of 1, 3, 4 units at $(0, -3, -1)$, $(4, 5, 3)$, $(1, -3, -4)$ respectively.   *Ans.* $(2, 0, -1)$.

6. Masses of 2, 3, 4 units at $(4, \frac{1}{2}, 1)$, $(3, 4, 0)$, $(-2, -1, 4)$ respectively.   *Ans.* $(1, 1, 2)$.

7. Two posts of equal radius, 6 ft. and 4 ft. tall, stand upright 5 ft. apart. Find the centroid.

Ans. 2 ft. from taller post, 2.6 ft. above the ground.

8. Two posts of equal radius, 7 ft. and 3 ft. tall, stand upright 20 ft. apart. Find the centroid.

Ans. 6 ft. from taller post, 2.9 ft. above the ground.

9. Show that the centroid of two particles divides the line joining them into segments inversely proportional to the masses.

10. Show that the centroid of three equal particles lies at the intersection of the medians of the triangle having the three points as vertices. (Deduce from Ex. 9.)

11. A slender rod 40 in. long is bent so as to form a right angle. If the segments are 8 in. and 32 in. long, find the centroid.

Ans. Coördinates in inches relative to the corner: $(12.8, 0.8)$.

12. Three rods, of lengths 10, 10, 16 ft., form a triangle. Find the centroid.   *Ans.* On the altitude to the longest side, $\frac{5}{3}$ ft. from that side.

13. Weights of 2, 3, 7, and 8 lbs. rest on the four corners of a table 5 ft. square. Find the centroid of the four weights.

14. Find the centroid of a cross-section of an angle-iron (Fig. 156), the outside flange width L being 3 in. and the thickness $\frac{1}{2}$ in.

15. Solve Ex. 14, if the flange width remains 3 in., and the thickness is increased to 1 in.

16. For the angle-iron of Fig. 156, for what proportions does the centroid lie at the inner corner?   *Ans.* $L = 2.62t$.

17. Find the centroid of a nonsymmetrical angle-iron, like that of Fig. 156, except that one flange is 3 in. wide and $\frac{1}{2}$ in. thick, the other 4 in. wide and $\frac{3}{4}$ in. thick.

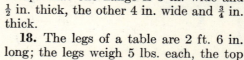

Fig. 156

18. The legs of a table are 2 ft. 6 in. long; the legs weigh 5 lbs. each, the top 10 lbs. Find the centroid.   *Ans.* 20 in. above the floor.

19. If in Ex. 18, the top of the table is taken as one inch thick, how much does the centroid rise?   *Ans.* $\frac{1}{6}$ in.

20. From a square of side $2a$ a circle of radius $b (b < a)$ is stamped out. If the circle is tangent to two sides of the square, find the centroid (tangents as axes).

$$Ans. \ \bar{x} = \bar{y} = \frac{4a^3 - \pi b^3}{4a^2 - \pi b^2}.$$

21. Check the answer to Example (*a*) by solving in another way (different subdivision).

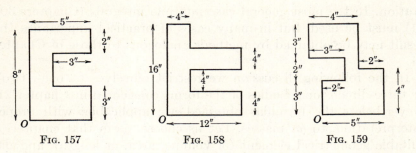

Fig. 157   Fig. 158   Fig. 159

22. Find the centroid of the area in Fig. 157. Check by solving in two ways.

23. Find in two ways the centroid of the area in Fig. 158.

24. In Fig. 159, find the centroid. *Ans.* $(\frac{125}{62}, \frac{231}{62})$.

25. The base of a box is 4×3 ft., the depth is 2 ft. If there is no top, find the centroid. *Ans.* 0.7 ft. from the base.

26. Solve Ex. 25 if the bottom is twice as heavy, per unit area, as the sides. *Ans.* 0.54 ft. from the base.

27. A sphere of radius 3 in. rests on a cylinder of radius 4 in. and height 8 in. Find the height of the centroid. *Ans.* 5.54 in.

28. Find the centroid of a cylindrical basin of radius 4 in. and depth 3 in. *Ans.* $\frac{9}{10}$ in. above the base.

29. Solve Ex. 28 if the bottom is twice as heavy, per unit area, as the sides. *Ans.* $\frac{9}{14}$ in. above the base.

30. A circular disk of radius b, density k, is inset in a disk of radius a, density 1. If the two circles are tangent, find the centroid.

$$Ans. \text{ From point of tangency, } \bar{x} = \frac{a^3 + (k-1)b^3}{a^2 + (k-1)b^2}.$$

31. Solve Ex. 30 if the circumference of the smaller passes through the center of the larger ($2b < a$). *Ans.* From center, $\bar{x} = \dfrac{(k-1)b^3}{a^2 + (k-1)b^2}.$

32. A sphere of radius a and density 2 is imbedded in a sphere of radius $2a$ and density 3, the two spheres being tangent (internally). Find the centroid. *Ans.* $\bar{x} = -\frac{1}{23}a.$

33. A metal sphere 1 ft. in diameter, of specific gravity 9, is dropped into a cylindrical tank 2 ft. in diameter and 10 ft. deep. The tank is then filled with water. Neglecting the weight of the tank, find the height of the centroid. *Ans.* 4.47 ft.

34. A cubical container of edge 3 ft. is filled with water, except that a stone slab 2 ft. by 1 ft. by 3 in., of specific gravity 2, lies on the bottom. Neglecting the weight of the container, find the height of the centroid. *Ans.* 1 ft. 5.7 in.

170. Determination of centroids by integration. To find the centroid of a continuous mass, we must as a rule resort to integration. In the most general case multiple integrals (Chapters 30–31) must be used, but in many cases of practical importance the result may be obtained by methods analogous to those of Chapter 21.

In the following discussion we restrict ourselves to one-, two-, or three-dimensional bodies of the forms considered in Chapter 21. Nevertheless the formulas obtained are applicable, with proper interpretation, to *all* masses. Let us choose, as in that chapter, a suitable geometrical element (of volume, area, or length), and denote the mass contained in this element by Δm_i. Let x_i, y_i, z_i be the *coördinates of the centroid of* Δm_i. Then the product $x_i \, \Delta m_i$ is the simple mass-moment of Δm_i with respect to the yz-plane (or the y-axis, for a plane mass in the xy-plane), and the limit of the sum of all such moments is the moment of the whole mass. In this way we obtain the following formulas:

$$(1) \qquad M\bar{x} = \lim_{n \to \infty} \sum_{i=1}^{n} x_i \, \Delta m_i = \int x_c \, dm,$$

$$(2) \qquad M\bar{y} = \lim_{n \to \infty} \sum_{i=1}^{n} y_i \, \Delta m_i = \int y_c \, dm,$$

$$(3) \qquad M\bar{z} = \lim_{n \to \infty} \sum_{i=1}^{n} z_i \, \Delta m_i = \int z_c \, dm,$$

where x_c, y_c, z_c are the *coordinates of the centroid of the element.*

The subscript is inserted to make sure that we never forget the meaning of the multipliers x_c, y_c, z_c. Of course in any problem these variables, as well as the mass-element, must be expressed in terms of some one variable.

It should be noted that, in the expressions for the coördinates of the centroid of the element, *all infinitesimals may be neglected.* For instance, it often happens that the x-coördinate is, exactly, $x_i + \frac{1}{2}\Delta x$, so that the first limit above, in its primary form, is

$$M\bar{x} = \lim_{n \to \infty} \sum_{i=1}^{n} (x_i + \tfrac{1}{2}\Delta x) \, \Delta m_i.$$

But the term $\frac{1}{2}\Delta x \, \Delta m_i$, being infinitesimal of higher order, may be dropped.

171. Centroid of a plane area: Cartesian coördinates. In any system of coördinates, formulas (1) and (2) above become, for a plane area,

$$(1) \qquad A\bar{x} = \int x_c \, dA, \quad A\bar{y} = \int y_c \, dA.$$

In Cartesian coördinates, the area-element dA is of course the usual rectangular element.

Example: Find the centroid of the area in the first quadrant bounded by the parabola $y^2 = 4ax$ and its latus rectum.

With the vertical element, the area is

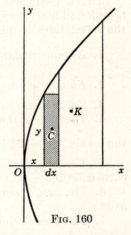

$$A = \int_0^a y \, dx = 2\sqrt{a} \int_0^a \sqrt{x} \, dx = \tfrac{4}{3}a^2.$$

The centroid C of the element is $(x, \tfrac{1}{2}y)$: by (1),

$$A\bar{x} = \int_0^a xy \, dx = 2\sqrt{a} \int_0^a x^{\frac{3}{2}} \, dx = \tfrac{4}{5}a^3,$$

$$A\bar{y} = \int_0^a \tfrac{1}{2}y \cdot y \, dx = 2a \int_0^a x \, dx = a^3.$$

Thus the coördinates of the centroid K are

$$\bar{x} = \tfrac{3}{5}a, \quad \bar{y} = \tfrac{3}{4}a,$$

which checks very well by estimate.*

Fig. 160

Anyone who thoroughly understands this simple example should have little difficulty, either here or later, with the subject of centroids. One has not fully mastered it, however, until he sees clearly that this example is exactly the same, in kind, as Example (a), § 169. There, we replaced three rectangles by equivalent particles at the respective centroids, and found the total moment by simple arithmetic; here, we replace n rectangles by particles in exactly the same way, and find the limit of the sum of elementary moments by integration.

We shall have occasion to use the following theorem.

THEOREM: *The centroid of a triangular area is at the intersection of the medians.*

* The student is strongly advised not to write out formulas for $\bar{x}$, $\bar{y}$, as quotients of integrals. Aside from clumsiness of form, the continual turning back and forth from one integral to the other wastes time and increases the likelihood of mistake. The best technique is to take up in turn the three tasks — of finding A, $A\bar{x}$, $A\bar{y}$ — and complete each before the next is started.

The proof of this theorem is a very easy problem in integration (Ex. 9 below). Also, a special device may be noted. Divide the

triangle into strips parallel to the base. The centroid of each strip is in the median, so that the same must be true for the centroid of the whole. And by symmetry of argument, if the centroid lies in one median it must lie in all three.

Fig. 161

EXERCISES

In Exs. 1–31, find the centroid of the area. (Where A is given, it has been found in a previous exercise.) In each case, draw a figure and estimate the coördinates of the centroid.

1. A semicircular area. Solve in two ways. *Ans.* $\bar{x} = \dfrac{4a}{3\pi}$.

2. An elliptic quadrant. Solve in two ways. *Ans.* $\left(\dfrac{4a}{3\pi}, \dfrac{4b}{3\pi}\right)$.

3. Ex. 2, using the equations $x = a \cos \phi$, $y = b \sin \phi$.

4. The area in the first quadrant under that arch of $y = \sin \frac{1}{2}x$ nearest the y-axis. ($A = 4$.) *Ans.* $\left(\pi, \dfrac{\pi}{8}\right)$.

5. The area in the first quadrant under the curve $y = 4 - x^2$. Find each coördinate in two ways.

6. The area bounded by the curve $y = 2(1 + x^3)$ and the coördinate axes. *Ans.* $(-\frac{2}{5}, \frac{6}{7})$.

7. The area bounded by the curve $y^2 = 4ax$, the x-axis, and the line $x = x_1$. ($A = \frac{2}{3}x_1y_1$.) *Ans.* $(\frac{3}{5}x_1, \frac{3}{8}y_1)$.

8. The area bounded by the curve $x^2 = 4ay$, the x-axis, and the line $x = x_1$. Find each coördinate in two ways. *Ans.* $(\frac{3}{4}x_1, \frac{3}{10}y_1)$.

9. A triangle. (Solve for a right triangle by integration; deduce the general answer.)

10. The area in the first quadrant bounded by the curve $y = e^{-x}$, the axes, and the ordinate $x = \ln 5$. *Ans.* $(1 - \frac{1}{4}\ln 5, \frac{3}{10})$.

11. The whole area in the first quadrant between the curve $y = e^{-x}$ and the axes. *Ans.* $(1, \frac{1}{4})$.

12. The area bounded by the curve $2y^2 + 2y - x - 2 = 0$ and the line $x = 2y$. ($A = \frac{8}{3}$.) *Ans.* $(-\frac{4}{5}, 0)$.

13. The area bounded by the curve $y = \ln x$, the x-axis, and the line $x = e$. ($A = 1$.) *Ans.* $\left(\dfrac{e^2 + 1}{4}, \dfrac{e - 2}{2}\right)$.

14. The area bounded by the curve $y^2 = \dfrac{1}{(1 - x)^3}$, the y-axis, and the line $x = -1$. $A = 2(2 - \sqrt{2})$. *Ans.* $(1 - \sqrt{2}, 0)$.

15. One arch of the cycloid $x = a(\theta - \sin \theta)$, $y = a(1 - \cos \theta)$. ($A = 3\pi a^2$.) *Ans.* $(\pi a, \frac{5}{6}a)$.

—**16.** The area between the curves $2y = x^2$, $y = x^3$. *Ans.* $(\frac{3}{10}, \frac{3}{70})$.

17. The area in the first quadrant under the curve $y = \dfrac{a^3}{x^2 + a^2}$. ($A = \frac{1}{2}\pi a^2$.) *Ans.* Nonexistent.

18. The area in the first quadrant under the curve $y = \dfrac{x}{(1 + x^2)^2}$. ($A = \frac{1}{2}$.)

19. The area bounded by the parabola $y^2 = 4ax$, its axis prolonged, and the tangent at the upper end of the latus rectum. *Ans.* $\left(-\dfrac{a}{5}, \dfrac{a}{2}\right)$.

20. The area bounded by the parabola $x^2 - 4x + y = 5$ and the lines $x = 0$, $y = 9$. *Ans.* $(\frac{1}{2}, \frac{39}{5})$.

21. The fourth-quadrant area bounded by the parabola $y^2 + 2x - 2y = 3$. Obtain each coördinate in two ways. *Ans.* $(0.53, -0.35)$.

22. The area bounded by the curve $xy^3 = 1$ and the lines $x = 0$, $y = 1$. *Ans.* $(\frac{1}{5}, 2)$.

23. The area between the curve $y = xe^x$ and its asymptote. *Ans.* $(-2, -\frac{1}{8})$.

24. The area in the first quadrant bounded by the hypocycloid $x = a\cos^3 t$, $y = a\sin^3 t$. ($A = \frac{3}{32}\pi a^2$.) *Ans.* $\bar{x} = \bar{y} = \dfrac{256a}{315\pi}$.

25. The area in the first quadrant between the two parabolas $x^2 - 4ay + a^2 = 0$, $x^2 = 2ay$. *Ans.* $(\frac{3}{8}a, \frac{1}{5}a)$.

26. The area in Fig. 162.

27. The area in Fig. 163.

28. The area in Fig. 164.

29. The area of the loop of the curve $y^2 = x(1 - x^2)^2$. ($A = \frac{16}{21}$.) *Ans.* $(\frac{7}{15}, 0)$.

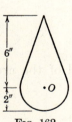

Fig. 162

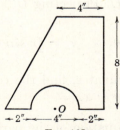

Fig. 163

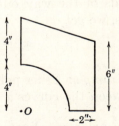

Fig. 164

30. The area in the first quadrant enclosed by the curve $a^2y^2 = x^2(a^2 - x^2)$ and the axes. $\left(A = \dfrac{a^2}{3}.\right)$ *Ans.* $\left(\dfrac{3\pi a}{16}, \dfrac{a}{5}\right)$.

31. The area of the loop of the curve $y^2 = x^2(1 - x)$. ($A = \frac{8}{15}$.) *Ans.* $(\frac{4}{7}, 0)$.

32. Devise a method for finding graphically the centroid of any quadrilateral.

172. Centroid of a plane area: polar coördinates. In a definite integration, if we always make sure that the *limit of the sum of elements* represents the quantity required, nothing else matters. In two different problems using the same coördinates and dealing with the same kind of physical entity (*e.g.*, a plane area), or even at different stages of the same problem, we may at any time shift from one type of element to another, according to convenience.

Figure 165 represents an enlargement of a single element of polar area. The area of the *sector* bounded by arc PP' is $\frac{1}{2}r_i^2 \, \Delta\theta$. For the *triangle* whose base is the straight line PP', the height is $r_i\cos \frac{1}{2} \, \Delta\theta$, base $2r_i \sin \frac{1}{2} \, \Delta\theta$, area

$$r_i^2 \cos \tfrac{1}{2} \, \Delta\theta \sin \tfrac{1}{2} \, \Delta\theta = \tfrac{1}{2}r_i^2 \sin \Delta\theta.$$

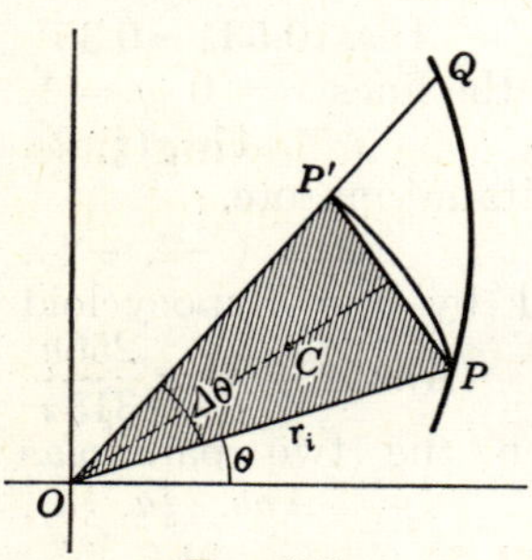

Now (§ 11)

$$\lim_{\Delta\theta\to 0} \frac{\frac{1}{2}r_i^2 \sin \Delta\theta}{\frac{1}{2}r_i^2 \, \Delta\theta} = 1.$$

Thus the sector and the triangle are equal, except for infinitesimals of higher order. This means that, keeping always the same value $\frac{1}{2}r^2 \, d\theta$, we may at any time think of the element as a sector or a triangle, whichever is handier at the moment.

Fig. 165

In building up the moment-integrals (1) of § 171, the triangle is most convenient, because we know that its centroid C is two-thirds of the way out from O. Projecting OC into the x- and y-axes, we get

$$x_c = \tfrac{2}{3}r \cos \theta, \qquad y_c = \tfrac{2}{3}r \sin \theta.$$

Example: Using polar coördinates, find the centroid of the area between the curves $x^2 = ay$, $y = x$.

In polar coördinates, the equation of the parabola is

$$r^2 \cos^2 \theta = ar \sin \theta, \qquad r = a \tan \theta \sec \theta:$$

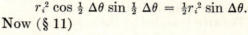

$$A = \frac{1}{2}\int_0^{\frac{\pi}{4}} r^2 \, d\theta = \frac{1}{2}a^2 \int_0^{\frac{\pi}{4}} \tan^2 \theta \sec^2 \theta \, d\theta = \frac{1}{6}a^2 \left[\tan^3 \theta \right]_0^{\frac{\pi}{4}} = \frac{1}{6}a^2;$$

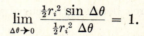

$$A\bar{x} = \frac{1}{2}\int_0^{\frac{\pi}{4}} \tfrac{2}{3}r \cos \theta \cdot r^2 \, d\theta$$

$$A\bar{x} = \tfrac{1}{3}a^3 \int_0^{\frac{\pi}{4}} \tan^3 \theta \sec^2 \theta \, d\theta$$

$$= \tfrac{1}{12}a^3,$$

$$\bar{x} = \tfrac{1}{2}a;$$

$$A\bar{y} = \tfrac{1}{2}\int_0^{\frac{\pi}{4}} \tfrac{2}{3}r \sin \theta \cdot r^2 \, d\theta$$

$$= \tfrac{1}{3}a^3 \int_0^{\frac{\pi}{4}} \tan^4 \theta \sec^2 \theta \, d\theta$$

$$= \tfrac{1}{15}a^3,$$

$$\bar{y} = \tfrac{2}{5}a.$$

173. The Second Proposition of Pappus. The following theorem, known as the *Second Proposition of Pappus*, is useful in a variety of ways (see also Ex. 19, p. 327):

The volume of any solid of revolution is equal to the generating area times the circumference of the circle described by the centroid of the area.*

For definiteness, take the axis of revolution as x-axis, and suppose first that this forms part of the boundary of the rotating area (Fig. 167). The proof is very easy. By §§ 159, 171,

$$V = \pi \int_a^b y^2 \, dx, \qquad A\bar{y} = \int_a^b \tfrac{1}{2}y \cdot y \, dx,$$

so that

$$V = 2\pi A\bar{y} = A \cdot 2\pi\bar{y}.$$

But this last formula, translated into words, is the theorem.

The proof is readily extended to cover the situation shown in Fig. 168.

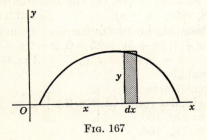

FIG. 167

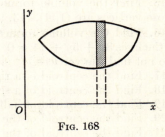

FIG. 168

*The case in which the axis of revolution crosses the generating area is excluded.

The figure at top right is labeled FIG. 166, with points K, C marked.

EXERCISES

In Exs. 1–10, find the centroid, using polar coördinates.

1. A semicircular area.

2. Half of a circular ring. $Ans. \ \bar{x} = \dfrac{4}{3\pi} \cdot \dfrac{a^2 + ab + b^2}{a + b}.$

3. A circular sector of half-angle α. $Ans. \ \bar{x} = \dfrac{2}{3} r \dfrac{\sin \alpha}{\alpha}.$

4. The upper half of the area bounded by the curve $r^2 = a^2 \cos \theta$. ($A = a^2$.) $Ans. \ \bar{y} = \tfrac{4}{15}a.$

5. One-half the area of the curve $r = a(1 - \sin \theta)$. ($A = \tfrac{3}{4}\pi a^2$.)

$$Ans. \ \left(\dfrac{16a}{9\pi}, \dfrac{-5a}{6} \right).$$

6. One quadrant of the area of the curve $r = 2a \cos^2 \theta$. ($A = \tfrac{3}{8}\pi a^2$.)

$$Ans. \ \left(\dfrac{1024a}{315\pi}, \dfrac{64a}{21\pi} \right).$$

7. The area bounded by the curves $y = 2x$, $y^2 = 4ax$. $Ans. \ (\tfrac{2}{5}a, a).$

8. The area in the first quadrant bounded by the curves $y = x^3$, $y = 2x$. ($A = 1$.)

9. One loop of the curve $r = a \cos 2\theta$. ($A = \tfrac{1}{8}\pi a^2$.)

10. The area between the curves $x^2 = ay$, $y^2 = ax$. (Deduce from the example of § 172.)

In. Exs. 11–21, use the Second Proposition of Pappus.

11. Find the volume of a circular cylinder.

12. Find the volume of a torus. $Ans. \ 2\pi^2 a^2 b.$

13. Find the volume generated by rotating an ellipse about the tangent at one end of the minor axis. $Ans. \ 2\pi^2 ab^2.$

14. The ellipse $\dfrac{x^2}{a^2} + \dfrac{y^2}{b^2} = 1$ and the circle $x^2 + y^2 = ab$ are rotated about the line $x = a$. Compare the volumes obtained.

15. Find the volume formed by rotating about Oy the quadrilateral whose vertices are $(1, 4)$, $(13, 9)$, $(18, -3)$, $(6, -8)$. $Ans. \ 3211\pi.$

16. Find the volume formed by rotating about Ox the area bounded by the lines $3x + 5y + 14 = 0$, $2y = x + 1$, $3x + 5y + 25 = 0$, $x - 2y = 10$. (Do not find the vertices.) $Ans. \ 66\pi.$

17. Find the centroid of a right triangle.

18. Find the centroid of a semicircular area.

19. Find the centroid of half of a circular ring. (Cf. Ex. 2.)

20. Find the centroid of the area in Fig. 163.

21. Find the centroid of the area in Fig. 164.

22. Prove the Second Proposition of Pappus by another method.

23. Prove the Second Proposition for the case shown in Fig. 168.

174. Centroid of a solid of revolution. Since the centroid of a solid of revolution lies on the axis, a single coördinate determines its position. If, say, the revolution takes place around the x-axis, the general formulas of § 170 reduce to

$$V\bar{x} = \int x_c \, dV,$$

where of course dV is a disk, ring, or shell, according to convenience, and x_c is the x-coördinate of the centroid of the volume-element.

Example (a): The area bounded by the parabola $y^2 = 4ax$, the x-axis, and the latus rectum revolves about the x-axis. Find the centroid of the solid generated.

Cutting the generating area into rectangles as shown, we have as the element a circular disk of volume $\pi y^2 \, dx$. The centroid C of the element is of course at its center, *i.e.*, on the x-axis at a distance x from O. Hence

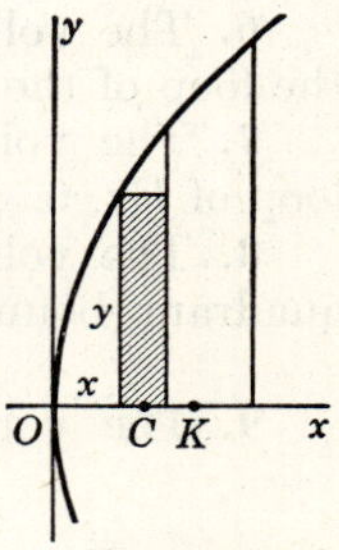

$$V\bar{x} = \pi \int_0^a xy^2 \, dx = 4\pi a \int_0^a x^2 \, dx = \tfrac{4}{3}\pi a^4.$$

By Example (a), § 159, $V = 2\pi a^3$, so that

Fig. 169

$$\bar{x} = \frac{\tfrac{4}{3}\pi a^4}{2\pi a^3} = \frac{2}{3}a.$$

Example (b): Solve Example (a) by another method.

With the cylindrical shell as element,

$$dV = 2\pi y(a - x) \, dy.$$

By the midpoint formula of analytic geometry,

$$x_c = \tfrac{1}{2}(a + x).$$

Thus

$$V\bar{x} = 2\pi \cdot \tfrac{1}{2} \int_0^{2a} y(a^2 - x^2) \, dy.$$

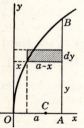

Fig. 170

Putting $y \, dy = 2a \, dx$ and changing limits, we get

$$V\bar{x} = 2\pi a \int_0^a (a^2 - x^2) \, dx = 2\pi a \left[a^2 x - \tfrac{1}{3}x^3 \right]_0^a = \tfrac{4}{3}\pi a^4,$$

as before.

EXERCISES

In Exs. 1–28, find the centroid.

1. A hemisphere of radius R. Solve in two ways.

Ans. At distance $\frac{3}{8}R$ from the center.

2. The volume formed by revolving about Oy the area in the first quadrant bounded by $y^2 = 4ax$, $y = 0$, $x = a$. Solve in two ways.

Ans. $(0, \frac{5}{6}a, 0)$.

3. The volume formed by rotating the area of Ex. 2 about the latus rectum. Solve in two ways.   *Ans.* $(a, \frac{5}{8}a, 0)$.

4. The upper half of the oblate spheroid formed by revolving the ellipse $\dfrac{x^2}{a^2} + \dfrac{y^2}{b^2} = 1$ about Oy. Solve in two ways.   *Ans.* $(0, \frac{3}{8}b, 0)$.

5. A circular cone. Solve in two ways.

Ans. At distance $\frac{1}{4}h$ from the base.

6. The volume formed by revolving about Ox the area enclosed by the loop of the curve $y^2 = x^2(1 - x)$.   *Ans.* $(\frac{3}{5}, 0, 0)$.

7. The volume formed by revolving about Oy the top half of the loop of Ex. 6.   *Ans.* $(0, \frac{21}{128}, 0)$.

8. The volume formed by revolving about Ox the area in the first quadrant bounded by the curve $y^2 = x^2(1 - x^2)$ and the x-axis.

Ans. $(\frac{5}{8}, 0, 0)$.

9. The volume formed by revolving about Oy the area of Ex. 8.

Ans. $\left(0, \dfrac{2}{3\pi}, 0\right)$.

10. The volume formed by revolving about the line $x = -1$ the area bounded by $y = x^3$, $y = 0$, $x = 1$.   *Ans.* $(-1, \frac{25}{84}, 0)$.

11. The volume generated by revolving about Ox the area in the second quadrant under the curve $y = e^x$. $(V = \frac{1}{2}\pi.)$ *Ans.* $\bar{x} = -\frac{1}{2}$.

12. The volume generated by revolving about Oy the area in the second quadrant under the curve $y = e^x$. $(V = 2\pi.)$ *Ans.* $\bar{y} = \frac{1}{8}$.

13. The volume formed by revolving about the line $x = 2a$ the area bounded by that line, the x-axis, and the curve $a^2y = x^3$. $(V = \frac{16}{5}\pi a^3.)$

Ans. $\bar{y} = \frac{10}{7}a$.

14. The volume generated by revolving about Ox the area in the third quadrant under the curve $y^2 = \dfrac{1}{(1 - x)^3}$.   *Ans.* $\bar{x} = -1$.

15. The volume formed by revolving about Ox the area under the curve $xy = 1$, from $x = 1$ to $x = b$. What happens as b increases?

Ans. $\bar{x} = \dfrac{b \ln b}{b - 1}$.

16. One-half of a torus (cut by a plane perpendicular to the axis). Solve in two ways. $\left(V = \pi^2 a^2 b.\right)$ *Ans.* $\bar{y} = \dfrac{4a}{3\pi}$.

17. The volume formed by rotating about Oy the area in the third quadrant bounded by the curve $y^2 = x + 1$. Solve in two ways.

Ans. $\bar{y} = -\frac{5}{16}$.

18. The volume formed by rotating the area of Ex. 17 about Ox. Solve in two ways. $\qquad$ *Ans.* $\bar{x} = -\frac{1}{3}$.

19. The volume generated by revolving about the directrix the area in the first quadrant bounded by the parabola $y^2 = 4ax$, its axis, and its latus rectum. ($V = \frac{64}{15}\pi a^3$.) $\qquad$ *Ans.* $\bar{y} = \frac{25}{32}a$.

20. The volume generated by revolving about Ox the area bounded by $y = \text{in } x$, $y = 0$, $x = e$. $\qquad$ *Ans.* $\bar{x} = \dfrac{e^2 - 1}{4(e - 2)}$.

21. The volume generated by revolving the area of Ex. 20 about Oy.
$$\text{*Ans.* } \bar{y} = \frac{e^2 - 1}{2(e^2 + 1)}.$$

22. The volume cut off from the hyperboloid $x^2 + y^2 - z^2 + a^2 = 0$ by the plane $z = 2a$. $\qquad$ *Ans.* $\bar{z} = \frac{27}{16}a$.

23. The upper half of the solid bounded by the surfaces $x^2 + y^2 = 2a^2$, $x^2 + y^2 - z^2 = a^2$. ($V = \frac{2}{3}\pi a^3$.) $\qquad$ *Ans.* $\bar{z} = \frac{3}{8}a$.

24. The upper half of the solid bounded by the surfaces $x^2 + y^2 - z^2 = a^2$, $x^2 + y^2 = 2z^2$. ($V = \frac{2}{3}\pi a^3$.) $\qquad$ *Ans.* $\bar{z} = \frac{3}{8}a$.

25. The volume inside the surfaces $x^2 + y^2 = z^2$, $x^2 + y^2 + az = 2a^2$. ($V = \frac{5}{6}\pi a^3$.) $\qquad$ *Ans.* $\bar{z} = \frac{11}{10}a$.

26. The volume bounded by the surfaces $x^2 + y^2 = 3a^2 - 2az$, $x^2 + y^2 = az$. $\qquad$ *Ans.* $\bar{z} = \frac{5}{6}a$.

27. The volume formed by revolving about Ox the area in the first quadrant between the parabolas $x^2 = 2ay$, $x^2 = 4ay - a^2$. ($V = \frac{1}{15}\pi a^3$.)
$$\text{*Ans.* } \bar{x} = \frac{15}{32}a.$$

28. The volume formed by revolving the area of Ex. 27 about Oy. ($V = \frac{1}{8}\pi a^3$.) $\qquad$ *Ans.* $\bar{y} = \frac{1}{4}a$.

29. A top consists of a cone of radius 2 in. and height 2 in., surmounted by a cylinder of radius $\frac{1}{4}$ in. and height 2 in. Find the centroid. $\qquad$ *Ans.* 1.57 in. from vertex of cone.

30. A wooden buoy consists of a cone and hemisphere placed base to base; the common radius is 2 ft., the height of the cone 6 ft. Find the centroid. $\qquad$ *Ans.* 5.4 ft. from vertex.

31. Find the centroid of the volume formed by rotating about Oy the area under the curve $y = e^{-\frac{1}{2}x^2}$. $\qquad$ *Ans.* $\bar{y} = \frac{1}{4}$.

32. Solve Ex. 31 by inspection. (In $V\bar{y}$, put $x^2 = \frac{1}{2}z^2$; compare $V\bar{y}$ and V.)

33. If a plane area, *symmetric to* Oy, rotates about an external line parallel to Oy, show that $\bar{y}$ for the solid thus formed is equal to $\bar{y}$ for the area. State the result as a general theorem. Check Ex. 16 above with Ex. 1, p. 316.

34. Find the centroid of the solid formed by rotating an isosceles triangle about an external line perpendicular to the base. (Ex. 33.)

35. Find graphically the centroid of the solid formed by rotating an isosceles trapezoid about an external line perpendicular to the base. (Ex. 32, p. 317, and Ex. 33 above.)

36. If V_x, V_y denote the volumes formed by revolving a plane area (lying all in one quadrant) about Ox and Oy in turn, show that the mass-moments $V_x\bar{x}$, $V_y\bar{y}$ are equal. Check Ex. 16.

175. Centroids of miscellaneous solids.

Example (*a*): Find the centroid of one-half of the solid in the examples of § 163.

With the triangular element (Fig. 148), we know by § 171 that the centroid of the element is $(x_c, y_c, z_c) \equiv (x, \frac{2}{3}y, \frac{1}{3}z)$. Thus

$$V\bar{x} = \int_0^a x \cdot \tfrac{1}{2}yz \, dx.$$

But $z = y$, $x \, dx = -y \, dy$:

$$V\bar{x} = \tfrac{1}{2}\int_0^a xy^2 \, dx$$

$$= -\tfrac{1}{2}\int_a^0 y^3 \, dy = \tfrac{1}{8}a^4.$$

In § 163 we found $V = \frac{1}{3}a^3$, so that

$$\bar{x} = \frac{\frac{1}{8}a^4}{\frac{1}{3}a^3} = \tfrac{3}{8}a.$$

Next,

$$V\bar{y} = \int_0^a \tfrac{2}{3}y \cdot \tfrac{1}{2}yz \, dx$$

$$= \tfrac{1}{3}\int_0^a y^3 \, dx = \tfrac{1}{3}\int_0^a (a^2 - x^2)^{\frac{3}{2}} \, dx.$$

Putting $x = a \sin \theta$, we find

$$V\bar{y} = \tfrac{1}{16}\pi a^4,$$

$$\bar{y} = \frac{\frac{1}{16}\pi a^4}{\frac{1}{3}a^3} = \tfrac{3}{16}\pi a.$$

Since for all the elements $z_c = \frac{1}{3}z = \frac{1}{3}y = \frac{1}{2}y_c$,

$$\bar{z} = \tfrac{1}{2}\bar{y} = \tfrac{3}{32}\pi a.$$

Example (*b*): Solve Example (*a*) by another method.

For the rectangular element (Fig. 149), the centroid is easily seen to be $(x_c, y_c, z_c) \equiv (\frac{1}{2}x, y, \frac{1}{2}z)$. Thus

$$V\bar{x} = \int_0^a \tfrac{1}{2}x \cdot xz \, dy = \tfrac{1}{2}\int_0^a x^2y \, dy = -\tfrac{1}{2}\int_a^0 x^3 \, dx,$$

as before. Next,

$$V\bar{y} = \int_0^a y \cdot xz \, dy = \int_0^a y^2x \, dy = \int_0^a y^2\sqrt{a^2 - y^2} \, dy.$$

Putting $y = a \sin \theta$, we obtain the same result as above.

EXERCISES

Find the centroid of the given solid.

1. An elliptic cone cut off by a right section. $(V = \frac{1}{3}\pi abh.)$

$$Ans. \ \bar{z} = \frac{1}{4}h.$$

2. The volume cut from the paraboloid $\dfrac{x^2}{a^2} + \dfrac{y^2}{b^2} = \dfrac{z}{c}$ by the plane $z = c$.

$$Ans. \ \bar{z} = \frac{2}{3}c.$$

3. The volume in the first octant under the plane $z = y$ and inside the parabolic cylinder $y^2 = 4 - x$. Solve in two ways. $(V = 4.)$

$$Ans. \ (\tfrac{4}{3}, \tfrac{16}{15}, \tfrac{8}{15}).$$

4. A pyramid with a square base, whose apex lies vertically above one corner of the base. $\qquad Ans. \ (\tfrac{3}{8}a, \tfrac{3}{8}a, \tfrac{1}{4}h).$

5. The volume in the first octant inclosed by the cylinder $y^2 = ax$ and the planes $x = a$, $z = x$. $(V = \frac{2}{5}a^3.)$ $\qquad Ans. \ (\tfrac{5}{7}a, \tfrac{5}{12}a, \tfrac{5}{14}a).$

6. The volume in the first octant bounded by the surfaces $y + z = a$, $z^2 = ax$. $(V = \frac{1}{12}a^3.)$

7. The volume in the first octant bounded by the surfaces $x^2 = y + 2z$, $x = 1$. $(V = \frac{1}{20}.)$

8. The volume in the first octant inside the cylinder $y^2 + z^2 = a^2$ and outside the cylinder $y^2 = ax$. $(V = \frac{1}{16}\pi a^3.)$ $\qquad Ans. \ \left(\dfrac{a}{4}, \dfrac{32a}{15\pi}, \dfrac{16a}{15\pi}\right).$

9. One-eighth of the solid bounded by two equal circular cylinders whose axes intersect at right angles. $(V = \frac{2}{3}a^3.)$ $\qquad Ans. \ (\tfrac{9}{64}\pi a, \tfrac{9}{64}\pi a, \tfrac{3}{8}a).$

10. The volume in the first octant bounded by the surfaces $y + z = a$, $x^2 + ay = a^2$. $(V = \frac{2}{5}a^3.)$

11. The volume bounded by the cylinder $x^2 = ay$ and the planes $z = 0$, $y = x$, $y = z$. $(V = \frac{1}{15}a^3.)$

12. The volume in the first octant bounded by the surfaces $yz = z - x$, $z = 1$. Solve in two ways. $(V = \frac{1}{4}.)$

13. The volume in the first octant bounded by the surfaces $y^2 = 4a^2 - ax$, $az = xy$. $(V = \frac{16}{3}a^3.)$

14. The volume in the first octant bounded by the surfaces $x + y = a$, $z^2 = 4ay$. Solve in two ways. $(V = \frac{8}{15}a^3.)$

15. The volume inclosed by the plane $y = x$, the xy-plane, and the hyperbolic paraboloid with rulings parallel to the zx-plane intersecting the lines $x = a$, $z = 0$ and $x = y = z$. $(V = \frac{1}{12}a^3.)$

16. One-quarter of the circular conoid generated by a line parallel to the xy-plane following the line $y = h$, $x = 0$ and the circle $x^2 + z^2 = a^2$, $y = 0$. $(V = \frac{1}{8}\pi a^2 h.)$ $\qquad Ans. \ \left(\dfrac{8a}{9\pi}, \dfrac{h}{3}, \dfrac{4a}{3\pi}\right).$

17. The volume of Ex. 16 by a second method. (Ex. 30, p. 301, and Ex. 2, p. 316.)

18. The volume in the first octant inside the cylinder formed by a line parallel to the line $y + z = a$, $x = 0$, and following the circle $x^2 + y^2 = a^2$, $z = 0$. $(V = \frac{1}{3}a^3.)$ $\qquad Ans. \ (\tfrac{3}{8}a, \tfrac{3}{32}\pi a, \tfrac{3}{32}\pi a).$

176. Centroid of an arc; of a surface of revolution. The centroid of a curved arc or of a surface of revolution can be found by choosing an element as in § 164 or § 165 respectively.

Example: Find the centroid of a semicircular wire.

Taking the bounding diameter as axis of y, we have $\bar{y} = 0$, and

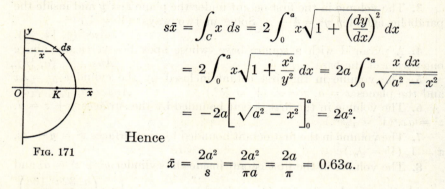

$$s\bar{x} = \int_C x \, ds = 2 \int_0^a x\sqrt{1 + \left(\frac{dy}{dx}\right)^2} \, dx$$

$$= 2 \int_0^a x\sqrt{1 + \frac{x^2}{y^2}} \, dx = 2a \int_0^a \frac{x \, dx}{\sqrt{a^2 - x^2}}$$

$$= -2a\left[\sqrt{a^2 - x^2}\,\right]_0^a = 2a^2.$$

Hence

$$\bar{x} = \frac{2a^2}{s} = \frac{2a^2}{\pi a} = \frac{2a}{\pi} = 0.63a.$$

Fig. 171

EXERCISES

In Exs. 1–16, find the centroid.

1. The example above, using y as the variable of integration.

2. The example above, using the equations $x = a \cos \theta$, $y = a \sin \theta$.

3. A circular arc of half-angle α. *Ans.* $\bar{x} = \dfrac{a \sin \alpha}{\alpha}$.

4. Half the arc of the hypocycloid $x^{\frac{2}{3}} + y^{\frac{2}{3}} = a^{\frac{2}{3}}$. $(s = 3a.)$ *Ans.* $\bar{x} = \frac{2}{5}a$.

5. Half the arc of the hypocycloid $x = a \cos^3 \phi$, $y = a \sin^3 \phi$.

6. The arc from cusp to vertex of the cycloid $x = a(\theta - \sin \theta)$, $y = a(1 - \cos \theta)$. $(s = 4a.)$ *Ans.* $(\frac{4}{3}a, \frac{4}{3}a)$.

7. The entire arc which is cut off on the curve $9y^2 = 4x^3$ by the line $x = 3$. *Ans.* $(\frac{58}{35}, 0)$.

8. The entire arc of the loop of the curve $9ay^2 = x(x - 3a)^2$. $(s = 4\sqrt{3}\,a.)$ *Ans.* $\left(\dfrac{7a}{5}, 0\right)$.

9. The entire arc of the loop of the curve $9y^2 = x^2(2x + 3)$. $(s = 2\sqrt{3}.)$ *Ans.* $(-\frac{4}{5}, 0)$.

10. The two arcs of the curve $9y^2 = 4(1 + x^2)^3$ between $x = 0$ and $x = 2$. $(s = \frac{44}{3}.)$ *Ans.* $(\frac{15}{11}, 0)$.

11. A hemispherical surface. *Ans.* $\bar{x} = \frac{1}{2}a$.

12. A hemispherical surface, using the equations $x = a \cos \theta$, $y = a \sin \theta$.

13. A spherical zone. *Ans.* Midway between the bounding planes.

14. The lateral surface of a circular cone. *Ans.* $\bar{x} = \frac{1}{3}h$.

15. The surface area cut from a sphere by one sheet of a cone of half-angle 60°.   *Ans.* $\bar{x} = \frac{3}{4}a$.

16. One-half the surface area of a torus (cut by a plane at right angles to the axis). ($A = 2\pi^2 ab$.)   *Ans.* $\bar{y} = \dfrac{2a}{\pi}$.

17. If an arc, *symmetric to Oy*, rotates about an external axis parallel to Oy, show that $\bar{y}$ for the surface area thus formed is the same as $\bar{y}$ for the arc. Formulate the result as a theorem. Check Ex. 16.

18. One arch of the cycloid $x = a(\theta - \sin \theta)$, $y = a(1 - \cos \theta)$ rotates about Oy. Find the centroid of the surface area generated. (Exs. 6, 17.)   *Ans.* $\bar{y} = \frac{4}{3}a$.

19. Prove the First Proposition of Pappus:

The surface area of a solid of revolution is equal to the length of the generating arc times the circumference of the circle described by the centroid of the arc.

Solve Exs. 20–24 by the First Proposition of Pappus.

20. Find the surface area of a circular cone.

21. Find the surface area of a torus.

22. Find the centroid of a semicircular wire.

23. Find the surface area of a circular cone frustum.

24. Find the centroid of a semicircular wire plus a wire of the same density joining the ends.   *Ans.* $\bar{x} = \dfrac{2a}{\pi + 2}$.

CHAPTER 23 *MOMENTS OF INERTIA*

177. Moment of inertia. The product of a mass m, concentrated at a point P, by the square of the distance r of P from a fixed line, or *axis*, is called the moment of the second order, or *moment of inertia*, of m with respect to that axis:

$$I = mr^2.$$

The moment of inertia of a system of such masses is of course the sum

FIG. 172   (1) $$I = \sum_{i=1}^{n} m_i r_i^2.$$

Moment of inertia with respect to the x-axis will be denoted by I_x; similarly I_y and I_z. Since the distance from the x-axis to a point (x, y, z) is $\sqrt{y^2 + z^2}$, we have by (1)

(2) $$I_x = \sum_{i=1}^{n} m_i(y_i^2 + z_i^2); \text{ etc.}$$

It is fundamentally important to realize that the moment of inertia of a particle of given mass, with respect to a given axis, is *independent of the direction* from that axis, being dependent on the distance only. Thus for a given particle, I_z is the same whether the particle is at $(5, 0, 0)$, or $(0, 5, 2)$, or $(3, -4, 6)$, or any other point for which

$$x^2 + y^2 = 25.$$

Example: Find I_z for the following set of particles: 2 units at $(1, 3, -2)$, 3 units at $(-3, 2, 6)$, 4 units at $(0, 0, 2)$, 1 unit at $(-3, 0, 1)$.

By (2), properly adapted, we have

$$I_z = 2(1 + 9) + 3(9 + 4) + 4(0) + 1(9) = 68.$$

By thinking of a continuous mass as an aggregate of particles, we may obtain an intuitive conception of the meaning of moment on inertia for such a mass. A formal definition will be stated in § 244.

178. Radius of gyration. Let M denote the mass of the physical object (solid, plane sheet, system of particles, etc.) under consideration. Since $M \neq 0$, we may always divide I by M; from the fact that moment of inertia is mass times square of distance, it appears that $\dfrac{I}{M}$ will be the square of a length:

$$\frac{I}{M} = R^2,$$

or

(1) $$I = MR^2.$$

The length R is called the *radius of gyration*, or *radius of inertia*, of M with respect to the given axis of moments. The meaning of the radius of gyration is obvious: it is the distance from the axis at which a *particle* of mass M must be placed in order to have the same moment of inertia as the original mass.

Example: In the example of § 177,

$$I_z = 68, \qquad M = 2 + 3 + 4 + 1 = 10,$$

$$R_z = \sqrt{\frac{I}{M}} = \sqrt{\frac{68}{10}} = 2.608.$$

That is, if the four particles were concentrated in a single one at this distance from the z-axis, I_z would be unchanged.

We confine our attention now to *homogeneous* bodies. In this case, the mass M is proportional to the density δ. It follows from the definition of moment of inertia that I is also proportional to δ. Thus in (1) the density-factor δ cancels out, so that the radius of gyration of a homogeneous body, with respect to any axis, is *independent of the density*.

Just as in the case of first-order moment, by taking $\delta = 1$, we may speak of "moment of inertia" of areas, volumes, etc., no idea of mass being involved.*

* In some important applications, this is just the case in which we are interested.

179. Moment of inertia by integration. The actual computation of the moment of inertia of a continuous mass is effected by integration in much the same way that the moment of the first order (§ 170) is determined.

Choose an element (of volume, area, or length) in some suitable way, and denote the mass of this element by Δm_i. Let r_i denote the radius of gyration of the element. (In the expression for the radius of gyration, infinitesimals may as usual be neglected.) Then $r_i^2 \Delta m_i$ is the moment of inertia of the element. Add together all the elementary moments and take the limit of the sum:

$$(1) \qquad I = \lim_{n \to \infty} \sum_{i=1}^{n} r_i^2 \Delta m_i = \int r^2 \, dm,$$

where r is the *radius of gyration of the mass-element* with respect to the axis of moments. Of course the integrand must be expressed in terms of a single variable, and the integration must be extended over the whole mass.

Just as, in finding centroids, we must take an element the position of whose centroid is known, so here the essential point is to *choose an element whose radius of gyration is known*. The way in which the integral (1) is built up will be explained piecemeal, for the cases of greatest importance.

180. Moment of inertia of a plane area. To find the moment of inertia of a plane area with respect, say, to the y-axis, let us take as element a rectangle parallel to that axis. [A second method will appear in Example (b) below.] Then, the radius of gyration r of the element is simply x, since (apart from infinitesimals) every particle is at distance x from the axis of moments:

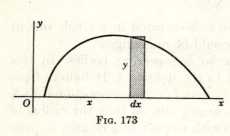

FIG. 173

$$I_y = \int_a^b x^2 y \, dx.$$

It is definitely inadvisable to memorize this formula; again, the reader should concentrate on understanding the argument.

Example (a): Find the moment of inertia of the area bounded by a parabola, its axis, and its latus rectum, with respect to the axis.

Taking the horizontal element, we have

$$I_x = \int_0^{2a} y^2(a - x)\, dy = \int_0^{2a} y^2\left(a - \frac{y^2}{4a}\right) dy$$

$$= \left[\frac{ay^3}{3} - \frac{y^5}{20a}\right]_0^{2a} = \frac{16}{15}a^4.$$

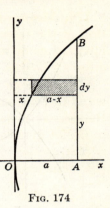

Fig. 174

By Example (a), § 67, the mass, or area, is $M = \frac{4}{3}a^2$, so that

$$I_x = \frac{16}{15}a^4 \cdot \frac{M}{\frac{4}{3}a^2} = \frac{4}{5}Ma^2.$$

This shows that the square of the radius of gyration is

$$R^2 = \tfrac{4}{5}a^2.$$

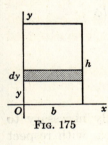

Fig. 175

To find the moment of inertia of a rectangle with respect to the base, we have

$$I_x = \int_0^h y^2 x\, dy = b\int_0^h y^2\, dy = \tfrac{1}{3}bh^3.$$

Since $M = bh$, the result may be written as

(1) $$I_x = \frac{bh^3}{3} = \frac{1}{3}Mh^2.$$

This formula, which should be memorized, says in words:

The moment of inertia of a rectangle with respect to the base is one-third the mass, or area, times the square of the altitude.

Example (b): Solve Example (a) by another method.

Taking the vertical element, we have by (1)

$$I_x = \int_0^a \tfrac{1}{3}y^2 \cdot y\, dx = \tfrac{1}{3}\int_0^a y^3\, dx$$

$$= \tfrac{8}{3}a^{\frac{3}{2}}\int_0^a x^{\frac{3}{2}}\, dx = \tfrac{16}{15}a^4.$$

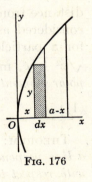

Fig. 176

Example (c): Find the moment of inertia, with respect to the line $x = 1$, of the area enclosed by the loop of the curve $y^2 = x^2(1 - x)$.

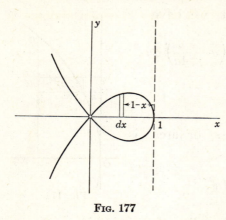

FIG. 177

Choosing a vertical element (Fig. 177), one parallel to the line $x = 1$, we obtain at once

$$I_{x=1} = 2 \int_0^1 (1 - x)^2 y \, dx.$$

Here $y = x\sqrt{1 - x}$, so that we have

$$I_{x=1} = 2 \int_0^1 x(1 - x)^{\frac{5}{2}} \, dx.$$

It is interesting to evaluate this integral with the aid of Wallis' Formula. Put $x = \sin^2 \phi$, and thus obtain

$$I_{x=1} = 4 \int_0^{\frac{\pi}{2}} \sin^2 \phi \cos^5 \phi \sin \phi \cos \phi \, d\phi$$

$$= 4 \int_0^{\frac{\pi}{2}} \sin^3 \phi \cos^6 \phi \, d\phi$$

$$= 4 \frac{2 \cdot 5 \cdot 3 \cdot 1}{9 \cdot 7 \cdot 5 \cdot 3 \cdot 1} = \frac{8}{63}.$$

181. Polar moment of inertia. It is frequently necessary to find the moment of inertia of a plane mass, or area, with respect to a line perpendicular to the plane. Take the plane in which the area lies as xy-plane, and the perpendicular line as z-axis. Obviously, the distance of each particle from the z-axis is merely its distance from the origin, so that this moment may equally well be considered as moment of inertia *with respect to the origin*. Since, for a particle at (x, y), the distance is the polar radius vector $\sqrt{x^2 + y^2}$, moment of inertia with respect to the origin is called *polar moment of inertia*. For a system of particles,

$$(1) \qquad I_z = I_0 = \sum_{i=1}^{n} m_i(x_i^2 + y_i^2).$$

THEOREM: *The moment of inertia of a plane mass with respect to a line perpendicular to its plane is equal to the sum of the moments with respect to two lines in the plane intersecting at right angles in the foot of the perpendicular.*

That is, for a mass (or area) in the xy-plane,

$$I_z = I_0 = I_x + I_y.$$

For a system of particles, the truth of this theorem appears at once from (1):

$$I_z = \sum_{i=1}^{n} m_i(x_i^2 + y_i^2) = \sum_{i=1}^{n} m_i y_i^2 + \sum_{i=1}^{n} m_i x_i^2 = I_x + I_y.$$

Later (§ 244), it will be a simple matter to complete the proof.

EXERCISES

In Exs. 1–4, find the moment of inertia with respect to each of the coördinate axes.

1. Masses of 2 units at $(0, -4)$, 2 units at $(3, 0)$, 3 units at $(1, 4)$, and 5 units at $(-2, -2)$. *Ans.* $I_x = 100; I_y = 41$.

2. Masses of 2 units at $(1, 0)$, 2 units at $(1, -3)$, 3 units at $(0, -2)$, and 1 unit at $(-1, 1)$. *Ans.* $I_x = 31; I_y = 5$.

3. Masses of 2 units at $(0, 3, 0)$, 3 units at $(2, -4, 1)$, and 1 unit at $(-1, -2, -3)$. *Ans.* $I_x = 82; I_y = 25; I_z = 83$.

4. Masses of 2 units at $(1, 1, 4)$, 3 units at $(2, 0, 0)$, and 4 units at $(-2, -3, 1)$. *Ans.* $I_x = 74; I_y = 66; I_z = 68$.

In Exs. 5–38, find the moment of inertia. The symbol M denotes the total mass of the system.

5. Equal particles at each corner of a square, with respect to one side of the square. *Ans.* $\frac{1}{2}Ma^2$.

6. Equal particles at three corners of a square, with respect to a side through the vacant corner. *Ans.* $\frac{2}{3}Ma^2$.

7. Equal particles at each corner of a cube, with respect to an edge of the cube. *Ans.* Ma^2.

8. Equal particles at seven corners of a cube, with respect to an edge through the vacant corner. *Ans.* $\frac{8}{7}Ma^2$.

9. A straight rod or wire with respect to a perpendicular through one end. *Ans.* $\frac{1}{3}Ml^2$.

10. A straight rod with respect to a perpendicular through a trisection point. Solve by integration; check by Ex. 9.

11. A wire bent in the form of a square, with respect to one side. *Ans.* $\frac{5}{12}Ma^2$.

12. A circular wire with respect to its axis (line through the center perpendicular to the plane).

13. The area bounded by the parabola $y^2 = 4ax$ and the latus rectum, with respect to Oy. *Ans.* $\frac{3}{7}Ma^2$.

14. The area bounded by $y^2 = 4ax$ and its latus rectum, with respect to the latus rectum. *Ans.* $\dfrac{64a^4}{105}$.

15. The area of the loop of $y^2 = x^2(1 - x)$, Fig. 177, with respect to Oy. *Ans.* $\frac{64}{315}$.

16. The area of the loop of $y^2 = x^4(1 - x)$ with respect to Oy.

$$Ans. \; \frac{2^9}{11 \cdot 9 \cdot 7 \cdot 5} = \frac{512}{3465}.$$

17. The area of Ex. 16, with respect to the line $x = 1$. $Ans. \; \frac{32}{693}$.

18. The area enclosed by the curve $y^2 = x^5(1 - x)^3$, with respect to Oy.

$$Ans. \; \frac{9\pi}{1024}.$$

19. The area of Ex. 18, with respect to the line $x = 1$. $Ans. \; \frac{5\pi}{1024}$.

20. The area bounded by $y^2 = 4ax$ and its latus rectum, with respect to the line $y = 2a$. $Ans. \; \frac{64a^4}{5}$.

21. The area bounded by the curve $2x^2 + 2x - y - 2 = 0$ and the line $y = 2x$, with respect to the line $x = 1$. $Ans. \; \frac{16}{5}$.

22. A triangle with respect to the line through the vertex parallel to the base. (Solve for the right triangle and deduce the general answer.) $Ans. \; \frac{1}{2}Mh^2$.

23. A triangle with respect to the base. $Ans. \; \frac{1}{6}Mh^2$.

24. Ex. 23 another way.

25. A circular area with respect to a diameter. $Ans. \; \frac{1}{4}Ma^2$.

26. Solve Ex. 25 by inspection. (Set up I_y and I_x, each with vertical element; add the former to three times the latter and note that $I_z = I_y$.)

27. An ellipse with respect to each of its axes. $Ans. \; \frac{1}{4}Ma^2, \; \frac{1}{4}Mb^2$.

28. The area in the fourth quadrant bounded by the curve $y = \ln x$, with respect to Oy. $Ans. \; \frac{1}{9}$.

29. A rectangle of sides b, h, with respect to the line bisecting the sides of length h. $Ans. \; \frac{1}{12}bh^3$.

30. The area bounded by the curve $y = 1 + x^3$ and the axes, with respect to Oy.

31. The area in Fig. 159, p. 313, with respect to the right side. $Ans. \; 348.3$.

32. The area in Fig. 154, p. 311, with respect to the base. $Ans. \; 1728$.

33. The area in Fig. 154, with respect to the left side. $Ans. \; 640$.

34. The area in Fig. 154, with respect to O. (Exs. 32–33.)

35. The area in Fig. 156, p. 312, with respect to the base.

36. The area in Fig. 162, p. 317, with respect to the line of symmetry.

37. The area in Fig. 164, p. 317, with respect to the left side. $Ans. \; 417.7$.

38. A circular area with respect to a perpendicular to the plane through the center. (Ex. 25 and § 181.) $Ans. \; \frac{1}{2}Ma^2$.

39. Solve Ex. 38 by integration. (Take as element a circular ring.)

40. Find the moment of inertia of a circular sector of angle α, with respect to a line through the center perpendicular to the plane. (Deduce the answer from Ex. 38.) $Ans. \; \frac{1}{2}Ma^2$.

41. Using the answer to Ex. 40, show that the polar moment of inertia of an area bounded by a polar curve and two radius vectors is

$$I_0 = \tfrac{1}{4} \int_\alpha^\beta r^4 \, d\theta.$$

In Exs. 42–46, find the moment of inertia with respect to the origin. (Ex. 41.)

42. The area of the curve $r^2 = a^2 \cos \theta$.   *Ans.* $\tfrac{1}{4}\pi a^4$.

43. The area of the curve $r^2 = a^2 \cos 2\theta$.   *Ans.* $\tfrac{1}{8}\pi a^4$.

44. The triangle bounded by the lines $y = 0,\ x = b,\ y = \dfrac{h}{b}x$. Check by § 181 (Exs. 22-23).   *Ans.* $\tfrac{1}{12}bh(h^2 + 3b^2)$.

45. The area bounded by the parabola $y^2 = ax$ and the line $y = x$.

46. The area bounded by the curve $a^2y = x^3$ and the line $y = x$.

47. Find the moment of inertia of a circular area with respect to a point on the circumference.   *Ans.* $\tfrac{3}{2}Ma^2$.

48. Find the moment of inertia of a rectangle with respect to one corner. (Deduce the answer from Ex. 44; check by § 181.)
     Ans. $\tfrac{1}{3}bh(b^2 + h^2)$.

182. Moment of inertia of a solid of revolution. No additional theory is needed to find the moment of inertia of a solid of revolution with respect to its axis, but other solids are out of reach at present (§ 244).

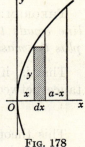

Example (a): A solid is generated by revolving about Oy the area bounded by the parabola $y^2 = 4ax$, the x-axis, and the latus rectum. Find the moment of inertia of the solid with respect to Oy.

Take as volume-element the cylindrical shell $2\pi xy \, dx$. The radius of gyration of this shell is evidently x, since every particle of the shell is at that distance (apart from infinitesimals) from the axis:

Fig. 178

$$I_y = 2\pi \int_0^a x^2 \cdot xy \, dx = 4\pi \sqrt{a} \int_0^a x^{\frac{7}{2}} \, dx = \tfrac{8}{9}\pi a^5.$$

The mass, or volume, is

$$M = 2\pi \int_0^a xy \, dx = \tfrac{8}{5}\pi a^3,$$

whence

$$I_y = \tfrac{5}{9}Ma^2.$$

To find the moment of inertia of a circular cylinder with respect to its axis, divide the cylinder into shells:

$$I_y = 2\pi \int_0^r x^2 \cdot xy \; dx = 2\pi h \int_0^r x^3 \; dx,$$

or

(1) $$I_y = \frac{\pi r^4 h}{2} = \frac{1}{2}Mr^2.$$

That is, *the moment of inertia of a cylinder with respect to its axis is one-half the mass times the square of the radius.*

Since the circular disk is merely a cylinder of small altitude, this gives us a valuable second method for moment of inertia of a solid of revolution with respect to its axis.

Example (b): Find I_x for the solid formed by revolving about Ox the area of Fig. 178.

Take as volume element the disk $\pi y^2 \; dx$. Then by (1),

$$I_x = \pi \int_0^a \frac{1}{2}y^2 \cdot y^2 \; dx = \frac{\pi}{2} \cdot 16a^2 \int_0^a x^2 \; dx$$
$$= \tfrac{8}{3}\pi a^5.$$

183. The translation theorem. Let the term *centroidal line* be used to denote a line through the centroid.

THEOREM: *The moment of inertia of a mass with respect to any line equals the moment with respect to the parallel centroidal line plus the mass times the square of the distance between the lines.*

That is, if l is any line, $\bar{l}$ the parallel centroidal line, h the distance between them, then

$$I_l = I_{\bar{l}} + Mh^2.$$

This theorem applies to *all* masses. For brevity, the proof will be deferred to § 245, at which time the general proof can be given.

Example: Find the moment of inertia of a right triangle with respect to its centroid (*i.e.*, with respect to a line through the centroid perpendicular to the plane).

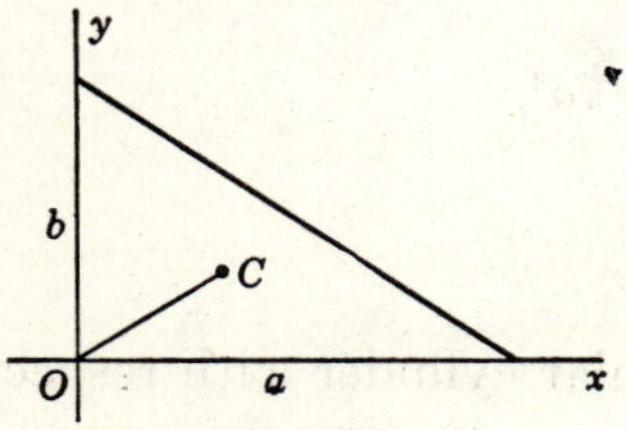

By Ex. 23, p. 334,

$$I_y = \tfrac{1}{6}Ma^2, \qquad I_x = \tfrac{1}{6}Mb^2,$$

so that

$$I_0 = \tfrac{1}{6}M(a^2 + b^2),$$
$$I_c = I_0 - M \cdot \overline{OC}^2 = I_0 - M \cdot \tfrac{1}{9}(a^2 + b^2)$$
$$= \tfrac{1}{18}M(a^2 + b^2).$$

FIG. 179

EXERCISES

In Exs. 1–18, find the moment of inertia with respect to the axis of revolution.

1. A sphere. $Ans.\ \frac{2}{5}Ma^2.$

2. A circular cone. $Ans.\ \frac{3}{10}Ma^2.$

3. An oblate spheroid. Solve by two methods. $Ans.\ \frac{2}{5}Ma^2.$

4. A prolate spheroid, using the equations $x = a\cos\phi,\ y = b\sin\phi.$ $Ans.\ \frac{2}{5}Mb^2.$

5. A torus. $Ans.\ (b^2 + \frac{3}{4}a^2)M.$

6. The volume formed by revolving about Ox the area bounded by $y^2 = 4ax,\ x = 0,\ y = 2a.$

7. The volume formed by revolving the area of Ex. 6 about the line $y = 2a.$ $Ans.\ \dfrac{8\pi a^5}{15}.$

8. The volume formed by revolving about Ox the area in the first quadrant under the curve $y = e^{-x}.$ $Ans.\ \dfrac{\pi}{8}.$

9. The volume formed by revolving about Ox the area bounded by the curve $y = \ln x$ and the lines $x = e,\ y = 0.$ $Ans.\ \frac{3}{2}\pi(3e - 8).$

10. The volume generated by revolving the area of Ex. 9 about $Oy.$ $Ans.\ \dfrac{\pi(3e^4 + 1)}{8}.$

11. The volume formed by revolving the area of Fig. 154, p. 311, about the left side.

12. The volume formed by revolving the area of Fig. 154 about the base.

13. The volume formed by revolving the area of Fig. 157, p. 313 about the base.

14. The volume generated by revolving the area of Fig. 156, p. 312, about its base.

15. The volume bounded by the surfaces $x^2 + y^2 = 4az,\ x^2 + y^2 = 4z^2.$ $Ans.\ \frac{16}{15}\pi a^5.$

16. The volume bounded by the quadric surfaces $x^2 + y^2 - z^2 = a^2,$ $x^2 + y^2 = 2a^2.$ $Ans.\ \frac{32}{15}\pi a^5.$

17. The volume bounded by the quadric surfaces $x^2 + y^2 - z^2 = a^2,$ $x^2 + y^2 = 2z^2.$ $Ans.\ \frac{16}{15}\pi a^5.$

18. The volume inside the surfaces $x^2 + y^2 = 3z^2,\ x^2 + y^2 + az = 4a^2.$

In Exs. 19–23, find the moment of inertia.

19. A circular wire with respect to a diameter, using Cartesian coordinates. $Ans.\ \frac{1}{2}Ma^2.$

20. The wire of Ex. 19, using the equations $x = a\cos\theta,\ y = a\sin\theta.$

21. A circular wire with respect to a tangent. (Use $x = a\cos\theta,$ $y = a\sin\theta.$) $Ans.\ \frac{3}{2}Ma^2.$

22. Solve Ex. 21 in Cartesian coördinates.

23. The arc of the catenary $y = a \cosh \dfrac{x}{a}$, from the vertex to the point

(x_1, y_1), with respect to Ox. $\left(s = a \sinh \dfrac{x_1}{a}. \right)$ *Ans.* $a^2s + \tfrac{1}{3}s^3$.

In Exs. 24–28, find the moment of inertia with respect to the axis of revolution.

24. A spherical surface, using Cartesian coördinates.   *Ans.* $\tfrac{2}{3}Ma^2$.
25. A spherical surface, using the equations $x = a \cos \theta, \, y = a \sin \theta$.   *Ans.* $\tfrac{1}{2}Ma^2$.
26. The lateral surface of a cone of revolution.   *Ans.* $\tfrac{1}{2}Ma^2$.
27. The surface of a torus.   *Ans.* $(b^2 + \tfrac{3}{2}a^2)M$.
28. A cylindrical drum.   *Ans.* $\pi r^4 + 2\pi r^3 h$.

In Exs. 29–39, obtain the required moment of inertia by using the theorem of § 183, with reference to previous exercises.

29. A square plate with respect to (a) a line through the center parallel to a side; (b) a perpendicular through the center; (c) a line trisecting two opposite sides (two cases); (d) a diagonal.
    Ans. (a) $\tfrac{1}{12}Ma^2$; (b) $\tfrac{1}{6}Ma^2$; (d) $\tfrac{1}{12}Ma^2$.
30. An isosceles triangle with respect to a line (a) parallel to the base bisecting the altitude; (b) through the vertex perpendicular to the plane.
    Ans. (a) $\tfrac{1}{12}Mh^2$; (b) $\tfrac{1}{2}M(h^2 + \tfrac{1}{3}a^2)$.
31. A circular wire with respect to (a) a tangent; (b) any line perpendicular to the plane.   *Ans.* (a) $\tfrac{3}{2}Ma^2$; (b) $M(a^2 + h^2)$.
32. A circular area with respect to (a) a tangent; (b) a perpendicular through a point in the circumference.
33. A sphere with respect to a tangent.
34. A spherical surface with respect to a tangent.
35. A torus with respect to a tangent parallel to the axis.
36. The area of Fig. 154, p. 311, with respect to a line through the centroid parallel to the base.   *Ans.* 528.
37. The area of Fig. 154 with respect to a line through the centroid parallel to the sides.   *Ans.* 208.
38. The area of Fig. 154 with respect to the centroid. (Exs. 36–37.)
39. The area of Fig. 154 with respect to a line through P perpendicular to the plane. (Ex. 38.)   *Ans.* 1552.

CHAPTER 24 *FLUID PRESSURE.*

WORK

184. Distributed force. In Chapter 6 we have touched briefly upon the problem of a force or forces acting upon a single particle.

We have frequently to consider a force not acting at a single point, but distributed over an area or throughout a volume. Examples are the pressure of a carload of sand against the sides of the car, the attraction between two electrified plates, the gravitational attraction between two spheres or other solids. If the mass upon which the force acts be thought of as composed ultimately of particles, such a distributed force may be regarded as comprising the totality of forces acting on the separate particles.

185. Fluid pressure. Given a plane area submerged vertically in a homogeneous fluid, let us for definiteness take the x-axis in the surface with the y-axis *positive downward*. (Of course in any particular problem the axes should be so chosen as to make the analytic geometry simple.) Divide the area into rectangles of length x_i, width Δy, and depth y_i below the surface. Now the force on any submerged *horizontal* area is equal to the weight of the column of fluid standing on this area. Hence the force on our elementary rectangle is, apart from infinitesimals of higher order,*

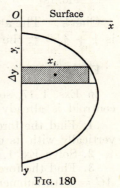

Fig. 180

$$\Delta F_i = w y_i x_i \, \Delta y,$$

* The reasoning is as follows. If the rectangle were rotated about its upper side through 90° into a horizontal position at depth y_i, the force would be $w y_i x_i \, \Delta y$; if it were rotated about the lower side to a horizontal position at depth $y_i + \Delta y$, the force would be $w(y_i + \Delta y) x_i \, \Delta y$. The actual force is greater than the former and less than the latter.

where w is the weight of the fluid per unit volume. Therefore

$$F = \lim_{n \to \infty} \sum_{i=1}^{n} w y_i x_i \, \Delta y = w \int_c^d yx \, dy,$$

where c and d are the least and greatest depths below the surface.

Under the integral sign, we have evidently multiplied the area $x \, dy$ of the element by its depth y below the surface, so that the integral represents the first-order moment of the submerged area with respect to the axis in the surface.

THEOREM: *The force on a submerged vertical plane area equals the product of the weight per unit volume, the submerged area, and the depth of the centroid of the area below the surface:*

(1) $$F = wA\bar{y}.$$

Example: Find the force on one face of the submerged triangle of Fig. 181.

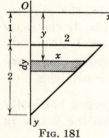

FIG. 181

The equation of the line through $(0, 3)$, $(2, 1)$ is

$$x + y = 3.$$

Thus the force is

$$F = w \int_1^3 yx \, dy = w \int_1^3 y(3 - y) \, dy$$

$$= w\left[\tfrac{3}{2}y^2 - \tfrac{1}{3}y^3\right]_1^3 = \tfrac{10}{3}w.$$

Check: The area is $A = \tfrac{1}{2} \cdot 2 \cdot 2 = 2$, the depth of the centroid is $1 + \tfrac{2}{3} = \tfrac{5}{3}$; the force, by (1), is $F = w \cdot 2 \cdot \tfrac{5}{3} = \tfrac{10}{3}w$.

EXERCISES

In Exs. 1–17, solve by direct integration. When the position of the centroid is already known, check by the theorem of § 185.

1. Find the force on one face of a plank 12 ft. by 6 in., submerged vertically with its upper end in the surface.

2. Solve Ex. 1, if the upper end is 6 ft. below the surface.

3. Find the force on one face of a right triangle of sides $AB = 3$ ft., $AC = 4$ ft., submerged with AC vertical and AB in the surface.

Ans. 8w.

4. Solve Ex. 3 if AB is 4 ft., C 8 ft., below the surface.

5. Solve Ex. 3 if AB is 8 ft., C 4 ft., below the surface.

6. What force must be withstood by a vertical dam 100 ft. long and 20 ft. deep?

Ans. 620 tons.

7. What force must be withstood by a trapezoidal dam 100 ft. long at the top, 80 ft. long at the bottom, and 20 ft. deep? *Ans.* 17,333*w*.

8. A horizontal cylindrical boiler 4 ft. in diameter is half full of water. Find the force on one end. *Ans.* 330 lbs.

9. Solve Ex. 8 if the boiler is full of water. *Ans.* 8π*w*.

10. Find the force that must be withstood by a bulkhead closing a water main 4 ft. in diameter, if the surface of the water in the reservoir is 40 ft. above the center of the bulkhead. *Ans.* 16 tons.

11. Find the force on one end of a parabolic trough full of water, if the depth is 2 ft. and the width across the top 2 ft. *Ans.* $\frac{32}{15}w$.

12. The ends of a trough have the shape of an inverted arch of the curve

$$y = a \cos \frac{x}{a}.$$ If the trough is filled with a liquid weighing *w* lbs. per cu. ft.,

find the force on one end. *Ans.* $\frac{1}{4}\pi wa^3$.

13. The vertical face of a dam is in the shape of an inverted arch of the cycloid $x = a(\theta - \sin \theta)$, $y = a(1 - \cos \theta)$. Find the maximum force that the dam must withstand. *Ans.* $\frac{5}{2}\pi wa^3$.

14. A trough 4 ft. deep and 6 ft. wide has semi-elliptical ends. If the trough is full of water, find the force on one end. *Ans.* 32*w*.

15. Solve Ex. 14, using the equations $x = 3 \cos \phi$, $y = 4 \sin \phi$.

16. Find the force on one face of a square 2 ft. on a side, submerged with one diagonal vertical and one corner in the surface. *Ans.* $4\sqrt{2}\ w$.

17. A triangular trough of width 2*a* and depth 2*a* is filled to depth *a* with a liquid of unit weight 2*w*, this overlaid with a stratum of depth *a* and unit weight *w*. (*a*) Find the force on one end; (*b*) find the force if the liquids were thoroughly mixed.

Ans. (*a*) $\frac{3}{2}wa^3$; (*b*) $\frac{5}{3}wa^3$.

18. Show that for an area submerged as in Fig. 182, the force is

$$F = \tfrac{1}{2}w \int_a^b y^2 \, dx.$$

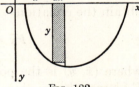

Fig. 182

Solve Exs. 19–24 by the method of Ex. 18.

19. Ex. 3.   **20.** Example, § 185.   **21.** Ex. 8.
22. Ex. 11.   **23.** Ex. 12.   **24.** Ex. 13.

186. Resultant of parallel forces. Given a set of parallel forces $f_1, f_2, \ldots, f_n$ whose resultant (algebraic sum) is not 0, the problem of finding the line of action of the resultant is analogous to that of finding the centroid of a set of mass particles.

The simplest case arises when all the forces lie in one plane: for concreteness, consider a straight beam bearing concentrated loads. Take the line of the beam as *x*-axis, and mark an origin—say at the left end. Multiply each force by its distance (*i.e.*, the distance of its line of action) from the origin. *The sum of these first-order moments must equal the moment of the resultant:* that is,

$$F\bar{x} = \sum_{i=1}^{n} f_i x_i.$$

Example (a): A straight beam bears concentrated loads as shown. Find the position of the resultant, and the reactions at the ends.

Taking moments about A, we have

$$F\bar{x} = 4 \cdot 60 + 8 \cdot 40 + 16 \cdot 100 = 2160, \qquad \bar{x} = \tfrac{2160}{200} = 10.8 \text{ ft.}$$

The moment, about A, of the reaction R_2 must balance the mo-

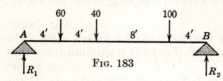

FIG. 183

ments of the forces, so that
$$20R_2 = 2160, \qquad R_2 = 108 \text{ lbs.}$$
We could find R_1 from the fact that
$$R_1 + R_2 = 200,$$

but as a check let us find it independently, by taking moments about B:

$$20R_1 = 16 \cdot 60 + 12 \cdot 40 + 4 \cdot 100 = 1840, \qquad R_1 = 92 \text{ lbs.}$$

If the parallel forces do not all lie in the same plane, take the xy-plane perpendicular to the forces. Let (x_i, y_i) be the point where the line of action of f_i pierces the xy-plane. Taking moments first with respect to the y-axis, then with respect to the x-axis, we obtain the equations

$$F\bar{x} = \sum_{i=1}^{n} f_i x_i, \qquad F\bar{y} = \sum_{i=1}^{n} f_i y_i,$$

where $(\bar{x}, \bar{y})$ is the point where the line of action of the resultant F pierces the xy-plane.

Example (b): A table 20×10 ft., weighing 4 oz. per sq. ft., bears loads at the corners as shown. Find the point of application of the resultant.

The weight of the table-top may be replaced by a force of 50 lbs. at the center. Taking moments about OC as y-axis and about OA as x-axis, we find

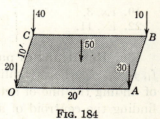

FIG. 184

$$F\bar{x} = 10 \cdot 50 + 20 \cdot 30 + 20 \cdot 10 = 1300, \qquad \bar{x} = \tfrac{1300}{150} = 8\tfrac{2}{3} \text{ ft.};$$
$$F\bar{y} = 5 \cdot 50 + 10 \cdot 40 + 10 \cdot 10 = 750, \qquad \bar{y} = \tfrac{750}{150} = 5 \text{ ft.}$$

187. Center of pressure. Let us return to the problem of fluid pressure. In taking moments, we may replace the force

$$\Delta F_i = wy_ix_i\,\Delta y,$$

acting on the elementary rectangle, by a concentrated force of the same magnitude at the center of the rectangle (just as, in the example above, we replaced the weight of the table by a force at its center). The moments of this force with respect to Oy and Ox are respectively $wy_ix_i\,\Delta y \cdot \frac{1}{2}x_i$, $wy_ix_i\,\Delta y \cdot y_i$. Adding all these elementary moments and taking the limits of the sums, we obtain the formulas

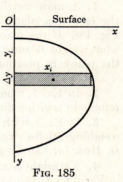

FIG. 185

$$F\bar{x} = \lim_{n\to\infty} \sum_{i=1}^{n} \tfrac{1}{2}wy_ix_i^2\,\Delta y = \tfrac{1}{2}w\int_c^d yx^2\,dy,$$

$$F\bar{y} = \lim_{n\to\infty} \sum_{i=1}^{n} wy_i^2x_i\,\Delta y = w\int_c^d y^2x\,dy,$$

where $(\bar{x}, \bar{y})$ is the point of application of a single force F that would balance the distributed force. This point is called the *center of pressure.*

Once more, the student is advised not to memorize these formulas, but to concentrate on understanding the mechanics of the problem.

Example: Find the center of pressure on the submerged triangle of Fig. 181. (Example, § 185.)

We have

$$F\bar{x} = \frac{1}{2}w\int_1^3 yx^2\,dy = \frac{1}{2}w\int_1^3 y(3-y)^2\,dy$$

$$= \frac{1}{2}w\left[\frac{9y^2}{2} - 2y^3 + \frac{1}{4}y^4\right]_1^3 = 2w,$$

$$\bar{x} = \frac{2w}{\frac{10}{3}w} = \frac{3}{5};$$

$$F\bar{y} = w\int_1^3 y^2x\,dy = w\int_1^3 y^2(3-y)\,dy$$

$$= w\left[y^3 - \frac{1}{4}y^4\right]_1^3 = 6w,$$

$$\bar{y} = \frac{6w}{\frac{10}{3}w} = \frac{9}{5}.$$

EXERCISES

1. A man weighing 200 lbs. stands on
the end of a plank supported as shown in
Fig. 186. If the plank weighs 4 lbs. per ft.,
what weight W must be applied at A to hold
the plank in position?

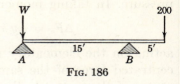

Fig. 186

Ans. 40 lbs. (critical value).

2. In Ex. 1, what must be the weight of the plank per foot, if it is to
remain in position due to its own weight?

3. In Ex. 1, with W removed, a child
weighing 60 lbs. walks from A toward
B. How far can he go?   *Ans.* 5 ft.

4. A straight beam is loaded as shown
in Fig. 187. If the weight of the beam is
negligible, find (a) the point of application of the resultant; (b) the reactions at

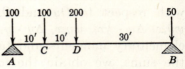

Fig. 187

the supports. *Ans.* (a) $\bar{x} = 16$ ft. 8 in.; (b) 300 lbs., 150 lbs.

5. Solve Ex. 4 if the beam weighs 2 lbs. per foot.

6. Solve Ex. 4 if the segment AD bears a uniformly distributed load
of 5 lbs. per ft.

7. Solve Ex. 4 if the segment AD bears a uniformly distributed load of
5 lbs. per ft. and the segment DB a distributed load increasing uniformly
from 5 lbs. per ft. at D to 15 lbs. per ft. at B.   *Ans.* (a) $\bar{x} = 23$ ft. 3 in.

8. A platform 20 ft. square, weighing $1\frac{1}{2}$ lbs. per sq. ft., bears loads of
100 lbs. at (5, 4), 200 lbs. at (15, 5), 50 lbs. at (8, 12), 50 lbs. at (20, 0).
At what point would a single support hold the platform in place?

Ans. (10.9, 8).

9. A weight W is to be raised by a lever with the force F at one end
and the fulcrum A at the other. If the weight is a ft. from the fulcrum,
and the lever weighs w lbs. per ft., what should be the length of the lever

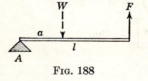

Fig. 188

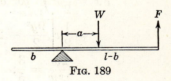

Fig. 189

to lift the weight most easily? (Fig. 188.)   *Ans.* $l = \sqrt{\dfrac{2Wa}{w}}$.

10. Solve Ex. 9 if the lever projects a distance b beyond the fulcrum
(Fig. 189).   *Ans.* If $\sqrt{\dfrac{2Wa - b^2w}{w}} > a, l = b + \sqrt{\dfrac{2Wa - b^2w}{w}}$;

otherwise (§ 79), $l = a + b$.

11. A platform 20 ft. square, of negligible weight, bears a single concentrated load. The reactions are, at (0, 0), 50 lbs.; at (20, 0), 80 lbs.; at (20, 20), 100 lbs.; at (0, 20), 70 lbs. Where is the load?

12. Solve Ex. 11 if the platform weighs 4 oz. per sq. ft.   *Ans.* (13, 12).

In Exs. 13–18, find the depth of the center of pressure.

13. A rectangle submerged vertically with one edge in the surface.
Ans. $\frac{2}{3}a$.

14. A rectangle submerged vertically with its upper edge at depth c.

15. An isosceles triangle submerged with the line of symmetry vertical and the vertex in the surface.   *Ans.* $\frac{3}{4}h$.

16. An isosceles triangle submerged with the line of symmetry vertical and the base in the surface.   *Ans.* $\frac{1}{2}h$.

17. One end of a horizontal cylindrical tank, half filled.

18. One end of the parabolic trough of Ex. 11, p. 341.

19. Find the center of pressure in Ex. 3, p. 340.

20. Find the center of pressure in Ex. 4, p. 340.

21. Find the center of pressure in Ex. 5, p. 340.

22. Find the center of pressure on the right half of the square of Ex. 16, p. 341.

23. Find integrals for the center of pressure on the submerged area of Ex. 18, p. 341. (Ex. 13.)

In Exs. 24–29, solve by the method of Ex. 23.

24. Ex. 17.	**25.** Ex. 18.	**26.** Ex. 19.
27. Ex. 20.	**28.** Ex. 21.	**29.** Ex. 22.

188. Work. Let a constant force be acting continuously upon a body so as to move it through a distance d. The product of the magnitude F of the force, and the distance d, is called the work done in moving the body through the distance d,

> **Work = (magnitude of force) (distance over which it acts),**
> **W = F· d.**

If, for instance, you use a constant 20-lb. force to push a block 10 ft., then the work you do is

$$W = (20 \text{ lbs.})(10 \text{ ft.})$$
$$= 200 \text{ ft-lbs.}$$

The above basic concept of work is readily extended to the determination of the work done by a variable force, as is illustrated in the example below.

Example: A cylindrical tank, with a base radius of 5 ft. and a height of 20 ft., is filled with water. Find the work done in pumping all the water out the top of the tank.

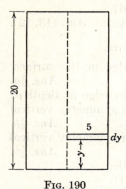

A cross-section of the tank is exhibited in Fig. 190. Consider a representative element, as shown, at a distance y from the base of the tank. The circular disk, formed by revolving that element about the axis of the tank, has a volume $\pi(5^2)\ dy$ cu. ft. Water weighs about 62.5 lbs. per cu. ft. Therefore, the circular disk of water weighs $62.5(25\pi)\ dy$ lbs., and it is to be raised a distance of $(20 - y)$ ft.

Fig. 190

The work to be done in raising the circular disk of water to the top of the tank is $62.5(25\pi)(20 - y)\ dy$.

To empty the whole tank, the work required is

$$(1) \qquad W = 62.5(25\pi) \int_0^{20} (20 - y)\ dy,$$

the limit of the sum of the infinitesimal elements of work.

From (1) it follows that

$$W = \frac{3125\pi}{2}\left[-\frac{(20 - y)^2}{2} \right]_0^{20}$$

$$= 9.82(10)^5 \text{ ft-lbs.}$$

EXERCISES

In order to simplify the numerical work, let w denote the weight in pounds per cubic foot of the liquid in Exs. 1–13.

1. Suppose the tank of the example above is only half full (the bottom half!); find the work done in pumping the water out the top of the tank.
Ans. $3750\pi w$ ft-lbs.

2. A hemispherical tank of diameter 6 ft. is full of liquid. Find the work done in pumping the liquid out the top of the tank. *Ans.* $\dfrac{81\pi w}{4}$ ft-lbs.

3. For the tank of Ex. 2, suppose the surface of the liquid is one foot from the top of the tank. Find the work done in pumping the liquid out the top. *Ans.* $16\pi w$ ft-lbs.

4. A cistern is built in the form of a hemisphere of radius r, surmounted by a right circular cylinder with base radius r and height h. If the cistern is full of water, find the work done in pumping the water out the top of the cistern. *Ans.* $\frac{1}{12}\pi w r^2 (3r^2 + 8rh + 6h^2)$.

5. Let a cistern of the shape of that in Ex. 4 have its cylinder height equal its hemisphere radius, $h = r$. If the cistern is half full, 50% of capacity volume, find the work done in pumping the water out the top of the cistern. $\qquad$ *Ans.* $\dfrac{77\pi wr^4}{72}$.

6. Let the cistern of Ex. 5 be three-fourths full. Find the work done in pumping the water out the top. $\qquad$ *Ans.* $\dfrac{383\pi wr^4}{288}$.

7. If the cistern of Ex. 4 is filled only to the top of the hemisphere, find the work done in pumping the water out the top.

Ans. $\tfrac{1}{12}\pi wr^3\,(3r + 8h)$.

8. A tank is made in the shape of a right-circular cylinder surmounted by a frustum of a cone, a vertical cross-section being shown in Fig. 191. The tank is full of water. Find the work needed to pump all the water out the top.

Ans. $\dfrac{314\pi w}{3}$ ft-lbs.

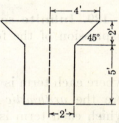

FIG. 191

9. A conical reservoir of top radius r and height h is filled with oil. Find the work needed to pump the oil out the top of the reservoir.

Ans. $\tfrac{1}{12}\pi wr^2h^2$.

10. If the reservoir of Ex. 9 is filled only to one-eighth of its capacity, find the work needed.

Ans. $\tfrac{5}{192}\pi wr^2h^2$.

11. A tank is made in the form of a cone, of base radius r and height h, surmounted by a right-circular cylinder of base radius r and height H. The tank is full of water. Find the work done in pumping all the water out the top of the tank. $\qquad$ *Ans.* $\tfrac{1}{12}\pi wr^2\,(h^2 + 4hH + 6H^2)$.

12. If the tank of Ex. 11 is filled only to a distance c units ($c < H$) from the top of the tank, find the work done.

Ans. $\tfrac{1}{12}\pi wr^2\,(h^2 + 4hH + 6H^2 - 6c^2)$.

13. Solve Ex. 12, if $H < c < H + h$.

Ans. $\dfrac{\pi wr^2}{12h^2}\,(h + H - c)^3(h + H + 3c)$.

It is known empirically that (within the so-called elastic limit) for an elastic spring, the force f needed to stretch it beyond its natural length is proportional to the elongation s; $f = k \cdot s$. The number k is called the spring constant.

14. A spring of natural length 10 in. is such that a force of 6 lbs. will stretch it 2 in. Show that the spring constant is 3 lbs. per in., and find the work done in stretching the spring from its natural length to a length of 14 in. $\qquad$ *Ans.* 24 in-lbs.

15. Find the work necessary to stretch the spring of Ex. 14 an additional 4 in., from a length of 14 in. to one of 18 in. $\qquad$ *Ans.* 72 in-lbs.

16. It takes twice as much work to stretch a certain spring from 9 to 10 in., as it does to stretch it from 8 to 9 in. Find the natural length of the spring. $\qquad$ *Ans.* 7.5 in.

CHAPTER 25 SERIES OF
CONSTANT TERMS

189. Infinite series. A *finite series*, or *series of n terms*, is an expression of the form

$$u_1 + u_2 + u_3 + \cdots + u_n,$$

where each term is formed by some definite rule. Familiar examples are the *arithmetic series* (also called arithmetic progression), in which each term is formed by adding a fixed amount to the preceding term; the *geometric series* (progression), in which each term bears a constant ratio to the preceding; and the expansion of $(1 + x)^m$ by the Binomial Theorem, where m is a positive integer.

Cases frequently arise where the generating law may be supposed to apply over and over indefinitely, so that the number of terms is unlimited. When this occurs, the series is called an *infinite series*, denoted by the symbol

$$u_1 + u_2 + u_3 + \cdots + u_n + \cdots.$$

This symbol may be more compactly expressed by a simple extension of the $\sum$-notation introduced in § 64:

$$u_1 + u_2 + u_3 + \cdots + u_n + \cdots = \sum_{n=1}^{\infty} u_n.$$

Example: The geometric series with first term 1 and ratio $\frac{1}{2}$ is

(1) $$1 + \frac{1}{2} + \frac{1}{4} + \frac{1}{8} + \cdots + \frac{1}{2^{n-1}} + \cdots = \sum_{n=1}^{\infty} \frac{1}{2^{n-1}}.$$

Instead, we may write either

$$1 + \sum_{n=1}^{\infty} \frac{1}{2^n} \quad \text{or} \quad \sum_{n=0}^{\infty} \frac{1}{2^n}.$$

190. Sum of an infinite series. The *sum* of a finite series is merely the algebraic sum of all the terms, and can always be found (theoretically at least) by direct addition.

On the other hand, an infinite series has no sum in the ordinary sense of the term, since no matter how many terms we might add up, there would always be more to come.

Let us return to the example of the preceding section. Let the sum of the first n terms of the series

(1) $$1 + \frac{1}{2} + \frac{1}{2^2} + \cdots + \frac{1}{2^{n-1}} + \cdots$$

be S_n; that is,

(2) $$S_n = 1 + \frac{1}{2} + \frac{1}{2^2} + \cdots + \frac{1}{2^{n-1}}.$$

Since this is a finite geometric series, we know its sum from elementary algebra,

$$S_n = \frac{1 - (\frac{1}{2})^n}{1 - \frac{1}{2}} = 2 - \frac{1}{2^{n-1}}.$$

Note that, as n increases, $S_n \to 2$; that is,

(3) $$\lim_{n \to \infty} S_n = \lim_{n \to \infty} \left(2 - \frac{1}{2^{n-1}} \right) = 2.$$

It is only natural, then, to define as the sum of the series (1) the value of the limit in (3), a number which can be approached as closely as desired by adding a sufficient number of terms of the original series.

DEFINITION: *The* **sum** *of an infinite series is the limit, if it exists, of the sum of a finite number of terms, as the number of terms approaches infinity,*

$$S = \lim_{n \to \infty} S_n.$$

Example: The sum of the first n terms of the infinite geometric series

$$a + ar + ar^2 + \cdots + ar^{n-1} + \cdots$$

is

$$S_n = \frac{a - ar^n}{1 - r} \qquad (r \neq 1).$$

Hence the sum of the series, if the sum exists, is

$$S = \lim_{n \to \infty} \frac{a - ar^n}{1 - r}.$$

When $|r| < 1$, the quantity ar^n approaches zero as n increases, and

$$S = \frac{a}{1 - r}.$$

When r is numerically greater than 1, the quantity ar^n increases indefinitely, and the above limit does not exist: the series has no sum. The reader may show that the same is true if $r = \pm 1$.

191. Convergence and divergence. If the series has a sum S, *i.e.*, if S_n approaches a limit when n increases, the series is said to be *convergent*, or to *converge to the value S;* if the limit does not exist, the series is *divergent*.

For instance, the above example shows that a geometric series converges to the value $\dfrac{a}{1 - r}$ if $|r| < 1$; it diverges if $|r| \geqq 1$.

A series may diverge because S_n increases indefinitely as n increases; or it may diverge because S_n fails in some other way to approach a limit. A common type of divergence is that in which S_n increases and decreases alternately, or *oscillates*, without approaching any limit. In the latter case the series is called *oscillatory*. A very simple example of oscillatory divergence is furnished by the geometric series for which $r = -1$:

$$a - a + a - a + \cdots + (-1)^{n-1}a + \cdots.$$

Here $S_n = a$ or $S_n = 0$ alternately, according as n is odd or even.

In the elementary applications divergent series are of no importance. Before being able to use a given series we must determine whether it converges or diverges. If S_n can be expressed explicitly as a simple function of n, as in the case of the arithmetic and geometric series, we can usually determine the convergence or divergence of the series directly, and find the sum if it exists; but S_n cannot be so expressed in most cases.

If the series $\sum\limits_{n=1}^{\infty} u_n$ converges, then S_n approaches a limit S, as $n \to \infty$. But then also $S_{n-1} \to S$, as $n \to \infty$, since it is purely a matter of notation, whether $(n - 1)$ or n terms are taken in the finite sum. Then, if the series converges, $\lim\limits_{n \to \infty} S_{n-1} = \lim\limits_{n \to \infty} S_n$, so that

$$\lim_{n \to \infty} (S_n - S_{n-1}) = \lim_{n \to \infty} u_n = 0.$$

A necessary condition for convergence is that the general term approach zero as its limit:

$$\lim_{n \to \infty} u_n = 0.$$

This condition, though necessary, is not sufficient; *i.e.*, if the n-th term does not approach zero, the series diverges, but if the n-th term does approach zero, the series still may diverge. This is illustrated by the "harmonic series"

$$1 + \frac{1}{2} + \frac{1}{3} + \frac{1}{4} + \cdots + \frac{1}{n} + \cdots,$$

which will be shown in § 192 to be divergent, although its n-th term approaches zero as $n \to \infty$.

We shall make use of the following fundamental result without proof.

Theorem: *If a variable steadily $\begin{Bmatrix} increases \\ decreases \end{Bmatrix}$ but never becomes $\begin{Bmatrix} greater \\ less \end{Bmatrix}$ than some fixed number A, the variable approaches a limit which is not $\begin{Bmatrix} greater \\ less \end{Bmatrix}$ than A.*

192. The harmonic series. The series

(1) $$1 + \frac{1}{2} + \frac{1}{3} + \frac{1}{4} + \cdots + \frac{1}{n} + \cdots = \sum_{n=1}^{\infty} \frac{1}{n}$$

is called the *harmonic series*.

A common notation for the sum of the first n terms of this important series is H_n:

$$H_n = 1 + \frac{1}{2} + \frac{1}{3} + \cdots + \frac{1}{n} = \sum_{k=1}^{n} \frac{1}{k}.$$

We shall prove that the harmonic series diverges; $H_n \to \infty$, as $n \to \infty$. Of course, $1 + \frac{1}{2} > 1 + \frac{1}{3}, \frac{1}{3} + \frac{1}{4} > \frac{1}{4} + \frac{1}{4}, \frac{1}{5} + \frac{1}{6} > \frac{1}{6} + \frac{1}{6}$, etc. That is, the following n inequalities are true:

$$1 + \tfrac{1}{2} > 1 + \tfrac{1}{3},$$
$$\tfrac{1}{3} + \tfrac{1}{4} > \tfrac{1}{2},$$
$$\tfrac{1}{5} + \tfrac{1}{6} > \tfrac{1}{3},$$
$$\vdots$$
$$\frac{1}{2n-1} + \frac{1}{2n} > \frac{1}{n}.$$

Adding the corresponding members of these inequalities, we obtain

$$H_{2n} > H_n + \tfrac{1}{3}.$$

Thus $H_{2n} - H_n > \tfrac{1}{3}$. But, if the harmonic series converges, then a limit H exists such that as $n \to \infty$, $H_n \to H$, and also $H_{2n} \to H$. Then $H_{2n} - H_n \to 0$, which contradicts the inequality $H_{2n} - H_n > \tfrac{1}{3}$. Hence, the harmonic series cannot converge; it must diverge.

193. The factorial notation. The symbol $n!$ (read *factorial n*) is used to denote the *product of all the integers from 1 to n inclusive:*

$$\boldsymbol{n! = n(n-1)(n-2)\cdots 3\cdot 2\cdot 1.}$$

By special definition (introduced to facilitate the writing of certain formulas),

$$\boldsymbol{0! = 1.}$$

It will be found as we proceed that factorials occur prominently in many important series.

In manipulating the factorial symbol, we must have constant recourse to the definition. For example,

$$\frac{6!}{3!} = \frac{6\cdot 5\cdot 4\cdot 3\cdot 2\cdot 1}{3\cdot 2\cdot 1} = 6\cdot 5\cdot 4;$$

$$\frac{n!}{3!\cdot(n-3)!} = \frac{n(n-1)(n-2)}{3\cdot 2\cdot 1}.$$

EXERCISES

In Exs. 1–6, write out the first five terms of each series.

1. $\displaystyle\sum_{n=1}^{\infty} \frac{1}{n^2}.$

2. $\displaystyle\sum_{n=1}^{\infty} \frac{(-1)^n}{n!}.$

3. $\displaystyle\sum_{n=1}^{\infty} \frac{2n^2 - 9n + 13}{6(n-1)!}.$ *Ans.* $1 + \tfrac{1}{2} + \tfrac{1}{3} + \tfrac{1}{4} + \tfrac{1}{8} + \cdots.$

4. $\displaystyle\sum_{n=1}^{\infty} \frac{1}{3n^4 - 30n^3 + 105n^2 - 149n + 72}.$ *Ans.* $1 + \tfrac{1}{2} + \tfrac{1}{3} + \tfrac{1}{4} + \tfrac{1}{77} + \cdots.$

5. $\displaystyle\sum_{n=2}^{\infty} \frac{1 + (-1)^n}{n^2 + 1}.$ *Ans.* $\tfrac{2}{5} + 0 + \tfrac{2}{17} + 0 + \tfrac{2}{37} + \cdots.$

6. $\displaystyle\sum_{n=0}^{\infty} \frac{(-1)^n(n+1)}{(2n+1)!}.$

Prove that the series in Exs. 7–14 are divergent.

7. $\displaystyle\sum_{n=0}^{\infty} \frac{n^2 + 1}{2n + 5}.$

8. $1 - 2 + 3 - \cdots + (-1)^{n-1}n + \cdots.$

9. $1 + \dfrac{2}{4} + \dfrac{3}{8} + \dfrac{4}{12} + \cdots + \dfrac{n+1}{4n} + \cdots.$

10. $\dfrac{1}{3} + \dfrac{3}{5} + \dfrac{5}{7} + \cdots + \dfrac{2n-1}{2n+1} + \cdots.$

11. $1 + \dfrac{e}{2^2} + \dfrac{e^2}{3^2} + \dfrac{e^3}{4^2} + \cdots + \dfrac{e^{n-1}}{n^2} + \cdots.$

12. $\dfrac{1}{2} + \dfrac{1}{4} + \dfrac{1}{6} + \dfrac{1}{8} + \cdots + \dfrac{1}{2n} + \cdots.$

13. $\displaystyle\sum_{n=1}^{\infty} \sin\dfrac{n\pi}{2}.$ **14.** $\displaystyle\sum_{n=0}^{\infty} \dfrac{\pi^n}{e^n}.$

15. Show that every infinite arithmetic series, with terms not all zero, is divergent.

In each of Exs. 16–19, show that the given series are identical.

16. $\displaystyle\sum_{n=0}^{\infty} \dfrac{x^n}{n!}$ and $1 + x + \displaystyle\sum_{n=2}^{\infty} \dfrac{x^n}{n!}.$

17. $\displaystyle\sum_{n=0}^{\infty} \dfrac{x^{n+1}}{n+1}$ and $\displaystyle\sum_{n=1}^{\infty} \dfrac{x^n}{n}.$ In the first series replace n everywhere by $(n-1)$. This is called a shift in index.

18. $\displaystyle\sum_{n=0}^{\infty} \dfrac{(-1)^n y^{2n+1}}{(2n+1)!}$ and $\displaystyle\sum_{n=1}^{\infty} \dfrac{(-1)^{n-1} y^{2n-1}}{(2n-1)!}.$

19. $\displaystyle\sum_{n=1}^{\infty} (n^2+1)z^{n+2}$ and $\displaystyle\sum_{n=3}^{\infty} (n^2-4n+5)z^n.$

194. Comparison test. Let

$$u_1 + u_2 + u_3 + \cdots + u_n + \cdots$$

be a series of *positive terms* to be tested.

(a) *If a series*

$$a_1 + a_2 + a_3 + \cdots + a_n + \cdots$$

of positive terms, known to be convergent, can be found such that

$$u_n \leqq a_n,$$

then the series to be tested is convergent.

(b) *If a series*

$$b_1 + b_2 + b_3 + \cdots + b_n + \cdots$$

of positive terms, known to be divergent, can be found such that

$$u_n \geqq b_n,$$

then the series to be tested is divergent.

To prove (*a*), let S_n be the sum of the first *n* terms of the *u*-series, T_n the sum of the first *n* terms of the *a*-series, and T the sum of the *a*-series. Since all the terms u_n and a_n are positive, both S_n and T_n increase, as *n* increases. On the other hand, we have

$$S_n < T_n < T.$$

Therefore, S_n always increases with *n*, but never exceeds the fixed number T. Hence S_n approaches a limit, not greater than T, by the theorem quoted at the end of § 191.

The proof of (*b*) is left to the student.

The success of the test depends on our ability to find a *convergent* series whose terms are *greater* than the corresponding terms of the series to be tested, or a *divergent* series whose terms are *less* than those of the series to be tested. To show that the terms of the *u*-series are greater than those of some convergent series, or less than those of some divergent series, proves nothing.

Since the convergence of a series is not affected by discarding any finite number of terms, it is clear that the conditions of the test do not need to be satisfied from the very beginning of the series, but only *after a certain point,* all the terms up to that point being neglected.

If we change the signs of all the terms, the sign of the sum S (if the sum exists) is changed, but its existence is not affected. Thus if all the terms are negative, we may change all the signs before testing.

Example: Test for convergence the series

$$\frac{2}{1^2} + \frac{3}{2^2} + \frac{4}{3^2} + \cdots + \frac{n+1}{n^2} + \cdots.$$

We know (§ 192) that the harmonic series

$$1 + \frac{1}{2} + \frac{1}{3} + \cdots + \frac{1}{n} + \cdots$$

is divergent. Since

$$\frac{n+1}{n^2} = \frac{1}{n} + \frac{1}{n^2} > \frac{1}{n},$$

the given series is divergent.

195. An integral test. Consider an infinite series,

$$\sum_{n=1}^{\infty} u_n,$$

of positive terms, such that the terms never increase with increasing

n; *i.e.*, $0 < u_{n+1} \leq u_n$. For such a series the following test may*
determine whether the series converges or diverges.

Integral test: If, for $x \geq 1$, the function $f(x)$ is positive, continuous, and never increases with increasing x, then

(a) If $\int_1^\infty f(x)\, dx$ exists, the series $\sum_{n=1}^\infty f(n)$ converges;

(b) If $\int_1^\infty f(x)\, dx$ does not exist, the series $\sum_{n=1}^\infty f(n)$ diverges.

Let us prove part (a) of the test. Put

$$S_n = f(1) + f(2) + f(3) + \cdots + f(n).$$

Now, as shown in Fig. 192, the
area under the curve $y = f(x)$,
from $x = 1$ to $x = n$, is

$$\int_1^n f(x)\, dx,$$

and the sum of the areas of the
rectangles, from $x = 1$ to $x = n$,
is

$$f(2) + f(3) + \cdots + f(n) = S_n - f(1).$$

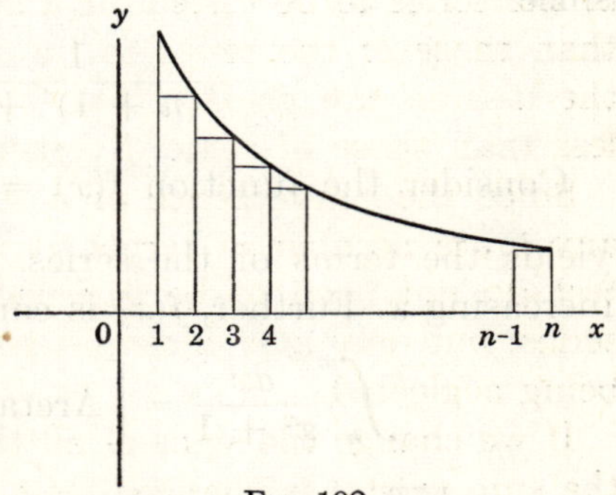

Since $f(x)$ never increases with increasing x,

FIG. 192

$$S_n - f(1) \leq \int_1^n f(x)\, dx.$$

But $\int_1^\infty f(x)\, dx$ exists; call its value A. Then

$$S_n - f(1) \leq A,$$

or $S_n \leq A + f(1)$, by which we have shown that S_n, always increasing, is bounded above. Then S_n approaches a limit as $n \to \infty$;
the series $\sum_{n=1}^\infty f(n)$ converges.

The proof of part (b) is similar to the above, with rectangles
formed by using horizontal lines drawn to the right where each
ordinate, $x = 1, 2, 3, \cdots, n$, intersects the curve. Completion of the
proof is left as an exercise.

* No test for convergence is capable of effective testing of all series. At best, a test
will show that certain series converge, that others diverge, but there will remain series
for which it gives no answer.

Since, for continuous $f(x)$, $\int_a^\infty f(x)\,dx$ and $\int_1^\infty f(x)\,dx$ exist, or do not exist, together, the lower limit in the integral need not be taken as one; its value is unessential.

It is important to notice that, in order to apply the integral test, it is necessary to find a continuous function $f(x)$ for which the values $f(n)$, for integral n, coincide with the terms of the series to be tested. That is not a serious matter for elementary problems.

Example (a): Test the series $\displaystyle\sum_{n=0}^\infty \frac{1}{n^2 + 1}$.

The terms of this series are all positive, and they decrease steadily, since

$$\frac{1}{(n + 1)^2 + 1} < \frac{1}{n^2 + 1}.$$

Consider the function $f(x) = \dfrac{1}{x^2 + 1}$. For $x = n$, this function yields the terms of the series. Also, $f(x)$ decreases steadily with increasing x. Further, $f(x)$ is continuous, and

$$\int_k^\infty \frac{dx}{x^2 + 1} = \Big[\operatorname{Arctan} x\Big]_k^\infty = \frac{\pi}{2} - \operatorname{Arctan} k,$$

so that $\displaystyle\int_k^\infty f(x)\,dx$ exists. Hence the series $\displaystyle\sum_{n=0}^\infty \frac{1}{n^2 + 1}$ converges.

Note that the lower limit k played no essential role, and also note that the fact that the series starts with the $n=0$ term has no bearing whatever on the question of convergence.

Example (b): Test the series $\displaystyle\sum_{n=2}^\infty \frac{1}{n \ln n}$.

Here the series starts with $n = 2$, which does not interfere at all with the application of the integral test. We could shift the index, if we wished, to get $\displaystyle\sum_{n=1}^\infty \frac{1}{(n + 1) \ln (n + 1)}$.

The function $f(x) = \dfrac{1}{x \ln x}$ yields the general term of our series for integral values, $x = n$. Now

$$f'(x) = -\frac{1 + \ln x}{x^2 \ln^2 x},$$

which is negative for $x \geq 2$ (even for $x > 1$), so $f(x)$ decreases steadily. Consider the appropriate integral,

$$\int_2^\infty \frac{dx}{x \ln x} = \left[\ln \ln x \right]_2^\infty,$$

which does not exist. It follows that $\sum_{n=2}^\infty \frac{1}{n \ln n}$ is divergent.

196. The p-series. The series

(1) $$1 + \frac{1}{2^p} + \frac{1}{3^p} + \cdots + \frac{1}{n^p} + \cdots = \sum_{n=1}^\infty \frac{1}{n^p}$$

is called the *p-series*.

If $p = 1$, this is the harmonic series, which we know is divergent. If $p < 1$,

$$\frac{1}{n^p} > \frac{1}{n},$$

so that the series (1) diverges for $p < 1$ by comparison with the harmonic series.

If $p > 1$, we use the integral test. From $f(x) = \frac{1}{x^p}$, for fixed p, we obtain $f'(x) = -\frac{p}{x^{p+1}}$, which is negative, for $x \geq 1$; the function decreases with increasing x. The integral

$$\int_1^\infty \frac{dx}{x^p} = \left[\frac{1}{(1 - p)x^{p-1}} \right]_1^\infty = 0 - \frac{1}{1 - p}$$

exists, for $p > 1$. Hence the series (1) converges for $p > 1$.

In recapitulation, the p-series $\sum_{n=1}^\infty \frac{1}{n^p}$ diverges for $p \leq 1$, converges for $p > 1$. It is quite useful in applying the comparison test.

Example: Test the series

(2) $$\frac{1}{1 \cdot 2} + \frac{1}{2 \cdot 3} + \frac{1}{3 \cdot 4} + \cdots + \frac{1}{n(n + 1)} + \cdots.$$

The series

$$\frac{1}{1^2} + \frac{1}{2^2} + \frac{1}{3^2} + \frac{1}{4^2} + \cdots + \frac{1}{n^2} + \cdots$$

is the p-series with $p = 2$, therefore convergent. Since

$$\frac{1}{n^2 + n} < \frac{1}{n^2}$$

for all (positive integral) values of n, the series (2) converges.

EXERCISES

In Exs. 1–6, test for convergence, employing the comparison test.

1. $\displaystyle\sum_{n=1}^{\infty} \frac{1}{n^n}.$ *Ans.* Convergent.

2. $\dfrac{1}{2} + \dfrac{1}{2 \cdot 4} + \dfrac{1}{3 \cdot 8} + \dfrac{1}{4 \cdot 16} + \cdots + \dfrac{1}{n \cdot 2^n} + \cdots.$

3. $\dfrac{1}{5} + \dfrac{1}{11} + \dfrac{1}{17} + \cdots + \dfrac{1}{6n - 1} + \cdots.$

4. $\displaystyle\sum_{n=0}^{\infty} \frac{1}{(2n - 1)(n^2 + 1)}.$ *Ans.* Convergent.

5. $\displaystyle\sum_{k=2}^{\infty} \frac{\sqrt{k - 1}}{k}.$ *Ans.* Divergent.   6. $\displaystyle\sum_{k=1}^{\infty} \frac{k^2 + 1}{k^3 - 7}.$

In Exs. 7–12, test for convergence, using the integral test.

7. $\displaystyle\sum_{n=1}^{\infty} ne^{-n^2}.$ *Ans.* Convergent.   8. $\displaystyle\sum_{n=1}^{\infty} \frac{1}{1 + \sqrt{n}}.$

9. $\dfrac{1}{2\sqrt{2}} + \dfrac{1}{5\sqrt{5}} + \dfrac{1}{10\sqrt{10}} + \cdots + \dfrac{1}{(1 + k^2)^{\frac{3}{2}}} + \cdots.$

10. $\displaystyle\sum_{k=2}^{\infty} \frac{1}{k(\ln k)^2}.$ *Ans.* Convergent.   11. $\displaystyle\sum_{j=2}^{\infty} \frac{\ln j}{j}.$ *Ans.* Divergent.

12. $\displaystyle\sum_{n=1}^{\infty} \frac{n}{(1 + n^2)^2}.$

13. Show that the series $\displaystyle\sum_{n=1}^{\infty} \frac{1}{an + b}$ is divergent for all values * of a and b.

$\left(\text{Compare with } \displaystyle\sum_{n=1}^{\infty} \frac{1}{2an}.\right)$

14. Show that the series $\displaystyle\sum_{n=1}^{\infty} \frac{1}{an^2 + bn + c}$ is convergent for all values *
of a, b, c $(a \neq 0)$. (Adapt the suggestion in Ex. 13.)

15. Show that the series $\displaystyle\sum_{n=1}^{\infty} \frac{a_0 n + a_1}{b_0 n^2 + b_1 n + b_2}$ is divergent.

16. Do Ex. 13 by the integral test.

17. Complete the proof of part (b) of the integral test.

18. If $\displaystyle\sum_{n=1}^{\infty} u_n, \sum_{n=1}^{\infty} a_n$ are two series of *positive terms* such that

$\displaystyle\lim_{n \to \infty} \frac{u_n}{a_n} = k(k > 0)$, show that the u-series converges or diverges according
as the a-series converges or diverges.

---

* The case in which the denominator vanishes for a positive integral value of n is
tacitly excluded, since then the series would not be defined.

19. Using the theorem of Ex. 18 with $u_n = \dfrac{P(n)}{Q(n)}$, $a_n = \dfrac{1}{n^{q-p}}$, prove the validity of the following test.

POLYNOMIAL TEST: *If $P(n)$ is a polynomial of degree p, $Q(n)$ a polynomial of degree q, the series $\displaystyle\sum_{n=1}^{\infty} \dfrac{P(n)}{Q(n)}$ converges if $q > p + 1$, otherwise diverges.*

In Exs. 20–29, test by using the polynomial test.

20. $\displaystyle\sum_{n=2}^{\infty} \dfrac{n^3 + 1}{n^4(3n + 1)}.$

21. $\displaystyle\sum_{k=0}^{\infty} \dfrac{1}{(2k + 1)^2}.$

22. $\dfrac{3 \cdot 4}{2 + 1} + \dfrac{4 \cdot 5}{16 + 1} + \dfrac{5 \cdot 6}{54 + 1} + \cdots + \dfrac{(n + 2)(n + 3)}{2n^3 + 1} + \cdots.$

23. $\displaystyle\sum_{n=0}^{\infty} \dfrac{2n - 1}{4(n + 4)(n + 1)}.$

24. Ex. 3.   **25.** Ex. 4.   **26.** Ex. 6.
27. Ex. 12.   **28.** Ex. 13.   **29.** Ex. 14.

In Exs. 30–41, test by any available means.

30. $1 + \dfrac{1}{2^1} + \dfrac{1}{2^4} + \dfrac{1}{2^9} + \cdots + \dfrac{1}{2^{n^2}} + \cdots.$

31. $\displaystyle\sum_{m=0}^{\infty} \dfrac{\sin^2 (2m + 1)}{(m + 1)^2}.$ *Ans.* Convergent.

32. $\displaystyle\sum_{n=0}^{\infty} \dfrac{(-1)^n n^2}{n + 1}.$ *Ans.* Divergent.

33. $\displaystyle\sum_{n=0}^{\infty} \dfrac{2n + 1}{(2n - 1)^3 + n^2}.$

34. $\displaystyle\sum_{n=1}^{\infty} n^2 e^{-sn}, \, s > 0.$ **35.** $\displaystyle\sum_{n=1}^{\infty} n^2 e^{-sn}, \, s < 0.$

36. $\displaystyle\sum_{k=2}^{\infty} \dfrac{\sqrt{k}}{k^2 + 1}.$ *Ans.* Convergent.   **37.** $\displaystyle\sum_{n=1}^{\infty} \dfrac{n}{e^n}.$

38. $\dfrac{e + 1}{\pi} + \dfrac{(e + 1)^2}{\pi^2} + \dfrac{(e + 1)^3}{\pi^3} + \cdots + \dfrac{(e + 1)^n}{\pi^n} + \cdots.$

39. $\displaystyle\sum_{n=0}^{\infty} \dfrac{1}{2^{3n}}.$ **40.** $\displaystyle\sum_{n=1}^{\infty} \dfrac{1}{7n + 1}.$

41. $\displaystyle\sum_{n=1}^{\infty} \dfrac{100n^2}{\pi^n}.$

42. Show, by using examples such as $\displaystyle\sum_{n=0}^{\infty} (-1)^n$, that you cannot, in general, test for convergence by grouping terms together before testing.

43. Show that for series of positive terms it is legitimate to group terms before testing for convergence.

44. Use the integral test on the harmonic series.

45. Show that the harmonic series is divergent by grouping the terms as follows:

$$1 + \left(\frac{1}{2}\right) + \left(\frac{1}{3} + \frac{1}{4}\right) + \left(\frac{1}{5} + \frac{1}{6} + \frac{1}{7} + \frac{1}{8}\right) + \cdots$$
$$+ \left(\frac{1}{2^k + 1} + \frac{1}{2^k + 2} + \cdots + \frac{1}{2^k + 2^k}\right) + \cdots,$$

and proving that the sum of the terms in each group $\geq \frac{1}{2}$.

46. Adapt the suggestion of Ex. 45 to a new proof of the convergence of $\sum\limits_{n=1}^{\infty} \frac{1}{n^p}$ for $p > 1$. Group the terms as follows:

$$1 + \left(\frac{1}{2^p} + \frac{1}{3^p}\right) + \left(\frac{1}{4^p} + \frac{1}{5^p} + \frac{1}{6^p} + \frac{1}{7^p}\right) + \cdots$$
$$+ \left(\frac{1}{2^{np}} + \frac{1}{(2^n + 1)^p} + \cdots + \frac{1}{(2^{n+1}-1)^p}\right) + \cdots,$$

and show that the new series has its terms less than the corresponding terms of the convergent geometric series

$$1 + \frac{1}{2^{p-1}} + \frac{1}{(2^{p-1})^2} + \cdots + \frac{1}{(2^{p-1})^n} + \cdots.$$

197. Absolute convergence. First we prove the following important result.

THEOREM: *If the series* $\sum\limits_{n=1}^{\infty} |u_n|$ *converges, then* $\sum\limits_{n=1}^{\infty} u_n$ *converges.*

In the finite sum

$$S_n = u_1 + u_2 + u_3 + \cdots + u_n,$$

let the positive terms be denoted by a's, the numerical values of the negative ones by b's. Then

$$S_n = A_k - B_m,$$

where $A_k = \sum a$'s, $B_m = \sum b$'s, and $k + m = n$.

For the series $\sum\limits_{n=1}^{\infty} |u_n|$, the corresponding finite sum is

$$|u_1| + |u_2| + |u_3| + \cdots + |u_n| = A_k + B_m.$$

The theorem states that, if $(A_k + B_m)$ approaches a limit, then $(A_k - B_m)$ does also. But, since A_k and B_m are positive and increasing, if $(A_k + B_m)$ approaches a limit, then A_k and B_m must do so separately. Hence $(A_k - B_m)$ approaches a limit, and the proof is ended.

DEFINITION: *A series is said to be* **absolutely convergent** *if the series formed from it by replacing all its terms by their absolute values is convergent.*

The theorem above may now be reworded.

THEOREM: *If a series is absolutely convergent, it is convergent.*

A series which is convergent, but not absolutely convergent, is called *simply convergent.*

Example: Test the series $\sum_{n=1}^{\infty} \dfrac{\sin\frac{n\pi}{4}}{n^2}$.

The numerator takes on values which are positive, negative, or zero, depending on the value of n. However, $\left|\sin\dfrac{n\pi}{4}\right| \leqq 1$, so

$$\left|\frac{\sin\frac{n\pi}{4}}{n^2}\right| < \frac{1}{n^2}$$

and we know $\sum_{n=1}^{\infty} \dfrac{1}{n^2}$ is convergent. Hence, the given series is absolutely convergent by the comparison test, so it is also convergent.

198. Ratio test. Given the series

(1) $u_1 + u_2 + u_3 + \cdots + u_n + \cdots,$

form the ratio $\dfrac{u_{n+1}}{u_n}$ of a general term to the one *preceding* it. Then,

(a) *If* $\lim\limits_{n\to\infty}\left|\dfrac{u_{n+1}}{u_n}\right| < 1,$ *the series converges; indeed, converges absolutely.*

(b) *If* $\lim\limits_{n\to\infty}\left|\dfrac{u_{n+1}}{u_n}\right| > 1,$ *or if* $\left|\dfrac{u_{n+1}}{u_n}\right|$ *increases indefinitely, the series diverges.*

(c) *If* $\lim\limits_{n\to\infty}\left|\dfrac{u_{n+1}}{u_n}\right| = 1,$ *the test fails.*

(d) *If* $\left|\dfrac{u_{n+1}}{u_n}\right|$ *does not approach a limit and does not increase indefinitely, the test fails.*

Since the ratio test deals with absolute values, it applies to series in general, not merely to series of positive terms.

Consider the first case: $\lim\limits_{n\to\infty}\left|\dfrac{u_{n+1}}{u_n}\right| = L < 1$. Let us choose some number r between L and 1. By the definition of limit, the difference between the ratio $\left|\dfrac{u_{n+1}}{u_n}\right|$ and its limit L can be made as small as desired, by choosing n large enough; therefore a number k can be found such that for all values of $n \geq k$, we have

$$\left|\frac{u_{n+1}}{u_n}\right| < r.$$

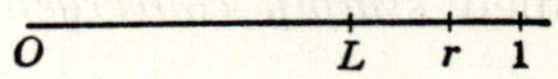

Hence

FIG. 193

$$|u_{k+1}| < |u_k|\,r,$$

$$|u_{k+2}| < |u_{k+1}|\,r < |u_k|\,r^2,$$

$$|u_{k+3}| < |u_{k+2}|\,r < |u_k|\,r^3,$$

$$\vdots \qquad\qquad \vdots \qquad\qquad \vdots \qquad .$$

Discarding the first k terms of $\sum\limits_{n=1}^{\infty}|u_n|$, we see that the remaining terms are less than the corresponding terms of the series

$$|u_k|\,r + |u_k|\,r^2 + |u_k|\,r^3 + \cdots + |u_k|\,r^m + \cdots.$$

But this last, being a geometric series with ratio $r < 1$, is convergent; hence the given series converges by the comparison test.

In case (b), it is easy to show that u_n does not approach zero.

Example (a): In the series

$$1 - \frac{1}{2} + \frac{2}{2^2} - \frac{3}{2^3} + \cdots + \frac{(-1)^n \cdot n}{2^n} + \frac{(-1)^{n+1}(n+1)}{2^{n+1}} + \cdots,$$

$$\lim_{n\to\infty}\left|\frac{u_{n+1}}{u_n}\right| = \lim_{n\to\infty}\frac{\dfrac{n+1}{2^{n+1}}}{\dfrac{n}{2^n}} = \lim_{n\to\infty}\frac{n+1}{2n} = \frac{1}{2}.$$

Thus the series converges.

Example (b): In the series

$$1 + 1 + \frac{1}{2!} + \frac{1}{3!} + \frac{1}{4!} + \cdots + \frac{1}{n!} + \frac{1}{(n+1)!} + \cdots,$$

$$\lim_{n\to\infty}\left|\frac{u_{n+1}}{u_n}\right| = \lim_{n\to\infty}\frac{\dfrac{1}{(n+1)!}}{\dfrac{1}{n!}} = \lim_{n\to\infty}\frac{n!}{(n+1)!},$$

so that

$$\lim_{n\to\infty}\left|\frac{u_{n+1}}{u_n}\right| = \lim_{n\to\infty}\frac{1\cdot2\cdot3\cdots n}{1\cdot2\cdot3\cdots n(n+1)} = \lim_{n\to\infty}\frac{1}{n+1} = 0.$$

Hence the series converges.

Example (c): For the *p*-series $\sum_{n=1}^{\infty}\dfrac{1}{n^p}$, we have

$$\lim_{n\to\infty}\frac{\dfrac{1}{(n+1)^p}}{\dfrac{1}{n^p}} = \lim_{n\to\infty}\frac{n^p}{(n+1)^p} = \lim_{n\to\infty}\frac{1}{\left(1+\dfrac{1}{n}\right)^p} = 1.$$

This is sufficient to show that the test fails in case (c); for the *p*-series converges if $p>1$, diverges if $p\leqq1$, so that there are both convergent and divergent series for which $L=1$.

Failure of the test in case (d) is obvious, since the limit L, which is our criterion, is nonexistent. See Ex. 25 below.

EXERCISES

In Exs. 1–14, test for convergence by the ratio test.

1. $\sum_{n=1}^{\infty}\dfrac{(-1)^{n+1}n}{3^n}.$ *Ans.* Convergent.

2. $\dfrac{2^5}{\pi^2}+\dfrac{3^5}{\pi^3}+\dfrac{4^5}{\pi^4}+\cdots+\dfrac{n^5}{\pi^n}+\cdots.$

3. $\dfrac{1^2}{2^0}+\dfrac{2^2}{2^1}+\dfrac{3^2}{2^2}+\cdots+\dfrac{k^2}{2^{k-1}}+\cdots.$

4. $\sum_{n=0}^{\infty}\dfrac{(-1)^n}{(2n)!}.$ *Ans.* Convergent.

5. $\sum_{n=1}^{\infty}\dfrac{(n-2)(n+3)}{2\cdot4\cdot6\cdots(2n)}.$ *Ans.* Convergent.

6. $\sum_{n=1}^{\infty}\dfrac{1\cdot4\cdot7\cdots(3n+1)}{n^5}.$ *Ans.* Divergent.

7. $\sum_{n=0}^{\infty}\dfrac{(-1)^n(n+1)}{(2n+1)!}.$

8. $\sum_{n=2}^{\infty}\dfrac{4n+1}{2^n n!\,(2n+1)}.$

9. $\sum_{n=1}^{\infty}\dfrac{1\cdot3\cdot5\cdot7\cdots(2n-1)}{3\cdot6\cdot9\cdots(3n)}.$ *Ans.* Convergent.

10. $\dfrac{\pi}{3} - 2\left(\dfrac{\pi}{3}\right)^2 + 3\left(\dfrac{\pi}{3}\right)^3 - \cdots + (-1)^{n+1}n\left(\dfrac{\pi}{3}\right)^n + \cdots.$

11. $\displaystyle\sum_{n=1}^{\infty} \dfrac{n^{100}}{e^n}.$

12. $\displaystyle\sum_{k=0}^{\infty} \dfrac{1}{(2k+1)\cdot 5^{2k+1}}.$

13. $\displaystyle\sum_{n=1}^{\infty} \dfrac{3\cdot 6\cdot 9\cdots(3n)}{1\cdot 5\cdot 9\cdots(4n+1)}.$ *Ans.* Convergent.

14. $\displaystyle\sum_{n=1}^{\infty} \dfrac{(-1)^{n-1}(2n+1)!}{n!}.$ *Ans.* Divergent.

15. If $P(n)$ is a polynomial of any degree in n, show that *the series* $\displaystyle\sum_{n=1}^{\infty} \dfrac{P(n)}{k^n}$ *converges provided* $|k| > 1$.

In Exs. 16–27, show that the ratio test fails; test for convergence by some other method.

16. $\displaystyle\sum_{n=1}^{\infty} \dfrac{n+2}{n(n+3)(2n-1)}.$

17. $\displaystyle\sum_{n=2}^{\infty} \dfrac{\sqrt{n-1}}{n^2(n+1)}.$

18. $\dfrac{1}{1\cdot 3} + \dfrac{1}{3\cdot 5} + \dfrac{1}{5\cdot 7} + \cdots + \dfrac{1}{(2n-1)(2n+1)} + \cdots.$

19. $\dfrac{1}{2^3} + \dfrac{2^2}{3^3} + \dfrac{3^2}{4^3} + \cdots + \dfrac{(n-1)^2}{n^3} + \cdots.$

20. $\displaystyle\sum_{n=1}^{\infty} \dfrac{(-1)^n 3n}{n+1}.$ *Ans.* Divergent.

21. $\displaystyle\sum_{n=1}^{\infty} \dfrac{\sec^2 n}{n}.$ *Ans.* Divergent.

22. $\displaystyle\sum_{n=1}^{\infty} \dfrac{1}{n^2}\cos\dfrac{2n\pi}{n+1}.$ *Ans.* Convergent.

23. $\displaystyle\sum_{n=0}^{\infty} \dfrac{e^{\cos\frac{n\pi}{4}}}{(n+1)(n+2)}.$

24. $\displaystyle\sum_{n=1}^{\infty} (-1)^n n^3.$ *Ans.* Divergent.

25. $\displaystyle\sum_{n=1}^{\infty} u_n,$ where $u_n = \dfrac{1}{n}$ if n is odd, $u_n = \dfrac{1}{2^n}$ if n is even.   *Ans.* Divergent.

26. $\displaystyle\sum_{n=0}^{\infty} \dfrac{\cos\dfrac{n\pi}{6}}{e^n}.$

27. $\displaystyle\sum_{n=1}^{\infty} \dfrac{(3+\cos n\pi)n}{2^n}.$ *Ans.* Convergent.

199. Alternating series. A series whose terms are alternately positive and negative is called an *alternating series*. We shall obtain two extremely useful results concerning such series.

ALTERNATING SERIES TEST: *If after a certain point the terms of an alternating series never increase numerically, and if the limit of the n-th term is zero, the series is convergent.*

THEOREM: *If a series has been shown to be convergent by the alternating series test, then the difference between the sum of the series and the sum of the first n terms is numerically less than the $(n + 1)$-th term:*

$$| S - S_n | < | u_{n+1} |.$$

While formal proofs of these theorems are easily written out, the situation may be shown more vividly by plotting the successive terms as distances laid off end-to-end on an axis. Let $OP_1 = u_1$, $P_1P_2 = u_2$, $P_2P_3 = u_3$, and for any n, $P_nP_{n+1} = u_{n+1}$. It follows from the hypotheses that the successive segments are measured alternately right and left and become shorter and shorter, approaching the limit zero. For any n, the segment OP_n represents

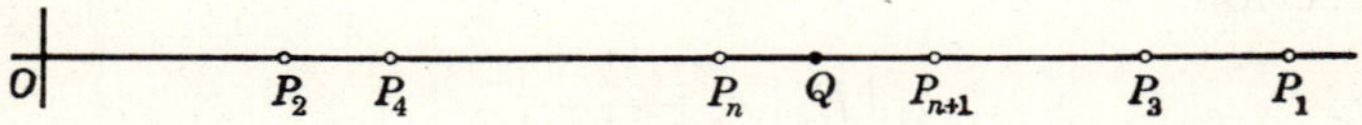

FIG. 194

the sum S_n of the first n terms. Evidently P_n must approach some fixed limit-point Q, and OP_n, or S_n, approaches the limiting value $OQ = S$. This proves the validity of the alternating series test.

To prove the theorem following the test, note that any two successive points P_n, P_{n+1} must fall on opposite sides of Q. Hence $| P_nQ | < | P_nP_{n+1} |$. But

$$P_nQ = OQ - OP_n = S - S_n, \quad P_nP_{n+1} = u_{n+1}.$$

It is important to realize that the theorem does not state a bound on the error for any convergent alternating series, but only for those whose convergence can be demonstrated by the alternating series test.

Example (a): Test the series $\sum\limits_{n=1}^{\infty} \frac{(-1)^{n-1}}{n}$.

This series is not absolutely convergent, since the series of absolute values is the harmonic series.

Let
$$u_n = \frac{(-1)^{n-1}}{n}.$$
Then

(1) The u_n alternate in sign;

(2) $\lim\limits_{n \to \infty} u_n = 0$;

(3) $\dfrac{1}{n+1} < \dfrac{1}{n}$, so $|u_{n+1}| < |u_n|$; the terms steadily decrease in numerical value.

Hence, the series in question converges by the alternating series test. Since it is convergent, but not absolutely convergent, it is simply convergent.

Let
$$S_n = 1 - \frac{1}{2} + \frac{1}{3} - \frac{1}{4} + \cdots + \frac{(-1)^{n-1}}{n},$$

the sum to n terms of the series, and let E_n be the error made by stopping with the n-th term. Thus, E_n is the difference between the sum of the series and the approximation S_n. By the theorem of this section,

$$|E_n| < \frac{1}{n+1},$$

which in this instance is not particularly helpful, as is pointed out in Ex. 23 below. The next example has a more cheerful ending.

Example (b): Test the series $\sum\limits_{n=0}^{\infty} \dfrac{(-1)^n}{(2n)!}$

We already know (Ex. 4, p. 363) that this series is absolutely convergent. Let us, in order to bound the error in computation with the series, test it by the alternating series test. It is easily seen that

(1) The terms alternate in sign;

(2) $\lim\limits_{n \to \infty} \dfrac{(-1)^n}{(2n)!} = 0$;

(3) $\dfrac{1}{(2n+2)!} < \dfrac{1}{(2n)!}$.

Therefore the alternating series test applies. Now consider the error made in using only the terms out to $n = 4$. Because the alternating series test worked, we know that

$$|E_4| < \frac{1}{(2 \cdot 5)!} = \frac{1}{10!} = \frac{1}{3,628,800} = 0.000\,000\,3.$$

That is, the approximation

$$S_4 = 1 - \frac{1}{2!} + \frac{1}{4!} - \frac{1}{6!} + \frac{1}{8!}$$

yields the sum of the series correct to six decimal places!

200. Evaluation of the sum of a series. So far we have striven merely to determine whether a given series is convergent or divergent—*i.e.*, whether it does or does not have a sum. The existence of a sum having been established, the next problem is to determine its value. It follows from the definition of convergence that this can be done to any desired degree of approximation by merely adding together a sufficient number of terms at the beginning of the series. However, unless the series is "rapidly convergent" —*i.e.*, unless the successive terms diminish rapidly in numerical value—the amount of computation involved in this process is apt to be prohibitive. (See Ex. 23 below.) More elaborate methods, beyond the range of this book, make it possible to sum many slowly convergent series with comparative ease.

In computing the sum of a series by addition of terms, it is necessary to know an upper limit for the error committed by stopping with any given term. In this connection the theorem of the preceding section is useful, as we saw in Example (*b*) of that section.

If a series converges rapidly, it is usually easy to show that, even though the succeeding terms all have the same sign, the error committed by stopping at any point is only slightly greater than the first term neglected (cf. the example below).

As a rule, the terms retained in the computation are replaced by decimal approximations, and care must be taken to see that the errors thus introduced do not accumulate sufficiently to affect the result. If the sum is to be correct to k decimal places, each term must be computed to at least $k + 1$ places, and frequently more. The reader is warned against the very common mistake of stopping at too early a point in the series, so that the terms neglected are sufficient to vitiate the result.

Example: Find the sum of the series

$$\frac{1}{5} + \frac{1}{3 \cdot 5^3} + \frac{1}{5 \cdot 5^5} + \frac{1}{7 \cdot 5^7} + \cdots + \frac{1}{(2n-1) \cdot 5^{2n-1}} + \cdots,$$

correct to four decimal places. (Ex. 12, p. 364.)

To find the sum, we have

$$\frac{1}{5} = 0.2, \qquad \frac{1}{3 \cdot 5^3} = 0.002\,67, \qquad \frac{1}{5 \cdot 5^5} = 0.000\,06.$$

The fourth term is evidently far too small in itself to affect the fifth place, and the error committed by stopping with the third term is but slightly greater than the fourth term.* Adding the three terms computed above, and discarding the fifth place as untrustworthy, we find the sum to be 0.2027.

EXERCISES

In Exs. 1–16, test the series (a) for convergence; (b) for absolute convergence.

1. $\sum\limits_{n=1}^{\infty} \dfrac{(-1)^{n+1}}{2n+1}.$ *Ans.* Convergent.

2. $\sum\limits_{n=1}^{\infty} \dfrac{(-1)^{n+1}}{(2n+1)^2}.$ *Ans.* Absolutely convergent.

3. $\sum\limits_{n=2}^{\infty} \dfrac{(-1)^n(n+2)}{3n-1}.$ *Ans.* Divergent.

4. $\sum\limits_{n=1}^{\infty} \dfrac{(-1)^{n-1}1000n^2}{3^n}.$ *Ans.* Absolutely convergent.

5. $\sum\limits_{k=0}^{\infty} \dfrac{(-1)^k\,k!}{100^k}.$ *Ans.* Divergent.

6. $\sum\limits_{k=0}^{\infty} \dfrac{(-1)^k(2k)!}{10^k}.$ 7. $\sum\limits_{n=0}^{\infty} \dfrac{(-1)^n 10^{4n}}{n!}.$

* The argument is as follows:

$$\frac{1}{7 \cdot 5^7} + \frac{1}{9 \cdot 5^9} + \frac{1}{11 \cdot 5^{11}} + \cdots + \frac{1}{(2n-1)5^{2n-1}} + \cdots < \frac{1}{7 \cdot 5^7} + \frac{1}{7 \cdot 5^9} + \frac{1}{7 \cdot 5^{11}}$$

$$+ \cdots + \frac{1}{7 \cdot 5^{2n-1}} + \cdots < \frac{1}{7 \cdot 5^7}\left(1 + \frac{1}{5^2} + \frac{1}{5^4} + \cdots + \frac{1}{5^{2k}} + \cdots\right).$$

The series in parentheses is a geometric series whose sum is $\dfrac{1}{1 - \frac{1}{25}} = \frac{25}{24}.$ Thus the error in stopping with the third term is less than $\frac{25}{24}$ times the fourth term.

8. $\displaystyle\sum_{n=0}^{\infty} \frac{(-1)^n}{n^3 + 1}.$

9. $\displaystyle\sum_{n=0}^{\infty} \frac{(-1)^n(n + 1)}{n^2 + 4n + 5}.$

10. $\displaystyle\sum_{n=1}^{\infty} \frac{(-1)^{n+1} n \pi^n}{e^{2n} + 1}.$

11. $1 - \dfrac{1}{2\sqrt{1}} + \dfrac{1}{3\sqrt{2}} - \dfrac{1}{4\sqrt{3}} + \cdots + \dfrac{(-1)^{n-1}}{n\sqrt{n-1}} + \cdots.$

12. $1 - \dfrac{1}{\sqrt{2}} + \dfrac{1}{\sqrt{3}} - \dfrac{1}{\sqrt{4}} + \cdots + \dfrac{(-1)^{n-1}}{\sqrt{n}} + \cdots.$

13. $\displaystyle\sum_{n=1}^{\infty} \frac{1}{n^2} \sin n.$ **14.** $\displaystyle\sum_{n=1}^{\infty} \frac{\sin \frac{1}{4} n \pi}{n^4}.$ **15.** $\displaystyle\sum_{n=1}^{\infty} \frac{n \cos \frac{1}{4} n \pi}{n + 1}.$

16. $\displaystyle\sum_{n=1}^{\infty} u_n,$ where $u_n = \dfrac{1}{n}$ if n is odd, $u_n = -\dfrac{1}{n^{\frac{3}{2}}}$ if n is even.   *Ans.* Divergent.

In Exs. 17–22, find the sum of the series, correct to the number of decimal places indicated in the respective answers.

17. $1 - \dfrac{1}{10} + \dfrac{2}{10^2} - \dfrac{3}{10^3} + \cdots + \dfrac{(-1)^n \cdot n}{10^n} + \cdots.$ *Ans.* 0.91736.

18. $1 - \dfrac{1}{3!} + \dfrac{1}{5!} - \cdots + \dfrac{(-1)^{n-1}}{(2n-1)!} + \cdots.$ *Ans.* 0.84147.

19. $1 - \dfrac{1}{2!} + \dfrac{2}{3!} - \dfrac{3}{4!} + \cdots + \dfrac{(-1)^{n-1}(n-1)}{n!} + \cdots.$ *Ans.* 0.736.

20. $\dfrac{1}{10} - \dfrac{1}{2 \cdot 10^2} + \dfrac{1}{3 \cdot 10^3} - \cdots + \dfrac{(-1)^{n-1}}{n \cdot 10^n} + \cdots.$ *Ans.* 0.0953.

21. $\dfrac{1}{5} + \dfrac{2}{5^2} + \dfrac{3}{5^3} + \cdots + \dfrac{n}{5^n} + \cdots.$ *Ans.* 0.3125.

22. $\dfrac{1}{1 \cdot 2} + \dfrac{1}{2 \cdot 3} \cdot \dfrac{1}{10} + \dfrac{1}{3 \cdot 4} \cdot \dfrac{1}{10^2} + \cdots + \dfrac{1}{n(n+1)10^{n-1}} + \cdots.$

Ans. 0.5176.

23. How many terms of the series $1 - \dfrac{1}{2} + \dfrac{1}{3} - \dfrac{1}{4} + \cdots + \dfrac{(-1)^{n-1}}{n} + \cdots$ must be taken to insure correctness of the sum to four places, with an error of not more than 5 points in the fifth place?   *Ans.* 20,000.

CHAPTER 26 *POWER SERIES*

201. Power series. A series of the form

$$a_0 + a_1 v + a_2 v^2 + \cdots + a_n v^n + \cdots = \sum_{n=0}^{\infty} a_n v^n,$$

where v is a variable and a_0, a_1, a_2, $\cdots$ are constants, is called a *power series*. Such series will be studied in this chapter.

A power series may converge for all values of the variable v, or for no values except zero; but usually it will converge for all values in some interval of definite length greater than zero, and diverge for all values outside that interval. The interval of convergence always extends equal distances on each side of the point $v = 0$.

In simple cases, the interval of convergence can be determined by the ratio test.

Example (a): Find the interval of convergence of the series

$$1 + x + \frac{x^2}{2} + \frac{x^3}{3} + \cdots + \frac{x^n}{n} + \cdots.$$

Here

$$\lim_{n \to \infty} \left| \frac{u_{n+1}}{u_n} \right| = \lim_{n \to \infty} \left| \frac{\dfrac{x^{n+1}}{n+1}}{\dfrac{x^n}{n}} \right| = \lim_{n \to \infty} \frac{n}{n+1} \cdot |x| = |x|.$$

Therefore:

(a) The series converges when $|x| < 1$, *i.e.*, $-1 < x < 1$.
(b) The series diverges when $|x| > 1$.
(c) The test fails when $x = \pm 1$. But when $x = 1$, the series is

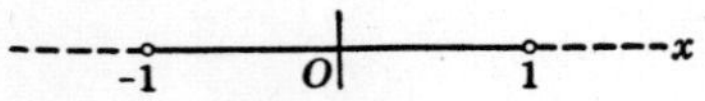

Fig. 195

$$1 + 1 + \frac{1}{2} + \frac{1}{3} + \cdots + \frac{1}{n} + \cdots,$$

370

and therefore diverges; when $x = -1$, the series is

$$1 - 1 + \frac{1}{2} - \frac{1}{3} + \frac{1}{4} - \cdots + \frac{(-1)^n}{n} + \cdots,$$

which converges by § 199.

Hence the interval of convergence is $-1 \leq x < 1$.

Example (b): Find the interval of convergence of the series

$$(x - 3) + 2(x - 3)^2 + 3(x - 3)^3 + \cdots + n(x - 3)^n + \cdots.$$

In this case

$$\lim_{n \to \infty} \left| \frac{(n + 1)(x - 3)^{n+1}}{n(x - 3)^n} \right| = \lim_{n \to \infty} \frac{n + 1}{n} \cdot |x - 3| = |x - 3|.$$

(a) The series converges if $|x - 3| < 1$, or $2 < x < 4$.
(b) The series diverges if $|x - 3| > 1$, or $x > 4$, $x < 2$.
(c) By § 191, the series diverges if $x = 2$ or $x = 4$.

Thus the interval is $2 < x < 4$.

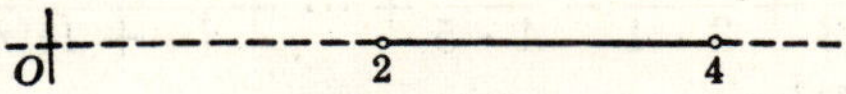

Fig. 196

Example (c): Find the region of convergence of the series

$$\frac{1}{x} + \frac{2}{x^3} + \frac{2^2}{x^5} + \frac{2^3}{x^7} + \cdots + \frac{2^n}{x^{2n+1}} + \cdots.$$

The test-limit is

$$\lim_{n \to \infty} \frac{\frac{2^{n+1}}{x^{2n+3}}}{\frac{2^n}{x^{2n+1}}} = \lim_{n \to \infty} \frac{2}{x^2} = \frac{2}{x^2}.$$

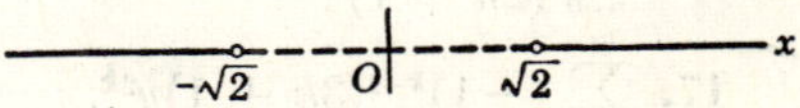

Fig. 197

Thus the series converges if $\frac{2}{x^2} < 1$, $|x| > \sqrt{2}$; it diverges at both endpoints.

EXERCISES

In Exs. 1–28, find the interval of convergence and test the series at the endpoints of the interval.

1. $\displaystyle\sum_{n=0}^{\infty} (-1)^n x^n.$ *Ans.* $-1 < x < 1.$

2. $\displaystyle\sum_{n=1}^{\infty} \frac{x^n}{2n - 1}.$ *Ans.* $-1 \leq x < 1.$

3. $\displaystyle\sum_{n=0}^{\infty} \frac{(-1)^n y^n}{(2n+1)^2 3^{n+1}}.$ *Ans.* $-3 \leqq y \leqq 3.$

4. $\displaystyle\sum_{n=1}^{\infty} \frac{(n+1)y^{2n}}{5^n}.$ *Ans.* $-\sqrt{5} < y < \sqrt{5}.$

5. $\displaystyle\sum_{n=0}^{\infty} (-1)^n n!\, x^n.$ *Ans.* $x = 0.$

6. $\displaystyle\sum_{n=1}^{\infty} \frac{n!\, x^n}{2n-1}.$ *Ans.* $x = 0.$

7. $\displaystyle\sum_{n=0}^{\infty} \frac{x^n}{n!}.$ *Ans.* All values of $x.$

8. $\displaystyle\sum_{n=0}^{\infty} \frac{(-1)^n x^{2n}}{(2n)!}.$ *Ans.* All values of $x.$

9. $y + \dfrac{y^2}{1+2^2} + \dfrac{y^3}{1+3^2} + \cdots + \dfrac{y^n}{1+n^2} + \cdots.$

10. $z - \dfrac{z^3}{4} + \dfrac{z^5}{7} - \dfrac{z^7}{10} + \cdots + \dfrac{(-1)^n z^{2n+1}}{3n+1} + \cdots.$

11. $\dfrac{x}{2\cdot3\cdot4} - \dfrac{x^2}{5\cdot6\cdot7} + \dfrac{x^3}{8\cdot9\cdot10} - \cdots + \dfrac{(-1)^{n-1}x^n}{(3n-1)(3n)(3n+1)} + \cdots.$

12. $\dfrac{1}{1\cdot2} - \dfrac{x^2}{2\cdot3} + \dfrac{x^4}{3\cdot4} - \dfrac{x^6}{4\cdot5} + \cdots + \dfrac{(-1)^n x^{2n}}{(n+1)(n+2)} + \cdots.$

13. $\displaystyle\sum_{n=0}^{\infty} \frac{(-1)^n x^{n+2}}{(n+1)^2 2^{2n}}.$ *Ans.* $-4 \leqq x \leqq 4.$

14. $\displaystyle\sum_{n=1}^{\infty} \frac{n x^{2n+3}}{(n+1)^2}.$ *Ans.* $-1 < x < 1.$

15. $\displaystyle\sum_{n=0}^{\infty} \frac{(-1)^n x^{2n+1}}{(2n+1)!}.$ *Ans.* All values of $x.$

16. $\displaystyle\sum_{n=0}^{\infty} \frac{n!\, x^n}{(2n+1)!}.$ *Ans.* All values of $x.$

17. $\displaystyle\sum_{k=1}^{\infty} (-1)^{k-1}(3k+1)y^{2k}.$ **18.** $\displaystyle\sum_{k=0}^{\infty} \frac{(-1)^k(3k+1)y^{2k}}{2^k}.$

19. $\displaystyle\sum_{n=1}^{\infty} n^2(x+1)^n.$ *Ans.* $-2 < x < 0.$

20. $\displaystyle\sum_{n=0}^{\infty} \frac{(-1)^n(x-4)^{n+1}}{(n+1)^3}.$ *Ans.* $3 \leqq x \leqq 5.$

21. $\displaystyle\sum_{n=1}^{\infty} n(x-2)^n.$ **22.** $\displaystyle\sum_{n=1}^{\infty} \frac{n(x+3)^n}{(2n-1)^3}.$

23. $\displaystyle\sum_{n=0}^{\infty} \frac{(n+2)(x-1)^n}{n!}.$ **24.** $\displaystyle\sum_{n=1}^{\infty} \frac{(-1)^n(2n-1)x^{2n-1}}{(2n)!}.$

25. $\displaystyle\sum_{n=1}^{\infty} \frac{(-1)^n}{n x^n}.$ *Ans.* $x \geqq 1,$ and $x < -1.$

26. $\displaystyle\sum_{n=0}^{\infty} \frac{n+1}{2^{n+2}x^n}.$ *Ans.* $x > \frac{1}{2},$ and $x < -\frac{1}{2}.$

27. $\displaystyle\sum_{n=0}^{\infty} \frac{(-1)^n 5^n}{(3n+1)x^n}$.

28. $\displaystyle\sum_{n=2}^{\infty} \frac{(-1)^n 2^{n+1}}{n^2 x^{n+2}}$.

In Exs. 29–33, find the interval of convergence, but do not test the series at the endpoints of the interval.

29. $\displaystyle\sum_{n=1}^{\infty} \frac{1 \cdot 3 \cdot 5 \cdot 7 \cdots (2n-1)x^{2n}}{2^n n!}$.

30. $\displaystyle\sum_{n=1}^{\infty} \frac{n^n x^n}{n!}$. *Ans.* $|x| < \dfrac{1}{e}$.

31. $\displaystyle\sum_{n=1}^{\infty} \frac{n! \, x^n}{n^n}$.

32. $\displaystyle\sum_{n=1}^{\infty} \frac{1 \cdot 3 \cdot 5 \cdot 7 \cdots (2n-1)x^{2n}}{2 \cdot 4 \cdot 6 \cdot 8 \cdots (2n+2)}$.

33. $1 + \displaystyle\sum_{n=1}^{\infty} \frac{m(m-1)\cdots(m-n+1)x^n}{n!}$. *Ans.* $|x| < 1$.

202. Maclaurin's Series. Being given a power series in x, if we substitute for x any value within the interval of convergence, the sum of the series is determined; *i.e.*, the sum is a function of x. This suggests a very important problem: Being given a function of x, to determine whether it has a power series expansion and, if it has one, to find that expansion.

The job of determining conditions under which $f(x)$ has a power series expansion belongs to a more advanced course. The more elementary problem of determining the coefficients in the expansion will be treated here. The existence of all the expansions in this book rests on well-known proofs in more advanced books.

Let us assume that such a series exists, and write

$$(1) \qquad f(x) = c_0 + c_1 x + c_2 x^2 + \cdots + c_n x^n + \cdots,$$

where the coefficients c_0, c_1, c_2, $\cdots$ are constants to be determined. Setting $x = 0$, we get

$$f(0) = c_0;$$

i.e., c_0 is the value of the given function at $x = 0$. Differentiating (1) (see Theorem IV, § 210),

$$f'(x) = c_1 + 2\,c_2 x + 3\,c_3 x^2 + \cdots,$$

and setting $x = 0$, we find

$$f'(0) = c_1.$$

Proceeding in this way, we get successively

$$f''(0) = 2 \cdot 1\, c_2,$$
$$f'''(0) = 3 \cdot 2 \cdot 1\, c_3,$$
$$\vdots \qquad \vdots$$
$$f^{(n)}(0) = n!\, c_n,$$
$$\vdots \qquad \vdots$$

Hence (1) takes the following form, called *Maclaurin's Series:*

$$(2) \quad f(x) = f(0) + f'(0)x + \frac{f''(0)}{2!}x^2 + \cdots + \frac{f^{(n)}(0)}{n!}x^n + \cdots.$$

It should be noted that we have not proved the validity of this result; we have merely proved that if there is a series of the form (1) whose sum is $f(x)$, that series is given by equation (2). Evidently the series (2) can always be formally written down whenever the function and its successive derivatives are defined at $x = 0$, but cases can be found in which the sum of the series is not the given function (see Ex. 49 below).

For all functions that we shall consider, *the interval within which Maclaurin's Series is valid coincides with the interval of convergence of the series.* Within that interval the series is said to *represent the function,* and the function is said to be *developed* or *expanded* in powers of x.

Example (a): Develop e^x in Maclaurin's Series.

$$f(x) = e^x, \qquad\qquad f(0) = 1,$$
$$f'(x) = e^x, \qquad\qquad f'(0) = 1,$$
$$\vdots \qquad \vdots \qquad\qquad \vdots \qquad \vdots$$
$$f^{(n)}(x) = e^x, \qquad\qquad f^{(n)}(0) = 1.$$

Therefore

$$e^x = 1 + x + \frac{x^2}{2!} + \frac{x^3}{3!} + \cdots + \frac{x^n}{n!} + \cdots.$$

This series converges for all values of x. (Ex. 7, p. 372.)

Example (b): Expand $\sin x$ in powers of x.

Here

$$f(x) = \sin x, \qquad\qquad f(0) = 0,$$
$$f'(x) = \cos x, \qquad\qquad f'(0) = 1,$$
$$f''(x) = -\sin x, \qquad\qquad f''(0) = 0,$$
$$f'''(x) = -\cos x, \qquad\qquad f'''(0) = -1,$$
$$f^{(4)}(x) = \sin x, \qquad\qquad f^{(4)}(0) = 0.$$

Since we have now returned to the original function, it is clear that the sequence 0, 1, 0, −1, occurring in the right-hand column, must repeat over and over. Hence, substituting in (2), we find

$$\sin x = x - \frac{x^3}{3!} + \frac{x^5}{5!} - \cdots + \frac{(-1)^n x^{2n+1}}{(2n+1)!} + \cdots.$$

The series converges for all values of x. (Ex. 15, p. 372.)

The rather cumbersome* method, using Maclaurin's formula directly to obtain power series for elementary functions, is to be used only on certain basic functions, those given in the next section. For other elementary functions, we obtain their power series expansions by suitable manipulations performed on the basic series. For details, see § 209–211.

203. The basic expansions. We list for reference:

(1) $$e^x = \sum_{n=0}^{\infty} \frac{x^n}{n!}; \text{ for all values of } x.$$

(2) $$\cos x = \sum_{n=0}^{\infty} \frac{(-1)^n x^{2n}}{(2n)!}; \text{ for all values of } x.$$

(3) $$\sin x = \sum_{n=0}^{\infty} \frac{(-1)^n x^{2n+1}}{(2n+1)!}; \text{ for all values of } x.$$

(4) $$\frac{1}{1-x} = \sum_{n=0}^{\infty} x^n; \; -1 < x < 1.$$

(5) $$\ln(1+x) = \sum_{n=1}^{\infty} \frac{(-1)^{n+1} x^n}{n}; \; -1 < x \leq 1.$$

(6) $$(1+x)^m = 1 + \sum_{n=1}^{\infty} \frac{m(m-1)(m-2)\cdots(m-n+1)x^n}{n!}; \; |x| < 1.$$

It is advisable that the student write out several terms of each series, as an aid in remembering these important expansions.

---

* Try this method for getting the general term of the series for $\frac{x^3}{(1+x^2)^2}$, and then compare with the neat device used in Ex. 7, p. 389.

204. Taylor's Series. As a natural generalization of the problem stated in § 202 (first paragraph), we may think of our function of x as the sum of a power series proceeding not in powers of x, but in powers of $x - a$, where a is some constant.

To determine this series, write

$$f(x) = c_0 + c_1(x - a) + c_2(x - a)^2 + \cdots + c_n(x - a)^n + \cdots,$$

and set $x = a$, which gives

$$c_0 = f(a).$$

We now differentiate and set $x = a$; etc. The process is identical with that of § 202; the result is *Taylor's Series:*

$$(1) \quad f(x) = f(a) + f'(a)(x - a) + \frac{f''(a)}{2!}(x - a)^2 + \cdots$$

$$+ \frac{f^{(n)}(a)}{n!}(x - a)^n + \cdots.$$

Thus Maclaurin's Series is a special case of Taylor's Series, viz., the case $a = 0$. The remarks made in § 202 concerning the validity of Maclaurin's Series apply here as well.

Example: Expand the function $\ln x$ in powers of $x - 1$.
In this case $a = 1$:

$$f(x) = \ln x, \qquad\qquad f(1) = 0,$$

$$f'(x) = \frac{1}{x}, \qquad\qquad f'(1) = 1,$$

$$f''(x) = -\frac{1}{x^2}, \qquad\qquad f''(1) = -1,$$

$$f'''(x) = \frac{2}{x^3}, \qquad\qquad f'''(1) = 2,$$

$$f^{(4)}(x) = -\frac{2 \cdot 3}{x^4}, \qquad\qquad f^{(4)}(1) = -2 \cdot 3,$$

$$\vdots \qquad \vdots \qquad\qquad\qquad \vdots \qquad \vdots$$

$$f^{(n)}(x) = (-1)^{n-1}\frac{(n-1)!}{x^n}, \qquad f^{(n)}(1) = (-1)^{n-1}(n-1)!$$

$$\vdots \qquad \vdots \qquad\qquad\qquad \vdots \qquad \vdots.$$

Hence, by (1),

$$\ln x = (x - 1) - \frac{(x-1)^2}{2} + \frac{(x-1)^3}{3}$$

$$- \cdots + (-1)^{n-1}\frac{(x-1)^n}{n} + \cdots.$$

The series converges for $0 < x \leqq 2$.

In the higher development of mathematics, it would be hard to overstress the importance of the general Taylor's Series; but in the specific elementary applications to which we are necessarily limited in this beginning course, the special case, Maclaurin's Series, is more useful than the general formula.

EXERCISES

In Exs. 1–10, use the Maclaurin Series directly to expand the given function in powers of x; then determine the interval of convergence.

1. $\cos x$. See (2), § 203.

2. $\dfrac{1}{1-x}$. See (4), § 203.

3. $\ln (1+x)$. See (5), § 203.   4. $\dfrac{1}{1+x}$.

5. $\sin 3x$.   6. $e^{-\frac{1}{2}x}$.   7. $\ln (1-3x)$.

8. $\sqrt{1+x}$.   *Ans.* $1 + \dfrac{1}{2}x + \sum\limits_{n=2}^{\infty} \dfrac{(-1)^{n+1} 1 \cdot 3 \cdot 5 \cdots (2n-3)x^n}{2^n n!}$.

9. $\dfrac{1}{\sqrt{1+x}}$.   *Ans.* $1 + \sum\limits_{n=1}^{\infty} \dfrac{(-1)^n 1 \cdot 3 \cdot 5 \cdots (2n-1)x^n}{2^n n!}$.

10. $(1+x)^m$. See (6), § 203.

In Exs. 11–20, obtain the power series expansion for the given function by making an appropriate substitution in one of the basic expansions of § 203.

11. $\dfrac{1}{1-x^2}$. Put x^2 for x in (4), § 203.

12. $\ln (1-x^2)$. Put $(-x^2)$ for x in (5), § 203.

13. $e^{-\frac{1}{2}x^2}$.   14. $\cos 4x$.   15. Ex. 4.

16. Ex. 5.   17. Ex. 6.   18. Ex. 7.

19. $\ln (1+4x^2)$.   20. $\dfrac{1}{1+3x^4}$.

21. Obtain the power series for $\dfrac{1}{\sqrt{1-x^2}}$ from the result of Ex. 9.

22. Obtain the power series for $\dfrac{x^4}{1-x^3}$ from (4), § 203.

23. Obtain the power series for $\dfrac{x^3}{\sqrt{1-x^3}}$ from Ex. 9.

24. Obtain the power series for $\ln (3-x)$ from (5), § 203, with the aid of the relation

$$\ln (3-x) = \ln \left[3\left(1 - \frac{x}{3}\right) \right] = \ln 3 + \ln \left(1 - \frac{x}{3}\right).$$

25. Obtain the power series for $\ln (5 - 2x)$ from (5), § 203.

26. Obtain the power series for $\sin x \cos x$ from (3), § 203.

27. Obtain the power series for $x^3 e^{-x^2}$ from (1), § 203.

28. Show that $\csc x$ cannot be expanded in powers of x.

29. Show that $x \cot^2 x$ cannot be expanded in powers of x.

30. Show that $x^2 \ln x$ cannot be expanded in powers of x.

In Exs. 31–39, use Taylor's Series directly to obtain the desired expansion.

31. e^x in powers of $(x - 2)$.   *Ans.* $\displaystyle\sum_{n=0}^{\infty} \frac{e^2(x-2)^n}{n!}$.

32. $\ln x$ in powers of $(x - 3)$.

33. $\sin x$ in powers of $(x - \frac{1}{4}\pi)$.

34. $\sqrt{x}$ in powers of $(x - 2)$.   **35.** $\dfrac{1}{1 + x}$ in powers of $(x + 4)$.

36. e^x in powers of $(x + 1)$.   **37.** $\ln x$ in powers of $(x - \frac{1}{2})$.

38. $\cos x$ in powers of $(x + \frac{1}{4}\pi)$.   **39.** $\dfrac{1}{1 - x}$ in powers of $(x - 3)$.

In Exs. 40–45, use appropriate devices to obtain the desired expansion from the basic formulas of § 203 without resorting to Taylor's expansion directly.

40. Ex. 31. Write $e^x = e^2 \cdot e^{x-2}$.

41. Ex. 32. Write $\ln x = \ln [3 + (x - 3)] = \ln \left[3\left(1 + \dfrac{x - 3}{3}\right)\right]$, etc.

42. Ex. 35. Use $\dfrac{1}{1 + x} = \dfrac{1}{-3 + (x + 4)}$, etc.

43. Ex. 36.   **44.** Ex. 37.   **45.** Ex. 39.

46. Show that, if $P(x)$ is a polynomial of the n-th degree in x,

$$P(x) = P(a) + P'(a)(x - a) + \frac{P''(a)}{2!}(x - a)^2 + \cdots + \frac{P^{(n)}(a)}{n!}(x - a)^n,$$

whatever may be the values of a and x.

47. Arrange the function $y = x^3 - 3x^2 + 2x - 5$ in powers of $x - 3$. (Ex. 46.)   *Ans.* $y = 1 + 11(x - 3) + 6(x - 3)^2 + (x - 3)^3$.

48. Arrange the function $y = x^4 - 3x^2 - 6x + 8$ in powers of $x - 2$. (Ex. 46.)   *Ans.* $y = 14(x - 2) + 21(x - 2)^2 + 8(x - 2)^3 + (x - 2)^4$.

49. The Maclaurin Series for the function $f(x) = e^{-\frac{1}{x^2}}$ may be formally obtained, provided we define $f(0) = 0$. Prove that the series converges for all values of x, but does not represent the function.

It is proved in more advanced courses that the derivatives of $f(x)$ exist and are continuous at $x = 0$.

The reader should show that the n-th derivative of $f(x)$ is the product of $e^{-\frac{1}{x^2}}$ and a polynomial in $\dfrac{1}{x}$.

205. Applications of Maclaurin's Series. The most elementary application of series, and one of great importance, is in computing tables of values of various functions, *e.g.*, logarithms, trigonometric functions, etc.

Example (a): Compute $\sin 3°$ to five decimal places.

Setting $x = 3° = \dfrac{\pi}{60}$ in the series for $\sin x$ (§ 203), we get

$$\sin 3° = \sin \frac{\pi}{60} = \frac{\pi}{60} - \frac{1}{6}\left(\frac{\pi}{60}\right)^3 + \frac{1}{120}\left(\frac{\pi}{60}\right)^5 - \cdots$$
$$= 0.052\,360 - 0.000\,024 + \cdots.$$

Without computing the third term, we see that it is much too small to affect the sixth decimal place, and the error committed by stopping with any term is less than the next term (by the theorem, § 199). Hence we need keep only two terms:

$$\sin 3° = 0.05234.$$

Example (b): Since

$$\lim_{\theta \to 0} \frac{\sin \theta}{\theta} = 1,$$

it follows that for small values of the angle, $\sin \theta$ and θ are nearly equal. Within what interval can the sine be replaced by the angle if the allowable error is 0.0005?

From the equation

$$\sin \theta = \theta - \frac{\theta^3}{3!} + \frac{\theta^5}{5!} - \cdots,$$

it appears that the error committed by stopping with the first term, *i.e.*, by setting

$$\sin \theta = \theta,$$

is less than $\frac{1}{6}\theta^3$ for sufficiently small θ (say, $\theta < 1$), by the theorem of § 199. We therefore have

$$\frac{1}{6}\theta^3 < 0.0005,$$
$$\theta^3 < 0.003,$$
$$\theta < 0.1442 \ (\text{radian})$$
$$< 8° \ 15', \text{approximately.}$$

That is, the sine of any angle less than $8° \ 15'$ can be replaced by the angle with an error less than 0.0005.

Example (c): Find the amount by which an arc of a great circle of the earth 1 mi. long recedes from its chord.

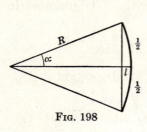

FIG. 198

We have to find

$$l = R - R \cos \alpha = R(1 - \cos \alpha).$$

Since α is very small, we may safely take, in (2) of § 203,

$$\cos \alpha = 1 - \tfrac{1}{2}\alpha^2,$$

$$l = \frac{1}{2}R\alpha^2 = \frac{(R\alpha)^2}{2R}.$$

By hypothesis, $R\alpha = \tfrac{1}{2}$, so that, with $R = 4000$ mi.,

$$l = \frac{\tfrac{1}{4}}{8000} \text{ mi.} = \frac{5280 \cdot 12}{4 \cdot 8000} \text{ in.} = 2 \text{ in., nearly.}$$

206. The value of e. As a further application of Maclaurin's Series, let us derive the value of e given in § 94. Taking $x = 1$ in (1), § 203, we have

$$e = 1 + 1 + \frac{1}{2!} + \frac{1}{3!} + \frac{1}{4!} + \cdots.$$

This gives*

1.
1.
0.5
0.166 667
0.041 667
0.008 333
0.001 389
0.000 198
0.000 025
0.000 003
───────
2.718 28.

The sum of all the remaining terms is but little greater than the first term neglected. Compare the terms neglected with the

geometric series $\dfrac{1}{10!}\left(1 + \dfrac{1}{11} + \dfrac{1}{11^2} + \cdots + \dfrac{1}{11^n} + \cdots\right).$

---

* Note that the fourth term can be obtained by dividing the third by 3, the fifth by dividing the fourth by 4, etc.

EXERCISES

In Exs. 1–8, use series to make the required computations.

1. cos 3° to five places.   **2.** sin 4° to four places.
3. cos 6° to four places.   **4.** sin 2° to five places.
5. sin 88° to four places.   **6.** cos 85° to four places.
7. ln (1.05) to four places.   **8.** ln (0.97) to six places.

9. Compute $\dfrac{1}{e}$ by series.   *Ans.* 0.3679.

10. Find the tenth root of e.   *Ans.* 1.10517.

11. Compute $(1.01)^7$ by the Binomial Theorem.   *Ans.* 1.0721.

12. Raise 0.99 to the tenth power.   *Ans.* 0.9044.

13. Extract the square root of 102 to four decimal places by using power series, first writing

$$\sqrt{102} = \sqrt{100 + 2} = 10(1 + 0.02)^{\frac{1}{2}}.$$

Ans. 10.0995.

14. Extract the square root of 101 to four decimal places by using series.

15. Within what interval can sin θ be replaced by θ, if the allowable error is 0.005? Check by the table.

16. Within what interval can cos θ be taken equal to 1, with accuracy to three places (allowable error 0.0005)? Check by the table, pp. 520–521.

17. Solve the equation cos $x = 5x$ to three figures by using series.

Ans. $x = 0.196.$

18. Solve the equation cos $x = 10x$.   *Ans.* $x = 0.0995.$

19. Solve Example (c), § 205, if the arc is 10 mi. long.   *Ans.* 16 ft.

20. In Example (c), § 205, how much longer is the arc than the chord?

Ans. $\frac{1}{6000}$ in.

21. If a straight tunnel were to be bored through the earth from Detroit to Chicago (say 300 mi.), how much distance would be saved?

Ans. 371 ft.

22. In Ex. 21, find the greatest depth of the tunnel.   *Ans.* 2.8 mi.

23. The gravitational attraction of the earth at a height h above sea-level is

$$A = \frac{gR^2}{(R + h)^2},$$

where R is the radius of the earth and $g = 32.16$ ft. per sec. per sec. At what altitude is $A = 32.00$?

24. Taking the earth's circumference as 40,000,000 meters, find the difference between the circumference and the perimeter of a regular inscribed polygon of 1,000,000 sides.   *Ans.* Less than $\frac{1}{15}$ mm.

25. In the computation of e, § 206, find an upper limit for the error caused by stopping with 10 terms.   *Ans.* 0.0000003.

207. Applications of Taylor's Series.

Obviously, if a power series is to be used for computation, the coefficients must be known numbers. Hence, even though it may be theoretically possible to expand a function $f(x)$ in powers of $x - a$ for any value of a (this is true, for instance, for e^x, sin x, and cos x), actually, for purposes of computation, the only readily available values of a are those for which $f(a)$, $f'(a)$, $f''(a)$, $\cdots$ are known, since these quantities appear in the coefficients. For example, if we wish to use the Taylor Series for sin x for computation, the only values of a ready to hand $(0 < a < \frac{1}{2}\pi)$ are $\frac{1}{6}\pi$, $\frac{1}{4}\pi$, or $\frac{1}{3}\pi$.

Maclaurin's Series converges rapidly, in general, for *small* values of x. Taylor's Series converges rapidly for values of x near a—*i.e.*, such that $x - a$ is small. Hence, of the available values of a [viz. those for which $f(a)$, $f'(a)$, $\cdots$ are known], we should as a rule choose the one that is *nearest the value of x for which $f(x)$ is to be computed*. For example, to compute sin 46°, we would take $a = \frac{1}{4}\pi$; to compute sin 58°, we would take $a = \frac{1}{3}\pi$.

Example: Find the value of $e^{1.04}$ to four decimal places.

Maclaurin's Series for e^x would converge fairly rapidly for $x = 1.04$, but the successive terms would not be easy to compute. Knowing the value of e from § 206, we may use $e^{1.04} = e \cdot e^{0.04}$,

$$e^{1.04} = e\left[1 + 0.04 + \frac{0.0016}{2!} + \frac{0.000\,064}{3!} + \frac{0.000\,002\,56}{4!} + \cdots\right]$$

$$= 2.718\,28\,(1 + 0.04 + 0.000\,8 + 0.000\,01) = 2.829\,2.$$

208. Approximate formulas for Δy. In (1), § 204, let us replace a by x and x by $x + \Delta x$. The formula then becomes

(1) $$f(x + \Delta x) = f(x) + f'(x)\,\Delta x + \frac{f''(x)}{2!}\,\overline{\Delta x}^2 + \frac{f'''(x)}{3!}\,\overline{\Delta x}^3 + \cdots$$

$$+ \frac{f^{(n)}(x)}{n!}\,\overline{\Delta x}^n + \cdots,$$

or, with

$$y = f(x), \qquad \Delta y = f(x + \Delta x) - f(x),$$

(2) $$\Delta y = y'\Delta x + \frac{y''}{2!}\,\overline{\Delta x}^2 + \frac{y'''}{3!}\,\overline{\Delta x}^3 + \cdots + \frac{y^{(n)}}{n!}\,\overline{\Delta x}^n + \cdots.$$

For values of x and Δx that cause the terms of the series to diminish rapidly, we have, as a first approximation to the value of Δy, the formula used in § 47, viz.

$$\Delta y = y'\,\Delta x = dy,$$

the error in using this formula being approximately $\frac{1}{2}y'' \ \overline{\Delta x^2}$; as a second approximation we have

$$\Delta y = y' \ \Delta x + \frac{1}{2}y'' \ \overline{\Delta x^2},$$

with an error nearly equal to $\frac{1}{6}y''' \ \overline{\Delta x^3}$; etc.

Example: Taking $f(x) = \cos x$ in (1), we get

$$\cos (x + \Delta x) = \cos x - \sin x \ \Delta x - \tfrac{1}{2} \cos x \ \overline{\Delta x^2} + \cdots,$$

which gives the first approximation

(3) $$\cos (x + \Delta x) = \cos x - \sin x \ \Delta x.$$

If the allowable error in the cosine is 0.0005, within what range may this formula be used to compute the cosines of angles near 45°?

The error in using (3) is approximately $-\frac{1}{2} \cos x \ \overline{\Delta x^2}$. Since $x = 45°$, we have, numerically,

$$\tfrac{1}{2} \cdot 0.7071 \ \overline{\Delta x^2} < 0.000\,5,$$
$$\overline{\Delta x^2} < 0.001\,414,$$
$$\Delta x < 0.037\,6 = 2°, \text{ roughly.}$$

Hence the approximate formula (3) may safely be used to compute the cosines of angles between 43° and 47°.

EXERCISES

1. Using $e^x = e \cdot e^{x-1}$, compute $e^{0.98}$ to four figures. *Ans.* 2.664.
2. Using Ex. 33, p. 378, compute sin 44°. *Ans.* 0.695.
3. Compute cos 44°. *Ans.* 0.719.

4. Apply (1), § 208, to $y = \dfrac{1}{x}$.

Ans. $\dfrac{1}{x + \Delta x} = \displaystyle\sum_{n=0}^{\infty} \dfrac{(-1)^n \ \overline{\Delta x^n}}{x^{n+1}} = \dfrac{1}{x} - \dfrac{\Delta x}{x^2} + \dfrac{\overline{\Delta x^2}}{x^3} - \cdots + \dfrac{(-1)^n \ \overline{\Delta x^n}}{x^{n+1}} + \cdots.$

5. Compute $\frac{1}{102}$ to eight decimal places. (Ex. 4.)
6. Compute $\frac{1}{997}$ to fifteen decimal places by mental arithmetic.
7. Given cos 6° = 0.994 52, find sec 6°. *Ans.* 1.005 51.
8. Show that the error in using the approximate formula of Example (*a*), § 47, is $\pi \ \overline{\Delta r^2}$. When $r = 10$ ft., what is the greatest allowable value of Δr if accuracy to 5% is required? *Ans.* About 1 ft.
9. Find the error in the approximate formula for the volume of a thin spherical shell (Ex. 1, p. 82). What is the greatest allowable thickness for a radius of 5 ft., if accuracy to 1% is required? *Ans.* About 0.6 in.

10. Solve the example of § 208 for angles near 60°.

Ans. 57° 30′ < x < 62° 30′.

11. From (1), § 208, obtain an approximate formula for $\dfrac{1}{(x + \Delta x)^2}$.

Ans. $\dfrac{1}{(x + \Delta x)^2} = \dfrac{1}{x^2} - \dfrac{2\,\Delta x}{x^3} + \dfrac{3\,\overline{\Delta x^2}}{x^4} - \dfrac{4\,\overline{\Delta x^3}}{x^5} + \cdots$.

12. Compute $(\tfrac{1}{98})^2$ to ten places by mental arithmetic.

13. Use (1), § 208, to obtain an approximate formula for $\dfrac{1}{(x + \Delta x)^3}$.

Ans. $\dfrac{1}{(x + \Delta x)^3} = \dfrac{1 \cdot 2}{2x^3} - \dfrac{2 \cdot 3\,\Delta x}{2x^4} + \dfrac{3 \cdot 4\,\overline{\Delta x^2}}{2x^5} - \dfrac{4 \cdot 5\,\overline{\Delta x^3}}{2x^6} + \cdots$.

14. Compute $\tfrac{1}{729}$ to seven places.

15. Show that $\ln (x + \Delta x) = \ln x + \dfrac{\Delta x}{x} - \dfrac{\overline{\Delta x^2}}{2x^2} + \dfrac{\overline{\Delta x^3}}{3x^3} - \cdots$.

16. If the allowable error in a logarithm is 0.00005, within what range can the formula $\ln (x + \Delta x) = \ln x + \dfrac{\Delta x}{x}$ be used?

17. Show that $(x + \Delta x)^{\frac{1}{2}} = x^{\frac{1}{2}} + \dfrac{\Delta x}{2x^{\frac{1}{2}}} - \dfrac{1}{2} \cdot \dfrac{\overline{\Delta x^2}}{4x^{\frac{3}{2}}} + \dfrac{1 \cdot 3}{2 \cdot 4} \dfrac{\overline{\Delta x^3}}{6x^{\frac{5}{2}}} - \cdots$.

18. Extract $\sqrt{101}$ to seven decimal places. (Ex. 17).

19. Make an accurate detail of the curve $y = x^4 - 4x^3 + 6x^2$ near the point $x = 1$. (Ex. 46, p. 378.)

20. Solve Ex. 19 for the curve $y = \ln x$. (Example, § 204.)

CHAPTER *27* OPERATIONS WITH POWER SERIES

209. Algebraic operations with power series. Operations that can always be performed upon series of a finite number of terms, such as rearrangement of terms, insertion or removal of parentheses, etc., cannot be assumed offhand to be allowable with infinite series, and in fact it is easily shown that they are not allowable in all cases.

In dealing with power series, it is desirable to know whether certain elementary operations are permissible. We therefore state the following theorems regarding power series; the proofs belong to a more advanced treatment of the subject.

THEOREM I: ADDITION. *Within any common interval of convergence, the term-by-term sum of the power series for $f(x)$ and $g(x)$ is the power series for $[f(x) + g(x)]$.*

In rough language, two convergent power series may be added term by term. That is, within an interval where the series

$$f(x) = \sum_{n=0}^{\infty} a_n x^n,$$

$$g(x) = \sum_{n=0}^{\infty} b_n x^n,$$

are both convergent, the series obtained by adding them term by term will converge to $[f(x) + g(x)]$:

$$f(x) + g(x) = \sum_{n=0}^{\infty} (a_n + b_n)x^n.$$

Subtraction is included by a change of signs.

THEOREM II: MULTIPLICATION. *Within any common interval of convergence of the power series,*

$$f(x) = \sum_{n=0}^{\infty} a_n x^n,$$

$$g(x) = \sum_{n=0}^{\infty} b_n x^n,$$

the power series formed by multiplying each term of one series by every term of the other series* converges to the product $f(x)g(x)$,

$$f(x)g(x) = a_0 b_0 + (a_0 b_1 + a_1 b_0)\, x + (a_0 b_2 + a_1 b_1 + a_2 b_0) x^2$$

$$+ \cdots + (a_0 b_n + a_1 b_{n-1} + \cdots + a_n b_0) x^n + \cdots.$$

THEOREM III: DIVISION. *If the power series for $f(x)$ and $g(x)$ are convergent in some common interval, the power series formed by performing ordinary long division (as with polynomials) to form $\dfrac{f(x)}{g(x)}$ will converge in some interval including $x = 0$, provided the constant term in the denominator series is not zero.*

Neither the general term, nor the interval of convergence, of the quotient series can be determined by elementary means. Division of power series is one instance in which we are forced to be content with the first few terms of a series.

In using these theorems, the point to be noted is that within the limits indicated they enable us to treat infinite series *exactly like polynomials*, merely discarding all terms beyond those that we need to retain.

Example (a): Find the power series for $\dfrac{1}{x^2 - 3x + 2}$.

Since

$$\frac{1}{x^2 - 3x + 2} = \frac{1}{(1-x)(2-x)} = \frac{1}{1-x} - \frac{1}{2-x},$$

and

$$\frac{1}{1-x} = 1 + x + x^2 + \cdots + x^n + \cdots, \qquad -1 < x < 1,$$

---

* This is the "Cauchy product" of the two series. A similar result holds for the product of any two *absolutely convergent* series, the product series being absolutely convergent to the product of the sums of the series being multiplied.

and

$$\frac{-1}{2-x} = \frac{-\frac{1}{2}}{1-\frac{x}{2}}$$

$$= -\frac{1}{2}\left(1 + \frac{x}{2} + \frac{x^2}{2^2} + \cdots + \frac{x^n}{2^n} + \cdots\right), \qquad -2 < x < 2,$$

we add the series term by term to obtain

$$\frac{1}{x^2 - 3x + 2} = \frac{1}{2} + \left(1 - \frac{1}{2^2}\right)x + \left(1 - \frac{1}{2^3}\right)x^2 + \cdots$$

$$+ \left(1 - \frac{1}{2^{n+1}}\right)x^n + \cdots, \qquad -1 < x < 1.$$

Example (b): Expand $\sin^2 x$ in powers of x to x^6 inclusive.
We have

$$\sin x = x - \frac{x^3}{3!} + \frac{x^5}{5!} - \cdots$$

$$= x - \tfrac{1}{6}x^3 + \tfrac{1}{120}x^5 - \cdots.$$

Squaring the trinomial and discarding all terms after x^6, we find

$$\sin^2 x = x^2 - \tfrac{1}{3}x^4 + \tfrac{2}{45}x^6 + \cdots.$$

By Theorem II, this series converges for all values of x. See also
the much more efficient method in Ex. 18 below.

Example (c): Expand $x^2 \csc^2 x$ to x^4 inclusive.
By Example (b),

$$x^2 \csc^2 x = \frac{x^2}{\sin^2 x} = \frac{x^2}{x^2 - \tfrac{1}{3}x^4 + \tfrac{2}{45}x^6 + \cdots}$$

$$= \frac{1}{1 - \tfrac{1}{3}x^2 + \tfrac{2}{45}x^4 + \cdots}.$$

$$1 - \tfrac{1}{3}x^2 + \tfrac{2}{45}x^4 \overline{\big| 1} \qquad \qquad \big| 1 + \tfrac{1}{3}x^2 + \tfrac{1}{15}x^4$$

$$\underline{1 - \tfrac{1}{3}x^2 + \tfrac{2}{45}x^4}$$

$$\tfrac{1}{3}x^2 - \tfrac{2}{45}x^4$$

$$\underline{\tfrac{1}{3}x^2 - \tfrac{1}{9}x^4}$$

$$\tfrac{1}{15}x^4$$

Therefore

$$x^2 \csc^2 x = 1 + \tfrac{1}{3}x^2 + \tfrac{1}{15}x^4 + \cdots.$$

The interval of convergence, obtained by more advanced methods,
is $|x| < \pi$.

Example (d): In leveling, error is introduced due to the curvature of the earth. Find the correction for 1 mi.

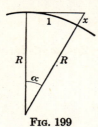

FIG. 199

By Ex. 11 below, we have

$$\sec \alpha = 1 + \frac{\alpha^2}{2} + \cdots,$$

and Fig. 199 shows that

$$\sec \alpha = \frac{R + x}{R} = 1 + \frac{x}{R}.$$

Since α is very small, we obtain

$$1 + \frac{\alpha^2}{2} = 1 + \frac{x}{R},$$

or

$$x = \frac{R\alpha^2}{2} = \frac{(R\alpha)^2}{2R} = \frac{1}{8000} \text{ mi.}$$

$$= \frac{5280 \cdot 12}{8000} \text{ in.} = 7.9 \text{ in.}$$

210. Differentiation of power series. Within its interval of convergence (endpoints excluded), term-by-term differentiation of a power series yields the power series for the derivative of the original sum-function, and the interval of convergence remains the same.

THEOREM IV: DIFFERENTIATION. *If*

$$f(x) = a_0 + a_1 x + a_2 x^2 + \cdots + a_n x^n + \cdots, \; | x | < h,$$

then

$$f'(x) = a_1 + 2 a_2 x + \cdots + n a_n x^{n-1} + \cdots,$$

for $| x | < h$.

Example: Derive the series for cos x from that for sin x.

We know that

$$\sin x = x - \frac{x^3}{3!} + \frac{x^5}{5!} - \cdots + \frac{(-1)^n x^{2n+1}}{(2n + 1)!} + \cdots,$$

for all x. Therefore

$$\cos x = 1 - \frac{3x^2}{3!} + \frac{5x^4}{5!} - \cdots + \frac{(-1)^n (2n + 1) x^{2n}}{(2n + 1)!} + \cdots$$

$$= 1 - \frac{x^2}{2!} + \frac{x^4}{4!} - \cdots + \frac{(-1)^n x^{2n}}{(2n)!} + \cdots,$$

for all x, as given in §203.

EXERCISES

In Exs. 1–23, expand the function in Maclaurin's Series by appropriate application of Theorems I–IV above. Determine the interval of convergence (not testing endpoints), wherever Theorem III is not involved. If Theorem III is used, the interval is enclosed in parentheses in the answer.

1. $\dfrac{4x}{(1+x)(1-3x)}$· Write as $\dfrac{1}{1-3x} - \dfrac{1}{1+x}$.

$$Ans. \sum_{n=1}^{\infty} [3^n - (-1)^n]x^n, \; -\tfrac{1}{3} < x < \tfrac{1}{3}.$$

2. cosh x. $\quad Ans.\; 1 + \dfrac{x^2}{2!} + \dfrac{x^4}{4!} + \cdots + \dfrac{x^{2n}}{(2n)!} + \cdots$, all values.

3. sinh x. $\quad Ans.\; x + \dfrac{x^3}{3!} + \dfrac{x^5}{5!} + \cdots + \dfrac{x^{2n-1}}{(2n-1)!} + \cdots$, all values.

4. ln $\dfrac{1+x}{1-x}$· $\quad Ans.\; 2\Big(x + \dfrac{x^3}{3} + \dfrac{x^5}{5} + \cdots + \dfrac{x^{2n-1}}{2n-1} + \cdots\Big)$, $|x| < 1$.

5. ln $(1 - 3x + 2x^2)$.

$$Ans. \; -3x - \frac{5}{2}x^2 - 3x^3 - \cdots - \frac{(1+2^n)x^n}{n} + \cdots, \; |x| < \frac{1}{2}.$$

6. From the basic series (§ 203) for $\dfrac{1}{1-x}$, find the series for $\dfrac{1}{(1-x)^2}$ by differentiation.

$$Ans.\; 1 + 2x + 3x^2 + \cdots + nx^{n-1} + \cdots, \; |x| < 1.$$

7. Obtain the series for $\dfrac{x^3}{(1+x^2)^2}$ by replacing x by $(-x^2)$ in the answer to Ex. 6 and then multiplying throughout by x^3.

$$Ans.\; \frac{x^3}{(1+x^2)^2} = \sum_{n=1}^{\infty} (-1)^{n-1}nx^{2n+1}, \; |x| < 1.$$

8. $e^{-x} \cos x$, to the term in x^4.
$$Ans.\; 1 - x + \tfrac{1}{3}x^3 - \tfrac{1}{6}x^4 + \cdots, \text{ all values of } x.$$

9. $e^{-x} \sin x$, to the term in x^5.
$$Ans.\; x - x^2 + \tfrac{1}{3}x^3 - \tfrac{1}{30}x^5 + \cdots, \text{ all values of } x.$$

10. tan x, to the term in x^5.
$$Ans.\; x + \tfrac{1}{3}x^3 + \tfrac{2}{15}x^5 + \cdots, \; (|x| < \tfrac{1}{2}\pi).$$

11. sec x, to the term in x^6.
$$Ans.\; 1 + \tfrac{1}{2}x^2 + \tfrac{5}{24}x^4 + \tfrac{61}{720}x^6 + \cdots, \; (|x| < \tfrac{1}{2}\pi).$$

12. ln$^2 (1 + x)$, to the term in x^5.
$$Ans.\; x^2 - x^3 + \tfrac{11}{12}x^4 - \tfrac{5}{6}x^5 + \cdots, \; |x| < 1.$$

13. $\dfrac{\ln (1 + x)}{1 + x}$· Check by Ex. 12.

14. x csc x, to the term in x^4.
$$Ans.\; 1 + \tfrac{1}{6}x^2 + \tfrac{7}{360}x^4 + \cdots, \; (|x| < \pi).$$

15. tan$^2 x$, to the term in x^6.
$$Ans.\; x^2 + \tfrac{2}{3}x^4 + \tfrac{17}{45}x^6 + \cdots, \; (|x| < \tfrac{1}{2}\pi).$$

16. $\sec^2 x$, to the term in x^6, by squaring the answer to Ex. 11. Check with Ex. 15.

17. $\cos^2 x$. Use $\cos^2 x = \frac{1}{2}(1 + \cos 2x)$.

$$Ans.\ 1 - \frac{2x^2}{2!} + \frac{2^3 x^4}{4!} - \frac{2^5 x^6}{6!} + \cdots + \frac{(-1)^n 2^{2n-1} x^{2n}}{(2n)!} + \cdots,\ \text{all values of } x.$$

18. $\sin^2 x$. Use $\sin^2 x = \frac{1}{2}(1 - \cos 2x)$; then check with Ex. 17.

19. From Ex. 5, find the power series for $\dfrac{4x - 3}{1 - 3x + 2x^2}$.

20. $\csc x - \cot x$, to the term in x^5.

$$Ans.\ \tfrac{1}{2}x + \tfrac{1}{24}x^3 + \tfrac{1}{240}x^5 + \cdots,\ (|x| < \pi).$$

21. $\dfrac{x}{(1 - 3x^4)^2}$. See Exs. 6–7.

22. $\dfrac{1 + 2x}{1 - x^3}$.

23. $e^x \cos 2x$, to the term in x^4.

24. Show that for values of x so small that the fourth and higher powers of $\dfrac{x}{a}$ may be neglected, the catenary $y = a \cosh \dfrac{x}{a}$ may be replaced by the parabola $x^2 = 2a(y - a)$.

25. Check Ex. 9 with Ex. 8, with the aid of differentiation.

26. Differentiate the series for e^x.

27. From Ex. 11, find the first three terms of the power series for $\sec x \tan x$. Then check with Exs. 10–11.

28. Obtain the series for $\sinh x$ from that for $\cosh x$.

29. Show that $\sin^3 x = \dfrac{3}{4} \displaystyle\sum_{n=1}^{\infty} \dfrac{(-1)^{n-1}(3^{2n} - 1)x^{2n+1}}{(2n + 1)!}$.

In Exs. 30–35, find the order and principal part of the given infinitesimal.

30. $\theta - \sin \theta$, when $\theta \to 0$. $Ans.\ \tfrac{1}{6}\theta^3$.

31. $1 - \cos \theta$, when $\theta \to 0$. $Ans.\ \tfrac{1}{2}\theta^2$.

32. $(1 + x)^m - (1 - x)^m$, when $x \to 0$. $Ans.\ 2mx$.

33. $\sinh x - \sin x$, when $x \to 0$. $Ans.\ \tfrac{1}{3}x^3$.

34. $\cosh x - \cos x$, when $x \to 0$. $Ans.\ x^2$.

35. $\sin x - \ln (1 + x)$, when $x \to 0$. $Ans.\ \tfrac{1}{2}x^2$.

36. In Example (d), § 209, find the correction for 4 mi. Solve in two ways. $Ans.\ 10.56$ ft.

37. Two ships have masts reaching 80 ft. above the water level. How far is each masthead visible from the other? $Ans.$ About 22 mi.

38. What is the radius of vision (theoretically) from the top of a building 200 ft. high? $Ans.\ 17.4$ mi.

In Exs. 39–45, evaluate the limits with the aid of series. Note that this is one application in which the general term of the series is not of use; a few terms suffice.

39. Evaluate $\displaystyle\lim_{x \to 0} \dfrac{\cos x - 1}{x \sin x}$. $Ans.\ -\tfrac{1}{2}$.

40. Evaluate $\lim\limits_{\theta \to 0} \dfrac{\sin \theta - \theta \cos \theta}{\sin^3 \theta}.$ *Ans.* $\tfrac{1}{3}$.

41. Evaluate $\lim\limits_{\theta \to 0} \dfrac{\tan \theta - \theta}{\theta^3}.$ *Ans.* $\tfrac{1}{3}$.

42. Evaluate $\lim\limits_{\theta \to 0} \dfrac{\tan^2 \theta - \theta^2}{\theta^4}.$ *Ans.* $\tfrac{2}{3}$.

43. Evaluate $\lim\limits_{x \to 0} \dfrac{\tan^2 x - \sin^2 x}{\sinh^3 x \, \ln (1 + x)}.$ *Ans.* 1.

44. Evaluate $\lim\limits_{\alpha \to 0} \dfrac{\tan 2\alpha - 2 \sin \alpha}{\alpha^3}.$

45. Evaluate $\lim\limits_{x \to 0} \dfrac{\sqrt{1 - x} - \sqrt{1 + x}}{x}.$

In Exs. 46–52, find the sum of the given series by using the appropriate value of x in some power series of known sum.

46. $1 + \dfrac{1}{2^2 \cdot 3} + \dfrac{1}{2^4 \cdot 5} + \cdots + \dfrac{1}{2^{2n} \cdot (2n + 1)} + \cdots.$ Put $x = \tfrac{1}{2}$ in Ex. 4.

Ans. ln 3.

47. $1 + \dfrac{2}{3} + \dfrac{3}{3^2} + \dfrac{4}{3^3} + \cdots + \dfrac{n}{3^{n-1}} + \cdots.$ Use Ex. 6.   *Ans.* $\tfrac{9}{4}$.

48. $1 - \dfrac{1}{2 \cdot 1!} + \dfrac{1}{2^2 2!} - \dfrac{1}{2^3 3!} + \cdots + \dfrac{(-1)^n}{2^n n!} + \cdots.$ *Ans.* $\dfrac{1}{\sqrt{e}}$.

49. $\sum\limits_{n=0}^{\infty} \dfrac{3^{2n}}{(2n)!}.$ *Ans.* cosh 3.

50. $\sum\limits_{n=0}^{\infty} \dfrac{(-1)^n}{(2n)!}.$

51. $\sum\limits_{n=0}^{\infty} \dfrac{(-1)^n}{3^{2n}(2n + 1)!}.$

52. $\sum\limits_{n=1}^{\infty} \dfrac{(-1)^{n-1}n}{2^{2n+1}}.$ (Ex. 7.)   *Ans.* $\tfrac{2}{25}$.

211. Integration of power series. Within its interval of convergence (sometimes even including endpoints), term-by-term integration of a power series yields the power series for the integral of the original sum-function, and the interval remains the same.

THEOREM V: INTEGRATION. *If*

$$f(x) = a_0 + a_1 x + a_2 x^2 + \cdots + a_n x^n + \cdots, \qquad |x| < h,$$

then

$$\int f(x)\, dx = C + a_0 x + \frac{a_1 x^2}{2} + \frac{a_2 x^3}{3} + \cdots + \frac{a_n x^{n+1}}{n + 1} + \cdots, \qquad |x| < h.$$

The theorem may also be worded as follows. If

$$f(x) = \sum_{n=0}^{\infty} a_n x^n, \qquad |x| < h,$$

then

$$\int_{\alpha}^{\beta} f(x)\, dx = \sum_{n=0}^{\infty} \frac{a_n}{n+1}\Big[\beta^{n+1} - \alpha^{n+1}\Big],$$

so long as $|\alpha|, |\beta| < h$.

Example: Derive the series for $\ln(1+x)$ from that for $\dfrac{1}{1+x}$.

We know, from the basic series (4), p. 375 (with x replaced by $-x$), that

$$\frac{1}{1+x} = 1 - x + x^2 - x^3 + \cdots + (-1)^n x^n + \cdots, \qquad |x| < 1.$$

Multiplying throughout by dx and integrating, we obtain

$$\ln(1+x) = C + x - \frac{x^2}{2} + \frac{x^3}{3} - \frac{x^4}{4} + \cdots + \frac{(-1)^n x^{n+1}}{n+1} + \cdots,$$
$$|x| < 1.$$

Putting $x = 0$, we find that $C = 0$, so that finally

$$\ln(1+x) = x - \frac{x^2}{2} + \frac{x^3}{3} - \frac{x^4}{4} + \cdots + \frac{(-1)^n x^{n+1}}{n+1} + \cdots, \qquad |x| < 1.$$

212. Application to definite integrals. An important application of Theorem V is in the approximate evaluation of definite integrals—particularly when the integral cannot be expressed in terms of elementary functions, but sometimes also when, although evaluation in the elementary sense is possible, the result would be of inconvenient form. Although the method is available, theoretically, whenever the interval of integration lies entirely within the interval of convergence of the series, it actually works well only if the integrated series converges rapidly at both limits.

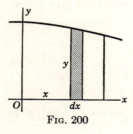

Fig. 200

Example (a): Find the area under the curve

$$y = \frac{\sin x}{x}$$

from $x = 0$ to $x = 1$.

The area is

$$A = \int_0^1 y\, dx = \int_0^1 \frac{\sin x}{x}\, dx.$$

The integral here occurring cannot be evaluated in terms of elementary functions. But we have

$$\sin x = x - \frac{x^3}{6} + \frac{x^5}{120} - \frac{x^7}{5040} + \cdots + \frac{(-1)^n x^{2n+1}}{(2n+1)!} + \cdots,$$

$$\frac{\sin x}{x} = 1 - \frac{x^2}{6} + \frac{x^4}{120} - \frac{x^6}{5040} + \cdots + \frac{(-1)^n x^{2n}}{(2n+1)!} + \cdots,$$

whence (Theorem V)

$$A = \int_0^1 \left(1 - \frac{x^2}{6} + \frac{x^4}{120} - \frac{x^6}{5040} + \cdots\right) dx$$

$$= \left[x - \frac{x^3}{18} + \frac{x^5}{600} - \frac{x^7}{35280} + \cdots\right]_0^1$$

$$= 1 - 0.05556 + 0.00167 - 0.00003 = 0.9461.$$

Example (b): Evaluate $\int_0^1 \dfrac{dx}{\sqrt{100 - x^3}}$.

This is an "elliptic integral," impossible to evaluate in elementary terms. But

$$\frac{1}{\sqrt{100 - x^3}} = \frac{1}{10\sqrt{1 - \frac{1}{100}x^3}}.$$

Expanding the integrand in powers of x (Ex. 9, p. 377), we find

$$\int_0^1 \frac{dx}{\sqrt{100 - x^3}} = \frac{1}{10}\int_0^1 \frac{dx}{\sqrt{1 - \frac{1}{100}x^3}} = \frac{1}{10}\int_0^1 \left(1 - \frac{1}{100}x^3\right)^{-\frac{1}{2}} dx$$

$$= \frac{1}{10}\int_0^1 \left(1 + \frac{1}{2}\frac{x^3}{10^2} + \frac{1\cdot 3}{2\cdot 4}\frac{x^6}{10^4} + \cdots\right) dx$$

$$= \frac{1}{10}\left[x + \frac{1}{2\cdot 4}\frac{x^4}{10^2} + \frac{1\cdot 3}{2\cdot 4\cdot 7}\frac{x^7}{10^4} + \cdots\right]_0^1$$

$$= 0.10013.$$

EXERCISES

1. From the basic series for $\dfrac{1}{1-x}$, write down the series for $\dfrac{1}{1+y^2}$, multiply by dy, and integrate from 0 to x.

Ans. $\operatorname{Arctan} x = \sum_{n=0}^{\infty} \dfrac{(-1)^n x^{2n+1}}{2n+1}$

$$= x - \frac{x^3}{3} + \frac{x^5}{5} - \cdots + \frac{(-1)^n x^{2n+1}}{2n+1} + \cdots, \quad |x| \leq 1.$$

2. From the series for $(1 + x)^{-\frac{1}{2}}$, Ex. 9, p. 377, obtain the series for $(1 - y^2)^{-\frac{1}{2}}$, and then that for Arcsin x.

$$\textit{Ans. } \mathbf{Arcsin\ } x = x + \sum_{n=1}^{\infty} \frac{1 \cdot 3 \cdot 5 \cdots (2n - 1)x^{2n+1}}{2^n n!(2n + 1)}, \; |x| < 1.$$

3. Investigate the result of integrating, term by term, the series for e^x.

4. Obtain the series for $\cos x$ by integration.

5. With the aid of Ex. 10, p. 389, obtain the terms, out to the x^6 term, in the power series for $\ln \cos x$.

$$\textit{Ans. } \ln \cos x = -\frac{x^2}{2} - \frac{x^4}{12} - \frac{x^6}{45} + \cdots, \; (|x| < \tfrac{1}{2}\pi).$$

6. Using the result in Ex. 11, p. 389, obtain the power series for $\ln (\sec x + \tan x)$, out to the term in x^7.

$$\textit{Ans. } \ln (\sec x + \tan x) = x + \frac{x^3}{6} + \frac{x^5}{24} + \frac{61x^7}{5040} + \cdots, \; (|x| < \tfrac{1}{2}\pi).$$

7. In Ex. 15, p. 389, we found that

$$\tan^2 x = x^2 + \tfrac{2}{3}x^4 + \tfrac{17}{45}x^6 + \cdots.$$

By integration of this series show that

$$\tan x = x + \frac{x^3}{3} + \frac{2x^5}{15} + \frac{17x^7}{315} + \cdots.$$

8. From the series for $\sinh x$, Ex. 3, p. 389, obtain by integration the series for $\cosh x$.

9. In Ex. 32, p. 152, we showed that

$$\text{Arctan } \tfrac{1}{3} + \text{Arctan } \tfrac{1}{2} = \tfrac{1}{4}\pi.$$

Use this result, and Ex. 1 above, to obtain a series for π.

$$\textit{Ans. } \pi = 4 \sum_{n=0}^{\infty} \frac{(-1)^n[(\frac{1}{3})^{2n+1} + (\frac{1}{2})^{2n+1}]}{2n + 1}.$$

10. Use Ex. 9 to compute π to three decimal places. It is best to compute $4 \text{ Arctan } \tfrac{1}{3}$ and $4 \text{ Arctan } \tfrac{1}{2}$, each from its own series, then add them to get π.

11. Put $x = \tfrac{1}{2}$ in the answer to Ex. 2, and compute π to two decimal places.

12. Integrate the series for $\dfrac{1}{1 - x^2}$, and compare with Ex. 4, p. 389.

13. Find, to three decimal places, the area under the curve $y = e^{-x^2}$, from $x = 0$ to $x = \tfrac{1}{2}$.   *Ans.* 0.461.

14. Find, to two decimal places, the centroid of the area in Ex. 13.   *Ans.* (0.24, 0.46).

15. Find, to four decimal places, the area under the curve $y = \cos (x^2)$ from $x = 0$ to $x = 1$.   *Ans.* 0.9045.

16. Find, to four decimal places, the area under the curve $y = \sin (x^2)$ from $x = 0$ to $x = 1$.

17. Evaluate $\displaystyle\int_0^{0.1} \frac{dx}{\sqrt{1 + x^5}}$ to eight decimal places.   *Ans.* 0.09999992.

18. Find the area under the curve $y = e^{-x^2}$, from $x = 0$ to $x = 1$.

Ans. 0.807.

19. Find the area under the curve $y = \dfrac{e^{-x}}{x}$ from $x = 0.001$ to $x = 0.002$.

Ans. $\ln 2 - 0.00100 = 0.69215$.

20. Evaluate $\displaystyle\int_0^1 \dfrac{x^4\,dx}{\sqrt{25 + x^4}}$ to three places.

21. Find the area under the curve $y = x^3 - 3x^2 + 2x - 5$ from $x = 2.999$ to $x = 3$. (Ex. 47, p. 378.)

22. Find the area under the curve $y = x^4 - 3x^2 - 6x + 8$ from $x = 1.99$ to $x = 2.01$. (Ex. 48, p. 378.)

23. Find to three places the area under the curve $y = \dfrac{\cos x}{x}$ from $x = \dfrac{1}{2}$ to $x = 1$.

Ans. 0.515.

24. Use Ex. 8, p. 377, and integration of series, to find to five decimal places the length of arc of the hyperbola $xy = 1$ from $x = 10$ to $x = 100$.

Ans. 90.00017.

25. Use Ex. 8, p. 377, Wallis' Formula, p. 267, and integration of series, to show that the length of one arch of the curve $y = \cos x$ is 1.24π.

26. Evaluate $\displaystyle\lim_{x \to 0} \int_x^{2x} \dfrac{\cos t\,dt}{t}$.

Ans. $\ln 2$.

27. Evaluate $\displaystyle\lim_{x \to 0} \int_x^{2x} \dfrac{e^{-t}}{t}\,dt$.

Ans. $\ln 2$.

28. Evaluate $\displaystyle\int_2^\infty \dfrac{dx}{\sqrt{x^4 + 1}} \left(\dfrac{1}{\sqrt{x^4 + 1}} = \dfrac{1}{x^2} \cdot \dfrac{1}{\sqrt{1 + x^{-4}}} \right.$; substitute x^{-4} for x in Ex. 9, p. 377.)

Ans. 0.497.

In Exs. 29–31, expand the integrand in powers of $\dfrac{1}{x}$. (Cf. Ex. 28.)

29. Find the area under the curve $y = \dfrac{1}{x^2 - 1}$, to the right of $x = 100$.

Ans. 0.010000333353.

30. Find the area under the curve $y = \dfrac{1}{x^4 + x^2}$, to the right of $x = 10$.

Ans. 0.000331.

31. For the curve $x^2y = 1$, show that from $x = 100$ to $x = 200$ the arc exceeds the chord by one ten-trillionth of its length.

213. Summation of power series.

The general problem, given a power series, to find the sum of the series in terms of known functions, is naturally incapable of solution. Even if the sum does happen to be expressible in terms of known functions, the actual determination of that sum may be prohibitively difficult.

There are instances in which the application of our knowledge of the basic series in § 203 will yield the desired sum.

Example (a): Sum the series $\sum\limits_{n=0}^{\infty} \dfrac{(-1)^n (n+2) x^n}{n!}$.

We start with a known series suggested by the series to be summed. We know that

$$(1) \qquad\qquad e^{-x} = \sum_{n=0}^{\infty} \frac{(-1)^n x^n}{n!},$$

for all finite x.

The series to be summed has a factor $(n+2)$ in the numerator. Such a factor can be introduced by differentiation of x^{n+2}. Therefore, we first introduce a factor x^2 on both sides of equation (1) to obtain

$$(2) \qquad\qquad x^2 e^{-x} = \sum_{n=0}^{\infty} \frac{(-1)^n x^{n+2}}{n!}.$$

Then differentiation of each member of equation (2) yields

$$(3) \qquad e^{-x}(2x - x^2) = \sum_{n=0}^{\infty} \frac{(-1)^n (n+2) x^{n+1}}{n!},$$

whereupon the desired sum is obtained by division of both members of (3) by x,

$$(4) \qquad e^{-x}(2 - x) = \sum_{n=0}^{\infty} \frac{(-1)^n (n+2) x^n}{n!},$$

valid for all finite x.

Example (b): Sum the series $\sum\limits_{n=1}^{\infty} \dfrac{(-1)^n x^{2n}}{(n+1)(n+3)}$.

A factor $(n+1)$ can be introduced into the denominator by integrating $x^n \, dx$, a factor $(n+3)$ by integrating $x^{n+2} \, dx$. But, in this instance, we can start off with a factor $(n+1)$ in the denominator by using the basic series

$$(5) \qquad \ln(1+x) = \sum_{n=1}^{\infty} \frac{(-1)^{n+1} x^n}{n}, \qquad |x| < 1,$$

and shifting index from n to $(n+1)$ to obtain

$$(6) \qquad \ln(1+x) = \sum_{n=0}^{\infty} \frac{(-1)^n x^{n+1}}{n+1}.$$

To get the desired power x^{n+2} into the numerator, we multiply throughout by x, obtaining

(7) $$x \ln (1 + x) = \sum_{n=0}^{\infty} \frac{(-1)^n x^{n+2}}{n + 1}.$$

Then an integration yields

$$\int x \ln (1 + x) \, dx = C + \sum_{n=0}^{\infty} \frac{(-1)^n x^{n+3}}{(n + 1)(n + 3)},$$

or

(8) $$\frac{1}{2}(x^2 - 1) \ln (1 + x) - \frac{1}{4}(x - 1)^2 = C + \sum_{n=0}^{\infty} \frac{(-1)^n x^{n+3}}{(n + 1)(n + 3)}.$$

Put $x = 0$ to obtain C. Thus we find that $C = -\frac{1}{4}$. Therefore we now have

(9) $$\frac{1}{2}(x^2 - 1) \ln (1 + x) - \frac{1}{4}x^2 + \frac{1}{2}x = \sum_{n=0}^{\infty} \frac{(-1)^n x^{n+3}}{(n + 1)(n + 3)}.$$

To obtain the desired power x^{2n} on the right, we first divide by x^3, exclude $x = 0$, and write

(10) $$\frac{x^2 - 1}{2x^3} \ln (1 + x) - \frac{1}{4x} + \frac{1}{2x^2} = \sum_{n=0}^{\infty} \frac{(-1)^n x^n}{(n + 1)(n + 3)}.$$

Finally, we replace x by x^2, thus obtaining the desired sum

(11) $$\frac{x^4 - 1}{2x^6} \ln (1 + x^2) - \frac{1}{4x^2} + \frac{1}{2x^4} = \sum_{n=0}^{\infty} \frac{(-1)^n x^{2n}}{(n + 1)(n + 3)},$$
$$0 < |x| < 1.$$

Note the implication that the left member, near $x = 0$, is an indeterminate form, as $x \to 0$, with limit $\frac{1}{3}$ ($n = 0$ term on the right).

EXERCISES

Sum the given series with the aid of the basic series in § 203.

1. $\sum_{n=0}^{\infty} \frac{(n + 1)(n + 2)x^n}{n!}$. Start with the series for $x^2 e^x$.

                            Ans. $e^x(x^2 + 4x + 2)$.

2. $\sum_{n=0}^{\infty} \frac{(-1)^n(n + 2)(n + 3)x^n}{n!}$.   *Ans.* $e^{-x}(x^2 - 6x + 6)$.

3. $\sum_{n=0}^{\infty} \frac{x^{n+4}}{n!(n + 2)}$.   *Ans.* $x^2(xe^x + 1 - e^x)$.

4. $\sum_{n=0}^{\infty} \frac{(-1)^n x^{2n+3}}{(2n)!(2n + 2)}$. Start with the series for $x \cos x$.

                          Ans. $x(x \sin x + \cos x - 1)$.

5. $\sum\limits_{n=0}^{\infty} \dfrac{(-1)^n x^{2n+5}}{(2n+1)!\,(2n+3)}.$ *Ans.* $x^2(\sin x - x \cos x).$

6. $\sum\limits_{n=0}^{\infty} (n+2)(n+1)x^{n+2}.$ *Ans.* $\dfrac{2x^2}{(1-x)^3}.$

7. $\sum\limits_{n=0}^{\infty} \dfrac{(n+3)(n-1)x^{n+1}}{n+1}.$ *Ans.* $4 \ln(1-x) + \dfrac{x}{(1-x)^2}.$

8. $\sum\limits_{n=0}^{\infty} (-1)^n(n+1)(n+2)x^{2n+1}.$ *Ans.* $\dfrac{2x}{(1+x^2)^3}.$

9. $\sum\limits_{n=0}^{\infty} \dfrac{(-1)^n(n+4)x^{n+3}}{n!\,(n+3)}.$ *Ans.* $2 + e^{-x}(x^3 - x^2 - 2x - 2).$

10. $\sum\limits_{n=0}^{\infty} \dfrac{1}{n!\,(n+3)}.$ Use the method of Ex. 3; then put $x=1.$

Ans. $e-2.$

11. $\sum\limits_{n=0}^{\infty} \dfrac{(-1)^n}{n!\,(n+3)}.$ See Ex. 10.   *Ans.* $2 - 5e^{-1}.$

12. $\sum\limits_{n=0}^{\infty} \dfrac{(-1)^n(n+1)}{4^n(2n)!}.$ *Ans.* $\cos \tfrac{1}{2} - \tfrac{1}{4}\sin \tfrac{1}{2}.$

CHAPTER *28* APPROXIMATE
INTEGRATION

214. Approximate integration. The Fundamental Theorem exhibits the limit of a sum of infinitesimal elements as a definite integral:

$$\lim_{n \to \infty} \sum_{i=1}^{n} f(x_i)\, \Delta x = \int_a^b f(x)\, dx.$$

This method of evaluating the limit may fail, however, for either of two principal reasons:

(*a*) It may not be possible to evaluate the integral in terms of known functions; or

(*b*) The function may have been determined empirically, so that no formula for it is available.

Under (*a*), we have just seen that the difficulty may frequently be overcome by expanding the integrand in a suitable power series and integrating term by term. But it is not always possible to find a power series convergent at both limits; if this is possible, the series may converge so slowly as to be useless.

Under (*b*), we may plot the points corresponding to the given (*x, y*)-pairs and find the equation of a curve which shall pass more or less closely through the given points. (There are several well-known methods for doing this; the process is called *curve-fitting.*) Then, of course, we may find the area under the approximation-curve in the usual way. But in a given case this method may be more trouble than it is worth; or, when a curve has been fitted, we may wish to have an independent means of checking the result.

In any of the above situations, we must have recourse to some form of approximate integration other than that of § 212. In addition to integrating machines, various analytic methods are known.

215. Simpson's Rule: geometric approach. When we are unable to evaluate the limit of a sum of n rectangles as n increases indefinitely, an obvious way of approximating the result would be to evaluate the sum itself for a reasonably large value of n—e.g., $n = 10$, in Fig. 57, p. 113. That is, measure or compute the successive ordinates, multiply by Δx to find the areas of the rectangles, and add the areas by simple arithmetic. Since the error is a rather small fraction of the total, this gives a moderately good approximation. But we can easily do better.

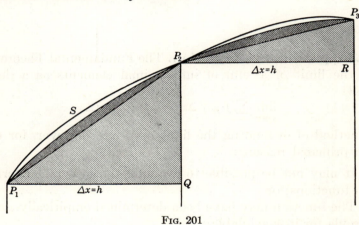

Fig. 201

Figure 201 shows a magnification of the top parts of two adjacent elementary strips. Consider the left-hand one, bounded by the arc P_1SP_2. The line P_1Q is the top of our usual rectangular element. If we replace this by the *chord* P_1P_2, thus replacing the rectangle by a trapezoid, we add to the counted area the triangle P_1QP_2, greatly improving the approximation. This method, leading to the "Trapezoidal Rule" stated below, is sufficiently accurate for many purposes, and is therefore quite often used. But we can do much better than this.

Consider the two adjacent strips simultaneously, and pass a parabola with vertical axis through the three consecutive division-points P_1, P_2, P_3; that is, replace the broken line $P_1P_2P_3$ by a *parabolic arc*. This adds to the count the narrow darker areas, again greatly improving the approximation.

To put this into effect, take the coördinates of P_1, P_2, P_3 as (x_0, y_0), $(x_0 + h, y_1)$, $(x_0 + 2h, y_2)$, where temporarily, to simplify the writing, we put $\Delta x = h$. The equation

(1) $$y - y_0 = a(x - x_0)^2 + b(x - x_0)$$

represents a parabola with vertical axis (since the only terms appearing are x^2, x, y, and constant), and it obviously passes through (x_0, y_0). Substituting $(x_0 + h, y_1)$ and $(x_0 + 2h, y_2)$, we get

$$y_1 - y_0 = ah^2 + bh,$$
$$y_2 - y_0 = 4ah^2 + 2bh.$$

Now let us compute the area under the parabola (1) from $x = x_0$ to $x = x_0 + 2h$:

$$
\begin{aligned}
A_1 &= \int_{x_0}^{x_0+2h} y \, dx = \int_{x_0}^{x_0+2h} [a(x - x_0)^2 + b(x - x_0) + y_0] \, dx \\
&= \left[\frac{a(x - x_0)^3}{3} + \frac{b(x - x_0)^2}{2} + y_0 x \right]_{x_0}^{x_0+2h} \\
&= \tfrac{8}{3}ah^3 + 2bh^2 + 2y_0 h \\
&= \frac{h}{3}(8ah^2 + 6bh + 6y_0) \\
&= \frac{h}{3}[(4ah^2 + 2bh) + 4(ah^2 + bh) + 6y_0] \\
&= \frac{h}{3}[y_2 - y_0 + 4(y_1 - y_0) + 6y_0] \\
&= \frac{h}{3}(y_0 + 4y_1 + y_2).
\end{aligned}
$$

Replacing h by Δx, we find

(2) $$A_1 = \int_{x_0}^{x_0+2\Delta x} y \, dx = \frac{\Delta x}{3}(y_0 + 4y_1 + y_2).$$

Now divide the whole area from $x = a$ to $x = b$ into an *even number* n of strips, each of width Δx, and integrate over two strips at a time, starting with $x_0 = a$:

$$A_1 = \int_a^{a+2\Delta x} y \, dx = \frac{\Delta x}{3}(y_0 + 4y_1 + y_2),$$

$$A_2 = \int_{a+2\Delta x}^{a+4\Delta x} y \, dx = \frac{\Delta x}{3}(y_2 + 4y_3 + y_4),$$

$$A_3 = \int_{a+4\Delta x}^{a+6\Delta x} y \, dx = \frac{\Delta x}{3}(y_4 + 4y_5 + y_6),$$

$$\vdots \qquad \vdots \qquad \qquad \vdots$$

$$A_{\frac{1}{2}n} = \int_{a+(n-2)\Delta x}^{b} y \, dx = \frac{\Delta x}{3}(y_{n-2} + 4y_{n-1} + y_n).$$

Adding all these, we obtain the approximate formula called *Simpson's Rule:*

$$\int_a^b y \, dx = \frac{\Delta x}{3}(y_0 + 4y_1 + 2y_2 + 4y_3 + 2y_4 + \cdots + 4y_{n-1} + y_n).$$

Although we shall not take time either to derive or to apply it, the reader may wish to have available, for possible future reference, the approximate formula known as the *Trapezoidal Rule:*

$$\int_a^b y \, dx = \frac{\Delta x}{2}(y_0 + 2y_1 + 2y_2 + 2y_3 + \cdots + 2y_{n-1} + y_n).$$

The notation is the same as in Simpson's Rule, except that here the number of divisions need not be even.

216. Simpson's Rule: analytic approach. In the examples of § 212 and exercises following, we expanded the integrand about the lower limit—*i.e.*, in powers of x. More generally, to evaluate $\int_a^b f(x) \, dx$, where $a \neq 0$, it is well to expand in powers of * $(x - a)$

(§ 204). Then, the indefinite integral proceeds in powers of $(x - a)$; the value at the upper limit proceeds in powers of $(b - a)$, and converges rapidly, in general, if $(b - a)$ is small—*i.e., if the interval of integration is short.* [For instance, Example (*a*), § 212, easy enough as it stands, would be much easier if the upper limit were 0.1, much more troublesome if the upper limit were 10.] When the interval is inconveniently long, an obvious device is to subdivide and integrate piecemeal: thus we arrive quite naturally at the same problem that appeared in § 215—viz., to find the area from $x = x_0$ to $x = x_0 + 2h$.

To do this, in accordance with the above discussion we expand the function

$$y = f(x)$$

in Taylor's Series about the point $x = x_0$:

$$(1) \quad f(x) = f(x_0) + f'(x_0)(x - x_0) + \frac{f''(x_0)}{2!}(x - x_0)^2$$
$$+ \frac{f'''(x_0)}{3!}(x - x_0)^3 + \cdots.$$

---

* Of course it is sometimes more convenient to expand in powers of $(x - b)$, or about some interior point (Exs. 21–22, p. 395).

Upon integrating term by term, it is easily seen that the result to four terms is

(2) $$\int_{x_0}^{x_0+2h} f(x)\,dx = f(x_0)(2h) + \frac{f'(x_0)}{2!}(2h)^2 + \frac{f''(x_0)}{3!}(2h)^3 + \frac{f'''(x_0)}{4!}(2h)^4.$$

Since h is small, and we are neglecting terms in h^5 and beyond, this formula will in most cases give a good approximation to the value of the integral.

Let (as in § 215)

$$y_0 = f(x_0), \qquad y_1 = f(x_0 + h), \qquad y_2 = f(x_0 + 2h).$$

By (1), if again we keep only four terms,

$$y_1 = f(x_0) + f'(x_0)h + \frac{f''(x_0)}{2!}h^2 + \frac{f'''(x_0)}{3!}h^3,$$

$$y_2 = f(x_0) + f'(x_0)(2h) + \frac{f''(x_0)}{2!}(2h)^2 + \frac{f'''(x_0)}{3!}(2h)^3.$$

It follows that, approximately,

(3) $$\int_{x_0}^{x_0+2h} f(x)\,dx = \frac{h}{3}(y_0 + 4y_1 + y_2):$$

to verify this, substitute the values of y_0, y_1, y_2 in (3) and compare with (2).

Since (3) is identical with (2), § 215, the remainder of the argument proceeds just as in that section.

217. Applications. We have developed Simpson's Rule in connection with plane area. But of course, the Rule applies quite independently of the physical meaning of the integral, for the same reason that the Fundamental Theorem applies generally: viz., that any function of one variable may be interpreted as the ordinate of a plane curve, so that its integral becomes the area under that curve.

Example (a): Compute ln 2 from the fact that

$$\int_0^1 \frac{dx}{1+x} = \Big[\ln(1+x)\Big]_0^1 = \ln 2.$$

The direct method of § 212 is out of the question here, due to the very slow convergence of the Maclaurin Series for $\ln(1+x)$ —see Ex. 23, p. 369. Let us apply Simpson's Rule with $n = 10$,

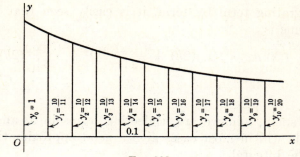

Fig. 202

$\Delta x = 0.1$, so that *

$$y_0 = \frac{1}{1}, \qquad y_1 = \frac{1}{1.1} = \frac{10}{11}, \qquad y_2 = \frac{1}{1.2} = \frac{10}{12}, \text{ etc.:}$$

$$\int_0^1 \frac{dx}{1+x} = \frac{1}{30}\left[\frac{10}{10} + \frac{40}{11} + \frac{20}{12} + \frac{40}{13} + \frac{20}{14} + \frac{40}{15} + \frac{20}{16}\right.$$
$$\left. + \frac{40}{17} + \frac{20}{18} + \frac{40}{19} + \frac{10}{20}\right]$$

(1)
$$= \frac{1}{3}\left[\frac{1}{10} + \frac{4}{11} + \frac{1}{6} + \frac{4}{13} + \frac{1}{7} + \frac{4}{15} + \frac{1}{8} + \frac{4}{17}\right.$$
$$\left. + \frac{1}{9} + \frac{4}{19} + \frac{1}{20}\right]$$

$$= \tfrac{1}{3}[0.100\,000$$
$$0.363\,636$$
$$0.166\,667$$
$$0.307\,692$$
$$0.142\,857$$
$$0.266\,667$$
$$0.125\,000$$
$$0.235\,294$$
$$0.111\,111$$
$$0.210\,526$$
$$\underline{0.050\,000}$$
$$2.079\,450] = 0.693\,15.$$

* Here and in a number of the exercises following, a table of reciprocals is handy: see, for instance, the *Macmillan Logarithmic and Trigonometric Tables*, Revised, New York, The Macmillan Co., p. 94. To use the table, write the second term in (1) as $\frac{4}{11} = \frac{1}{\frac{11}{4}}$ $= \frac{1}{2.75} = 0.363636$, the fourth term as $\frac{1}{\frac{13}{4}} = \frac{1}{3.25}$; etc.

If we were to keep the (quite untrustworthy) sixth place, the answer would be 0.693150. The correct value is 0.693147. Thus, with a six-place table of reciprocals, Simpson's Rule produces an error of 3 points in the sixth place. The Trapezoidal Rule gives an error of 6 points in the fourth place.

Example (b): Find the area under the curve determined by the following set of empirical data:

x	0	1	2	3	4	5	6	7	8
y	0	0.38	0.68	1.13	1.47	1.78	2.18	2.60	2.84

With $n = 8$, $\Delta x = 1$, we have

$$(2) \quad A = \int_0^8 y\, dx = \tfrac{1}{3}[0 + 1.52 + 1.36 + 4.52 + 2.94 + 7.12$$
$$+ 4.36 + 10.40 + 2.84]$$
$$= \tfrac{1}{3}(35.06) = 11.69.$$

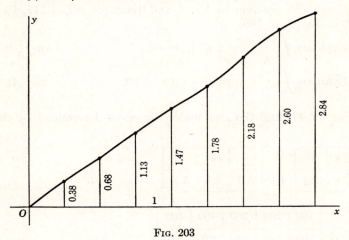

Fig. 203

The points, when plotted, follow fairly closely a straight line. The equation of this line, fitted to the data by the method of averages, is

$$y = 0.363\, x.$$

Using this in (2), we get

$$A = \int_0^8 y\, dx = 0.363\left[\frac{x^2}{2}\right]_0^8 = 11.62:$$

a difference of 0.6 of 1%.

EXERCISES

1. Evaluate $\int_1^2 \dfrac{dx}{1+x}$ with $n = 10$.

2. Check the answers to Ex. 1 and Example (a) by evaluating $\int_2^3 \dfrac{dx}{1+x}$ with $n = 10$.

3. Evaluate $\int_0^1 \dfrac{dx}{1+x^2}$ with $n = 10$.   *Ans.* $\dfrac{\pi}{4} = 0.78540$.

4. Evaluate $\int_0^1 e^{-x^2}\, dx$ with $n = 10$.   *Ans.* 0.7468.

5. Evaluate $\int_0^1 x^2 e^{-x^2}\, dx$ with $n = 10$.   *Ans.* 0.1895.

6. Check Ex. 5 by means of Ex. 4. (Integrate by parts.)

7. Show, by computation with power series, that the answer given in Ex. 4 is correct to four decimal places.

8. Show, by computation with power series, that the answer given in Ex. 5 is correct to four decimal places.

9. Check the answers to Ex. 1 and Example (a), § 217, by setting $x = 0.2$ in Ex. 4, p. 389.

10. Evaluate $\int_0^{\frac{1}{2}} \dfrac{dx}{\sqrt{1-x^2}}$ with $n = 4$.   *Ans.* $\dfrac{\pi}{6} = 0.5236$.

11. Evaluate $\int_0^1 \sqrt{1+x^4}\, dx$ with $n = 10$.   *Ans.* 1.090.

In Exs. 12–17, find the area under the curve determined by the given data.*

12.

x	2	4	6	8	10
v	3.4	4.8	5.9	6.9	7.8

Ans. 46.53.

13.

P	100	200	300	400	500
Q	95	185	270	350	415

Ans. 106,330.

14.

t	1	2	3	4	5
x	1.10	4.35	10.05	17.15	26.25

Ans. 44.48.

15.

x	8	10	12	14	16	18	20
y	26	115	227	358	515	684	880

Ans. 4679.

* In some cases, the answers are given to a number of places not justified by the data. This is done in order to show the difference in results by Simpson's Rule and by using the fitted equation: Exs. 12–17 vs. Exs. 18–23.

16.

x	0.6	0.8	1.0	1.2	1.4
y	0.161	0.374	0.806	1.302	2.150

Ans. 0.708.

17.

x	1	2	3	4	5	6	7
y	1.82	4.19	6.90	9.21	11.65	14.36	16.72

Ans. 55.56.

In Exs. 18–23, the given equation has been fitted to the data by the method of averages. Check the answer to the previous exercise by using the empirical formula.

18. Ex. 12: (a) $v^2 = 5.93x$; (b) by a variation of the same method, $v^2 = 5.90x$.   *Ans.* (a) 46.74; (b) 46.63.

19. Ex. 13: $Q = 0.95P - 0.0000005P^3$.   *Ans.* 106,200.

20. Ex. 14: $x = 1.071t^2$.   *Ans.* 44.29.

21. Ex. 15: $y = 2.55x^2 - 140.02$.   *Ans.* 4679.

22. Ex. 16: $y = 0.773x^3$.   *Ans.* 0.717.

23. Ex. 17: (a) $y = 2.49x - 0.69$; (b) by a slight variation of the method, $y = 2.48x - 0.66$.   *Ans.* (a) 55.62; (b) 55.56.

24. Draw a smooth curve through the points

x	0	3	5	7	9	11	12
y	0	0.59	1.56	2.83	4.36	6.05	6.90

and find the area under the curve, taking $n = 6$.

25. Solve Ex. 24 with $n = 12$.

26. Solve Ex. 24, using the fitted formula $y = 0.072x^2 - 0.002x^3$. Compare the results of Exs. 24–26.

27. Draw a smooth curve, on a large scale, through the points

x	0	50	100	150	220	300	500
y	0	22.8	49.8	85.0	128.6	192.4	328.4

and find the area under the curve, taking $n = 10$.

28. Solve Ex. 27, using the fitted formula $y = 0.233x^{1.171}$.

29. The velocity of a body, sliding from rest down a smooth inclined plane, is observed at the ends of successive seconds as shown in the table:

t	1	2	3	4	5	6	7	8
v	1.31	2.52	3.52	4.72	5.87	7.02	8.17	9.42

Find the distance traveled in 8 sec.   *Ans.* 37.8 ft.

30. In Ex. 29, the fitted formula is $v = 1.1784t$. Check the answer.   *Ans.* 37.7 ft.

CHAPTER 29 PARTIAL DIFFERENTIATION

218. Functions of several variables. So far, we have been concerned with functions of a single argument. A function may, however, depend upon several independent variables.

Example (a): The hypotenuse of a right triangle is a function of the perpendicular sides:

$$(1) \qquad\qquad h = \sqrt{a^2 + b^2}.$$

Example (b): The volume of a box is a function of its three dimensions:

$$V = xyz.$$

Geometrically a function of two variables x and y may be represented as the z-coördinate of a surface in space. Thus an equation of first degree represents a plane; equation (1) represents one sheet of a circular cone.

219. Limits; continuity. Consider a function

$$(1) \qquad\qquad z = f(x, y)$$

representing a surface in space. When x and y approach the respective values x_1, y_1, the function z is said to *approach a limit* z_1 if the point (x, y, z) of the surface (1) approaches a definite limiting point (x_1, y_1, z_1). In other words, if the difference between the variable z and the fixed value z_1 can be made as small as desired, by taking x sufficiently near the fixed x_1, and y sufficiently near the fixed y_1, then z is said to approach z_1; in symbols,

$$\lim_{\substack{x \to x_1 \\ y \to y_1}} f(x, y) = z_1.$$

A function $f(x, y)$ is *continuous* at the point (x_1, y_1) (compare § 12) if $f(x_1, y_1)$ exists, and *[f (x,y) is continuous for (x,y)]*
$$\lim_{\substack{x \to x_1 \\ y \to y_1}} f(x, y) = f(x_1, y_1).$$
[if f(x,y) exists at (x₁,y₁) & neighboring values if lim_{x,y} f(x,y) = f(x₁,y₁)]

Similar definitions are laid down for functions of more than two variables.

In what follows, it is assumed that all functions occurring are continuous at all points under consideration.

220. Partial derivatives. If y be kept *fixed*, the function
$$z = f(x, y)$$
[no matter how y approaches x, y, respectively]

becomes a function of x alone, and its derivative may be found by the ordinary rules. This derivative is called the *partial derivative of z with respect to x*, and is denoted by
$$\frac{\partial z}{\partial x}, \quad \frac{\partial f}{\partial x}, \quad \text{or} \quad f_x(x, y).$$

The partial derivative with respect to y has a similar meaning.

When z is defined implicitly as a function of x and y by the equation
$$F(x, y, z) = 0,$$
the partial derivatives may still be found by the rule of § 30.

The idea of partial differentiation may be extended at once to functions of any number of variables. We have only to remember that in differentiating with respect to any one variable, *all the other variables are treated as constants*.

Example (a): If $V = \pi r^2 h$, then
$$\frac{\partial V}{\partial r} = 2\pi r h, \qquad \frac{\partial V}{\partial h} = \pi r^2.$$

Thus, if the altitude of a circular cylinder is kept fixed, the volume changes at a rate equal to the lateral area; etc.

Example (b): If $z^2 + 2zx = x^2 - y^2$, then
$$2z\frac{\partial z}{\partial x} + 2z + 2x\frac{\partial z}{\partial x} = 2x, \qquad \frac{\partial z}{\partial x} = \frac{x - z}{x + z},$$
$$2z\frac{\partial z}{\partial y} + 2x\frac{\partial z}{\partial y} = -2y, \qquad \frac{\partial z}{\partial y} = \frac{-y}{x + z}.$$

221. Geometric interpretation. To keep y constant, say $y = y_1$, in the equation $z = f(x, y)$ means geometrically that we cut the surface by the plane $y = y_1$. The partial derivative $\dfrac{\partial z}{\partial x}$ is therefore the *slope of the curve of intersection* of the surface and the plane $y = y_1$: that is, the slope of the tangent PT. The partial derivative $\dfrac{\partial z}{\partial y}$ may be interpreted similarly.

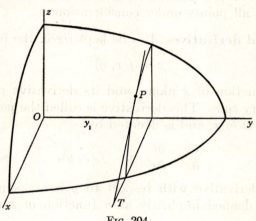

Fɪɢ. 204

Example: Find the equations of the tangent to the parabola $(x + y)^2 + 32z = 256$, $x = 5$ at P: $(5, 3, 6)$.

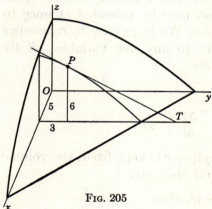

Fɪɢ. 205

Since x is constant, we differentiate partially with respect to y:

$$2(x + y) + 32\frac{\partial z}{\partial y} = 0,$$

$$\frac{\partial z}{\partial y} = -\frac{1}{16}(x + y),$$

$$\left[\frac{\partial z}{\partial y}\right]_P = -\frac{1}{2}.$$

Thus the equations of the tangent PT are

$$z - 6 = -\tfrac{1}{2}(y - 3), \quad x = 5,$$

or

$$y + 2z = 15, \qquad\qquad x = 5.$$

222. Higher derivatives. The derivatives $\dfrac{\partial z}{\partial x}$, $\dfrac{\partial z}{\partial y}$ are themselves functions of x and y, and their partial derivatives can in turn be found. They are denoted by the following symbols:

$$\frac{\partial}{\partial x}\left(\frac{\partial z}{\partial x}\right) = \frac{\partial^2 z}{\partial x^2} = f_{xx}(x, y),$$

$$\frac{\partial}{\partial y}\left(\frac{\partial z}{\partial x}\right) = \frac{\partial^2 z}{\partial y \, \partial x} = f_{xy}(x, y),$$

$$\frac{\partial}{\partial x}\left(\frac{\partial z}{\partial y}\right) = \frac{\partial^2 z}{\partial x \, \partial y} = f_{yx}(x, y),$$

$$\frac{\partial}{\partial y}\left(\frac{\partial z}{\partial y}\right) = \frac{\partial^2 z}{\partial y^2} = f_{yy}(x, y).$$

The process can of course be repeated to find still higher derivatives.

It can be shown that the two "cross-derivatives" $\dfrac{\partial^2 z}{\partial y \, \partial x}$, $\dfrac{\partial^2 z}{\partial x \, \partial y}$ are identical, provided they are continuous:

$$\frac{\partial^2 z}{\partial y \, \partial x} \equiv \frac{\partial^2 z}{\partial x \, \partial y}.$$

EXERCISES

In Exs. 1–16, find the first partial derivatives of the given function.

1. $z = x^3 - x^2 y + 4y^2$. *Ans.* $\dfrac{\partial z}{\partial x} = 3x^2 - 2xy$; $\dfrac{\partial z}{\partial y} = 8y - x^2$.

2. $z = 4x^2 y - y^2 + 3x - 1$. *Ans.* $\dfrac{\partial z}{\partial x} = 8xy + 3$; $\dfrac{\partial z}{\partial y} = 4x^2 - 2y$.

3. $z = \sin(xy)$. **4.** $z = \cot(xy)$.

5. $u = \sqrt{x^2 - v^2}$. **6.** $v = (x^2 + w^2)^{-\frac{1}{2}}$.

7. $x = \dfrac{u - v}{u^2 + v^2}$. **8.** $s = \left(\dfrac{t + 3y}{t}\right)^2$.

9. $r = \cos^2(\theta - 3\phi)$. **10.** $r = \sec^2(2\theta - 3\phi)$.

11. $y = \ln(z^2 + x^2)$. **12.** $u = \ln[z^2(x^2 - y^2)]$.

13. $v = e^{-xy}$. **14.** $u = z e^{-x^2 - y^2}$.

15. $w = \tan(x + 2y - z^2)$. **16.** $\alpha = \ln[xy(2t - 1)^2]$.

17. If (x, y) and (r, θ) are the Cartesian and polar coördinates of a point, find the partial derivatives of x and y with respect to r and θ.

Ans. $\dfrac{\partial x}{\partial \theta} = -r \sin \theta$.

18. In Ex. 17, find the partial derivatives of r and θ with respect to x and y.

Ans. $\dfrac{\partial \theta}{\partial x} = -\dfrac{y}{x^2 + y^2}$.

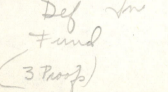

In Exs. 19–24, find $\dfrac{\partial z}{\partial x}, \dfrac{\partial z}{\partial y}$.

19. $x^2 - y^2 + z^2 = a^2$.   *Ans.* $\dfrac{\partial z}{\partial x} = \dfrac{-x}{z}; \dfrac{\partial z}{\partial y} = \dfrac{y}{z}$.

20. $z^2 - 4xz + y^2 = 4$.   *Ans.* $\dfrac{\partial z}{\partial x} = \dfrac{2z}{z - 2x}; \dfrac{\partial z}{\partial y} = \dfrac{y}{2x - z}$.

21. $xy + xz + yz = 3$.   **22.** $x^2 + z^2 = 4yz$.
23. $xyz = x + y + z$.   **24.** $2x^2z - z^3y = x$.

In Exs. 25–30, find the equations of the tangent line in the given plane.

25. Tangent to the parabola $z = x^2 + 4y^2$, $x = 2$, at the point $(2, 1, 8)$.
    Ans. $x = 2, z = 8y$.

26. Tangent to the parabola $z = y^2 - 4x^2 - 1$, $y = 4$, at the point $(-2, 4, -1)$.   *Ans.* $y = 4, 16x - z = -31$.

27. Tangent to the circle $x^2 + 3y^2 + z^2 = 13$, $y = -1$, at the point $(1, -1, 3)$.   *Ans.* $y = -1, x + 3z = 10$.

28. Tangent to the ellipse $x^2 + 3y^2 + z^2 = 13$, $x = 1$, at the point $(1, -1, 3)$.   *Ans.* $x = 1, z = y + 4$.

29. Tangent to the curve $z^2 = xy + x^2$, $z = 4$, at $(2, 6, 4)$. What kind of curve is this?   *Ans.* $z = 4, 5x + y = 16$.

30. Tangent to the curve $xy + xz + yz = 0$, $x = 6$, at $(6, -2, 3)$. What kind of curve is this?   *Ans.* $x = 6, 9y + 4z = -6$.

31. Given $z = (x - 2y^2)^3$, find $\dfrac{\partial^2 z}{\partial x^2}, \dfrac{\partial^2 z}{\partial x\,\partial y}, \dfrac{\partial^2 z}{\partial y\,\partial x}, \dfrac{\partial^2 z}{\partial y^2}$.

32. Given $v = (t - 3x)e^{-t}$, find $\dfrac{\partial^2 v}{\partial t^2}, \dfrac{\partial^2 v}{\partial x^2}, \dfrac{\partial^2 v}{\partial x\,\partial t}, \dfrac{\partial^2 v}{\partial t\,\partial x}$.

33. Given $u = \sin(x + 2y)$, verify that $\dfrac{\partial^3 u}{\partial y\,\partial x^2} = \dfrac{\partial^3 u}{\partial x\,\partial y\,\partial x} = \dfrac{\partial^3 u}{\partial x^2\,\partial y}$.

34. For the u of Ex. 33, obtain $\dfrac{\partial^3 u}{\partial x^3}, \dfrac{\partial^3 u}{\partial y^2\,\partial x}$, and $\dfrac{\partial^3 u}{\partial y\,\partial x\,\partial y}$.

35. If $w = x^3 - 7xy^2$, show that $x\dfrac{\partial w}{\partial x} + y\dfrac{\partial w}{\partial y} = 3w$.

36. If $u = 3x^2 + 2xz - y^2$, show that $x\dfrac{\partial u}{\partial x} + y\dfrac{\partial u}{\partial y} + z\dfrac{\partial u}{\partial z} = 2u$.

37. If $z = \dfrac{xy}{x^2 + y^2}$, show that $x\dfrac{\partial z}{\partial x} + y\dfrac{\partial z}{\partial y} = 0$.

38. If $u = \sqrt{x^3 - 2y^3}$, show that $x\dfrac{\partial u}{\partial x} + y\dfrac{\partial u}{\partial y} = \dfrac{3}{2}u$.

39. If $u = \ln(x^2 + y^2)$, show that $\dfrac{\partial^2 u}{\partial x^2} + \dfrac{\partial^2 u}{\partial y^2} = 0$.

40. If $\theta = \text{Arctan}\,\dfrac{y}{x}$, show that $\dfrac{\partial^2 \theta}{\partial x^2} + \dfrac{\partial^2 \theta}{\partial y^2} = 0$.

41. Show that $u = e^{-a^2 t}\sin \alpha x$ satisfies the equation $\dfrac{\partial u}{\partial t} = \dfrac{\partial^2 u}{\partial x^2}$ for all values of α.

42. Determine the relation that must hold between α and β if $u = e^{\alpha x} \sin \beta y$ is to satisfy the equation $\dfrac{\partial^2 u}{\partial x^2} + \dfrac{\partial^2 u}{\partial y^2} = 0$.   *Ans.* $\beta = \pm \alpha$.

43. If $u = e^{\sqrt{m^2+n^2}\,x} \cos my \sin nz$, show that $\dfrac{\partial^2 u}{\partial x^2} + \dfrac{\partial^2 u}{\partial y^2} + \dfrac{\partial^2 u}{\partial z^2} = 0$.

44. Find the relation connecting α, β, γ if $u = e^{\alpha t} \cos \beta x \sin \gamma y$ is to satisfy the equation $\dfrac{\partial^2 u}{\partial x^2} + \dfrac{\partial^2 u}{\partial y^2} = \dfrac{\partial u}{\partial t}$.

45. For the function $z = x^2 y^2 + y^{\frac{1}{3}}$, show that $\dfrac{\partial^2 z}{\partial y\, \partial x} \neq \dfrac{\partial^2 z}{\partial x\, \partial y}$ at $(0, 0, 0)$.

223. A formula for Δz. When x and y change by amounts Δx, Δy, the function

$$(1) \qquad\qquad z = f(x, y)$$

changes by an amount

$$\Delta z = f(x + \Delta x, y + \Delta y) - f(x, y).$$

In the Law of the Mean (§ 109),

$$f(b) - f(a) = (b - a)f'(x_1), \qquad\qquad a < x_1 < b,$$

let us put

$$a = x, \qquad b = x + \Delta x.$$

Then x_1 may be written in the form

$$x_1 = x + \alpha\, \Delta x, \qquad\qquad 0 < \alpha < 1,$$

since this merely says that any number lying between x and $x + \Delta x$ must be equal to x plus some part of Δx. (In the figure, $OP = x_1$.) Thus

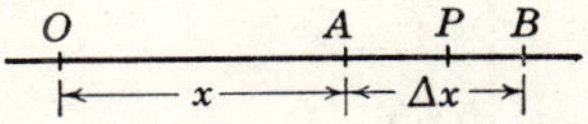

$$(2) \qquad f(x + \Delta x) - f(x) = f'(x + \alpha\, \Delta x)\, \Delta x,$$
$$0 < \alpha < 1.$$

Fig. 206

When y is kept fixed, the function (1) becomes a function of one variable, so that (2) applies; but the ordinary derivative $f'(x)$ must be replaced by the partial derivative $f_x(x, y)$. That is,

$$(3) \qquad f(x + \Delta x, y) - f(x, y) = f_x(x + \alpha\, \Delta x, y)\, \Delta x.$$

In the same way let us apply (2) to the function $f(x + \Delta x, y)$, keeping x and Δx fixed and letting y take an increment:

$$(4) \quad f(x + \Delta x, y + \Delta y) - f(x + \Delta x, y) = f_y (x + \Delta x, y + \beta\, \Delta y)\, \Delta y,$$
$$0 < \beta < 1.$$

Adding (3) and (4), we find

$$f(x + \Delta x, y + \Delta y) - f(x, y) = f_x(x + \alpha \Delta x, y) \Delta x$$
$$+ f_y(x + \Delta x, y + \beta \Delta y) \Delta y.$$

Since

$$\lim_{\Delta x \to 0} f_x(x + \alpha \Delta x, y) = f_x(x, y),$$
$$\lim_{\substack{\Delta x \to 0 \\ \Delta y \to 0}} f_y(x + \Delta x, y + \beta \Delta y) = f_y(x, y),$$

we may write this last formula in the form

$$f(x + \Delta x, y + \Delta y) - f(x, y) = f_x(x, y) \Delta x + f_y(x, y) \Delta y$$
$$+ \epsilon \Delta x + \eta \Delta y,$$

where ϵ and η are infinitesimals. This is equivalent to

$$(5) \qquad \Delta z = \frac{\partial z}{\partial x} \Delta x + \frac{\partial z}{\partial y} \Delta y + \epsilon \Delta x + \eta \Delta y.$$

224. Total differentials. In the formula just written, the quantity $\dfrac{\partial z}{\partial x} \Delta x + \dfrac{\partial z}{\partial y} \Delta y$ — *i.e.*, the group of infinitesimals of *first order* —is called the *total differential* of z (compare the similar procedure in § 45):

$$(1) \qquad dz = \frac{\partial z}{\partial x} \Delta x + \frac{\partial z}{\partial y} \Delta y.$$

In particular, if $z = x$, $\dfrac{\partial z}{\partial x} = 1$ and $\dfrac{\partial z}{\partial y} = 0$, so that

$$dx = \Delta x.$$

Similarly

$$dy = \Delta y.$$

(Here again, as in § 45, these results are to be considered as definitions of dx and dy.) Hence we may write (1) in the equivalent form

$$(2) \qquad dz = \frac{\partial z}{\partial x} dx + \frac{\partial z}{\partial y} dy.$$

If x and y are functions of a third variable t, then z becomes a function of t alone, and its differential has been defined in § 45. It can be shown that the value of dz as given by (2) agrees with the earlier definition.

For functions of more than two arguments a similar formula holds. Thus, if

$$u = f(x, y, z),$$

the total differential of u is

$$(3) \qquad du = \frac{\partial u}{\partial x}\, dx + \frac{\partial u}{\partial y}\, dy + \frac{\partial u}{\partial z}\, dz.$$

This formula is valid for any system of independent variables.

It follows from what has been said that the total differential of a function of any number of variables may be found by our ordinary rules (§ 45).

Example: If

$$u = x^3 - xy^2 + yt - t^3,$$
$$du = 3x^2\, dx - y^2\, dx - 2xy\, dy + y\, dt + t\, dy - 3t^2\, dt.$$

225. Approximate formulas. It appears from (5), § 223 and (1), § 224, that when Δx and Δy are both small, *dz and Δz are nearly equal.* Hence the differential can be used as an approximation to the increment, for functions of two (or more) variables, exactly as in § 47.

Example (a): Find the error in the value of a fraction produced by small errors in the numerator and denominator.

Let the fraction be

$$(1) \qquad f = \frac{y}{x}.$$

Then the change in f due to small changes in y and x is approximately, if Δx and Δy are small compared to x,

$$df = \frac{x\, \Delta y - y\, \Delta x}{x^2}.$$

Example (b): In Fig. 207, if $x = 9.986$, $y = 7.013$, find $\tan \theta$.

In Example (a), take $y = 7$, $\Delta y = 0.013$; $x = 10$, $\Delta x = -0.014$. Then

$$\tan \theta = \frac{7.013}{9.986} = 0.7 + \frac{10(0.013) - 7(-0.014)}{100}$$

$$= 0.7 + \frac{0.13 + 0.098}{100} = 0.7023.$$

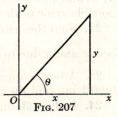

Fig. 207

EXERCISES

In Exs. 1–15, find the total differential.

1. $z = y^4 - 4xy^3$. $\qquad\qquad$ *Ans.* $dz = 4(y^3 - 3xy^2)\, dy - 4y^3\, dx$.

2. $z = x^2y - u^2 + x$. $\qquad$ *Ans.* $dz = (2xy + 1)\, dx + x^2\, dy - 2u\, du$.

3. $z = \sqrt{x^2 + y^2}$. $\qquad\qquad\qquad\qquad$ *Ans.* $dz = \dfrac{x\, dx + y\, dy}{\sqrt{x^2 + y^2}}$.

4. $\theta = \text{Arctan}\, \dfrac{y}{x}$. $\qquad\qquad\qquad$ *Ans.* $d\theta = \dfrac{x\, dy - y\, dx}{x^2 + y^2}$.

5. $\theta = \text{Arcsin}\, \dfrac{y}{r}$. $\qquad\qquad\qquad$ *Ans.* $d\theta = \dfrac{r\, dy - y\, dr}{r\sqrt{r^2 - y^2}}$.

6. $z = \dfrac{y}{\sqrt{x^2 + y^2}}$. $\qquad\qquad$ *Ans.* $dz = \dfrac{x(x\, dy - y\, dx)}{(x^2 + y^2)^{\frac{3}{2}}}$.

7. $V = \pi r^2 h$. $\qquad\qquad\qquad$ **8.** $S = 2\pi rh + 2\pi r^2$.

9. $x = \dfrac{u^2}{v}$. $\qquad\qquad\qquad$ **10.** $w = \ln \sqrt{x^2 + y^2 + z^2}$.

11. $y = e^{-xt^2}$. $\qquad\qquad\qquad$ **12.** $r = \cos \theta \sin \phi \sin \psi$.

13. $v = \ln (xyz)$. $\qquad\qquad\qquad$ **14.** $r = \sqrt{x^2 + y^2 + z^2}$.

15. $u = e^{-\alpha^2 t} \sin \alpha x$; α constant.

16. Find the error in the product xy, due to small errors in x and y. $\qquad\qquad\qquad\qquad\qquad\qquad$ *Ans.* $x\, \Delta y + y\, \Delta x$.

17. Compute the product 0.5102 by 0.6303 to four decimal places. (Ex. 16.)

18. A lot is approximately 60 by 140 ft. If each of the measurements is uncertain by 3 in., find the maximum uncertainty in the area.

19. A certain giant saguaro in the Arizona desert has no protruding limbs, and is roughly a circular cylinder in shape. At the present time, its rate of growth is found to be an increase in height of 0.8 in. per year, and an increase in diameter of 0.1 in. per year. Find the rate of increase of its volume, given that the saguaro is 40 ft. tall and 2 ft. in diameter. $\qquad\qquad$ *Ans.* 1.26 cu. ft. per year.

20. In Ex. 19, compute the rate of change of the lateral surface area (neglecting the spines, which is not always advisable). $\qquad\qquad$ *Ans.* 1.47 sq. ft. per year.

21. A sprinter runs 100 yd. in about 10 sec. If the time may be in error by as much as $\frac{1}{10}$ sec., and the distance by as much as 6 in., find the greatest possible error in the velocity. $\qquad\qquad$ *Ans.* 0.35 ft. per sec.

22. Find the error in the common logarithm of the product of two numbers x and y due to small errors in the numbers. $\qquad$ *Ans.* $M\!\left(\dfrac{\Delta x}{x} + \dfrac{\Delta y}{y}\right)$.

23. A box is approximately $3 \times 4 \times 5$ ft. If each dimension is in excess by 0.1 in., find the excess volume. $\qquad\qquad$ *Ans.* 677 cu. in.

24. In Ex. 23, find the length of a diagonal. (Ex. 14.)

25. A right angle is constructed and the tangent of one of the acute angles is found by measuring the opposite side y and the adjacent side x. If $y = 2.5 \pm 0.1$, $x = 1.5 \pm 0.1$, what is the greatest possible error in the tangent? [Example (a), § 225.]   *Ans.* About 0.18.

26. In Ex. 25, find the greatest possible error in the angle. (Ex. 4.)
                    Ans. About 2° 42′.

27. In Ex. 25, find the greatest possible error in the sine of the angle.

28. It is desired to draw a line through the points $(0, 0)$, $(3, 4)$. If the line is actually drawn through $(-0.04, 0.11)$ and $(3.01, 3.94)$, find the error in the slope of the line.   *Ans.* −0.08.

29. Find approximately the error in the function x^2y due to small errors in x and y.

30. The base of a box is a square of side 6.005; the depth is 8.997. Find the volume. (Ex. 29.)

31. Find the hypotenuse of a right triangle whose sides are 6.03, 7.96.

32. The cosine of an angle is measured: $\cos \theta = \dfrac{x}{r}$. Find the error in $\cos 2\theta$ due to errors in x and r.

226. Differentiation of implicit functions. Let z be defined implicitly as a function of the two independent variables x and y by the equation

$$(1) \qquad\qquad F(x, y, z) = 0.$$

We already know how to obtain the derivatives of z with respect to x, and with respect to y, in an efficient manner; see Example (b), § 220. There are times, as in the next section, when it is expedient to have a formula for each of these derivatives.

For the function in equation (1), put

$$u = F(x, y, z);$$

then

$$du = \frac{\partial F}{\partial x}\, dx + \frac{\partial F}{\partial y}\, dy + \frac{\partial F}{\partial z}\, dz.$$

But since $u = 0$, $du = 0$ likewise, and

$$\frac{\partial F}{\partial x}\, dx + \frac{\partial F}{\partial y}\, dy + \frac{\partial F}{\partial z}\, dz = 0.$$

Further, since z is a function of x and y, we may write

$$dz = \frac{\partial z}{\partial x}\, dx + \frac{\partial z}{\partial y}\, dy.$$

Eliminating dz between these two equations, we find

$$\left(\frac{\partial F}{\partial x} + \frac{\partial F}{\partial z}\frac{\partial z}{\partial x}\right) dx + \left(\frac{\partial F}{\partial y} + \frac{\partial F}{\partial z}\frac{\partial z}{\partial y}\right) dy = 0.$$

To find $\dfrac{\partial z}{\partial x}$, keep y fixed, so that $dy = 0$. Then

$$\frac{\partial F}{\partial x} + \frac{\partial F}{\partial z}\frac{\partial z}{\partial x} = 0,$$

whence

(2) $$\frac{\partial z}{\partial x} = -\frac{\dfrac{\partial F}{\partial x}}{\dfrac{\partial F}{\partial z}} \qquad \left(\frac{\partial F}{\partial z} \neq 0\right).$$

Similarly

(3) $$\frac{\partial z}{\partial y} = -\frac{\dfrac{\partial F}{\partial y}}{\dfrac{\partial F}{\partial z}} \qquad \left(\frac{\partial F}{\partial z} \neq 0\right).$$

227. Tangent plane to a surface. It can be shown that all the lines tangent to a surface

(1) $$z = f(x, y)$$

at a point P: (x_1, y_1, z_1) lie in a plane, the *tangent plane* to the surface at that point. (It is assumed that z, $\dfrac{\partial z}{\partial x}$, and $\dfrac{\partial z}{\partial y}$ are continuous at P.) This plane is determined by any two tangent lines.

Let us assume the equation of the tangent plane in the form

$$z - z_1 = m_1(x - x_1) + m_2(y - y_1),$$

where m_1 and m_2 are to be determined. Now the line of intersection of this plane with the plane $y = y_1$ has the slope m_1. But this line is the tangent lying in the plane $y = y_1$, and, by § 221, its slope is the value of $\dfrac{\partial z}{\partial x}$ at P:

$$m_1 = \left[\frac{\partial z}{\partial x}\right]_P.$$

Similarly we find

$$m_2 = \left[\frac{\partial z}{\partial y}\right]_P.$$

Thus the equation of the plane tangent to the surface (1) at (x_1, y_1, z_1) is

(2) $$z - z_1 = \left[\frac{\partial z}{\partial x}\right]_P (x - x_1) + \left[\frac{\partial z}{\partial y}\right]_P (y - y_1).$$

More generally, let the equation of the surface be given in the implicit form

(3) $$F(x, y, z) = 0.$$

We may imagine equation (3) solved for z, and may then write the equation of the tangent plane by (2). Substituting for $\dfrac{\partial z}{\partial x}$ and $\dfrac{\partial z}{\partial y}$ the values given by (2) and (3) of § 226, and clearing of fractions, we find

(4) $$\left[\frac{\partial F}{\partial x}\right]_P (x - x_1) + \left[\frac{\partial F}{\partial y}\right]_P (y - y_1) + \left[\frac{\partial F}{\partial z}\right]_P (z - z_1) = 0.$$

228. Normal line. The *normal* to a surface at a point P is the line through P perpendicular to the tangent plane.

It will be recalled from solid analytic geometry that the direction cosines of any line perpendicular to the plane

$$Ax + By + Cz + D = 0$$

are *proportional to the coefficients* A, B, C. Hence, since the normal is perpendicular to the tangent plane (4), § 227, we have at once the following theorem.

THEOREM: *The direction cosines of the normal to the surface*

$$F(x, y, z) = 0$$

at a point are proportional to the values of $\dfrac{\partial F}{\partial x}, \dfrac{\partial F}{\partial y}, \dfrac{\partial F}{\partial z}$ *at that point.*

This theorem is fundamental in the geometry of surfaces.

By analytic geometry, the equations of a line through (x_1, y_1, z_1) with direction cosines proportional to a, b, c are

(1) $$\frac{x - x_1}{a} = \frac{y - y_1}{b} = \frac{z - z_1}{c}.$$

From this the equations of the normal at any point may be written down at once.

Example: Find the tangent plane and normal line to the sphere

(2) $$x^2 + y^2 + z^2 = a^2$$

at any point P: (x_1, y_1, z_1) on the surface.

With
$$F(x, y, z) = x^2 + y^2 + z^2 - a^2 = 0,$$
we have
$$\frac{\partial F}{\partial x} = 2x, \qquad \frac{\partial F}{\partial y} = 2y, \qquad \frac{\partial F}{\partial z} = 2z,$$
or at P,
$$\left[\frac{\partial F}{\partial x}\right]_P = 2x_1, \qquad \left[\frac{\partial F}{\partial y}\right]_P = 2y_1, \qquad \left[\frac{\partial F}{\partial z}\right]_P = 2z_1.$$

Substituting in (4), § 227, and simplifying, we find
$$x_1 x + y_1 y + z_1 z = x_1^2 + y_1^2 + z_1^2,$$
or, since the coördinates of P satisfy (2),
$$x_1 x + y_1 y + z_1 z = a^2.$$

By the theorem and equations (1) above, the equations of the normal are
$$\frac{x - x_1}{x_1} = \frac{y - y_1}{y_1} = \frac{z - z_1}{z_1}.$$

These equations may be simplified (Ex. 20 below).

EXERCISES

In Exs. 1–13, find the equation of the tangent plane and the equations of the normal line at the given point.

1. The ellipsoid $x^2 + 4y^2 + z^2 = 36$ at $(2, -2, 4)$. Draw the figure.
$$Ans. \ x - 4y + 2z = 18; \ \frac{x - 2}{1} = \frac{y + 2}{-4} = \frac{z - 4}{2}.$$

2. The cone $x^2 + 2z^2 = y^2$ at $(1, 3, -2)$.
$$Ans. \ \text{Tangent plane: } x = 3y + 4z.$$

3. The paraboloid $z = xy$ at $(3, 4, 12)$.
$$Ans. \ \text{Normal: } \frac{x - 3}{4} = \frac{y - 4}{3} = \frac{z - 12}{-1}.$$

4. The paraboloid $z = x^2 - y^2$ at $(3, 3, 0)$.
$$Ans. \ \text{Tangent plane: } z = 6(x - y).$$

5. The hyperboloid $x^2 - 3y^2 - z^2 + 3 = 0$ at $(2, 1, -2)$.
$$Ans. \ \text{Normal: } \frac{x - 2}{2} = \frac{y - 1}{-3} = \frac{z + 2}{2}.$$

6. The paraboloid $4z = x^2 + 4y^2$ at $(2, 1, 2)$. Draw the figure.
$$Ans. \ \text{Tangent plane: } x + 2y - 2z = 0.$$

7. The cylinder $y^2 = 4ax$ at $(a, 2a, a)$. Draw the figure.
$$Ans. \ x - y + a = 0; \ \frac{x - a}{1} = \frac{y - 2a}{-1} = \frac{z - a}{0}.$$

8. The paraboloid $yz = x$ at the origin.   *Ans.* $x = 0; y = z = 0.$

9. The cubic surface $xy^2 + 3x - z^2 = 4$ at $(2, 1, -2)$.
$$\text{\textit{Ans.} Tangent plane: } x + y + z = 1.$$

10. The surface $y = x(2z - 1)$ at $(4, 4, 1)$.

11. The paraboloid $Ax^2 + Cz^2 = 2Gy$ at (x_1, y_1, z_1).
$$\text{\textit{Ans.} Tangent plane: } Ax_1x + Cz_1z = G(y + y_1).$$

12. The cylinder $Ax^2 + Cz^2 = 1$ at (x_1, y_1, z_1).
$$\text{\textit{Ans.} Tangent plane: } Ax_1x + Cz_1z = 1.$$

13. The quadric surface $Ax^2 + By^2 + Cz^2 = K$ at (x_1, y_1, z_1).
$$\text{\textit{Ans.} Tangent plane: } Ax_1x + By_1y + Cz_1z = K.$$

14. Find the equations of the tangent at the point $(1, 2, 2)$ to the circle $x^2 + y^2 + z^2 = 9$, $x + y + z = 5$; draw the figure.

15. Find the equations of the tangent at the point $(1, 1, 1)$ to the ellipse $x^2 + y^2 = 2z^2$, $x + y + 2z = 4$.

16. Show that the surfaces $x^2 - y^2 + 4z^2 = 1$ and $x^2 - y^2 + 2(z + 1)^2 = 5$ are tangent at the point $(1, 2, 1)$.

17. Show that the sphere $x^2 + y^2 + z^2 = 2a^2$ and the hyperbolic cylinder $xy = a^2$ are tangent to each other at the point $(a, a, 0)$. Draw the figure.

18. Show that the surfaces $2x^2 + 2y^2 - z^2 = 25$, $x^2 + y^2 = 5z$ are tangent to each other at $(4, 3, 5)$. Draw the figure.

19. Prove that the tetrahedron formed by the coördinate planes and a tangent plane to the surface $xyz = a^3$ is of constant volume.

20. Prove that every normal to a sphere passes through the center.

21. State and prove a converse of the theorem of Ex. 20.

22. Two surfaces are said to intersect at right angles (or be perpendicular to each other) at a common point P if their normals at P intersect at right angles. Prove that two surfaces

$$F(x, y, z) = 0, \quad G(x, y, z) = 0$$

intersect at right angles at P if

$$\left[\frac{\partial F}{\partial x}\right]_P \cdot \left[\frac{\partial G}{\partial x}\right]_P + \left[\frac{\partial F}{\partial y}\right]_P \cdot \left[\frac{\partial G}{\partial y}\right]_P + \left[\frac{\partial F}{\partial z}\right]_P \cdot \left[\frac{\partial G}{\partial z}\right]_P = 0.$$

23. Prove that the ellipsoid $2x^2 + y^2 + z^2 = 7$ and the cylinder $y^2 = 4x$ are perpendicular to each other at $(1, 2, 1)$. (Ex. 22.)

24. Prove that the paraboloid $2x^2 + y^2 = 6az + 6a^2$ and the cone $z^2 = xy$ intersect at right angles at $(a, 4a, 2a)$.

25. Determine a and b so as to make the paraboloid $y = ax^2 + bz^2$ perpendicular to the ellipsoid $x^2 + y^2 + 2z^2 = 7$ at the point $(1, 2, 1)$.
$$\text{\textit{Ans.} } a = 3, b = -1.$$

26. Determine b and c so as to make the surfaces $x^2 = by + cz$ and $x^2 + y^2 = 2z(y - 4) + 25$ perpendicular at the point $(3, -2, 1)$.
$$\text{\textit{Ans.} } b = -4, c = 1.$$

27. Find the angle between the sphere $x^2 + y^2 + z^2 = 14$ and the ellipsoid $3x^2 + 2y^2 + z^2 = 20$ at the point $(1, 2, 3)$.   *Ans.* $23° 33'.$

CHAPTER *30* DOUBLE INTEGRALS

229. Volume under a surface. The method employed in § 163 for finding the volume of a solid succeeds only when the solid can be cut into slices such that the area of the face of each slice is

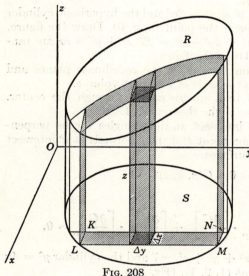

known. We proceed to develop a method that is free of this restriction.

Consider the solid bounded by a portion R of the surface

$$z = f(x, y), \qquad z \geqq 0,$$

the area S into which R projects in the xy-plane, and the vertical cylinder through the boundaries of S and R. We may compute the volume V of this solid as follows.

FIG. 208

Draw in S a set of n lines parallel to the y-axis and a set of m lines parallel to the x-axis, thus dividing S into rectangles of area $\Delta y \, \Delta x$, together with a number of irregular portions around the boundary. By passing through each line of the two sets a plane perpendicular to the xy-plane we divide V into vertical rectangular columns, together with smaller irregular columns. The upper boundary of each rectangular column is a portion of the surface R.

Through that point of the upper boundary of each column which is nearest the xy-plane, pass a horizontal plane, thus forming a set of rectangular prisms lying wholly within V. As Δx and Δy both approach 0, the *limit of the sum* of all these prisms is the volume under the surface:*

(1)
$$V = \lim_{\substack{\Delta x \to 0 \\ \Delta y \to 0}} \sum_{i=1}^{n} \sum_{j=1}^{m} f(x_i, y_j) \, \Delta y \, \Delta x.$$

From the critical standpoint this formula, based directly on our intuitive conception of volume, may be regarded as a *definition*, analogous to the definition of area in § 65. The definition is valid whenever the limit exists. If z is a continuous function, existence of the limit can be proved.

230. Volume found by integration. The "double limit" (1) above may be evaluated by two successive applications of the theorem of § 65, as follows.

Let us fix our attention on the rectangle $KLMN$ in S (Fig. 208), keeping x and Δx constant for the time being. The volume $\Delta V_i'$ whose base is this rectangle may be found by adding the volumes of all the included elementary prisms and then taking the limit as Δy approaches zero. Hence, by § 65,

$$\Delta V_i' = \lim_{m \to \infty} \sum_{j=1}^{m} f(x_i, y_j) \, \Delta y \, \Delta x = \left[\int_{y_i'}^{y_i''} f(x_i, y) \, dy \right] \Delta x.$$

In the expression for $\Delta V_i'$ the coefficient of Δx is a function of x_i alone, since the limits y_i' and y_i'' are functions of x_i alone. Thus we may apply again the theorem of § 65, and find that the required volume under the surface $z = f(x, y)$ is

$$V = \lim_{n \to \infty} \sum_{i=1}^{n} \left[\int_{y_i'}^{y_i''} f(x_i, y) \, dy \right] \Delta x = \int_{a}^{b} \left[\int_{y'}^{y''} f(x, y) \, dy \right] dx,$$

where a and b are the extreme values of x on the boundary of S.

The quantity just found is usually written without the brackets:

(1)
$$V = \int_{a}^{b} \int_{y'}^{y''} f(x, y) \, dy \, dx.$$

* This is illustrated by the common sawmill practice of cutting slabs and edgings into lath or other thin, narrow boards. By reducing the width and thickness of the product the volume of waste is reduced toward the ideal limit zero.

It is called a *double integral*, or more properly an *iterated integral*, being merely an integral of an integral. It is to be noted that *the inner integral sign belongs with the inner differential*, and that *during the integration with respect to y, x remains constant*. Further, the first or inner limits of integration are in general variables, but the outer limits are always constants.

Of course we might integrate first with respect to x, then with respect to y. The same reasoning as before would lead to the formula

$$(2) \qquad V = \int_c^d \int_{x'}^{x''} f(x, y) \; dx \; dy,$$

y remaining constant during the first integration. The change from (1) to (2) is called *inverting the order* of integration.

In the foregoing argument, we have assumed our solid to be divided into rectangular columns perpendicular to the xy-plane. Sometimes, however, it is more convenient to erect columns perpendicular to one of the other coördinate planes. Such variations offer no difficulty provided the geometric meaning of the successive integrations be kept clearly in mind. In every problem, a sketch of the required volume should be made, and the double integral built up by inspection of the figure.

Any function $f(x, y)$ of two independent variables may be interpreted as the z-coördinate of a variable point on a surface. If, then, in any problem, we can express the required quantity as a double limit of the form (1), § 229, *no matter what may be the geometric or physical meaning of the given function $f(x, y)$*, the limit may be evaluated by an iterated integration (1) or (2). Thus the method described above is by no means confined to the determination of volumes—it applies to a great variety of problems.

Example (a): Find the volume in the first octant bounded by the plane $z = 2 - x - y$ and the cylinder $y = 1 - x^2$. (Fig. 209.)

By means of planes parallel to the yz-plane, cut the solid into thin slabs. Then, by planes parallel to the zx-plane, cross-cut the slabs into slender vertical columns of base $dy \, dx$, height z, volume $z \, dy \, dx$. (Since we are intending to integrate first with respect to y, we write $z \, dy \, dx$ rather than $z \, dx \, dy$.) In the first integration, adding up all the columns in the slab, x remains constant, and y varies from 0 (at P) to $1 - x^2$ (at Q). The second integration adds up all the slabs, from $x = 0$ (at O) to $x = 1$ (at A):

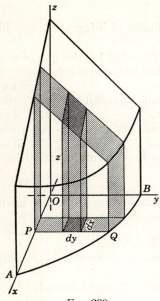

FIG. 209

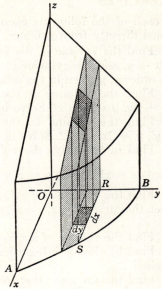

FIG. 210

$$V = \int_0^1 \int_0^{1-x^2} z \, dy \, dx$$

$$= \int_0^1 \int_0^{1-x^2} (2 - x - y) \, dy \, dx$$

$$= -\tfrac{1}{2} \int_0^1 \left[(2 - x - y)^2 \right]_0^{1-x^2} dx$$

$$= -\tfrac{1}{2} \int_0^1 \left[(1 - x + x^2)^2 - (2 - x)^2 \right] dx = \tfrac{49}{60}.$$

Example (b): Solve Example (a) by a second method.

Cut the solid into slabs by planes parallel to the zx-plane, the slabs into columns by planes parallel to the yz-plane (Fig. 210). In the first integration, x varies from 0 (at R) to $\sqrt{1 - y}$ (at S); then y varies from 0 (at O) to 1(at B):

$$V = \int_0^1 \int_0^{\sqrt{1-y}} z \, dx \, dy = \int_0^1 \int_0^{\sqrt{1-y}} (2 - x - y) \, dx \, dy$$

$$= -\tfrac{1}{2} \int_0^1 \left[(2 - x - y)^2 \right]_0^{\sqrt{1-y}} dy$$

$$= -\tfrac{1}{2} \int_0^1 \left[(2 - \sqrt{1 - y} - y)^2 - (2 - y)^2 \right] dy = \tfrac{49}{60}.$$

EXERCISES

In each of the following exercises, the limits of integration should be obtained directly from a figure.

1. Find the volume in the first octant bounded by the planes $x = 1$, $z = 2x + y$, and the cylinder $y^2 = x$. Solve in two ways, integrating once in the order x, y, then in the order y, x.   *Ans.* $\frac{21}{20}$.

2. Find the volume in the first octant bounded by the surfaces $z = 1 + xy$, $y = 1 - x^2$. Solve in two ways.   *Ans.* $\frac{3}{4}$.

3. Find the volume in the first octant bounded by the surfaces $z = xy^2$, $y = 2x$, $y = 2$. Solve in two ways.   *Ans.* $\frac{4}{5}$.

4. Find in two ways the volume in the first octant bounded by the surfaces $az = x^2 + 2ay$, $y = x$, $x = a$.   *Ans.* $\dfrac{7a^3}{12}$.

5. Find the volume of a cylindrical column having as its base the area between the curves $y = x$, $y = x^2$, and cut off by the plane $x - y - z + 1 = 0$.   *Ans.* $\frac{11}{60}$.

6. Find the volume of a sphere by double integration.

7. Find by double integration the volume of a segment of an elliptic paraboloid.

8. Find in two ways the volume in the first octant bounded by the surfaces $yz = ax$, $y^2 = az$, $z = a$.   *Ans.* $\frac{1}{6}a^3$.

9. Find the volume in the first octant bounded by the surfaces $y^2 + z^2 = ax$, $2y + z = 2a$.   *Ans.* $\frac{5}{6}a^3$.

10. Find in two ways the volume in the first octant bounded by the surfaces $z = x^2y$, $y^2 = x$, $y = x^2$.   *Ans.* $\frac{3}{56}$.

11. Find the volume in the first octant bounded by the surfaces $az = xy$, $x^2 = 4ay$, $x - y = a$.   *Ans.* $\frac{1}{24}a^3$.

12. Find the volume under the surface $az = xy$, whose base is the area in the xy-plane bounded by the curves $y^2 = ax$, $x + y = 2a$, $y = 0$.

13. Find in two ways the volume in the first octant under the plane $x + z = 1$, cut off by the surface $x^2 + y + z = 4$.   *Ans.* $\frac{7}{4}$.

14. Find the volume in the first octant bounded by the surfaces $y^2 + az = a^2$, $y^2 + z^2 = ax$. Solve in two ways.   *Ans.* $\frac{2}{7}a^3$.

15. Find the volume inclosed by the surfaces $az = y^2 + ax$, $y = x$, $x + y = 2a$, $y = 0$, $z = 0$.   *Ans.* $\frac{7}{6}a^3$.

16. Find the volume inclosed by the surfaces $az = y^2 + ax$, $x + y = 2a$, $y = x$, $x = 0$, $z = 0$.   *Ans.* $\frac{3}{2}a^3$.

17. Find the volume bounded by the coördinate planes and the surface $x^{\frac{1}{2}} + y^{\frac{1}{2}} + z^{\frac{1}{2}} = a^{\frac{1}{2}}$.   *Ans.* $\frac{1}{90}a^3$.

18. Find the entire volume inside the surface $x^{\frac{2}{3}} + y^{\frac{2}{3}} + z^{\frac{2}{3}} = a^{\frac{2}{3}}$.
    Ans. $\frac{4}{35}\pi a^3$.

19. Find the centroid of the solid in the first octant bounded by the surfaces $az = x^2 + y^2$, $y = x$, $x = a$.   *Ans.* $(\frac{4}{5}a, \frac{9}{20}a, \frac{7}{15}a)$.

20. Find the centroid of the solid in Ex. 2.

21. Find the centroid of the solid in Ex. 3.

22. Solve each part of Ex. 21 by a second method.

23. In Ex. 3, find the moment of inertia with respect to the z-axis.

24. Find the centroid of the solid in Ex. 10.

25. Find the centroid of the solid bounded by the surfaces $z = 0$, $z = x$, $y = x$, $x^2 = ay$. *Ans.* $(\frac{3}{5}a, \frac{1}{2}a, \frac{3}{10}a)$.

26. Solve each part of Ex. 25 by a second method.

27. In Ex. 25, find the moment of inertia with respect to the z-axis.

28. Show that when an area in the xy-plane rotates about the x-axis, the volume generated is

$$V = 2\pi \int_a^b \int_{y'}^{y''} y \, dy \, dx.$$

29. In Ex. 28, show that the result of the first integration is either the circular disk or the cylindrical shell, depending on the order of integration.

231. The double integral. Being given a function f of two independent variables, defined at all points of a plane region S, let us divide S into k elements ΔS_i ($i = 1, 2, \cdots, k$) in such a way that as k increases and ΔS_i approaches zero, the maximum distance between any two points on the boundary of ΔS_i approaches zero— *i.e.*, the elements ΔS_i are *infinitesimal of the second order*. Multiply the area ΔS_i of each element by the value f_i of the function at some point of ΔS_i, add all these products together, and take the limit of the sum. This limit is called the *double integral of f over the region S*, and is denoted by the symbol $\int_S\!\!\int f \, dS$:

$$(1) \qquad \lim_{k \to \infty} \sum_{i=1}^k f_i \, \Delta S_i = \int_S\!\!\int f \, dS.$$

Let us take a moment to tie this up with the argument of § 229. There, the independent variables were the Cartesian coördinates (x, y) of any point in S; the equation

$$z = f(x, y)$$

represented a surface in space; the elements of area ΔS were rectangles $\Delta y \, \Delta x$; and, since we took m cutting planes in one direction and n in the other, the number of elements was $k = mn$.

It is clear that the double in-

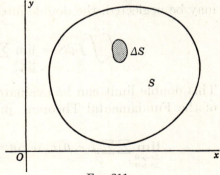

FIG. 211

tegral, like the "iterated" integral $\int_a^b \int_{y'}^{y''} f(x, y) \, dy \, dx$, may always be interpreted as the volume under a surface. Since this volume, for a given surface and given base S, is a definite fixed quantity, the value of a double integral is *independent of the mode of division* of S into elements, so long as the longest chord in every ΔS approaches zero.

Whenever the double integral exists, the iterated integral also exists, and gives us one means of evaluating the double integral. However, the latter does not tie us down to a particular coördinate system, or to any particular mode of division of S. We shall take advantage of this in the next section.

232. The double integral in polar coördinates. Let S be a plane area bounded by a curve whose equation is given in polar

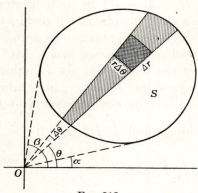

coördinates. We may divide S into elements ΔS by means of concentric circular arcs and radial lines, as in the figure. Then ΔS is the difference between two circular sectors of angle $\Delta \theta$ and radii r and $r + \Delta r$ respectively: *i.e.*,

$$\Delta S = \tfrac{1}{2}(r + \Delta r)^2 \, \Delta \theta - \tfrac{1}{2} r^2 \, \Delta \theta$$

$$= r \, \Delta r \, \Delta \theta + \tfrac{1}{2} \, \overline{\Delta r^2} \, \Delta \theta.$$

Fig. 212

Let $f(r, \theta)$ be a function of the polar coördinates defined at all points of S. Then, since the infinitesimal of higher order $\tfrac{1}{2} \, \overline{\Delta r^2} \, \Delta \theta$ may be neglected, the double integral of § 231 appears as

$$\int_S \int f \, dS = \lim_{\substack{\Delta r \to 0 \\ \Delta \theta \to 0}} \sum \sum f(r, \theta) r \, \Delta r \, \Delta \theta.$$

This double limit can be evaluated by two successive applications of the Fundamental Theorem, just as in § 230; the result is

$$\lim_{\substack{\Delta r \to 0 \\ \Delta \theta \to 0}} \sum \sum f(r, \theta) r \, \Delta r \, \Delta \theta = \int_\alpha^\beta \int_{r'}^{r''} f(r, \theta) r \, dr \, d\theta,$$

where α, β are the least and greatest values of θ (Fig. 212), and r', r'' are the least and greatest values of r in the typical sector— α and β constant, r' and r'' functions of θ, in general.

233. Plane area as a double integral. If in § 231 we take the function f as unity everywhere in S, the double integral $\int_S\!\!\int f\, dS$ reduces to $\int_S\!\!\int dS$. Since this is merely the limit of the sum of all the elements ΔS, the result is the area A of the region S itself:

$$A = \int_S\!\!\int dS.$$

In Cartesian coördinates,

$$A = \int_a^b \int_{y'}^{y''} dy\, dx = \int_c^d \int_{x'}^{x''} dx\, dy;$$

in polar coördinates,

$$A = \int_\alpha^\beta \int_{r'}^{r''} r\, dr\, d\theta.$$

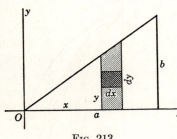

Fig. 213

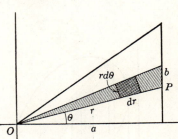

Fig. 214

Example (a): Find the area of a right triangle by double integration in Cartesian coördinates. (Fig. 213.)

The equation of the bounding line is

$$y = \frac{b}{a}x;$$

therefore

$$A = \int_0^a \int_0^{\frac{b}{a}x} dy\, dx = \int_0^a \Big[y \Big]_0^{\frac{b}{a}x} dx$$
$$= \frac{b}{a}\int_0^a x\, dx = \frac{1}{2}ab.$$

Example (b): Solve Example (a) in polar coördinates.

The upper limit for r is seen from Fig. 214 to be*

---

* Or, we may transform the equation $x = a$ to polar coördinates: $x = r \cos \theta = a$, $r = a \sec \theta$.

$$OP = a \sec \theta,$$

so that

$$A = \int_0^{\text{Arctan}\frac{b}{a}} \int_0^{a \sec \theta} r \, dr \, d\theta = \tfrac{1}{2}a^2 \int_0^{\text{Arctan}\frac{b}{a}} \sec^2 \theta \, d\theta$$

$$= \frac{1}{2}a^2 \Big[\tan \theta \Big]_0^{\text{Arctan}\frac{b}{a}} = \frac{1}{2}a^2 \cdot \frac{b}{a} = \frac{1}{2}ab.$$

234. Volume in cylindrical coördinates. Let (Fig. 215)

$$z = f(r, \theta)$$

be the equation of a surface in cylindrical coördinates (polar co-ordinates in the xy-plane with the Cartesian z). To find the volume under any portion of this surface, divide the base into polar ele-

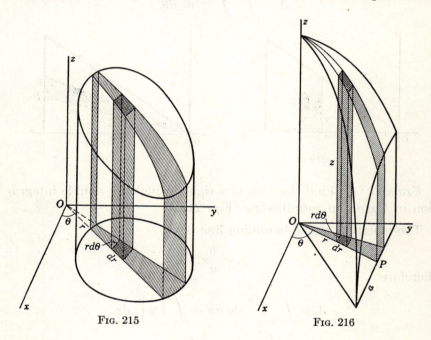

Fig. 215   Fig. 216

ments $r \, dr \, d\theta$ and erect on each element a column of height z, volume $zr \, dr \, d\theta$. Then the volume desired is the double integral over S:

$$V = \lim_{\substack{\Delta r \to 0 \\ \Delta\theta \to 0}} \sum\sum zr \, \Delta r \, \Delta\theta = \int_\alpha^\beta \int_{r'}^{r''} zr \, dr \, d\theta.$$

Example: Find the volume lying above the triangle bounded by the lines $x = 0$, $y = x$, $y = a$, and cut off by the surface

(1) $$x^2 + y^2 + az = 2a^2.$$

In cylindrical coördinates (1) becomes

$$r^2 + az = 2a^2;$$

the upper limit OP for r is found from

$$y = r \sin \theta = a,$$

so that

$$V = \frac{1}{a} \int_{\frac{\pi}{4}}^{\frac{\pi}{2}} \int_0^{a \csc \theta} (2a^2 - r^2) r \, dr \, d\theta$$

$$= \frac{1}{a} \int_{\frac{\pi}{4}}^{\frac{\pi}{2}} \left[a^2 r^2 - \frac{1}{4} r^4 \right]_0^{a \csc \theta} d\theta$$

$$= a^3 \int_{\frac{\pi}{4}}^{\frac{\pi}{2}} (\csc^2 \theta - \tfrac{1}{4} \csc^4 \theta) \, d\theta = \tfrac{2}{3} a^3.$$

EXERCISES

Solve Exs. 1–6 by iterated integration in rectangular coördinates.

1. Find the area of a circle.

2. Find the area between the cubic $xy^2 = a^3$ and the lines $y = a$ and $x = 0$.

3. Check the answer to Ex. 2 by inverting the order of integration.

4. Find the area bounded by the parabola $y^2 = 4ax$ and its latus rectum.

5. Check the answer to Ex. 3 by inverting the order of integration.

6. Find the area between the curves $x^2 = 2ay$, $x^2 = 4ay - a^2$.

                                                    Ans. $\tfrac{1}{3} a^2$.

Solve Exs. 7–10 by iterated integration in polar coördinates.

7. Find the area of the curve $r = a(1 - \cos \theta)$.   *Ans.* $\tfrac{3}{2} \pi a^2$.

8. Find the area of the curve $r = a(2 - \sin \theta)$.   *Ans.* $\tfrac{9}{2} \pi a^2$.

9. Find the area of the curve $r = 2a \cos^2 \theta$.   *Ans.* $\tfrac{3}{2} \pi a^2$.

10. Find the area of the curve $r^2 = a^2 \sin 2\theta$.   *Ans.* a^2.

In Exs. 11–34, use cylindrical coördinates.

11. Find the volume of a sphere.

12. A round hole of radius b is bored through the center of a sphere of radius a. Find the volume cut out.   *Ans.* $\dfrac{4\pi}{3} \left[a^3 - (a^2 - b^2)^{\frac{3}{2}} \right].$

13. Find the volume above the xy-plane, inside the cylinder $x^2 + y^2 = a^2$ and below the paraboloid $x^2 + y^2 = az$.   *Ans.* $\frac{1}{2}\pi a^3$.

14. Find the volume above the xy-plane common to the paraboloid $x^2 + y^2 + az = 4a^2$ and the cylinder $x^2 + y^2 = a^2$.   *Ans.* $\frac{7}{2}\pi a^3$.

15. Find the volume inside the cylinder $x^2 + y^2 = a^2$ and outside the cone $x^2 + y^2 = z^2$.   *Ans.* $\frac{4}{3}\pi a^3$.

16. Find the volume above the xy-plane bounded by the surfaces $x^2 + y^2 = a^2$, $z = y$, $z = 0$. (Examples, § 163.)   *Ans.* $\frac{2}{3}a^3$.

17. Find the volume in the first octant inside the cylinder $y^2 + z^2 = a^2$ and outside the cylinder $y^2 = ax$.   *Ans.* $\frac{1}{16}\pi a^3$.

18. Find the volume in the first octant bounded by the surfaces $y = x$, $x = a$, $xy = az$.   *Ans.* $\frac{1}{8}a^3$.

19. Find the volume in the first octant bounded by the surfaces $y = x$, $x = a$, $2az = x^2 + y^2$.   *Ans.* $\frac{1}{6}a^3$.

20. Find the volume in the first octant bounded by the surfaces $y = x$, $z = x$, $ay = x^2$.   *Ans.* $\frac{1}{12}a^3$.

21. Find the volume in the first octant bounded by the cylinder $x^2 + z^2 = a^2$ and the plane $x - y + z = 0$.   *Ans.* $\frac{2}{3}a^3$.

22. Find the volume inside the cylinder $x^2 + z^2 = 4a^2$ and outside the hyperboloid $x^2 + z^2 - y^2 = a^2$.   *Ans.* $4\sqrt{3}\,\pi a^3$.

23. Find the volume inside the cylinder $y^2 + z^2 = a^2$ and outside the hyperboloid $x^2 - y^2 - z^2 = a^2$.   *Ans.* $\frac{4}{3}\pi(2\sqrt{2} - 1)a^3$.

24. A square hole of side $2a$ whose axis is the z-axis is cut through the paraboloid of Ex. 14. Find the volume cut out.   *Ans.* $\frac{40}{3}a^3$.

25. A vertical cylinder is passed through the circle $r = a\cos\theta$. Find the volume of the cylinder inside a sphere of radius a with center at the origin.   *Ans.* $\frac{2}{3}(\pi - \frac{4}{3})a^3$.

26. Find the volume bounded by the surfaces $z = 0$, $x = 0$, $y = x$, $y = a$, $y^2 = a(z - x)$.   *Ans.* $\frac{5}{12}a^3$.

27. In Ex. **13**, find the centroid of that part of the solid that lies in the first octant.   *Ans.* $\left(\dfrac{8a}{5\pi}, \dfrac{8a}{5\pi}, \dfrac{a}{3}\right)$.

28. In Ex. **13**, find the moment of inertia with respect to the z-axis.   *Ans.* $\frac{2}{3}Ma^2$.

29. Find the centroid of half of a circular cone.   *Ans.* $\left(\dfrac{a}{\pi}, 0, \dfrac{h}{4}\right)$.

30. Find the moment of inertia of a sphere with respect to a diameter.

31. Find the centroid of one octant of a sphere.   *Ans.* $(\frac{3}{8}a, \frac{3}{8}a, \frac{3}{8}a)$.

32. In Ex. **15**, find the centroid of the volume lying in the first octant.   *Ans.* $\left(\dfrac{3a}{2\pi}, \dfrac{3a}{2\pi}, \dfrac{3a}{8}\right)$.

33. Find the centroid of the volume in the first octant bounded by the surfaces $y = x$, $x = a$, $zx = ay$.   *Ans.* $(\frac{2}{3}a, \frac{4}{9}a, \frac{1}{3}a)$.

34. In Ex. **33**, find the moment of inertia with respect to the z-axis.   *Ans.* $\frac{3}{16}a^5$.

35. Show that when an area bounded by the curve $r = f(\theta)$ rotates about the polar axis, the volume generated is

$$V = 2\pi \int_{\alpha}^{\beta} \int_{r'}^{r''} r^2 \sin\theta \, dr \, d\theta.$$

In Exs. 36–42, use the method of Ex. 35.

36. Find the volume of a sphere.

37. Find the volume of a circular cone.

38. Find the volume generated by revolving the cardioid $r = a(1 - \sin\theta)$ about its line of symmetry. *Ans.* $\frac{8}{3}\pi a^3$.

39. The curve $r^2 = a^2 \sin\theta$ revolves about the y-axis. Find the volume generated. *Ans.* $\frac{8}{15}\pi a^3$.

40. Find the volume of a torus.

41. Find the volume cut from a sphere by one sheet of a cone of half-angle α with its vertex at the center of the sphere. *Ans.* $\frac{2}{3}\pi a^3(1 - \cos\alpha)$.

42. Find the centroid of a circular cone.

235. Evaluation by inversion of order. We have seen that inversion of the order of integration frequently affords a useful check on the value of an iterated integral. There are important integrals which cannot be evaluated in terms of elementary functions, as they stand, but which yield to elementary methods, when the order of integration is inverted.

Example: Evaluate $\int_0^1 \int_x^1 e^{y^2} \, dy \, dx.$

Here the first integration is impossible by elementary methods. We shall invert the order of integration. The inner integration runs from $y = x$ to $y = 1$; the outer one from $x = 0$ to $x = 1$. Therefore, the integration covers the triangle bounded by $x = 0$, $y = x$, $y = 1$ (Fig. 217). The integrand is unaffected by a change of order of integration. Hence,

$$\int_0^1 \int_x^1 e^{y^2} \, dy \, dx = \int_0^1 \int_0^y e^{y^2} \, dx \, dy$$

$$= \int_0^1 \left[xe^{y^2} \right]_0^y dy$$

$$= \int_0^1 ye^{y^2} \, dy$$

$$= \left[\tfrac{1}{2}e^{y^2} \right]_0^1$$

$$= \tfrac{1}{2}(e - 1).$$

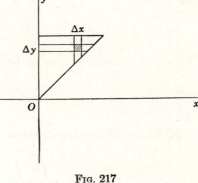

Fɪɢ. 217

236. Evaluation by change of coördinate system. An integration impossible, by elementary methods, in rectangular coördinates, may become possible (even simple) in polar coördinates, or vice versa. We shall use two examples, of which the second is of vital importance in many advanced applications of mathematics to engineering and physics.

Example (a): Evaluate $\displaystyle\int_0^a \int_0^{\sqrt{a^2-x^2}} \sqrt{x^2 + y^2}\, dy\, dx.$

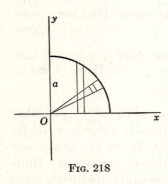

FIG. 218

Here we can perform the first integration, but not the second one, by elementary means. The integration runs from $y = 0$ to $y = \sqrt{a^2 - x^2}$, then from $x = 0$ to $x = a$; that is, over the first quadrant of a circle of radius a, center at the origin. This suggests polar coördinates. The new element of area is $r\, dr\, d\theta$, and $\sqrt{x^2 + y^2}$ becomes r. Therefore,

$$\int_0^a \int_0^{\sqrt{a^2-x^2}} \sqrt{x^2 + y^2}\, dy\, dx = \int_0^{\frac{\pi}{2}} \int_0^a r \cdot r\, dr\, d\theta$$

$$= \int_0^{\frac{\pi}{2}} \tfrac{1}{3}a^3\, d\theta = \frac{\pi a^3}{6}.$$

Example (b): Evaluate $\displaystyle\int_0^\infty e^{-x^2}\, dx.$

This involves only a single integration, but a non-elementary one. Put

$$B = \int_0^\infty e^{-x^2}\, dx.$$

Then, of course, it is also true that

$$B = \int_0^\infty e^{-y^2}\, dy.$$

Now, consider the iterated integral

$$\int_0^\infty \int_0^\infty e^{-x^2-y^2}\, dx\, dy.$$

Since $e^{-x^2-y^2} = e^{-x^2} \cdot e^{-y^2}$, we may write

$$\int_0^\infty \int_0^\infty e^{-x^2-y^2}\, dx\, dy = \int_0^\infty \left[\int_0^\infty e^{-x^2}\, dx \right] e^{-y^2}\, dy$$

$$= B \int_0^\infty e^{-y^2}\, dy = B^2.$$

Hence

$$B^2 = \int_0^\infty \int_0^\infty e^{-x^2-y^2}\, dx\, dy.$$

The region of integration in this last integral is the entire first quadrant. Turning to polar coördinates, we find that the element of area is $r\, dr\, d\theta$ and the integrand is e^{-r^2}. Therefore,

$$B^2 = \int_0^{\frac{\pi}{2}} \int_0^\infty e^{-r^2}\, r\, dr\, d\theta$$

$$= \int_0^{\frac{\pi}{2}} \left[-\tfrac{1}{2}e^{-r^2} \right]_0^\infty d\theta$$

$$= \int_0^{\frac{\pi}{2}} \tfrac{1}{2}\, d\theta = \tfrac{1}{4}\pi.$$

Since $B^2 = \tfrac{1}{4}\pi$, and $B > 0$, $B = \tfrac{1}{2}\sqrt{\pi}$. That is,

$$\int_0^\infty e^{-x^2}\, dx = \frac{\sqrt{\pi}}{2}.$$

EXERCISES

In Exs. 1–9, evaluate the integrals by inverting the order of integration.

1. $\displaystyle\int_0^1 \int_y^1 \frac{y\, dx\, dy}{\sqrt{x^2+y^2}}$.   *Ans.* $\tfrac{1}{2}(\sqrt{2}-1)$.

2. $\displaystyle\int_0^1 \int_{2y}^2 y\sqrt{x^2+y^2}\, dx\, dy$.   *Ans.* $\tfrac{1}{6}(5\sqrt{5}-8)$.

3. $\displaystyle\int_0^1 \int_x^1 x(x^2+y^2)^{\frac{3}{2}}\, dy\, dx$.   *Ans.* $\tfrac{1}{30}(4\sqrt{2}-1)$.

4. $\displaystyle\int_0^1 \int_x^1 x \sin y^3\, dy\, dx$.   *Ans.* 0.077.

5. $\displaystyle\int_0^1 \int_y^{\sqrt{y}} \frac{\sin x}{x}\, dx\, dy$.   *Ans.* 0.159.

6. $\displaystyle\int_{-1}^{0}\int_{-x}^{1}\frac{x^2\,dy\,dx}{1+y^4}.$ *Ans.* 0.058.

7. $\displaystyle\int_{0}^{2}\int_{\frac{1}{2}y}^{1}\frac{dx\,dy}{(1+x^2)^3}.$ *Ans.* $\frac{3}{8}$.

8. $\displaystyle\int_{0}^{1}\int_{\sqrt{x}}^{1}\sqrt{1+y^3}\,dy\,dx.$ *Ans.* 0.406.

9. $\displaystyle\int_{0}^{4}\int_{\sqrt{y}}^{2}\frac{y\,dx\,dy}{\sqrt{1+x^5}}.$ *Ans.* 0.949.

In Exs. 10–18, evaluate by transforming to polar coördinates.

10. $\displaystyle\int_{0}^{1}\int_{0}^{\sqrt{1-x^2}}e^{-x^2-y^2}\,dy\,dx.$ *Ans.* $\dfrac{\pi(e-1)}{4e}$.

11. $\displaystyle\int_{0}^{1}\int_{0}^{\sqrt{1-x^2}}e^{x^2+y^2}\,dy\,dx.$ *Ans.* $\frac{1}{4}\pi(e-1)$.

12. Ex. 1. **13.** Ex. 2.
14. Ex. 3. **15.** Ex. 4.
16. The example of § 235.

17. $\displaystyle\int_{0}^{a}\int_{0}^{\sqrt{a^2-x^2}}x^2\sqrt{x^2+y^2}\,dy\,dx.$ *Ans.* $\dfrac{\pi a^5}{20}$.

18. $\displaystyle\int_{0}^{a}\int_{0}^{x}\frac{x^2\,dy\,dx}{\sqrt{x^2+y^2}}.$ *Ans.* $\dfrac{a^3}{3}\ln(1+\sqrt{2})$.

19. Evaluate $\displaystyle\int_{0}^{\frac{\pi}{2}}\int_{0}^{\sec\theta}\frac{r\,dr\,d\theta}{1+r^2\sin^2\theta}$ by transforming to rectangular co-ordinates. *Ans.* $\frac{1}{2}\pi$.

20. Use the result in Example (*b*), § 236, to evaluate

$$\int_{0}^{\infty}e^{-a^2x^2}\,dx,\text{ for }a>0.\qquad Ans.\ \frac{\sqrt{\pi}}{2a}.$$

21. Evaluate the integral in Ex. 20 for $a<0$. *Ans.* $\dfrac{-\sqrt{\pi}}{2a}$.

22. Find the volume generated by revolving about the *x*-axis the area between $y=e^{-x^2}$ and its asymptote. *Ans.* $2\left(\dfrac{\pi}{2}\right)^{\frac{3}{2}}$.

23. For the area of Ex. 22, find the moment of inertia with respect to *Oy*.

24. For the area of Ex. 22, find the moment of inertia with respect to *Ox*.

25. Evaluate $\int_0^\infty x^{-\frac{1}{2}} e^{-ax}\, dx$, for $a > 0$. Put $x = v^2$.   *Ans.* $\sqrt{\dfrac{\pi}{a}}$.

26. Evaluate $\int_0^\infty x^{\frac{1}{2}} e^{-ax}\, dx$, for $a > 0$.   *Ans.* $\frac{1}{2}\sqrt{\dfrac{\pi}{a^3}}$.

27. Evaluate $\int_0^1 \left(\ln \dfrac{1}{x}\right)^{\frac{1}{2}} dx$.   *Ans.* $\frac{1}{2}\sqrt{\pi}$.

237. Area of a surface. We have seen (§ 165) that the area of a surface of revolution may be found by simple integration. To find areas of curved surfaces in general, double integration is required.

Consider a region R on the surface

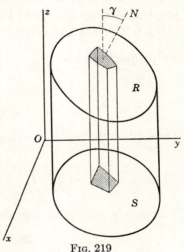

(1) $z = f(x, y)$.

Let us pass through the boundary of R a vertical cylinder, cutting from the xy-plane a region S—that is, S is the horizontal projection of R. Divide S into elements ΔS_i in any convenient way (§ 231), and denote by ΔR_i the portion of R lying above the i-th element. Draw the tangent plane at some point (any point) of ΔR_i, and denote by $\Delta R_i'$ the element of area (above ΔS_i) on the tangent plane. Now the

Fig. 219

two elements ΔR_i and $\Delta R_i'$, on the surface and on the tangent plane respectively, are sensibly equal—*i.e.*, they differ by infinitesimals of higher order—so that in taking the limit of the sum, we may *substitute the latter for the former.*[*]

It is known from geometry (or if not known, is easily established —Ex. 30 below) that if two planes intersect at an acute angle, an area in one plane may be projected into the other by multiplying by the cosine of the included angle. The angle between the xy-plane and the tangent plane equals the angle between their normals— *i.e.*, it is the angle between the z-axis and the normal to the surface at the point of contact of the tangent plane. Thus, if γ_i is the

---

[*] The questions that arise in justifying this statement analytically are exactly the same, in kind, as those that arose in § 164 when we replaced the element Δs_i on the curve by the element $\Delta s_i'$ on the tangent line. See the footnote, p. 302.

z-direction angle of the normal N_i,

$$\Delta R_i{'} \cos \gamma_i = \Delta S_i,$$

or

$$\Delta R_i{'} = \sec \gamma_i \, \Delta S_i.$$

Adding all the elements and taking the limit of the sum, we define the area R as

(2) $$R = \int_S \!\! \int \sec \gamma \; dS.$$

Of course if it is more convenient to project the area into the yz- or zx-plane, the same formula holds with α or β in place of γ.

By § 228, the direction cosines of the normal to the surface (1) are proportional to $-\dfrac{\partial z}{\partial x}$, $-\dfrac{\partial z}{\partial y}$, 1, so that

$$\cos \gamma = \frac{1}{\sqrt{\left(\dfrac{\partial z}{\partial x}\right)^2 + \left(\dfrac{\partial z}{\partial y}\right)^2 + 1}}.$$

Thus (2) becomes in Cartesian coördinates

(3) $$R = \int_a^b \int_{y'}^{y''} \sqrt{\left(\frac{\partial z}{\partial x}\right)^2 + \left(\frac{\partial z}{\partial y}\right)^2 + 1} \; dy \; dx.$$

Example (a): Find the area of the cylinder* (Fig. 220)

$$2az = 2a^2 - ax - y^2$$

intercepted in the first octant by the planes $y = x$, $y = a$. We find

$$\frac{\partial z}{\partial x} = -\frac{1}{2}, \qquad \frac{\partial z}{\partial y} = -\frac{y}{a}.$$

In the order x, y (which is in this case much the simpler),

$$\begin{aligned} R &= \int_0^a \int_0^y \sqrt{\frac{1}{4} + \frac{y^2}{a^2} + 1} \; dx \; dy \\ &= \frac{1}{2a} \int_0^a \int_0^y \sqrt{5a^2 + 4y^2} \; dx \; dy \\ &= \frac{1}{2a} \int_0^a \sqrt{5a^2 + 4y^2} \; y \; dy, \end{aligned}$$

---

* Sections by planes $y = k$ are easily seen to be parallel straight lines, the yz-trace is a parabola, so that the surface is a parabolic cylinder with generators parallel to the zx-plane.

so that

$$R = \frac{1}{16a} \cdot \frac{2}{3} \left[(5a^2 + 4y^2)^{\frac{3}{2}} \right]_0^a$$
$$= \frac{1}{24}(27 - 5^{\frac{3}{2}})a^2.$$

To use (2) in polar coördinates, we would usually work out sec γ in Cartesian coördinates and transform the result to the polar system.

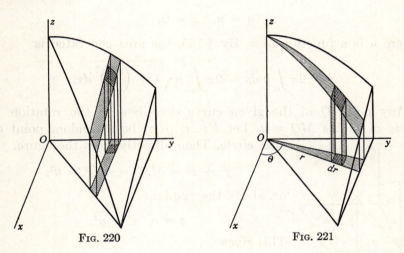

FIG. 220   FIG. 221

Example (*b*): Solve the problem above in polar coördinates.

Using the value of sec γ from Example (*a*), we have (Fig. 221)

$$R = \frac{1}{2a} \int_S \!\! \int \sqrt{5a^2 + 4y^2} \, dS$$

$$= \frac{1}{2a} \int_{\frac{\pi}{4}}^{\frac{\pi}{2}} \int_0^{a \csc \theta} \sqrt{5a^2 + 4r^2 \sin^2 \theta} \, r \, dr \, d\theta$$

$$= \frac{1}{16a} \cdot \frac{2}{3} \int_{\frac{\pi}{4}}^{\frac{\pi}{2}} \frac{\left[(5a^2 + 4r^2 \sin^2 \theta)^{\frac{3}{2}} \right]_0^{a \csc \theta}}{\sin^2 \theta} \, d\theta$$

$$= \frac{(27 - 5^{\frac{3}{2}})a^2}{24} \int_{\frac{\pi}{4}}^{\frac{\pi}{2}} \csc^2 \theta \, d\theta = \frac{(27 - 5^{\frac{3}{2}})a^2}{24}.$$

238. Surfaces of revolution. In § 165 we defined the area of a surface of revolution; in § 237 we defined curved area in general, including the former as a special case. Thus for the surface of revolution, area has been defined in two ways: obviously, this is allowable only if the two definitions are equivalent. It is interesting, and not difficult, to see how the general formula works out in the special case.

Let a surface of revolution be formed by revolving about Ox, from $x = a$ to $x = b$, the curve

$$y = u, \quad z = 0,$$

where u is a function of x. By § 165, the area generated is

$$S = 2\pi \int_C y \, ds = 2\pi \int_a^b u\sqrt{1 + \left(\frac{du}{dx}\right)^2} \, dx.$$

Any point Q of the given curve describes, in the rotation, a circle of radius $MQ = u$. Let $P: (x, y, z)$ be a random point of that circle. Then, directly from the figure,

$$y^2 + z^2 = \overline{MP}^2 = \overline{MQ}^2 = u^2,$$

or, above the xy-plane,

$$z = \sqrt{u^2 - y^2}.$$

This gives

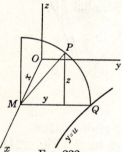

Fig. 222

$$\frac{\partial z}{\partial x} = \frac{u\dfrac{du}{dx}}{\sqrt{u^2 - y^2}}, \qquad \frac{\partial z}{\partial y} = \frac{-y}{\sqrt{u^2 - y^2}}.$$

Substituting in (3), § 237, and remembering that the first octant contains only one-fourth of the surface, we find after a trifle of simplifying

$$R = 4\int_a^b \int_0^u \frac{u\sqrt{1 + \left(\dfrac{du}{dx}\right)^2}}{\sqrt{u^2 - y^2}} \, dy \, dx$$

$$= 4\int_a^b u\sqrt{1 + \left(\frac{du}{dx}\right)^2} \left[\operatorname{Arcsin}\frac{y}{u}\right]_0^u dx$$

$$= 2\pi \int_a^b u\sqrt{1 + \left(\frac{du}{dx}\right)^2} \, dx = S.$$

EXERCISES

In Exs. 1–12, use rectangular coördinates.

1. Find the surface area of a sphere.

2. Find the area on the cylinder $y^2 + z^2 = a^2$ included between the planes $y = x$, $y = 3x$. 　　　　　　　　　　　　　　　*Ans.* $\frac{8}{3}a^2$.

3. Find the area of that part of the surface $az = ay + x^2$ lying above the xy-triangle bounded by the lines $y = 0, y = x, x = a$. 　*Ans.* $\frac{1}{12}(6^{\frac{3}{2}} - 2^{\frac{3}{2}})a^2$.

4. Find the area on the cylinder $x^2 + z^2 = a^2$ included between the planes $y = 0$, $y = mx$. 　　　　　　　　　　　　　*Ans.* $4ma^2$.

5. Solve Ex. 4, integrating in the other order.

6. Find the area of that part of the surface $9(z - y)^2 = 4x^3$ whose projection in the xy-plane is the triangle bounded by the lines $y = 0, y = x, x = 2$. 　　　　　　　　　　　　　*Ans.* $\frac{16}{15}(2 + \sqrt{2})$.

7. Solve Ex. 6, integrating in the other order.

8. Find the area cut off on the cylinder $y^2 + z^2 = a^2$ by the circular paraboloid $y^2 + z^2 = bx$. 　　　　　　　　　　*Ans.* $\dfrac{2\pi a^3}{b}$.

9. Find the area on the cylinder $z^2 = 4ax$ and inside the cylinder $y^2 = 4ax$, from $x = 0$ to $x = 3a$. 　　　　　　*Ans.* $\dfrac{112a^2}{3}$.

10. How much of the conical surface $z^2 = x^2 + y^2$ lies above a square of side $2a$ in the xy-plane whose center is the origin?

11. Find the area of that part of the surface $a^2z = a^2x + y^3$ intercepted in the first quadrant by the cylinder $y^3 = a^2x$ and the plane $y = a$. 　　　　　　　　　　　　　　　*Ans.* $\frac{1}{54}(11^{\frac{3}{2}} - 2^{\frac{3}{2}})a^2$.

12. A square hole of side $\sqrt{2}\,a$ is cut centrally through a sphere of radius a. Find the area cut from the surface of the sphere. 　*Ans.* $4\pi(\sqrt{2} - 1)a^2$.

In Exs. 13–20, use polar coördinates.

13. Ex. 1. 　　　　　　**14.** Ex. 2. 　　　　　　**15.** Ex. 3.
16. Ex. 4. 　　　　　　**17.** Ex. 8. 　　　　　　**18.** Ex. 9.

19. How much of the surface area of the hyperbolic paraboloid $az = xy$ lies within the cylinder $x^2 + y^2 = a^2$, in the first octant?

20. The center of a sphere of radius a is on the surface of a cylinder of diameter a. Find the surface area on the sphere cut out by the cylinder. 　　　　　　　*Ans.* $2(\pi - 2)a^2$.

21. A vertical cylinder is cut by a surface $z = f(x, y)$. Show that the area of the cylinder intercepted between the xy-plane and the cutting surface is

$$R = \int_C z \, ds,$$

where C is the horizontal projection of the curve of intersection.

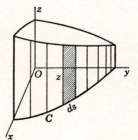

Fig. 223

In Exs. 22–29, use (or adapt) the formula of Ex. 21.

22. A woodsman chops halfway through a tree, the lower face of the cut being horizontal, the upper inclined at 45°. Find the area of bark cut out. (Examples, § 163.) *Ans.* $2a^2$.

23. Solve Ex. 22, integrating in the other order.

24. Solve Ex. 22 in polar coördinates.

25. Ex. 2. **26.** Ex. 8. **27.** Ex. 9.

28. In Ex. 20, find the surface area cut from the cylinder by the sphere.

29. A solid is bounded by two equal circular cylinders of radius a whose axes intersect at right angles. Find the total surface area of the solid. *Ans.* $16a^2$.

30. Two planes intersect at an angle α. (*a*) Given, in one plane, a rectangle of area A with its base parallel to the line of intersection, show that the projection of this area in the other plane is $A \cos \alpha$. (*b*) Show that this formula holds for an area of any shape. (Divide into rectangular strips with their ends parallel to the line of intersection, and integrate.)

CHAPTER *31* *TRIPLE INTEGRALS*

239. The triple integral in Cartesian coördinates. We have seen that the integral of a function of one variable, extended over a given interval, may be interpreted as the area under a plane curve. Again, the integral of a function of two variables extended over a plane region may be interpreted as the volume under a surface. If we have a function of three variables defined at all points of a portion of space, no similar geometric interpretation for the integral of the function throughout the given region is possible, since geometric intuition fails in space of four dimensions. Nevertheless the meaning of such an integral may be made plain by analogy with the earlier cases.

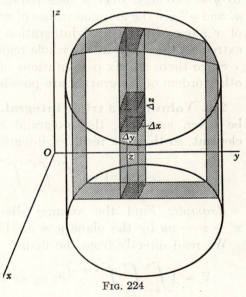

Suppose we have given a continuous function $f(x, y, z)$ defined at all points of a three-dimensional region V.

Fig. 224

Let us pass through V three sets of planes parallel to the coördinate planes, thus dividing V into elementary boxes of volume $\Delta x \, \Delta y \, \Delta z$, together with smaller irregular portions around the boundary. Now multiply the volume of each element by the value of the function at some point of the element, and form the sum of these products.

The triple limit

$$\lim_{\substack{\Delta z \to 0 \\ \Delta y \to 0 \\ \Delta x \to 0}} \sum \sum \sum f(x, y, z) \, \Delta z \, \Delta y \, \Delta x$$

is defined as the value of the *triple integral,* or *volume integral,* of $f(x, y, z)$ throughout the region V.

This limit may be evaluated by three successive integrations (cf. § 230):

$$T = \lim_{\substack{\Delta z \to 0 \\ \Delta y \to 0 \\ \Delta x \to 0}} \sum \sum \sum f(x, y, z) \, \Delta z \, \Delta y \, \Delta x$$

(1)
$$= \int_a^b \int_{y'}^{y''} \int_{z'}^{z''} f(x, y, z) \, dz \, dy \, dx.$$

The first integration extends over a vertical column of base $\Delta y \, \Delta x$; the limits z', z'' are the extreme values of z in this column, and in general are functions of both x and y. The integration with respect to y is extended over a slice parallel to the yz-plane; the limits y' and y'' are the extreme values of y in this slice, and are functions of x alone. In the final integration the limits are of course the extreme values of x in the whole region.

Since there are six permutations of the three letters x, y, z, five other orders of integration are possible, in addition to (1).

240. Volume as a triple integral. If in § 239 the given function be taken as unity, the integrand becomes merely the volume-element, so that the result of integration is the volume itself:

$$V = \int_a^b \int_{y'}^{y''} \int_{z'}^{z''} dz \, dy \, dx.$$

Example: Find the volume sliced off from the paraboloid $x^2 + z^2 = ay$ by the plane $y = a$. (Fig. 225.)

We read directly from the figure

$$V = 4 \int_0^a \int_{\frac{x^2}{a}}^a \int_0^{\sqrt{ay - x^2}} dz \, dy \, dx$$

$$= 4 \int_0^a \int_{\frac{x^2}{a}}^a \left[z \right]_0^{\sqrt{ay - x^2}} dy \, dx = 4 \int_0^a \int_{\frac{x^2}{a}}^a \sqrt{ay - x^2} \, dy \, dx$$

$$= \frac{8}{3a} \int_0^a \left[(ay - x^2)^{\frac{3}{2}} \right]_{\frac{x^2}{a}}^a dx = \frac{\pi}{2} a^3.$$

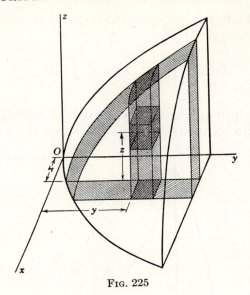

FIG. 225

For practice in reading limits, the student should verify the following integrals for the same volume:

$$V = 4 \int_0^a \int_0^{\sqrt{ay}} \int_0^{\sqrt{ay-x^2}} dz\ dx\ dy;$$

$$V = 4 \int_0^a \int_0^{\sqrt{ay}} \int_0^{\sqrt{ay-z^2}} dx\ dz\ dy;$$

$$V = 4 \int_0^a \int_0^{\sqrt{a^2-x^2}} \int_{\frac{x^2+z^2}{a}}^a dy\ dz\ dx.$$

A figure should be drawn for each case.

241. The triple integral: general formulation. We may generalize the set-up of § 239 in two ways. First, let the given function f be a function, not necessarily of the Cartesian x, y, z, but of any three independent variables. Second, let the region of integration be divided into k volume-elements ΔV_i of any shape whatever, subject to the single condition that as k increases, *the maximum distance between any two points of ΔV_i approaches* zero.*

Now, multiply each ΔV_i by the value of f at some point of the element, and add all these products. The *limit of this sum* as k

---

* It follows from this that in triple integration the element is an infinitesimal of third order.

increases indefinitely (always provided the limit exists) is the triple integral of f throughout V:

$$(1) \qquad \lim_{k \to \infty} \sum_{i=1}^{k} f_i \, \Delta V_i = \int\!\!\!\int_{V}\!\!\!\int f \, dV.$$

242. The triple integral in cylindrical coördinates. Divide the volume into elements by planes through the z-axis, cylinders

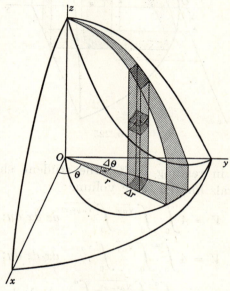

FIG. 226

around the z-axis, and planes perpendicular to the z-axis (Fig. 226). Then the base of the element (apart from infinitesimals of higher order) is $r \, \Delta r \, \Delta \theta$, the altitude Δz, volume $r \, \Delta z \, \Delta r \, \Delta \theta$, so that

$$\lim_{\substack{\Delta z \to 0 \\ \Delta r \to 0 \\ \Delta \theta \to 0}} \sum \sum \sum f(r, \theta, z) r \, \Delta z \, \Delta r \, \Delta \theta = \int_{\alpha}^{\beta}\!\!\int_{r'}^{r''}\!\!\int_{z'}^{z''} f(r, \theta, z) r \, dz \, dr \, d\theta.$$

In particular, if

$$f(r, \theta, z) = 1,$$

the integral represents the volume of the region in question:

$$V = \int_{\alpha}^{\beta}\!\!\int_{r'}^{r''}\!\!\int_{z'}^{z''} r \, dz \, dr \, d\theta.$$

Example: Find the volume in the first octant inside the cylinder $x^2 + y^2 = ay$ and the paraboloid $x^2 + y^2 + az = a^2$. (Fig. 226.)

In cylindrical coördinates, the given equations are

$$r = a \sin \theta, \qquad r^2 + az = a^2:$$

$$V = \int_0^{\frac{\pi}{2}} \int_0^{a \sin \theta} \int_0^{\frac{a^2 - r^2}{a}} r \, dz \, dr \, d\theta$$

$$= \int_0^{\frac{\pi}{2}} \int_0^{a \sin \theta} \left[z \right]_0^{\frac{a^2 - r^2}{a}} r \, dr \, d\theta = \frac{1}{a} \int_0^{\frac{\pi}{2}} \int_0^{a \sin \theta} (a^2 - r^2) r \, dr \, d\theta$$

$$= -\frac{1}{4a} \int_0^{\frac{\pi}{2}} \left[(a^2 - r^2)^2 \right]_0^{a \sin \theta} d\theta = \frac{a^3}{4} \int_0^{\frac{\pi}{2}} (1 - \cos^4 \theta) \, d\theta = \frac{5}{64} \pi a^3.$$

EXERCISES

In Exs. 1–16, use triple integration in rectangular coördinates.

1. Find the volume in the first octant bounded by the surfaces $a^2 z = xy^2$, $y = x$, $x = a$, integrating in the order z, x, y.

2. Check Ex. 1, by integrating in the order z, y, x.

3. Find the volume of a sphere.

4. Find the volume in the first octant bounded by the surfaces $yz = x^2 + z^2$, $z = x$, $z = a$, integrating in order y, z, x.   *Ans.* $\frac{4}{9}a^3$.

5. Ex. 4, integrating in order y, x, z.

6. Find the volume in the first octant bounded by the surfaces $z^2 = xy$, $y = x$, $x = a$, integrating in order z, y, x.   *Ans.* $\frac{2}{9}a^3$.

7. Ex. 6, integrating in order z, x, y.

8. Find the volume in the first octant bounded by the surfaces $a^2 z = a^3 - xy^2$, $y^2 = ax$, $y = a$, integrating in order z, y, x.   *Ans.* $\frac{11}{42}a^3$.

9. Ex. 8, integrating in order z, x, y.

10. Find the volume in the first octant bounded by the surfaces $z = x + y$, $y = 1 - x^2$.   *Ans.* $\frac{31}{60}$.

11. In Ex. 1, find the centroid.

12. In Ex. 4, find the centroid.   *Ans.* $(\frac{27}{64}a, \frac{21}{40}a, \frac{3}{4}a)$.

13. In Ex. 6, find the centroid.   *Ans.* $(\frac{3}{4}a, \frac{9}{20}a, \frac{9}{32}a)$.

14. In Ex. 8, find the centroid.   **15.** In Ex. 4, find I_x, I_y, I_z.

16. In Ex. 6, find I_x, I_y, I_z.   *Ans.* $I_y = \frac{18}{25}Ma^2$.

In Exs. 17–25, use triple integration with cylindrical coördinates.

17. Ex. 1.   **18.** Ex. 4.   **19.** Ex. 6.   **20.** Ex. 8.

21. Find the volume of a sphere.

22. Find the volume bounded by the xy-plane, the cylinder $x^2 + y^2 = ay$, and the paraboloid $x^2 + y^2 = az$.   *Ans.* $\frac{3}{32}\pi a^3$.

23. Find the volume in the first octant bounded by the cylinder $x^2 + y^2 = ay$ and the cone $a^2 z^2 = h^2(x^2 + y^2)$.   *Ans.* $\frac{2}{9}a^2 h$.

24. In Ex. 22, find the centroid.   *Ans.* $(0, \frac{2}{3}a, \frac{5}{18}a)$.

25. In Ex. 22, find I_x, I_y, I_z.   *Ans.* $I_x = \frac{175}{288}Ma^2$.

243. Heterogeneous masses. The density of a homogeneous mass has been defined in § 166 as the ratio of the mass to the volume it occupies:

$$\delta = \frac{M}{V}.$$

For a *heterogeneous* mass, *i.e.*, one whose density varies from point to point, we must introduce the idea of *density at a point*.

Consider an element of volume ΔV including a point P, where in general ΔV must be infinitesimal of the third order as in § 241, and let ΔM denote the mass contained in ΔV. Then the ratio $\frac{\Delta M}{\Delta V}$ is the *average density* of ΔV. If ΔV approaches zero in such a way that P is always included, the ratio $\frac{\Delta M}{\Delta V}$ in general approaches a limit δ, called the *density at the point P:*

$$\delta = \lim_{\Delta V \to 0} \frac{\Delta M}{\Delta V} = \frac{dM}{dV}.$$

If the density at any point is given as a function of the coördinates, the mass can be found by integration. In the most general case we divide the space occupied by the body into volume-elements ΔV_i as in § 241, multiply each element by the density δ_i at one of its points and add all these products. The limit of this sum is the mass:

$$M = \int\int_V\int \delta \, dV.$$

We shall use the term *homogeneous element* to mean that the density δ varies, within the element, only by infinitesimal amounts.* It is important to see two points clearly:

(*a*) The element must always be homogeneous, since otherwise, in building up the integral, we would not know what value to use for δ.

(*b*) Homogeneity of the element is the only requisite: the volume-element may be of any character whatever, provided the mass contained in it is homogeneous, since then we know the values of both δ and dV.

---

* These infinitesimal variations may be neglected, since when multiplied by dV they produce infinitesimals of higher order.

Now it is clear that the third-order infinitesimal element will always be homogeneous for any law of variation of density (since δ by tacit assumption is continuous); but if δ varies in some simple manner, it is possible in many cases to find a homogeneous element of one of the shapes used in Chapters 21 and 30; if so, we may find the volume by simple or at worst by double integration. See Examples (*a*) and (*b*).

Example (*a*)*:* Find the mass of a circular cone whose density varies as the distance from the axis. (Fig. 227.)

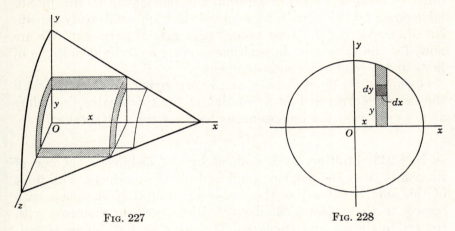

FIG. 227   FIG. 228

Let the cone be generated by revolving the line

$$\frac{x}{h} + \frac{y}{a} = 1$$

about Ox. If we divide the mass into cylindrical shells about the axis, each element will be homogeneous of density $\delta = ky$:

$$M = \int \delta \, dV = 2\pi k \int_0^a y \cdot yx \, dy$$

$$= 2\pi k \int_0^a y^2 \left(h - \frac{hy}{a} \right) dy = \tfrac{1}{6}\pi k a^3 h.$$

Example (*b*)*:* Find the mass of a circular plate if the density is proportional to the sum of the distances from two perpendicular diameters. (Fig. 228.)

With the two diameters as axes, $\delta = k(x + y)$, whence

$$M = 4k \int_0^a \int_0^{\sqrt{a^2 - x^2}} (x + y) \, dy \, dx, \text{ etc.}$$

Example (c): Find the mass of a sphere whose density is proportional to the sum of the distances from three mutually perpendicular diametral planes.

Since the density varies with all three coördinates, a triple integral is required: in Cartesian coördinates,

$$M = 8k \int_0^a \int_0^{\sqrt{a^2-x^2}} \int_0^{\sqrt{a^2-x^2-y^2}} (x + y + z) \, dz \, dy \, dx.$$

244. Centroids; moments of inertia. In Chapters 22–23, in order to make the ideas of centroid and moment of inertia intelligible on an intuitive basis, we adopted the rough-and-ready expedient of considering the mass as an "aggregate of particles." We are now, for the first time, in position to state analytic definitions of first- and second-order mass-moment.

Given a three-dimensional mass M occupying a volume V, with the density δ expressed as a function of the coördinates (including as a special case the homogeneous body—δ constant), take

$$\Delta M_i = \delta_i \, \Delta V_i$$

as in § 243. Multiply each element by the distance x_i of one of its points from the yz-plane, and add all the products. The limit of this sum is defined as the *first-order moment* of the mass with respect to the yz-plane. Similar definitions hold for moments with respect to the zx- and xy-planes. The point $(\bar{x}, \bar{y}, \bar{z})$ whose coördinates are given by the equations

$$M\bar{x} = \iiint_V x\delta \, dV,$$

$$M\bar{y} = \iiint_V y\delta \, dV,$$

$$M\bar{z} = \iiint_V z\delta \, dV$$

is the *centroid* of the mass.

In analogous fashion we arrive at a suitable definition for *moment of inertia* with respect to the x-axis:

$$I_x = \iiint_V (y^2 + z^2)\delta \, dV,$$

with similar definitions for I_y and I_z.

For area-masses or line-masses, the defining formulas are the two- and one-dimensional analogues of those above.

Example (a): In Example (a), § 243,

$$M\bar{x} = 2\pi k \int_0^a \frac{x}{2} \cdot y \cdot yx\, dy = \frac{\pi kh^2}{a^2} \int_0^a y^2 (a - y)^2\, dy$$

$$= \frac{1}{30}\pi ka^4 h,$$

$$\bar{x} = \frac{\frac{1}{30}\pi ka^4 h}{\frac{1}{6}\pi ka^3 h} = \frac{1}{5}a.$$

Example (b): In Example (b), § 243,

$$I_x = 4k \int_0^a \int_0^{\sqrt{a^2 - x^2}} y^2 (x + y)\, dy\, dx.$$

245. Translation theorem on moments of inertia. We are now able to prove the theorem of § 183, that if the lines l and $\bar{l}$ are parallel at a distance h apart, and if $\bar{l}$ passes through the centroid of the mass M, then

$$I_l = I_{\bar{l}} + Mh^2.$$

Take the line $\bar{l}$ as x-axis, the line l as $y = h$, $z = 0$. With a volume-element chosen in any suitable manner (the figure shows only one element), we have

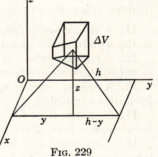

Fig. 229

$$I_{\bar{l}} = \int\int\int_V (y^2 + z^2)\, \delta\, dV,$$

$$I_l = \int\int\int_V [(h - y)^2 + z^2]\, \delta\, dV$$

$$= h^2 \int\int\int_V \delta\, dV - 2h \int\int\int_V y\delta\, dV + \int\int\int_V (y^2 + z^2)\, \delta\, dV.$$

By § 243, the first of these three integrals is Mh^2; by § 244, the second is $-2hM\bar{y}$, and therefore vanishes, since the centroid is in the zx-plane; the third is $I_{\bar{l}}$.

COROLLARY: *If two parallel lines l_1, l_2 are at distances h_1, h_2 from the centroid,*

$$I_{l_2} = I_{l_1} + M(h_2^2 - h_1^2).$$

EXERCISES

In Exs. 1–22, find the mass.

1. A straight rod, of length c, whose density is proportional to the distance from one end. *Ans.* $\frac{1}{2}kc^2$.

2. A straight rod, of length c, whose density is proportional to the square of the distance from one end. *Ans.* $\frac{1}{3}kc^3$.

3. A straight rod, of length c, whose density is proportional to the square of the distance from the center. *Ans.* $\frac{1}{12}kc^3$.

4. Four rods forming a square of side c, with the density varying as the square of the distance from one corner. *Ans.* $\frac{10}{3}kc^3$.

5. A rectangular plate, sides a and b, with density proportional to the square of the distance from a side of length b. *Ans.* $\frac{1}{3}ka^3b$.

6. A rectangular plate, sides a and b, with density proportional to the product of the distances to two adjacent sides. *Ans.* $\frac{1}{4}ka^2b^2$.

7. A semicircular wire, radius a, whose density varies as the distance from the bounding diameter. Use polar coördinates. *Ans.* $2ka^2$.

8. A semicircular wire, radius a, whose density varies as the fourth power of the distance from the bounding diameter. *Ans.* $\dfrac{3k\pi a^5}{8}$.

9. A circular plate, radius a, whose density varies as the square of the distance from a fixed diameter. *Ans.* $\frac{1}{4}k\pi a^4$.

10. A circular plate, radius a, with density varying as the cube of the distance from the center. *Ans.* $\dfrac{2k\pi a^5}{5}$.

11. A circular cylinder, base radius a and height h, whose density varies as the square of the distance from the base. *Ans.* $\frac{1}{3}k\pi a^2h^3$.

12. A circular cylinder, base radius a and height h, with density proportional to the distance from the axis of the cylinder. *Ans.* $\frac{2}{3}k\pi a^3h$.

13. A sphere, radius a, whose density varies as the distance from a fixed diametral plane. *Ans.* $\frac{1}{2}k\pi a^4$.

14. A spherical surface, radius a, with density proportional to the distance from a fixed diameter. *Ans.* $k\pi^2a^3$.

15. A spherical surface, radius a, with density proportional to the distance from a fixed diametral plane. *Ans.* $2k\pi a^3$.

16. A square, side a, whose density varies as the square of the distance from one corner. *Ans.* $\dfrac{2ka^4}{3}$.

17. A square, side a, whose density varies as the distance from one corner. Use polar coördinates. *Ans.* $\frac{1}{3}ka^3\left[\sqrt{2} + \ln(1 + \sqrt{2})\right]$.

18. A rectangular plate, sides a and b, whose density is proportional to the sum of the distances from two adjacent sides. *Ans.* $\frac{1}{2}kab(a + b)$.

19. A circular plate, radius a, whose density is proportional to the distance from a fixed point on the circumference. Use polar coördinates, with the equation $r = 2a\cos\theta$. *Ans.* $\frac{32}{9}ka^3$.

20. Use polar coördinates to solve Example (b), § 243. *Ans.* $\frac{8}{3}ka^3$.

21. A cube, edge length a, with density varying as the square of the distance from one corner.   *Ans.* ka^5.

22. A cube, edge length a, whose density varies as the sum of the distances from three adjacent faces.   *Ans.* $\frac{3}{2}ka^4$.

23. Complete the solution in Example (c), § 243.   *Ans.* $\frac{3}{2}k\pi a^4$.

24. Solve Example (c), § 243, in cylindrical coördinates.

25. Show that the problem of determining fluid pressure on a submerged vertical area (§ 185) is equivalent to that of finding the mass of a thin plate whose density is proportional to the distance from a line in the plane.

In Exs. 26–38, find the centroid.

26. Ex. 1.   *Ans.* $\frac{2}{3}$ way from the end of zero density.
27. Ex. 2.   **28.** Ex. 4.   **29.** Ex. 5.   **30.** Ex. 6.

31. A semicircular plate, radius a, whose density varies as the square of the distance from the bounding diameter. Use polar coördinates.

$$Ans. \text{ On the line of symmetry, } \frac{32a}{15\pi} \text{ from the center.}$$

32. A semicircular plate, radius a, whose density varies as the distance from the center.

33. One quadrant of a circular plate, radius a, with density proportional to the distance from one of the bounding radii.

34. One quadrant of a circular wire, radius a, with density varying as the distance from one of the bounding radii.

35. Ex. 19.
$$Ans. \text{ On the line of symmetry, } \frac{6a}{5} \text{ from the point of zero density.}$$

36. A circular plate, radius a, whose density is proportional to the square of the distance from a fixed point on the circumference.

$$Ans. \text{ On the line of symmetry, } \frac{4a}{3} \text{ from the point of zero density.}$$

37. Ex. 21.   *Ans.* $\left(\dfrac{7a}{12}, \dfrac{7a}{12}, \dfrac{7a}{12}\right)$.   **38.** Ex. 22.   *Ans.* $\left(\dfrac{5a}{9}, \dfrac{5a}{9}, \dfrac{5a}{9}\right)$.

In Exs. 39–48, find the indicated moment of inertia.

39. The rod of Ex. 1, with respect to the point of zero density.
                                                      Ans. $\frac{1}{4}kc^4$.

40. The rod of Ex. 1, with respect to the point of maximum density.
                                                      Ans. $\frac{1}{12}kc^4$.

41. The rod of Ex. 3, with respect to the center.   *Ans.* $\dfrac{kc^5}{80}$.

42. The rod of Ex. 3, with respect to one endpoint.   *Ans.* $\dfrac{kc^5}{30}$.

43. The circular plate of Ex. 9, with respect to the center.

44. The cylinder of Ex. 11, with respect to the plane of its base.
                                                      Ans. $\frac{3}{5}Mh^2$.

45. The cylinder of Ex. 11, with respect to the plane at the end of maximum density.   *Ans.* $\frac{1}{10}Mh^2$.

46. The sphere of Ex. 13, with respect to a diameter in the fixed plane (yz-plane).   *Ans.* $I_z = \frac{1}{2} M a^2$.

47. The sphere of Ex. 13, with respect to the diameter perpendicular to the fixed plane.   *Ans.* $I_x = \frac{1}{3} M a^2$.

48. The cube of Ex. 21, with respect to an edge through the corner of zero density.   *Ans.* $I_z = \frac{38}{45} M a^2$.

49. Prove the theorem of § 181 for any continuous plane mass.

50. Prove the corollary, § 245.

51. Solve Example (*b*), § 244. (Find I_0, using polar coördinates; $I_x = \frac{1}{2} I_0$.)

CHAPTER 32 DIFFERENTIAL EQUATIONS
OF THE FIRST ORDER

246. Definitions. A *differential equation* is an equation containing derivatives or differentials. Many examples have arisen in our previous work: for instance,

$$(1) \qquad x - yy' = 0, \qquad\qquad (\S\ 30)$$

$$(2) \qquad y'' = -\frac{a^2}{y^3}, \qquad\qquad (\S\ 30)$$

$$(3) \qquad r\frac{dh}{dr} + 2h = 0, \qquad\qquad (\S\ 41)$$

$$(4) \qquad \frac{d^2y}{dx^2} = -k^2 y, \qquad\qquad (\text{p. 140})$$

$$(5) \qquad \frac{\partial^2 u}{\partial x^2} + \frac{\partial^2 u}{\partial y^2} = 0, \qquad\qquad (\text{p. 412})$$

$$(6) \qquad \frac{\partial^2 u}{\partial x^2} + \frac{\partial^2 u}{\partial y^2} = \frac{\partial u}{\partial t}, \qquad\qquad (\text{p. 413})$$

$$(7) \qquad x\frac{\partial u}{\partial x} + y\frac{\partial u}{\partial y} + z\frac{\partial u}{\partial z} = 2u. \qquad\qquad (\text{p. 412})$$

Equations such as (1)–(4), involving only one independent variable and therefore containing only ordinary derivatives, are called *ordinary differential equations*. Equations containing partial derivatives (two or more independent variables) are *partial differential equations*—for example, (5)–(7).

The *order* of a differential equation is the order of the highest derivative that occurs in it. Thus (1), (3), (7) are of first order; (2), (4), (5), (6) are of second order.

A study of partial differential equations is beyond the limits of this book. In the elementary applications, ordinary equations of first or second order are of predominant importance.

455

247. Solutions of a differential equation. A *solution* of a differential equation is *any relation, free from derivatives, which involves one or more of the variables, and which is consistent with the differential equation.* For instance, the equation

$$(1) \qquad \frac{d^2x}{dt^2} + k^2x = 0$$

has the solution

$$(2) \qquad x = A \cos kt + B \sin kt,$$

with A and B arbitrary constants. That (2) is consistent with (1) is easily shown by twice differentiating (2) with respect to t.

In a like manner, the equation

$$(3) \qquad y(3x^2 + y^2)\,dx + (2xy^2 + 1)\,dy = 0$$

has the solution

$$(4) \qquad x^3 + xy^2 + \ln y = c,$$

with c arbitrary. To verify that equation (4) is a solution of (3), eliminate the arbitrary constant by differentiation, obtaining

$$(3x^2 + y^2)\,dx + \left(2xy + \frac{1}{y}\right) dy = 0,$$

and then multiply throughout by y to get equation (3).

Our aim in these concluding chapters is to solve simple ordinary differential equations, and to treat a few elementary applications which involve them.

By analogy with the integral calculus, a solution of a differential equation is often called an *integral* of the equation, and the arbitrary constants are called *constants of integration.*

248. General solutions; particular solutions. Under certain rather broad conditions, a differential equation of order n can be shown to have a solution involving n distinct arbitrary constants. Such a solution is called the *general solution.* Some differential equations have solutions which are not special cases of the general solution, but such matters are beyond a brief introduction to the subject. For the differential equations to be solved in this book, every solution is a special case (some choice of the arbitrary constants) of the general solution.

A *particular solution* is any solution, not general, of the differential equation. The particular solutions used most frequently contain no arbitrary constants. For equation (1) of § 247, some particular solutions are:

$$x = \cos kt,$$
$$x = 3 \cos kt - 2 \sin kt, \text{ etc.}$$

In applied problems involving differential equations we are in most cases concerned with a particular solution. Nevertheless the determination of the general solution is usually a necessary preliminary step,* after which the required particular solution is found by determining the arbitrary constant from given data, called *initial conditions*, or *boundary conditions*.

249. Separation of variables. Every differential equation of the first order, and of the first degree in y', can be written in the form

$$M\,dx + N\,dy = 0,$$

where in general M and N are functions of both x and y. It is sometimes possible to transform the equation into the form

$$A(x)\,dx + B(y)\,dy = 0.$$

When the variables can thus be separated, the solution follows at once by direct integration.

Example (a): Solve the equation

$$xy\,dx + (x^2 + 1)\,dy = 0.$$

After division by $y(x^2 + 1)$ the equation takes the form

$$\frac{x\,dx}{x^2 + 1} + \frac{dy}{y} = 0.$$

Then integration yields

$$\tfrac{1}{2} \ln (x^2 + 1) + \ln y = \tfrac{1}{2}c,$$

or

$$\ln (x^2 + 1) + 2 \ln y = c,$$
$$y^2 (x^2 + 1) = e^c = c_1.$$

This example illustrates the fact that the solution of a differential equation may be written in a variety of forms, frequently differing greatly in appearance. Where the answers to exercises

---

* As a rule, this is not true when we are dealing with a partial differential equation.

are given, it is not necessarily implied that the form in the book is simpler or better than any other. It furnishes good practice in manipulation, however, to reduce the answer to the form given, and it is recommended that this always be done.

Example (b): Solve the equation

$$(x^2 - 1)\, dx + xy\, dy = 0.$$

At once, we perform the separation of variables, obtaining

$$\frac{x^2 - 1}{x}dx + y\, dy = 0,$$

or

$$2\left(x - \frac{1}{x}\right)dx + 2y\, dy = 0.$$

Thus the required solution is

$$x^2 - 2 \ln x + y^2 = 2 \ln c,$$

or

$$x^2 + y^2 = 2 \ln (cx).$$

EXERCISES

In Exs. 1–19, find the general solution.

1. $dy = x^2 y\, dx.$ *Ans.* $x^3 = c + 3 \ln y.$
2. $dy = e^{x+y}\, dx.$ *Ans.* $e^x + e^{-y} = c.$
3. $dy = 2(xy - x)\, dx.$ *Ans.* $y = 1 + ce^{x^2}.$
4. $2x\, dy + y\, dx = 0.$ *Ans.* $xy^2 = c.$
5. $3y\, dx - 2x\, dy = 0.$ *Ans.* $y^2 = cx^3.$
6. $x^2 y' = y^2.$ *Ans.* $y - x = cxy.$

7. $\dfrac{dv}{dx} = v^2 x^2.$ *Ans.* $v(x^3 + c) + 3 = 0.$
8. $y^2\, dx = dy - a^2\, dx.$ *Ans.* $y = a \tan (ax + c).$
9. $y\, dx + x\, dy = xy(dx + dy).$ *Ans.* $e^{x+y} = cxy.$
10. $2(x + 1)(y + 1)\, dx + y\, dy = 0.$

               Ans. $(x + 1)^2 + y = c + \ln (y + 1).$

11. $(x - 1)\, dx + (x + 2)\, dy = 0.$ *Ans.* $x + y + c = 3 \ln (x + 2).$
12. $2(y - 1)\, dx - x^3 y\, dy = 0.$ *Ans.* $y + \ln (y - 1) = c - x^{-2}.$
13. $\sin x \cos y\, dx = \cos x \sin y\, dy.$ *Ans.* $\cos y = c \cos x.$
14. $y\, dx = xy\, dx + x^2\, dy.$ *Ans.* $x \ln (xy) + 1 = cx.$

15. $\dfrac{dy}{dx} + y^2 = a^2.$ *Ans.* $\dfrac{y + a}{y - a} = ce^{2ax}.$

16. $(x^2 + 1)\, dy + (y^2 + 1)\, dx = 0.$ See also Ex. 20, below.

           Ans. $\text{Arctan } y + \text{Arctan } x = \text{Arctan } c.$

17. $(y^2 + 9)\, dx = (x^2 + 9)\, dy$. See also Ex. 21, below.

$$Ans. \ \text{Arctan}\ \frac{x}{3} - \text{Arctan}\ \frac{y}{3} = \text{Arctan}\ \frac{c}{3}.$$

18. $\sqrt{1 - x^2}\, dy + \sqrt{1 - y^2}\, dx = 0$. See Ex. 22 below.

$$Ans. \ \text{Arcsin}\ y + \text{Arcsin}\ x = \text{Arcsin}\ c.$$

19. $\sqrt{4 - x^2}\, dy - \sqrt{4 - y^2}\, dx = 0$. See Ex. 23 below.

$$Ans. \ \text{Arcsin}\ \frac{y}{2} - \text{Arcsin}\ \frac{x}{2} = \text{Arcsin}\ \frac{c}{2}.$$

20. Show that the answer to Ex. 16 can be put in the form $c(1 - xy) = x + y$.

21. Show that the answer to Ex. 17 can be put in the form $c(9 + xy) = 9(x - y)$.

22. Show that the answer to Ex. 18 can be put in the form $x^2 + 2kxy + y^2 = 1 - k^2$, where $k = \sqrt{1 - c^2}$.

23. Show that the answer to Ex. 19 can be put in the form $x^2 - kxy + y^2 = 4 - k^2$, where $k = \sqrt{4 - c^2}$.

In Exs. 24–29, find the particular solution which satisfies the given condition.

24. $dx = -x^3 y^3\, dy$; when $x = 1$, $y = 0$.   *Ans.* $x^2\,(y^4 + 2) = 2$.

25. $\dfrac{d\phi}{dr} = r \csc \phi$; when $\phi = \pi$, $r = 3$.   *Ans.* $r^2 = 7 - 2 \cos \phi$.

26. $(x^2 + 2)(y + 1)^2\, dx + x^2\, dy = 0$; when $x = 1$, $y = 1$.
$$Ans. \ 2x^2 y + 2x^2 + 3xy - 4y + x - 4 = 0.$$

27. $xy(dx - dy) = y\, dy - x\, dx$; when $x = 1$, $y = 3$.
$$Ans. \ y + 1 = 2(x + 1)e^{y - x - 2}.$$

28. $\dfrac{dx}{d\theta} = -x \tan \theta$; $x = 0.421$ when $\theta = 10° 30'$.   *Ans.* $x = 0.428 \cos \theta$.

29. $dx - d\theta = x^2\, d\theta$; $x = -0.563$ when $\theta = 0$.
$$Ans. \ x = \tan (\theta - 0.513).$$

30. Find the family of curves having the property $\dfrac{dy}{dx} = -\dfrac{x}{y}$, and draw several of them.   *Ans.* $x^2 + y^2 = c^2$.

31. Find the family of curves whose slope at any point equals the ordinate of the point. Draw the curves $c = 1$, $c = 2$, $c = -1$, $c = 0$.
$$Ans. \ y = ce^x.$$

32. Find the family of curves whose slope equals the square of the ordinate. Draw the curves $c = 0$, $c = 1$, $c = -2$. What happens to the curve as c changes? What form is approached as c increases indefinitely?
$$Ans. \ xy - cy + 1 = 0.$$

33. Find the curves for which $\dfrac{dy}{dx} = -\dfrac{y}{x}$. Draw the curves $c = 1$, $c = 2$, $c = 0$, $c = -3$.   *Ans.* $xy = c$.

34. Draw the curve through $(3, 5)$ having the property $yy' = x$; also draw several other curves of the family.   *Ans.* $y^2 = x^2 + 16$.

250. Coefficients homogeneous of the same degree. A polynomial in x and y is said to be *homogeneous* if all the terms are of the same degree in x and y. More generally, any function of x and y is said to be *homogeneous of the n-th degree* if, when x and y are replaced by kx and ky, the result is the original function multiplied by k^n. Thus the function $x^3 - 3xy^2 + 2y^3$ is homogeneous of the third degree; the function $\sqrt{x^2 - y^2} + y \sin \dfrac{y^2}{x^2}$ is homogeneous of the first degree.

If, in the differential equation

$$(1) \qquad\qquad M\,dx + N\,dy = 0,$$

the coefficients M and N are homogeneous functions *of the same degree*, the equation when solved for y' takes the form

$$(2) \qquad\qquad y' = f\left(\frac{y}{x}\right):$$

i.e., y' is a function of $\dfrac{y}{x}$ alone. This suggests the substitution of a new variable v for the ratio $\dfrac{y}{x}$: *i.e.*, the substitution

$$(3) \qquad\qquad \boldsymbol{y = vx, \quad dy = v\,dx + x\,dv.}$$

This substitution always produces a differential equation in v and x in which *the variables are separable*.

Example: Solve the equation $(x + y)\,dx = x\,dy$.
Substituting for y and dy by (3), we find

$$(x + vx)\,dx = x(v\,dx + x\,dv),$$
$$dx - x\,dv = 0.$$

The variables can now be separated:

$$\frac{dx}{x} - dv = 0, \qquad \ln x - v + c = 0,$$

or, since

$$v = \frac{y}{x},$$
$$y = x \ln x + cx.$$

EXERCISES

In Exs. 1–13, obtain the general solution.

1. $(y^2 - xy)\,dx + x^2\,dy = 0.$ *Ans.* $x + cy = y \ln x.$
2. $2xy\,dx - (x^2 + y^2)\,dy = 0.$ *Ans.* $x^2 = y(c + y).$
3. $(x^2 - y^2)\,dx + 2xy\,dy = 0.$ *Ans.* $x^2 + y^2 = cx.$

4. $(u - v)\,du + (u + v)\,dv = 0.$

5. $(2z - 3x)\,dz + x\,dx = 0.$ *Ans.* $(x - 2z)^2 = c(x - z).$

6. $(y - 2x)\,dx + y\,dy = 0.$ *Ans.* $(y - x)(y + 2x)^2 = c.$

7. $(x^2 + 3w^2)\,dx - xw\,dw = 0.$ *Ans.* $2w^2 = x^2(cx^4 - 1).$

8. $(1 + b^2)\,da - a\,db = 0.$ **9.** $2y\,dx + (xy - x)\,dy = 0.$

10. $(x^2 + y^2)\,dx + xy\,dy = 0.$ **11.** $x^2y\,dx + (y^3 - x^3)\,dy = 0.$

12. $(2x - 5y)\,dx + (4x - y)\,dy = 0.$ *Ans.* $(2x + y)^2 = c(y - x).$

13. $y^2(x + 2y)\,dx - x(x^2 + xy + 2y^2)\,dy = 0.$

Ans. $y^2 + xy + x^2 \ln (cy) = 0.$

14. $(x - y)\,dx + (3x + y)\,dy = 0$; when $x = 2,\ y = -1.$

Ans. $2(x + 2y) + (x + y) \ln (x + y) = 0.$

15. $y(\ln y - \ln x - 1)\,dx + x\,dy = 0$; when $x = 1,\ y = e^2.$

Ans. $y = xe^{\frac{2}{x}}.$

16. $(2x + 3y)\,dx + x\,dy = 0$; when $x = 1,\ y = 0.$

Ans. $x^4 + 2x^3y - 1 = 0.$

17. $y(2x + 3y)\,dx - 3x(x + 2y)\,dy = 0$; when $x = 1,\ y = 1.$

Ans. $4y^3 - 3xy - x^2 = 0.$

18. In the answer to Ex. 2, draw the curves for $c = 4,\ c = -2,\ c = 0,$ $c \to \infty.$

19. In the answer to Ex. 3, draw the curves for $c = 2,\ c = 4,\ c \to \infty.$

20. Show that, if M and N are homogeneous of the same degree, equation (1) of § 250 can always be put in the form (2), and prove that the substitution $y = vx$ always separates the variables.

21. If $y' = F(ax + by + c)$, show that the substitution $ax + by + c = v$ produces an equation in which the variables can be separated.

22. Solve the equation $dy = (4x + y)^2\,dx.$ (Ex. 21.)

Ans. $y = 2 \tan (2x + c) - 4x.$

23. Solve the equation $dy = (x + 3y + 1)\,dx.$

Ans. $9y = ce^{3x} - 3x - 4.$

251. The linear equation. A differential equation is said to be *linear* if it is *of the first degree in y and y'* (or, what amounts to the same thing, in y and dy). By merely isolating y', every such equation may be put in the form

(1) $$dy + Py\,dx = Q\,dx,$$

where P and Q are functions of x alone. The first step in solving a linear equation is to reduce it to the standard form (1).

To solve this equation, let us multiply both members of (1) by the quantity* $e^{\int P\,dx}$:

(2) $$e^{\int P\,dx}(dy + Py\,dx) = Qe^{\int P\,dx}\,dx.$$

---

* Although it is possible to introduce this device somewhat less abruptly, there is no necessity for doing so. There can be no logical objection to the process regardless of its origin, since, just as in the evaluation of indefinite integrals, the only thing necessary is that the result shall be verifiable by differentiation.

Now by differentiating the quantity $ye^{\int P dx}$, it is easily verified that the entire left member of (2) is exactly $d(ye^{\int P dx})$, so that the integral of the left member is $ye^{\int P dx}$. Further, the right member involves x only, and therefore can be directly integrated.

A multiplier, such as $e^{\int P dx}$ in this case, which puts the equation in shape for direct integration is called an *integrating factor*.

In evaluating $\int P\ dx$, it is unnecessary to write the constant of integration; for,

$$e^{\int P dx + c} = e^c \cdot e^{\int P dx},$$

so that preservation of the constant merely multiplies the equation by the useless (constant) factor e^c.

The above process may be summarized as follows.

To solve any linear equation of the first order:

1. *Arrange the equation in the standard form* (1).
2. *Evaluate the expression* $e^{\int P dx}$, *and simplify if possible.*
3. *Multiply through by this expression as an integrating factor.*
4. *The entire left member then integrates as a unit, the result being y times the integrating factor, while the right member may be evaluated by an ordinary integration.*

It is hardly necessary to say that if an equation is *linear in x* (*i.e.*, of the first degree in x and dx) it may be solved in a similar way.

Example (a): Solve the equation $dy + 2y\ dx = x\ dx$. Here

$$P = 2, \quad \int P\ dx = 2x, \quad e^{\int P dx} = e^{2x}.$$

Introducing the integrating factor e^{2x}, and integrating, we find

$$ye^{2x} = \int xe^{2x}\ dx = \tfrac{1}{2}xe^{2x} - \tfrac{1}{4}e^{2x} + c,$$

whence

$$y = \tfrac{1}{2}x - \tfrac{1}{4} + ce^{-2x}.$$

Example (b): Solve the equation $xy' - x^3 - y = 0$.

Writing this in the form

$$(3) \qquad dy - \frac{y}{x}dx = x^2\ dx,$$

we have

$$P = -\frac{1}{x}, \qquad \int P \, dx = -\ln x,$$

whence

$$e^{\int P \, dx} = e^{-\ln x} = \frac{1}{x},$$

by formula (5) of § 92. Hence, dividing (3) by x and integrating, we get

$$\frac{y}{x} = \int x \, dx = \frac{x^2}{2} + c,$$

$$2y = x^3 + c_1 x.$$

EXERCISES

In Exs. 1–16, find the general solution.

1. $2(x - y) \, dx + dy = 0.$ *Ans.* $y = x + \frac{1}{2} + ce^{2x}.$
2. $dx + 3(x - 2y) \, dy = 0.$ *Ans.* $3x - 6y + 2 = ce^{-3y}.$
3. $3(y - 6x - 2) \, dx + dy = 0.$ *Ans.* $y = 6x + ce^{-3x}.$
4. $3(x^2 + y) \, dx - x \, dy = 0.$ *Ans.* $y = x^2(cx - 3).$
5. $3(x^5 y + 4) \, dx + x^6 \, dy = 0.$ *Ans.* $x^5 y = 6 + cx^2.$
6. $(3 + y - xy) \, dx + x \, dy = 0.$ *Ans.* $xy = 3 + ce^x.$
7. $(x + 1)y' = 2y + 2(x + 1)^4.$ *Ans.* $y = c(x + 1)^2 + (x + 1)^4.$
8. $\dfrac{dv}{dt} = g - kv.$ Solve in two ways.
9. $y' = 6 \cos^2 x - y \cot x.$ *Ans.* $y \sin x = c - 2 \cos^3 x.$
10. $t\dfrac{dx}{dt} + x + xt - e^t = 0.$ *Ans.* $2xte^t = c + e^{2t}.$
11. $(2y \sec x - \sin x) \, dx + \csc x \, dy = 0.$
    Ans. $y = \cos x \sin x + (c - x) \cos^2 x.$
12. $(y + 1) \, dx - (3x + y) \, dy = 0.$ *Ans.* $6x = c(y + 1)^3 - 3y - 1.$
13. $(x - 2)y' = 4y + x(x - 2)^4.$
    Ans. $y = (x - 2)^4(x + c) + 2(x - 2)^4 \ln (x - 2).$
14. $(xy + 3y - x - 2) \, dx + (x + 2) \, dy = 0.$
    Ans. $(x + 2)y = x + 1 + ce^{-x}.$
15. $y' = \sec x + 3y \tan x.$ *Ans.* $2y = (c + x) \sec^3 x + \sec x \tan x.$
16. $2r \cos \theta \, d\theta = \theta \, d\theta - \sin \theta \, dr.$ *Ans.* $r \sin^2 \theta = c - \theta \cos \theta + \sin \theta.$

In Exs. 17–24, find the particular solution indicated.

17. $y^2 \, dx + (3xy + 4) \, dy = 0;$ when $x = 2, y = 1.$
    Ans. $xy^3 = 2(2 - y^2).$
18. $2(4x - y - 2) \, dx + dy = 0;$ when $x = 0, y = 2.$
    Ans. $y = 2(e^{2x} + 2x).$
19. $\dfrac{dr}{d\theta} = \cot \theta \, (\cos \theta - r);$ when $\theta = \frac{1}{2}\pi, r = 2.$
    Ans. $2(2r - \cos \theta) \sin \theta = 2\theta + 8 - \pi.$

20. $xy' = 2 - y + 4x - 2xy$; when $x = 1$, $y = 1$.

$$Ans.\ xy = 2x - e^{2-2x}.$$

21. $\dfrac{du}{d\phi} = 2 \tan \phi \sin \phi + \sec \phi - 3u \tan \phi$; when $\phi = \frac{1}{4}\pi$, $u = \sqrt{2}$.

$$Ans.\ u = \sin \phi + 2 \cos^3 \phi.$$

22. $y' = x^2 + x - y + \dfrac{y}{x}$; when $x = 1$, $y = 2$. $Ans.\ y = x^2 + xe^{1-x}$.

23. $y' \cot 2x = 2y - x$; when $x = \frac{1}{2}\pi$, $y = \frac{1}{4}$.

$$Ans.\ 2(2y - x) \cos 2x = \pi - 1 - \sin 2x.$$

24. $(xy + x - y + 1)\, dx - x\, dy = 0$; when $x = 1$, $y = -2$.

$$Ans.\ xy = e^{x-1} - x - 2.$$

252. Summary. Even though able to solve any of the foregoing exercises, one has no proper grasp of the subject unless he can readily recognize the various types when they are not sorted out for him. To classify the equations below, it is recommended that the following questions be asked in order, until an affirmative answer is reached.

1. *Are the variables separable?* Collect terms in dx and dy and try to factor the coefficients.

2. *Is the equation linear—i.e., of the first degree in y and dy (or x and dx)?*

3. *Are the coefficients homogeneous of the same degree?*

MISCELLANEOUS EXERCISES

In Exs. 1–24, find the general solution.

1. $(x^3 + 4y)\, dx = x\, dy$.   **2.** $x^2y' + y^2 = 0$.

3. $(x^2 + y^2)\, dy + xy\, dx = 0$.   **4.** $2uv\, du + (v^2 - 3u^2)\, dv = 0$.

5. $\dfrac{dx}{dt} = tx^2$.

6. $(x + 3y - 1)\, dx + (x - 1)\, dy = 0$.

7. $x\, dy - 3y\, dx = x^2\, dx$.   **8.** $2y\, dx - x\, dy = 0$.

9. $(x + y)y' = y - x$.   **10.** $dy = 2(xy + x)\, dx$.

11. $(x - 2y + 5)\, dx + (2x + 4)\, dy = 0$.

12. $x^3\, dy - xy^2\, dx = 2ay^2\, dx$.   **13.** $x^3 - 2y^3 + 3xy^2 \cdot y' = 0$.

14. $(2x + y + 2)\, dy - y\, dx = 0$.   **15.** $x^3\, dy + y^3\, dx = 0$.

16. $(x^3 - y^3)\, dx + xy^2\, dy = 0$.   **17.** $y' = x + y$.

18. $2av^2\, du + u^3\, dv = 0$.   **19.** $(4u + 4v - 1)\, du = dv$.

20. $(3x - 2y + 6)\, dx = (x + 2)\, dy$.

21. $(3x - y)\, dy + dx = 0$.   **22.** $3xy' = y - xy$.

23. $y' = \sec^2 x \sec^3 y$.   **24.** $(xy^2 - 4)y' = -y^3$.

In Exs. 25–36, find the particular solution indicated.

25. $x^2\, dy - y^2\, dx = 0$; when $x = 2$, $y = 4$.

26. $\dfrac{dv}{dt} = \cos t - v$; when $t = 0$, $v = 0$.

27. $(x - 2y)\,dx + y\,dy = 0$; when $x = 1$, $y = 0$.

28. $(x^2 + 2y^2)\,dx = xy\,dy$; when $x = 1$, $y = 1$.

29. $\dfrac{dv}{dt} = -t - 4v$; when $t = 0$, $v = 1$.

30. $dx = (6t + 2)\,dt$; when $t = 0$, $x = -1$.

31. $(x^2 + y^2)\,dx - 2xy\,dy = 0$; when $x = 1$, $y = 2$.

32. $(xy - x^2)y' = y^2$; when $x = 1$, $y = 1$.

33. $\dfrac{dv}{dx} = \dfrac{2v - x}{x}$; when $x = 1$, $v = 0$.

34. $\dfrac{dy}{dx} = \dfrac{1 - x}{y}$; when $x = -3$, $y = 4$.

35. $y' \cos x = 1 - y - \sin x$; when $x = 0$, $y = 2$.

36. $\sin \theta \dfrac{dr}{d\theta} = 1 - 2r \cos \theta$; when $\theta = \dfrac{1}{2}\pi$, $r = 4$.

253. Equation of the catenary. Although the applications of differential equations are extremely varied, in this brief course we shall confine our attention almost entirely, in regard to applications, to the study of motion (Chapter 34). However, we have not yet found the equation of the catenary (§ 103) or of the tractrix (§ 105); since these problems may be solved by means of the work just completed, we shall take them up now.

When the vector sum of all the forces acting on a body is zero— *i.e.*, when all the forces balance—the corresponding vector polygon (§ 56) is a *closed polygon*. From this fact we can find the equation of the catenary.

Given a string suspended from two points, imagine the string cut at the lowest point V and a random point P (Fig. 230). If we apply at V and P forces equal to the tensions that were present before the cuts were made, the segment VP will remain in position. If the weight of the string per unit length is w, the segment is in equilibrium under the three forces ws, F_h, F_t, whose directions are, respectively, vertical,

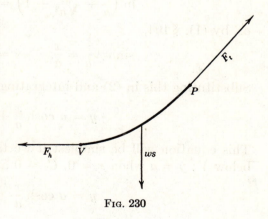

Fɪɢ. 230

horizontal, and along the tangent. Since the three forces form a closed triangle, it appears (Fig. 231) that

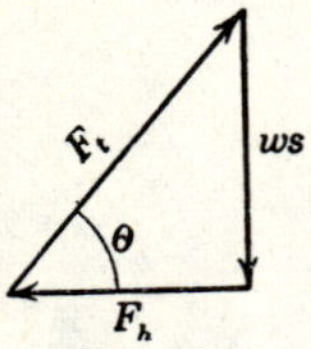

$$\tan \theta = \frac{ws}{F_h}.$$

For simplicity, put $\dfrac{F_h}{w} = a$:

(1) $$\tan \theta = \frac{s}{a}.$$

Fig. 231

Nothing has yet been said about coördinates. If we take the axes in the usual directions, θ is the slope-angle, and (1) becomes

(2) $$\frac{dy}{dx} = \frac{s}{a}.$$

Substituting this in the formula

$$\sqrt{1 + \left(\frac{dy}{dx}\right)^2} = \frac{ds}{dx},$$

we find

$$\sqrt{1 + \frac{s^2}{a^2}} = \frac{ds}{dx}, \qquad \frac{ds}{\sqrt{s^2 + a^2}} = \frac{dx}{a}.$$

Integration gives (Ex. 9, p. 250)

$$\ln(s + \sqrt{s^2 + a^2}) = \frac{x}{a} + C_1.$$

Take the y-axis through V, so that $s = 0$ when $x = 0$, and $C_1 = \ln a$:

$$\ln(s + \sqrt{s^2 + a^2}) = \frac{x}{a} + \ln a,$$

$$\ln\left(\frac{s}{a} + \sqrt{\frac{s^2}{a^2} + 1}\right) = \frac{x}{a},$$

or, by (1), § 104,

$$\sinh^{-1}\frac{s}{a} = \frac{x}{a}, \qquad s = a \sinh \frac{x}{a}.$$

Substituting this in (2) and integrating, we get

$$y = a \cosh \frac{x}{a} + C_2.$$

This equation will be simplest if we take the origin at distance a below V: $y = a$ when $x = 0$, $C_2 = 0$ and

$$y = a \cosh \frac{x}{a}.$$

254. Equation of the tractrix. By Ex. 19, p. 180, the slope of the tractrix at any point is

$$\frac{dy}{dx} = -\frac{y}{\sqrt{a^2 - y^2}}.$$

This gives

$$dx = -\frac{\sqrt{a^2 - y^2}\, dy}{y},$$

so that

$$x = -\sqrt{a^2 - y^2} + a \ln \frac{a + \sqrt{a^2 - y^2}}{y} + C.$$

Since the point $(0, a)$ is on the curve, $C = 0$. Thus

$$x = a \ln \frac{a + \sqrt{a^2 - y^2}}{y} - \sqrt{a^2 - y^2}$$

$$= a \operatorname{sech}^{-1} \frac{y}{a} - \sqrt{a^2 - y^2},$$

by (5), § 104.

25. Equation of the tractrix. Ex. 15, p. 150, the slope of
the tractrix at any point is

The first

CHAPTER 33 *LINEAR DIFFERENTIAL*
EQUATIONS

255. The linear equation. A differential equation of the n-th order is said to be *linear* if it is of *the first degree in* $y, y', \cdots, y^{(n)}$. Thus every linear differential equation of the n-th order can be written in the form

$$p_0 y^{(n)} + p_1 y^{(n-1)} + \cdots + p_n y = X,$$

where $p_0, p_1, \cdots, p_n$ and the right member X are functions of x.

In this chapter we shall confine our attention to the *linear differential equation with constant coefficients*

$$(1) \qquad a_0 y^{(n)} + a_1 y^{(n-1)} + \cdots + a_n y = X.$$

This equation is of prime importance in applied mathematics.

256. The homogeneous linear equation. A linear differential equation whose right-hand member is zero is said to be *homogeneous*. Thus the general form of the homogeneous linear equation with constant coefficients is

$$(1) \qquad a_0 y^{(n)} + a_1 y^{(n-1)} + \cdots + a_n y = 0.$$

If $y = y_1$ is a particular solution of (1), then $y = c_1 y_1$, where c_1 is arbitrary, is also a solution, as appears at once by substitution in (1). Further, if $y = y_2$ is a second particular solution, then not only $y = c_2 y_2$ but also

$$y = c_1 y_1 + c_2 y_2$$

is a solution. Finally, if

$$y = y_1, \quad y = y_2, \cdots, y = y_n$$

are n linearly independent* particular solutions, then

$$y = c_1 y_1 + c_2 y_2 + \cdots + c_n y_n$$

is a solution, and since it contains n arbitrary constants, it is the general solution.

We proceed to show that the general solution of equation (1) can always be written down, provided a certain algebraic equation of the n-th degree can be solved. The theory will be developed in detail only for the equation of the second order.

257. The characteristic equation. Given a homogeneous linear equation of the second order,

(1) $$a_0 y'' + a_1 y' + a_2 y = 0,$$

we seek y, as a function of x, such that a linear combination of y, y', and y'' will vanish identically. Intuitively, we react that y and its derivatives should be the same, except for constant factors. We already know that the exponential function $y = e^{mx}$ is the only one with that property; that is, we know the solution of $y' = my$. Hence let us try to determine m so that the function

$$y = e^{mx}$$

will satisfy the equation. Substituting in (1) the values

$$y = e^{mx}, \quad y' = me^{mx}, \quad y'' = m^2 e^{mx}$$

and dividing out the factor e^{mx}, we find that the differential equation is satisfied, provided

(2) $$a_0 m^2 + a_1 m + a_2 = 0.$$

Equation (2) is called the *characteristic equation*, or *auxiliary equation*, corresponding to (1). Thus

$$y = e^{mx}$$

is a solution of equation (1) *if and only if m is a root of the characteristic equation.*

---

* A set of functions $y_1, y_2, \cdots, y_n$ are *linearly dependent* if and only if there exists a set of constants $a_1, a_2, \cdots, a_n$ (not all zero) such that

$$a_1 y_1 + a_2 y_2 + \cdots + a_n y_n \equiv 0.$$

For example, $y_1 = e^x$, $y_2 = e^{-x}$, $y_3 = \sinh x$ are dependent, since $y_1 - y_2 - 2y_3 \equiv 0$. If the set of functions is not linearly dependent, the functions are said to be linearly independent.

258. Distinct roots. If the roots m_1, m_2 of the characteristic equation are *real and distinct*, we obtain at once two distinct particular solutions of the differential equation, viz.

$$y = e^{m_1 x}, \qquad y = e^{m_2 x}.$$

Hence, by § 256, the general solution is

(1) $$y = c_1 e^{m_1 x} + c_2 e^{m_2 x}.$$

Example: Solve the differential equation $2y'' - y' - y = 0$.

The characteristic equation is

$$2m^2 - m - 1 = 0,$$

whence

$$m = 1 \qquad \text{or} \qquad m = -\tfrac{1}{2}.$$

Thus the general solution of the given equation is

$$y = c_1 e^x + c_2 e^{-\frac{1}{2}x}.$$

EXERCISES

Find the general solution of the equations in Exs. 1–14.

1. $y'' - y' - 2y = 0$.

2. $y'' - 2y' - 8y = 0$.

3. $3y'' + 5y' - 2y = 0$.

4. $2y'' - 5y' - 3y = 0$.

5. $10\dfrac{d^2 y}{dt^2} - 3\dfrac{dy}{dt} - y = 0$.

6. $7\dfrac{d^2 x}{dt^2} - 5\dfrac{dx}{dt} - 2x = 0$.

7. $3\dfrac{d^2 x}{dy^2} = \dfrac{dx}{dy}$.

8. $\dfrac{d^2 x}{dt^2} = \beta^2 x$.

9. $y'' + 8y' + 15y = 0$.

10. $y'' - 7y' = 0$.

11. $4\dfrac{d^2 v}{du^2} - v = 0$.

12. $20\dfrac{d^2 x}{dt^2} = x + \dfrac{dx}{dt}$.

13. $3y'' + 14y' - 5y = 0$.

14. $12y'' = y - y'$.

In Exs. 15–24, find the particular solution which satisfies the given conditions.

15. $y'' + 3y' = 0$; when $x = 0$, $y = 0$ and $y' = 6$.

Ans. $y = 2(1 - e^{-3x})$.

16. $4y'' - 5y' + y = 0$; when $x = 0$, $y = -1$ and $y' = 0$.

Ans. $3y = e^x - 4e^{\frac{1}{4}x}$.

17. $\dfrac{d^2 x}{dt^2} - 3\dfrac{dx}{dt} + 2x = 0$; when $t = 0$, $x = 2$ and $\dfrac{dx}{dt} = 0$.

Ans. $x = 4e^t - 2e^{2t}$.

18. $2\dfrac{d^2x}{dt^2} - 3\dfrac{dx}{dt} + x = 0$; when $t = 0$, $x = -3$ and $\dfrac{dx}{dt} = -1$.

$$Ans. \; x = e^t - 4e^{\frac{1}{2}t}.$$

19. $y'' + ky' = 0$; when $x = 0$, $y = 0$ and $y' = 1$.

$$Ans. \; ky = 1 - e^{-kx}.$$

20. $y'' + 11y' + 28y = 0$; when $x = 0$, $y = 0$, and when $x = 1$, $y = 1$.

$$Ans. \; y = \frac{e^{-4x} - e^{-7x}}{e^{-4} - e^{-7}}.$$

21. $y'' + 11y' + 28y = 0$; when $x = 0$, $y = 0$, and when $x = 1$, $y' = 1$.

$$Ans. \; y = \frac{e^{-4x} - e^{-7x}}{7e^{-7} - 4e^{-4}}.$$

22. $6y'' = y + y'$; when $x = 0$, $y = 1$ and $y' = \frac{1}{6}$.

$$Ans. \; 5y = 3e^{\frac{1}{2}x} + 2e^{-\frac{1}{3}x}.$$

23. $y'' + 2y' = 0$; when $x = 0$, $y = 4$, and as $x \to \infty$, $y \to 3$.

$$Ans. \; y = 3 + e^{-2x}.$$

24. $y'' - 2y' - 3y = 0$; when $x = 0$, $y = 4$, and as $x \to \infty$, $y \to k$.

$$Ans. \; \text{If } k \neq 0, \text{ no solution; if } k = 0, \; y = 4e^{-x}.$$

259. Equal roots. When the characteristic equation has equal roots, the method of the previous article does not give the general solution. For, if $m_1 = m_2$, equation (1) above becomes

$$y = c_1 e^{m_1 x} + c_2 e^{m_1 x}$$
$$= (c_1 + c_2)e^{m_1 x} = C_1 e^{m_1 x};$$

hence the solution contains only a single constant, and is a particular solution.

To find a second particular solution, let us try

$$(1) \qquad\qquad y = xe^{m_1 x},$$

whence

$$y' = e^{m_1 x}(m_1 x + 1),$$
$$y'' = e^{m_1 x}(m_1^2 x + 2m_1).$$

Substituting in the differential equation, we find that (1) will be a solution, provided

$$(2) \qquad (a_0 m_1^2 + a_1 m_1 + a_2)x + 2a_0 m_1 + a_1 \equiv 0.$$

Now the coefficient of x vanishes because m_1 is a root of the characteristic equation

$$(3) \qquad\qquad a_0 m^2 + a_1 m + a_2 = 0.$$

Further, since by hypothesis equation (3) has *equal roots*, we know (Ex. 58, p. 39) that the first derivative of the polynomial in the left member of (3) vanishes for $m = m_1$ — *i.e.*, that

$$2a_0 m_1 + a_1 = 0.$$

Thus (2) holds, and $y = xe^{m_1 x}$ is a second particular solution.

Therefore the general solution of equation (1), § 257, in the case of equal roots is

$$y = c_1 e^{m_1 x} + c_2 x e^{m_1 x}.$$

Example: Solve the equation

$$\frac{d^2 z}{dt^2} - 10\frac{dz}{dt} + 25z = 0.$$

The characteristic equation is

$$m^2 - 10m + 25 = 0,$$

whence

$$m = 5, 5.$$

Thus the general solution is

$$z = c_1 e^{5t} + c_2 t e^{5t}.$$

260. The complex exponential function. By (1), § 203,

$$(1) \qquad e^x = 1 + x + \frac{x^2}{2!} + \frac{x^3}{3!} + \frac{x^4}{4!} + \frac{x^5}{5!} + \cdots + \frac{x^n}{n!} + \cdots$$

for all real values of x.

We use the above series as a guide to lead us to a reasonable definition of e^z, when z is complex, $z = x + iy$, $i = \sqrt{-1}$, x and y real. Then, in turn, that definition leads us to the discovery of the form of solution of a differential equation whose characteristic equation has conjugate complex roots.

Until we reach the desired definition of e^z, the work in this section is purely formal. It needs no justification, being only a sort of laboratory device used to decide upon a feasible starting point.

Write $e^z = e^{x+iy} = e^x \cdot e^{iy}$. Then a sensible meaning for e^{iy} is needed. In the series (1) replace x by iy to obtain

$$e^{iy} = 1 + \frac{iy}{1!} + \frac{i^2 y^2}{2!} + \frac{i^3 y^3}{3!} + \frac{i^4 y^4}{4!} + \frac{i^5 y^5}{5!} + \frac{i^6 y^6}{6!}$$

$$+ \cdots + \frac{i^{2k} y^{2k}}{(2k)!} + \frac{i^{2k+1} y^{2k+1}}{(2k+1)!} + \cdots,$$

or

$$(2) \quad e^{iy} = 1 + \frac{iy}{1!} - \frac{y^2}{2!} - \frac{iy^3}{3!} + \frac{y^4}{4!} + \frac{iy^5}{5!} - \frac{y^6}{6!}$$
$$+ \cdots + \frac{(-1)^k y^{2k}}{(2k)!} + i\frac{(-1)^k y^{2k+1}}{(2k+1)!} + \cdots.$$

In (2), separate the real from the imaginary terms, thus finding

$$(3) \quad e^{iy} = 1 - \frac{y^2}{2!} + \frac{y^4}{4!} - \frac{y^6}{6!} + \cdots + \frac{(-1)^k y^{2k}}{(2k)!} + \cdots$$
$$+ i\left[\frac{y}{1!} - \frac{y^3}{3!} + \frac{y^5}{5!} - \cdots + \frac{(-1)^k y^{2k+1}}{(2k+1)!} + \cdots\right].$$

The series on the right in (3) are those we have already obtained for cos y and sin y, so (3) can be written in the form

$$(4) \qquad e^{iy} = \cos y + i \sin y.$$

Equation (4) is our starting point. We use it as the *definition* of e^{iy} for y real and $i = \sqrt{-1}$. Then we further *define* e^{x+iy} by:

$$(5) \qquad e^{x+iy} = e^x(\cos y + i \sin y),$$

for x and y real, $i = \sqrt{-1}$.

That these are useful definitions will appear when we show that they lead to solutions of a differential equation which has a characteristic equation with conjugate complex roots.

261. Conjugate complex roots. Suppose the characteristic equation, *with real coefficients,*

$$(1) \qquad a_0 m^2 + a_1 m + a_2 = 0$$

has complex roots. Then those roots must be conjugates, $m = \alpha \pm i\beta$. Superficially, then, the differential equation

$$(2) \qquad a_0 y'' + a_1 y' + a_2 y = 0$$

appears to have the general solution

$$(3) \qquad y = c_1 e^{(\alpha + i\beta)x} + c_2 e^{(\alpha - i\beta)x}$$
$$= e^{\alpha x}(c_1 e^{i\beta x} + c_2 e^{-i\beta x}).$$

Now, by a definition in the preceding section,

$$e^{i\beta x} = \cos \beta x + i \sin \beta x$$

and

$$e^{-i\beta x} = \cos \beta x - i \sin \beta x.$$

Hence we consider as a tentative solution

$$y = e^{\alpha x}(c_1 \cos \beta x + ic_1 \sin \beta x + c_2 \cos \beta x - ic_2 \sin \beta x)$$

$$= (c_1 + c_2)e^{\alpha x} \cos \beta x + i(c_1 - c_2)e^{\alpha x} \sin \beta x,$$

or

(4) $$\boldsymbol{y = c_3 e^{\alpha x} \cos \beta x + c_4 e^{\alpha x} \sin \beta x,}$$

with new arbitrary constants* $c_3 = c_1 + c_2$ and $c_4 = i(c_1 - c_2)$.

Now comes a justification of our definition of e^z and our manipulations of the superficial solution (3) into the meaningful form (4). We show by direct substitution that (4) is a solution of the differential equation, with characteristic equation having roots $\alpha \pm i\beta$.

If the characteristic equation (1) has the solutions $m = \alpha \pm i\beta$, then that equation is

$$(m - \alpha)^2 = -\beta^2,$$

or

$$m^2 - 2\alpha m + \alpha^2 + \beta^2 = 0,$$

so that the corresponding differential equation is

(5) $$y'' - 2\alpha y' + (\alpha^2 + \beta^2)y = 0.$$

We need to show that (4) satisfies (5). From

$$y_1 = e^{\alpha x} \cos \beta x$$

we find that

$$y_1' = e^{\alpha x}(\alpha \cos \beta x - \beta \sin \beta x)$$

$$y_1'' = e^{\alpha x}[(\alpha^2 - \beta^2) \cos \beta x - 2\alpha\beta \sin \beta x],$$

from which

$$y_1'' - 2\alpha y_1' + (\alpha^2 + \beta^2)y_1 = 0$$

at once. Thus $y_1 = e^{\alpha x} \cos \beta x$ is a solution of (5). In the same way it can be shown that $y_2 = e^{\alpha x} \sin \beta x$ satisfies (5). It follows that equation (4), having the right number of arbitrary constants, is the general solution of equation (5).

It is important to note that we never use the form (3). From characteristic equation roots $m = \alpha \pm i\beta$, we write down the solution (4) directly.

---

* In a problem with a real solution, the original constants c_1 and c_2 would be conjugate complex numbers, and the new constants c_3 and c_4 would be real.

Example: Find a particular solution of the equation

(6) $$\frac{d^2x}{dt^2} - 4\frac{dx}{dt} + 13x = 0$$

satisfying the conditions $x = 1$, $\frac{dx}{dt} = 5$ when $t = 0$.

The characteristic equation is
$$m^2 - 4m + 13 = 0,$$
whence
$$m = 2 \pm \sqrt{-9} = 2 \pm 3i.$$

Thus the general solution is

(7) $$x = e^{2t}(c_1 \cos 3t + c_2 \sin 3t).$$

To find the desired particular solution, differentiate (7):

(8) $$\frac{dx}{dt} = e^{2t}(2c_1 \cos 3t + 2c_2 \sin 3t - 3c_1 \sin 3t + 3c_2 \cos 3t).$$

Substituting $x = 1$, $t = 0$ in (7) and $\frac{dx}{dt} = 5$, $t = 0$ in (8), we get

$$1 = c_1, \qquad 5 = 2c_1 + 3c_2,$$

whence $c_1 = 1$, $c_2 = 1$, and the solution is

$$x = e^{2t}(\cos 3t + \sin 3t).$$

EXERCISES

In Exs. 1–14, find the general solution.

1. $y'' + 6y' + 9y = 0$.   *Ans.* $y = c_1 e^{-3x} + c_2 x e^{-3x}$.

2. $4y'' - 4y' + y = 0$.   *Ans.* $y = c_1 e^{\frac{1}{2}x} + c_2 x e^{\frac{1}{2}x}$.

3. $\dfrac{d^2x}{dt^2} + 2\dfrac{dx}{dt} + 5x = 0$.   *Ans.* $x = e^{-t}(c_1 \cos 2t + c_2 \sin 2t)$.

4. $\dfrac{d^2x}{dt^2} + 9x = 0$.   *Ans.* $x = c_1 \cos 3t + c_2 \sin 3t$.

5. $\dfrac{d^2u}{dv^2} + 4\dfrac{du}{dv} + 5u = 0$.   6. $\dfrac{d^2u}{dv^2} + 4\dfrac{du}{dv} + 4u = 0$.

7. $y'' + 9y = 6y'$.   8. $9y'' = -4y$.

9. $\dfrac{d^2r}{d\theta^2} + 2\dfrac{dr}{d\theta} + 10r = 0$.   10. $\dfrac{d^2r}{d\theta^2} + 2\dfrac{dr}{d\theta} + r = 0$.

11. $y'' - 5y' + 4y = 0$.   12. $y'' = 16y$.

13. $25y'' + 4y = 20y'$.   14. $2(y'' + y') = -5y$.

In Exs. 15–24, find the particular solution indicated.

15. $y'' - 6y' + 9y = 0$; when $x = 0$, $y = 2$, and $y' = 5$.

                     Ans. $y = e^{3x}(2 - x)$.

16. $y'' - 6y' + 10y = 0$; when $x = 0$, $y = 2$, and $y' = 5$.

$Ans.$ $y = e^{3x}(2 \cos x - \sin x)$.

17. $y'' + 10y' + 29y = 0$; when $x = 0$, $y = 4$, and $y' = 20$.

18. $9y'' + y = 6y'$; when $x = 0$, $y = 0$, and $y' = 3$.

19. $4\left(\dfrac{d^2x}{dt^2} + \dfrac{dx}{dt}\right) = -25x$; when $t = 0$, $x = 2$, and $\dfrac{dx}{dt} = -1$.

20. $\dfrac{d^2x}{dt^2} + 2\dfrac{dx}{dt} + 17x = 0$; when $t = 0$, $x = 0$, and $\dfrac{dx}{dt} = 2$.

21. $y'' + 4y = 0$; when $x = 0$, $y = 3$, and when $x = \frac{1}{4}\pi$, $y = 2$.

22. $9y'' = -y$; when $x = \pi$, $y = 3$, and when $x = 2\pi$, $y = -3$.

23. $\dfrac{d^2x}{dt^2} + 2\dfrac{dx}{dt} + 5x = 0$; when $t = 0$, $x = 1$, and when $t = \frac{1}{4}\pi$, $x = -3$.

$Ans.$ $x = e^{-t}(\cos 2t - 3e^{\frac{\pi}{4}} \sin 2t)$.

24. $\dfrac{d^2x}{dt^2} + 2\dfrac{dx}{dt} + 5x = 0$; when $t = 0$, $x = 1$, and when $t = \frac{1}{2}\pi$, $x = -3$.

Compare with Ex. 23. $Ans.$ No solution.

In Exs. 25–28, for the indicated particular solution, find the values of y and y' at $x = 2$.

25. $4y'' + 4y' + y = 0$; when $x = 0$, $y = 2$ and $y' = 0$.

$Ans.$ At $x = 2$, $y = \dfrac{4}{e}$, $y' = -\dfrac{1}{e}$.

26. $4y'' = 3(4y' - 3y)$; when $x = 0$, $y = 4$ and $y' = 4$.

$Ans.$ At $x = 2$, $y = 0$, $y' = -2e^3$.

27. $16y'' + \pi^2 y = 0$; when $x = 0$, $y = 8$ and $y' = 0$.

$Ans.$ $y = 0$, $y' = -2\pi$.

28. $4y'' + y = 0$; when $x = 0$, $y = 3$, and when $x = \pi$, $y = 1$.

$Ans.$ $y = 2.46$, $y' = -0.99$.

In Exs. 29–34, use the definition of e^{iy} given in § 260.

29. Show that $e^{\frac{1}{2}\pi i} = i$, $e^{\pi i} = -1$, $e^{2\pi i} = 1$.

30. Show that $\ln (-1) = \pi i$, $\ln (-k) = \pi i + \ln k$, $\ln i = \frac{1}{2}\pi i$. (Ex. 29.)

31. Show that, if n is an integer, $e^{2n\pi i} = 1$, whence* $\ln 1 = 2n\pi i$.

32. From $e^{ix} = \cos x + i \sin x$, and the corresponding expression for e^{-ix}, form the product $e^{ix} \cdot e^{-ix} = e^0 = 1$, and draw what conclusion you can. $Ans.$ $\cos^2 x + \sin^2 x = 1$.

33. Square both members of the identity $e^{ix} = \cos x + i \sin x$, recall that x is real, and draw what conclusions you can.

$Ans.$ $\cos 2x = \cos^2 x - \sin^2 x$, $\sin 2x = 2 \sin x \cos x$.

34. Use $e^{ix} = \cos x + i \sin x$ and the same identity in y to obtain formulas for $\cos (x + y)$ and $\sin (x + y)$.

---

* In the domain of complex variables, the logarithm is an infinitely many-valued function. The value $\ln 1 = 0$ is the "principal value," analogous to the "principal values" of the inverse trigonometric functions (§ 87). Likewise the values given in Ex. 30 are the principal values.

262. Equations of higher order. The theory of §§ 257–261 is readily extended to equations of order higher than the second. We give the results without proof.

Let there be given a differential equation

(1) $$a_0 y^{(n)} + a_1 y^{(n-1)} + \cdots + a_n y = 0.$$

(*a*) If the roots m_1, $m_2 \cdots$, m_n of the characteristic equation

$$a_0 m^n + a_1 m^{n-1} + \cdots + a_n = 0$$

are all real and distinct, the general solution of (1) is

$$y = c_1 e^{m_1 x} + c_2 e^{m_2 x} + \cdots + c_n e^{m_n x}.$$

(*b*) Corresponding to a *double root* m_1, the terms in the general solution are

$$y = c_1 e^{m_1 x} + c_2 x e^{m_1 x};$$

corresponding to a *triple root,*

$$y = c_1 e^{m_1 x} + c_2 x e^{m_1 x} + c_3 x^2 e^{m_1 x}; \text{ etc.}$$

(*c*) A pair of roots $\alpha \pm i\beta$ give rise to the terms

$$y = e^{\alpha x}(c_1 \cos \beta x + c_2 \sin \beta x);$$

a pair of *double roots* $\alpha \pm i\beta$ give rise to the terms

$$y = e^{\alpha x}(c_1 \cos \beta x + c_2 \sin \beta x + c_3 x \cos \beta x + c_4 x \sin \beta x); \text{ etc.}$$

Example: Solve the equation

(2) $$y^{(4)} - 2y''' - 2y'' + 6y' + 5y = 0.$$

First we solve the characteristic equation

$$m^4 - 2m^3 - 2m^2 + 6m + 5 = 0,$$

by the method of synthetic division. The roots are found to be $m = -1, -1, 2 \pm i$. Therefore, the general solution of equation (2) is

$$y = c_1 e^{-x} + c_2 x e^{-x} + c_3 e^{2x} \cos x + c_4 e^{2x} \sin x.$$

EXERCISES

In Exs. 1–22, find the general solution.

1. $y''' - 4y'' + 4y' = 0.$ Ans. $y = c_1 + c_2 e^{2x} + c_3 x e^{2x}.$

2. $y''' + 2y'' - 3y' - 10y = 0.$

           Ans. $y = c_1 e^{2x} + e^{-2x}(c_2 \cos x + c_3 \sin x).$

3. $y''' + 9y' = 0.$ **4.** $y^{(4)} = y''.$

5. $y''' = 4y'.$ **6.** $y^{(4)} - 2y'' + y' = 0.$

7. $\dfrac{d^3x}{dt^3} + 3\dfrac{d^2x}{dt^2} - 4x = 0.$

8. $4\dfrac{d^3x}{dt^3} - 4\dfrac{d^2x}{dt^2} - 7\dfrac{dx}{dt} - 2x = 0.$

9. $2\dfrac{d^3u}{dy^3} - 3\dfrac{d^2u}{dy^2} + 2\dfrac{du}{dy} + 2u = 0.$

10. $\dfrac{d^4r}{d\theta^4} - 8\dfrac{d^2r}{d\theta^2} - 9r = 0.$ **11.** $y^{(4)} + 8y'' + 16y = 0.$

12. $4y^{(5)} + y''' = 0.$ **13.** $2y''' - 3y'' - 3y' + 2y = 0.$

14. $y''' - 3y'' + 3y' - y = 0.$

15. $y^{(4)} - 2y''' + 2y'' - 2y' + y = 0.$

16. $6\dfrac{d^5x}{dt^5} + 35\dfrac{d^4x}{dt^4} + 47\dfrac{d^3x}{dt^3} + 12\dfrac{d^2x}{dt^2} = 0.$

$\qquad\qquad\qquad$ *Ans.* $x = c_1 + c_2 t + c_3 e^{-4t} + c_4 e^{-\frac{1}{3}t} + c_5 e^{-\frac{3}{2}t}.$

17. $y^{(4)} - 4y''' + 14y'' - 20y' + 25y = 0.$

$\qquad\qquad$ *Ans.* $y = e^x(c_1 \cos 2x + c_2 \sin 2x + c_3 x \cos 2x + c_4 x \sin 2x).$

18. $y^{(4)} - 7y''' + 8y'' + 28y' - 48y = 0.$

19. $y^{(4)} + 2y''' + 5y'' + 8y' + 4y = 0.$

20. $4y''' - 12y'' + 13y' - 10y = 0.$

21. $y''' - 6y'' + 12y' - 8y = 0.$

22. $y^{(6)} + 9y^{(4)} + 24y'' + 16y = 0.$

In Exs. 23–31, find the indicated particular solution.

23. $y''' + 4y'' + 4y' = 0;$ when $x = 0,\ y = 4,\ y' = -1,\ y'' = -4.$

$\qquad\qquad\qquad\qquad$ *Ans.* $y = 2 + 2e^{-2x} + 3xe^{-2x}.$

24. $\dfrac{d^4x}{d\theta^4} + \dfrac{d^2x}{d\theta^2} = 0;$ when $\theta = 0,\ x = 0,\ \dfrac{dx}{d\theta} = 0,\ \dfrac{d^2x}{d\theta^2} = 2,\ \dfrac{d^3x}{d\theta^3} = 1.$

$\qquad\qquad\qquad\qquad$ *Ans.* $x = \theta + 2 - 2 \cos \theta - \sin \theta.$

25. $\dfrac{d^3x}{dt^3} + 4\dfrac{dx}{dt} = 0;$ when $t = 0,\ x = 0,$ when $t = \dfrac{1}{4}\pi,\ x = -1,$ and when

$t = \frac{1}{2}\pi,\ x = 2.$ $\qquad\qquad$ *Ans.* $x = 1 - \cos 2t - 2 \sin 2t.$

26. $y''' + 2y'' + 2y' = 0;$ when $x = 0,\ y = 0,\ y' = 3,\ y'' = -4.$

$\qquad\qquad\qquad$ *Ans.* $y = 1 + e^{-x}(2 \sin x - \cos x).$

27. $y''' + y'' + 4y' + 4y = 0;$ when $x = 0,\ y = 0,\ y' = 1,\ y'' = -5.$

$\qquad\qquad\qquad\qquad$ *Ans.* $y = \cos 2x - e^{-x}.$

28. $\dfrac{d^3x}{dt^3} - 2\dfrac{d^2x}{dt^2} - 3\dfrac{dx}{dt} + 10x = 0;$ when $t = 0,\ x = 0,\ \dfrac{dx}{dt} = -4,\ \dfrac{d^2x}{dt^2} = 1.$

$\qquad\qquad\qquad\qquad$ *Ans.* $x = e^{2t}(e^{-4t} - \cos t).$

29. $y^{(4)} - 2y''' + 2y'' - 2y' + y = 0;$ when $x = 0,\ y = 0,\ y' = 0,$
$y'' = 0,\ y''' = 4.$ $\qquad\qquad$ *Ans.* $y = 2(\cos x - e^x + xe^x).$

30. $\dfrac{d^4y}{dx^4} + 4\dfrac{d^2y}{dx^2} = 0;$ when $x = 0,\ y = 0,$ and when $x = \dfrac{1}{4}\pi,\ y = 0,\ y' = 0,$
$y'' = 4.$ $\qquad\qquad$ *Ans.* $y = \dfrac{2}{\pi - 2}(\cos 2x - 1 + 2x) - \sin 2x.$

31. $y''' + y'' - 6y' = 0$; when $x = 0$, $y = 2$, and when $x \to \infty$, $y \to 4$.

$$Ans. \ y = 2(2 - e^{-3x}).$$

263. The non-homogeneous linear equation. Let us consider now the *non-homogeneous* linear equation

(1) $$a_0 y^{(n)} + a_1 y^{(n-1)} + \cdots + a_n y = R.$$

In solving this equation, the first step is to write down the **general solution**

$$y_c = c_1 y_1 + c_2 y_2 + \cdots + c_n y_n$$

of the *homogeneous* equation obtained from (1) by *making the right member zero*. The quantity y_c is called the *complementary function*.

The next step is to obtain, by any means whatever, a *particular solution of* (1), say

$$y = y_p.$$

Then the equation

(2) $$y = y_c + y_p$$

is a solution of (1), as appears by substitution, and since it contains n arbitrary constants, it is the general solution.

Various methods exist for finding a particular solution

$$y = y_p.$$

The method given below, though not entirely general, is available in nearly all of the simpler applications.

Example: Solve the equation

(3) $$y'' - 5y' + 6y = x + e^{2x}.$$

The complementary function, *i.e.*, the solution of the equation

$$y'' - 5y' + 6y = 0,$$

is

$$y_c = c_1 e^{2x} + c_2 e^{3x}.$$

To obtain a particular integral of (3), proceed as follows.

Differentiating (3) twice, we obtain

(4) $$y^{(4)} - 5y''' + 6y'' = 4e^{2x}.$$

Differentiating again, we get

(5) $$y^{(5)} - 5y^{(4)} + 6y''' = 8e^{2x}.$$

Multiplying equation (4) by 2 and subtracting from (5), we get the *homogeneous* equation

(6) $$y^{(5)} - 7y^{(4)} + 16y''' - 12y'' = 0.$$

The complementary function y_c forms part of the solution of this equation; hence two of the roots of the characteristic equation

$$m^5 - 7m^4 + 16m^3 - 12m^2 = 0$$

are $m = 2, 3$. The other roots are $2, 0, 0$. Thus the general solution of (6) is

(7) $$y = c_1 e^{2x} + c_2 e^{3x} + c_3 + c_4 x + c_5 x e^{2x}.$$

Let us substitute y in the original equation as a trial solution, noting, however, that the terms arising from the complementary function must disappear identically after the substitution, so that it is sufficient to substitute*

(8) $$y = c_3 + c_4 x + c_5 x e^{2x}.$$

We have

$$y' = c_4 + 2c_5 x e^{2x} + c_5 e^{2x},$$
$$y'' = 4c_5 x e^{2x} + 4c_5 e^{2x}.$$

Substituting in (3), we find that (8) will be a particular integral provided the equation

$$4c_5 x e^{2x} + 4c_5 e^{2x} - 5c_4 - 10c_5 x e^{2x}$$
$$- 5c_5 e^{2x} + 6c_3 + 6c_4 x + 6c_5 x e^{2x} = x + e^{2x}$$

holds identically — *i.e.*, for all values of x. The terms in $x e^{2x}$ destroy each other. Equating coefficients of the other functions, we find the following:

Coefficients of e^{2x}: $4c_5 - 5c_5 = 1.$
Coefficients of x: $6c_4 = 1.$
Constant terms: $-5c_4 + 6c_3 = 0.$

This gives

$$c_5 = -1, \quad c_4 = \tfrac{1}{6}, \quad c_3 = \tfrac{5}{36}.$$

Substituting in (7), we get as the general solution of (3)

$$y = c_1 e^{2x} + c_2 e^{3x} + \tfrac{5}{36} + \tfrac{1}{6}x - x e^{2x}.$$

* That is, we place, temporarily, $c_1 = c_2 = 0$. This is of course allowable, since we are trying merely to find a particular solution y_p.

Thus the method consists of the following steps:

1. Write down the complementary function.

2. Differentiate both members of the given equation successively until the right member becomes zero, either directly or by elimination. The original equation is thus replaced by a derived *homogeneous* equation of higher order [equation (6) above].

3. Write down, by § 262, the general solution [equation (7) above] of this derived equation. The complementary function will always be a part of this solution, so that certain of the roots of the characteristic equation are known beforehand; these should be removed at once by division.

4. Of the arbitrary constants occurring in this general solution, those belonging to the complementary function (c_1, c_2 above) will remain arbitrary in the final result; they may therefore be placed temporarily equal to zero, since we are trying to find merely a particular solution of the original equation. The other constants, the so-called *superfluous constants*, are determined by substituting the value of y in the original equation as a trial solution and equating coefficients.

It is clear that the success of the method depends on our ability to reduce the right-hand member to zero by differentiation and elimination, as in the above example. Hence R and its successive derivatives must contain only a finite number of distinct functions of x. The method therefore applies whenever R contains only constants or terms of the form x^n, e^{ax}, $\sin^n ax$, $\cos^n ax$, or products of these, n being a positive integer.

In this brief introduction to linear equations, it seems unwise to attempt refinements of the technique given above. More efficient methods for solving these problems, and an exposition of methods which apply to linear equations not touched upon here, can be found in Rainville's *Elementary Differential Equations*, New York, The Macmillan Company, 1952.

EXERCISES

In Exs. 1–22, find the general solution.

1. $2y'' - y' = x - 5$.   *Ans.* $y = c_1 e^{\frac{1}{2}x} + c_2 + 3x - \frac{1}{2}x^2$.

2. $y'' + y' = (1 + x)^2$.   *Ans.* $y = c_1 e^{-x} + c_2 + x + \frac{1}{3}x^3$.

3. $\dfrac{d^2x}{dt^2} + 4x = \cos 3t$.   *Ans.* $x = c_1 \cos 2t + c_2 \sin 2t - \frac{1}{5}\cos 3t$.

4. $y'' + 4y' + 3y = 3e^x$.   *Ans.* $y = c_1e^{-x} + c_2e^{-3x} + \frac{3}{8}e^x$.

5. $z'' - 5z' + 6z = e^{4x}$.   *Ans.* $z = c_1e^{3x} + c_2e^{2x} + \frac{1}{2}e^{4x}$.

6. $y'' + y = 3x^2 - 5x$.   *Ans.* $y = $ C. F. $+ 3x^2 - 5x - 6$.

7. $\dfrac{d^2u}{dv^2} - 4v = u$.   **8.** $\dfrac{d^2\theta}{dt^2} = \theta + 2$.

9. $4\dfrac{d^2x}{dt^2} + 4\dfrac{dx}{dt} = 6 - x$.   **10.** $\dfrac{d^2\theta}{dt^2} = t^2$.

11. $y'' - 2y' + y = 2e^{3x} - 3x + 4$.

     Ans. $y = $ C. F. $+ \frac{1}{2}e^{3x} - 3x - 2$.

12. $y'' - 5y' + 6y = \cos x - e^{2x}$.

     Ans. $y = $ C. F. $+ \frac{1}{10}\cos x - \frac{1}{10}\sin x + xe^{2x}$.

13. $y'' + y = e^{2x} + 2e^x$.   *Ans.* $y = $ C. F. $+ \frac{1}{5}e^{2x} + e^x$.

14. $\dfrac{d^2x}{dt^2} = \cos t - x$.   *Ans.* $x = $ C. F. $+ \frac{1}{2}t \sin t$.

15. $\dfrac{d^2x}{dt^2} + 4x = \sin 3t + t^2$.   *Ans.* $x = $ C. F. $- \frac{1}{5}\sin 3t + \frac{1}{4}t^2 - \frac{1}{8}$.

16. $y'' - y = e^x \sin x$.   *Ans.* $y = $ C. F. $- \frac{2}{5}e^x \cos x - \frac{1}{5}e^x \sin x$.

17. $y'' + y = 4 \sin x \cos x$.   *Ans.* $y = $ C. F. $- \frac{2}{3}\sin 2x$.

18. $2y'' - 3y' + y = 3 \cos x - 2e^{-2x} + 5$.

     Ans. $y = $ C. F. $- \frac{3}{10}\cos x - \frac{9}{10}\sin x - \frac{2}{15}e^{-2x} + 5$.

19. $y'' - 2y' + y = xe^x$.   *Ans.* $y = e^x(c_1 + c_2x + \frac{1}{6}x^3)$.

20. $y'' + 2y' + y = \sin x + \sin 2x$.

     Ans. $y = $ C. F. $- \frac{1}{2}\cos x - \frac{3}{25}\sin 2x - \frac{4}{25}\cos 2x$.

21. $y'' + 4y = 2 \cos^2 x$.   *Ans.* $y = $ C. F. $+ \frac{1}{4} + \frac{1}{4}x \sin 2x$.

22. $y'' + 9y = \cos^3 x$.   *Ans.* $y = $ C. F. $+ \frac{3}{32}\cos x + \frac{1}{24}x \sin 3x$.

Find the following particular solutions.

23. $y'' = 4 - y$; $y = y' = 0$ when $x = 0$.   *Ans.* $y = 4(1 - \cos x)$.

24. $y'' - 3y' + 2y = 2e^{3x}$; $y = y' = 0$ when $x = 0$.

     Ans. $y = e^x - 2e^{2x} + e^{3x}$.

25. $y'' + y = 3 \sin x$; $y = 1$ when $x = 0$, $y = 0$ when $x = \frac{1}{2}\pi$.

     Ans. $y = (1 - \frac{3}{2}x) \cos x$.

26. $y'' - 4y' + 3y = x$; $y = -2$, $y' = 1$ when $x = 0$.

27. $y'' + y' = 3x^2$; $y = y' = 0$ when $x = 0$.

28. $\dfrac{d^2x}{dt^2} + \dfrac{dx}{dt} = 3t^2 - 2t$; $x = 0$, $v = 8$, when $t = 0$.

     Ans. $x = t^3 - 4t^2 + 8t$.

29. $y'' + 4y = \sin 2x + 2 \cos 2x$; $y = y' = 0$, when $x = 0$.

     Ans. $y = \frac{1}{8}\sin 2x - \frac{1}{4}x \cos 2x + \frac{1}{2}x \sin 2x$.

CHAPTER 34 *RECTILINEAR MOTION*

264. The equation of motion. Consider a point P moving in a straight line. If the acceleration (or force) is given as a function of time, two successive integrations give x in terms of t, after which the nature of the motion can be determined. (The reader should review §§ 51–54.)

In most cases of importance, however, the acceleration is a function of distance or velocity or both, perhaps time as well — say

$$(1) \qquad \frac{d^2x}{dt^2} = f(x,\, v,\, t),$$

or in terms of force,

$$(2) \qquad m\,\frac{d^2x}{dt^2} = F(x,\, v,\, t),$$

where of course

$$v = \frac{dx}{dt}.$$

Equation (1), or its mathematical equivalent (2), is called the *equation of motion*. It will be seen that this is a *differential equation of second order*.

In each problem there are in general three steps: first, *to write the equation of motion;* second, *to solve this equation*, determining the constants of integration in accordance with given boundary conditions; third, *to interpret the results*.

265. Motion in a resisting medium. When a body moves in a fluid medium, such as air or water, the medium offers a resistance to the motion. Experiment shows that the magnitude of this resistance depends upon the velocity, and that it increases with increasing velocity, but the law of variation is not known. However, valuable approximate results may be obtained by assuming the resistance *proportional to the velocity.*

Example: Study the motion of a body falling from rest under gravity, in a resisting medium.

With the downward sense as positive, we have

(1) $$\frac{dv}{dt} = g - kv; \quad x = v = 0 \text{ when } t = 0.$$

(The sign of the resistance is negative because when the body is falling — v positive — the resistance is directed upward.) Writing (1) in the form

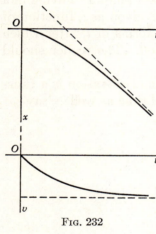

Fig. 232

$$\frac{dv}{g - kv} = dt,$$

we have

$$\ln (g - kv) = -kt + c_1.$$

Since $v = 0$ when $t = 0$, this becomes

$$\ln (g - kv) = -kt + \ln g,$$

or

(2) $$v = \frac{g}{k}(1 - e^{-kt}).$$

Replace v by $\frac{dx}{dt}$ and integrate:

$$x = \frac{g}{k}t + \frac{g}{k^2}e^{-kt} + c_2,$$

or finally, since $x = 0$ when $t = 0$,

$$x = \frac{g}{k}t + \frac{g}{k^2}e^{-kt} - \frac{g}{k^2}.$$

By (2), as t increases, v approaches asymptotically the "limiting velocity" $\frac{g}{k}$: *i.e.*, after some time* the motion is nearly uniform.

We note that (1) may also be solved by the method of § 263. $\left(\text{Put } v = \frac{dx}{dt}, \frac{dv}{dt} = \frac{d^2x}{dt^2}.\right)$ To find v in terms of x, solve (1) with $\frac{dv}{dt}$ replaced by $v\frac{dv}{dx}$.

---

* Unless k is small, the limiting velocity will be nearly reached in a few seconds, because of the rapid decrease of the exponential e^{-kt}. In some analogous electrical phenomena, the "transient term" sensibly disappears in a small fraction of a second.

EXERCISES

In Exs. 1–12, assume the resistance proportional to the velocity.

1. In the example of § 265, find the distance traveled in the first 10 sec., (a) if $k = 1$; (b) if $k = 0.01$. Compare with the case of negligible resistance.   *Ans.* (a) 288 ft.; (b) 1548 ft.

2. Solve the example of § 265 by the method of § 263.

3. In the example of § 265, find x in terms of v.

$$Ans. \quad x = \frac{g}{k^2} \ln \frac{g}{g - kv} - \frac{v}{k}.$$

4. A body is placed on a smooth horizontal table and given a velocity of 2 ft. per sec. After 2 sec. the velocity is 1.82 ft. per sec. Find k. *Ans.* 0.047.

5. Study the motion of a body in a resisting medium, with no other forces acting. Take $x = 0$, $v = v_0$ when $t = 0$. Interpret the results fully;*

draw the graph of x.   *Ans.* $x = \frac{v_0}{k}(1 - e^{-kt})$; $v = v_0 e^{-kt}$; $v = v_0 - kx.$

6. In Ex. 5, if $k = 2$, how long a time is required to dissipate 99% of the velocity?   *Ans.* $t = 2.3$ sec.

7. A body falling from rest in a heavy fluid acquires in 2 sec. a velocity of 9.33 ft. per sec. Find k.   *Ans.* 3.4.

8. A body falling from rest in a heavy fluid travels 1.68 ft. in the first second. Find k.   *Ans.* 18.0.

9. A body is projected upward against gravity in a resisting medium, with initial velocity $v_0 (v_0 < 0)$. Find v and x in terms of t. Solve in two ways (§§ 251, 263).

10. In Ex. 9, if $k = 0.01$, $v_0 = -1000$ ft. per sec., how far and for how long a time will the body rise?   *Ans.* 12,960 ft.; 27.2 sec.

11. A flier makes a parachute drop from a height of 5000 ft. Assuming $k = 1$ in § 265, find the time of fall. Can this drop be made with safety?
                    Ans. 2 min. 37 sec.

12. Solve the problem of § 265 if there is a downward initial velocity v_0.

Distinguish the cases $v_0 < \frac{g}{k}$, $v_0 = \frac{g}{k}$, $v_0 > \frac{g}{k}$.

13. Study the motion of a body under a force proportional to the velocity and *assisting* the motion. Take $x = 0$, $v = v_0$ when $t = 0$.

14. Study the motion $a = ct - kv$; when $t = 0$, $x = 0$ and $v = 0$.

15. Study the motion $a = 2 \cos t - v$; when $t = 0$, $x = 0$ and $v = 0$.

16. Study the motion $a = g + c \sin t - kv$; when $t = 0$, $x = 0$ and $v = 0$.

17. Solve Ex. 4, assuming the resistance to be proportional to v^2.
                    Ans. $k = 0.025$.

---

* Strictly interpreted, the solution shows that the body would never come to rest, a result which is not in accord with observation. The reason that theory and practice do not fully agree in this and similar problems is that the original assumption is only an approximation.

18. A body is thrown upward with a velocity of 80 ft. per sec. in a medium offering a resistance proportional to v^2. Taking $k = 0.005$, find how far and for how long a time the body will rise.   *Ans.* 69.3 ft.; 1.96 sec.

19. In Ex. 18, find when and with what velocity the body returns to the starting point.   *Ans.* 2.2 sec.; 56.6 ft. per sec.

20. A body moves in a vertical line under gravity, and under the action of a force proportional to the velocity and assisting the motion. Assuming $x = v = 0$ when $t = 0$, study the motion. Take $k = 4$.

> *Ans.* With the upward sense as positive, $x = 8t + 2 - 2e^{4t}$, etc.

21. Solve Ex. 20 if there is an upward initial velocity greater than 8 ft. per sec.

22. Solve Ex. 20 if there is an upward initial velocity of 8 ft. per sec.

23. Solve Ex. 20 if there is an upward initial velocity of 3 ft. per sec. For what time, and through what distance, does the body rise?

> *Ans.* $t = 0.12$ sec., $x = 0.19$ ft.

24. Study the motion of a body in a medium offering a resistance proportional to the square of the velocity, with no other forces acting.

$$Ans. \; v = \frac{v_0}{1 + kv_0 t}, \; x = \frac{1}{k} \ln (1 + kv_0 t), \; v = v_0 e^{-kx}.$$

266. Simple harmonic motion. If a particle moves in a straight line under the action of an acceleration directed toward a fixed point O in the line of motion, and proportional to the distance x from that point, it is said to have *simple harmonic motion*. The equation of motion is

$$(1) \qquad\qquad \frac{d^2x}{dt^2} = -k^2 x,$$

where k is a constant, the minus sign being chosen because the acceleration is always directed opposite to the "displacement" x.

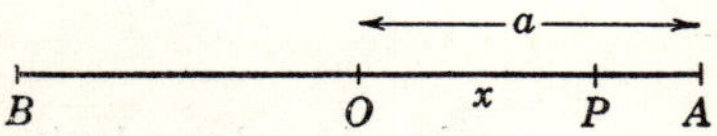

Let us study this motion with the body starting from rest at A, where $OA = a$: *i.e.*, with

Fig. 233

$$x = a, \quad v = 0 \text{ when } t = 0.$$

Solving by the method of § 261, we get the general solution

$$x = c_1 \cos kt + c_2 \sin kt,$$
$$v = -c_1 k \sin kt + c_2 k \cos kt.$$

The boundary conditions give very easily

$$(2) \qquad\qquad x = a \cos kt,$$
$$(3) \qquad\qquad v = -ak \sin kt.$$

Since the cosine is a periodic function, it follows from (2) that the body moves forever back and forth between the points $x = a$ and $x = -a$ (the points A, B in the figure), while (3) shows that v varies between the extreme values ak and $-ak$.

The time required for a complete oscillation, from A to B and back, is called the *period* of the motion. When $x = a$, $\cos kt = 1$, and the successive values of t are $0, \dfrac{2\pi}{k}, \dfrac{4\pi}{k}$, etc.; hence the period is $\dfrac{2\pi}{k}$. The extreme distance a is called the *amplitude*.

267. Hooke's Law. When a spiral steel spring of length $AO = l$ is stretched to a length $AP = l + x$, the tension in the spring, or the force tending to restore it to its natural length, is *proportional to the extension x.* This law, known as Hooke's Law, is obeyed very closely (provided the extension is not too great) by all so-called *elastic* materials.

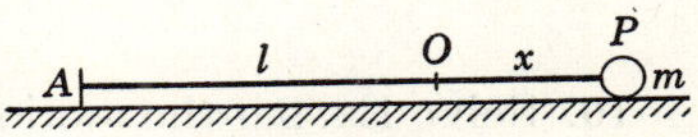

Fig. 234

Suppose a steel spring of negligible mass is placed on a smooth horizontal table with one end fast at A. Let the natural length of the spring be $AO = l$. A particle of mass m attached to the free end is drawn out to the position P and then released. The only force acting is the tension in the spring, which by Hooke's Law is directed toward the position of equilibrium O and is proportional to the distance from O. If the spring offers the same resistance to compression as to extension, it follows from § 266 that the particle performs simple harmonic oscillations about O, the equation of motion being

$$\frac{d^2x}{dt^2} = -k^2x.$$

Of course if the resistance to compression is not the same as to extension, a different equation comes into play as soon as the particle passes through O.

EXERCISES

In Exs. 1–6, solve the problem of simple harmonic motion (§ 266) with the given conditions.

1. When $t = 0$, $x = 0$ and $v = v_0$.   *Ans.* $x = \dfrac{v_0}{k} \sin kt$.

2. $k = 3$; when $t = 0$, $x = 1$ and $v = -6$.

Ans. $x = \cos 3t - 2 \sin 3t$.

3. $k = 3$; when $t = 0$, $x = -4$ and $v = 0$.

Ans. $x = -4 \cos 3t$.

4. $k = \frac{1}{2}$; when $t = 0$, $x = 2$, and when $t = \pi$, $x = 3$.

Ans. $x = 2 \cos \frac{1}{2}t + 3 \sin \frac{1}{2}t$.

5. $k = \frac{1}{2}$; when $t = 0$, $x = 1$ and $v = -2$.

6. Smallest positive k, and the corresponding x, to be determined; when $t = 0$, $x = 4$, $v = 0$, and when $t = \frac{1}{2}\pi$, $x = 2$.

Ans. $x = 4 \cos \dfrac{2t}{3}$.

7. A body falls from rest under gravity, and under the action of a force directed toward the starting point and proportional to the distance from that point. Show that the motion is simple harmonic, and find the center.

Ans. $x = \dfrac{g}{k^2}(1 - \cos kt)$.

8. Discuss the simple harmonic motion for which $k^2 = 9$, if $x = -3$, $v = 1$ when $t = 0$. *Ans.* $x = -3.02 \cos (3t + 0.11)$.

9. Study the motion $a = ct - k^2x$, $x = v = 0$ when $t = 0$.

Ans. $x = -\dfrac{c}{k^3} \sin kt + \dfrac{c}{k^2}t$.

10. Solve Ex. 9 if the motion takes place in a vertical line under gravity.

11. A particle is acted upon by a force of *repulsion* from a point O proportional to the distance from O. Write the equation of motion and solve it completely, taking $x = 0$ and $v = v_0$ when $t = 0$. Describe the motion. *Ans.* $kx = v_0 \sinh kt$, etc.

12. A body is acted upon by a force of repulsion from a point O proportional to the distance from O. If the motion takes place in a vertical line under gravity, with $x = v = 0$ when $t = 0$, discuss the motion.

13. Solve Ex. 12, with the upward sense as positive, if $v_0 > 0$. Discuss the cases $kv_0 < g$, $kv_0 = g$, $kv_0 > g$.

14. A steel spring offering the same resistance to compression as to extension is placed on a smooth horizontal table with one end fixed. The spring is stretched to a length 6 in. greater than the natural length and then released. Discuss the motion of a mass attached to the free end. Take $k^2 = 4$. Find the period. *Ans.* Period = 3.14 sec.

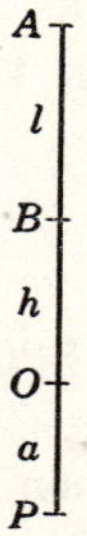

15. Work Ex. 14 if the resistance to compression is four times as great as to extension. *Ans.* Period = 2.36 sec.

16. Work Ex. 14 if the steel spring is replaced by a rubber band of natural length 1 ft. *Ans.* Period = 7.14 sec.

17. A rubber band of natural length $AB = l$ is suspended vertically with a weight attached. The effect of the weight is to stretch the band to a length $AO = l + h$. The weight is given a displacement $OP = a$ $(a < h)$ and then released. Write the equation of motion with O as origin, determining k^2 from the fact that at O the acceleration is 0. What is the nature of the motion?

Fig. 235

Ans. $\dfrac{d^2x}{dt^2} = -\dfrac{g}{h}x$.

18. In Ex. 17, the weight is let fall from a height b above B. What is the greatest extension? *Ans.* $h + \sqrt{h^2 + 2bh}$.

268. Damped vibrations. Consider next the case in which the body moves in a medium offering a resistance proportional to the velocity, and under an attraction proportional to the displacement. The equation of motion is evidently

$$\frac{d^2x}{dt^2} = -k^2 x - k'v,$$

or, if we put for convenience $k' = 2h$,

(1) $$\frac{d^2x}{dt^2} + 2h\frac{dx}{dt} + k^2 x = 0.$$

The characteristic equation is

$$m^2 + 2hm + k^2 = 0,$$

whence

$$m = -h \pm \sqrt{h^2 - k^2}.$$

The case of greatest interest is that in which $h < k$, so that the roots are imaginary. Setting

$$\beta = \sqrt{k^2 - h^2},$$

we have

$$m = -h \pm \beta i,$$

so that the general solution of (1) is

$$x = e^{-ht}(c_1 \cos \beta t + c_2 \sin \beta t).$$

With the initial conditions $x = 0$, $v = v_0$ when $t = 0$, we find (the details are left to the student)

(2) $$x = \frac{v_0}{\beta}e^{-ht} \sin \beta t,$$

(3) $$v = \frac{v_0}{\beta}e^{-ht}(\beta \cos \beta t - h \sin \beta t).$$

Thus v vanishes whenever

$$\tan \beta t = \frac{\beta}{h}, \qquad \beta t = \text{Arctan}\, \frac{\beta}{h} + n\pi,$$

i.e., when

(4) $$t = \frac{1}{\beta} \text{Arctan}\, \frac{\beta}{h} + \frac{n\pi}{\beta}.$$

The displacement x therefore has an infinite number of maxima and minima whose absolute values steadily diminish (see Ex. 2 below);

that is, the body vibrates back and forth indefinitely, but the resistance of the medium continually shortens the amplitude.

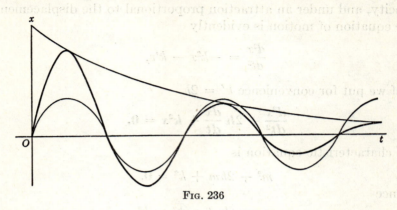

Fig. 236

Figure 236 shows the graph of x as given by (2), found by multiplying the ordinates of the curves

$$x = \frac{v_0}{\beta}e^{-ht}, \qquad x = \sin \beta t.$$

EXERCISES

1. Derive equations (2) and (3) above.

2. By substituting the value of t from (4) in (2), find the extreme
values of x, and obtain the ratio of two consecutive amplitudes.

Ans. The ratio is (numerically) $e^{-\frac{h\pi}{\beta}}$.

3. Show that the period of the damped vibrations is constant, and
greater than in the case of free oscillations (§ 266).

Ans. Period $= \dfrac{2\pi}{\sqrt{k^2 - h^2}}$.

4. Find when v assumes its maximum and minimum values.

Ans. $t = \dfrac{1}{\beta} \text{Arctan} \dfrac{2h\beta}{h^2 - \beta^2} + \dfrac{n\pi}{\beta}$.

5. How is the motion affected (*a*) if h is very small; (*b*) if h is but
slightly less than k?

6. In Fig. 236, do the maxima and minima on the product curve
coincide with its points of intersection with the exponential curve?

7. Solve the case $h < k$ with the initial conditions $x = a$, $v = 0$ when
$t = 0$.   *Ans.* $x = \dfrac{a}{\beta}e^{-ht}(\beta \cos \beta t + h \sin \beta t)$, $v = -\dfrac{ak^2}{\beta}e^{-ht} \sin \beta t$.

8. Solve equation (1), § 268, with $h = 5$, $k = 4$, taking $x = 12$, $v = 0$ when $t = 0$. Describe the motion.   *Ans.* $x = 16e^{-2t} - 4e^{-8t}$.

9. In Ex. 8, draw the graph of x.

10. Solve Ex. 8, taking $x = 0$, $v = v_0$ when $t = 0$. Show that the time of reaching the maximum displacement is independent of the initial velocity.
                                    Ans. $x = \frac{1}{6}v_0(e^{-2t} - e^{-8t})$.

11. Solve Ex. 8 if $x = 12$, $v = -300$ when $t = 0$. Find when the body passes through O, and when it reaches the maximum negative displacement.
                          Ans. $t = 0.05$ sec.; $t = 0.28$ sec.

12. Discuss fully the case $h = k$, taking $x = 0$, $v = v_0$ when $t = 0$. Find the maximum displacement.   *Ans.* $x = v_0 t e^{-ht}$.

13. In Ex. 12, draw the graph of x.

14. Solve the case $h = k$ if $x = a$, $v = 0$ when $t = 0$. Find the maximum velocity.   *Ans.* $x = ae^{-kt}(1 + kt)$.

15. Discuss the case $h = k$, taking $x = -a$, $v = v_0$ when $t = 0$. Distinguish the cases $v_0 < ah$, $v_0 = ah$, $v_0 > ah$.

16. Solve the case $h = k = 1$ if $x = 1$ when $t = 0$, $x = 0$ when $t = 1$.
                                    Ans. $x = e^{-t}(1 - t)$.

17. Solve the case $h = 1$, $k = \sqrt{2}$, taking $x = 1$, $v = -1$ when $t = 0$.
                                    Ans. $x = e^{-t} \cos t$.

18. In Ex. 17, draw the graph of x as a function of t.

19. Solve the case $h = 1$, $k = \sqrt{2}$, taking $x = 1$ when $t = 0$, $x = 2$ when $t = 1$.   *Ans.* $x = 5.88e^{-t} \cos (t - 1.40)$.

20. Solve the case $h = 1$, $k = \sqrt{2}$ if $v = 0$ when $t = 0$, $v = 1$ when $t = \frac{1}{2}\pi$.   *Ans.* $x = -3.41e^{-t} \cos (t - \frac{1}{4}\pi)$.

21. Solve the case $h = 1$, $k = \sqrt{2}$, taking $x = 1$, $v = 10$ when $t = 0$. Find the maximum displacement.
                    Ans. $x = 11.05e^{-t} \cos (t - 1.48)$; $x_{\max.} = 3.9$.

22. Solve the case $h = k$ if the motion takes place in a vertical line under gravity. Assume $x = v = 0$ when $t = 0$. Compare with the case of negligible resistance (Ex. 7, p. 488).   *Ans.* $x = \frac{g}{k^2}(1 - e^{-kt} - kte^{-kt})$.

23. Solve Ex. 22 if $h = k = \frac{1}{2}$, assuming $x = 0$ and $v = 64$ ft. per sec. upward when $t = 0$. Find the highest and lowest points.
          Ans. $x = 128(1 - e^{-\frac{1}{2}t} - te^{-\frac{1}{2}t})$; 27.3 ft., 128 ft.

24. Solve the problem of damped vibrations in a vertical line under gravity, taking $h = \frac{1}{6}$, $k^2 = \frac{1}{48}$, and the initial velocity 100 ft. per sec. upward. For how long a time does the body rise?
              Ans. $x = 1536 + 1368\, e^{-\frac{1}{4}t} - 2904\, e^{-\frac{1}{12}t}$; 2.08 sec.

25. Solve the problem of damped vibrations in a vertical line under gravity for the case $h < k$, taking $x = v = 0$ when $t = 0$.
          Ans. $x = \frac{g}{k^2} - \frac{g}{k\beta}e^{-ht} \cos (\beta t - \epsilon)$, where $\epsilon = \text{Arctan } \frac{h}{\beta}$.

In Exs. 26–30, investigate the motion resulting from the given acceleration a, and the given initial conditions.

26. $a = \cos 2t - \frac{1}{2} \cos t$, if $x = v = 0$ when $t = 0$. Draw the graph of x.

27. $a = \sin t + 2 \cos 2t$, if $x = 0$ when $t = 0$, $x = 0$ when $t = \frac{1}{2}\pi$.

$$Ans. \ x = \sin^2 t - \sin t.$$

28. $a = -k^2x + b \cos 2kt$, with $x = v = 0$ when $t = 0$.

$$Ans. \ x = \frac{b}{3k^2}(\cos kt - \cos 2kt).$$

29. $a = -k^2x + b \sin kt$, $x = v = 0$ when $t = 0$.

$$Ans. \ x = \frac{b}{2k^2} \sin kt - \frac{b}{2k}t \cos kt.$$

30. Study the motion $a = -k^2x - 2hv + bt$. (That is, in the problem of § 268 superimpose a force proportional to the time.) Show that if $h \geqq k$, the motion ultimately becomes practically uniform.

31. In Ex. 30, replace the term bt by bt^2. Show that the effect of this term is to superimpose a uniformly accelerated motion.

32. Study the motion $a = k^2x - 2hv$, with $x = 0$, $v = v_0$ when $t = 0$.

Put $\sqrt{h^2 + k^2} = \alpha$.　　　　　　　　　　　$Ans. \ x = \dfrac{v_0}{\alpha}e^{-ht} \sinh \alpha t.$

33. Solve Ex. 32 with $x = c$, $v = -(h + \alpha)c$ when $t = 0$.

$$Ans. \ x = ce^{-(h+\alpha)t}.$$

APPENDIX

APPENDIX

APPENDIX

A1. Definition of a limit. We say that

(1) $$\lim_{x \to a} f(x) = L,$$

if for every positive number ϵ (arbitrarily small), there exists a number δ such that, in order to make

(2) $$|f(x) - L| < \epsilon,$$

it is sufficient that x satisfy

(3) $$|x - a| < \delta, \qquad x \neq a.$$

Example (a): Show that

$$\lim_{x \to 3} (2x + 1) = 7.$$

Analysis of the problem: Given an ϵ, we wish to satisfy the inequality

$$|(2x + 1) - 7| < \epsilon$$

by choosing x "sufficiently close" to 3. The inequality yields

$$|2x - 6| < \epsilon,$$

or

$$|x - 3| < \frac{\epsilon}{2}.$$

Proof of the desired limit property: We are now in a position to choose the δ in (3) for this problem.

Let $\delta = \dfrac{\epsilon}{2}$. Then for all x such that

$$|x - 3| < \frac{\epsilon}{2}, \qquad x \neq 3,$$

495

it follows that
$$|2x - 6| < \epsilon,$$
from which
$$|(2x + 1) - 7| < \epsilon,$$
so that, by the definition of this section,
$$\lim_{x \to 3} (2x + 1) = 7,$$
as was desired.

Example (*b*): Show that
$$\lim_{x \to 2} (x^2 + 1) = 5.$$

Analysis: Since we wish to obtain
$$|x^2 + 1 - 5| < \epsilon,$$
we write it in the form
$$|x^2 - 4| < \epsilon,$$
or
$$|x - 2| \cdot |x + 2| < \epsilon.$$

Recall that one property of the absolute value symbol is that
$$|A + B| \leqq |A| + |B|.$$
Since $x + 2 = x - 2 + 4$, it follows that
$$|x + 2| \leqq |x - 2| + 4.$$
Thus, if we choose
$$|x - 2| < \delta,$$
then
$$|x + 2| < \delta + 4.$$
Therefore, it is desirable to find a δ such that
$$\delta(\delta + 4) = \epsilon.$$
Since δ is required to be positive, we find that
$$\delta = -2 + \sqrt{4 + \epsilon}.$$

Proof of the desired limit property: Choose
$$\delta = \sqrt{4 + \epsilon} - 2,$$
then, for
$$|x - 2| < \sqrt{4 + \epsilon} - 2,$$

it can be seen, because $|x + 2| \leqq |x - 2| + 4$, that

$$|x + 2| < \sqrt{4 + \epsilon} + 2.$$

By multiplication of corresponding members of the above two inequalities, it follows that

$$|x - 2| \cdot |x + 2| < (\sqrt{4 + \epsilon})^2 - (2)^2,$$

or

$$|x^2 - 4| < 4 + \epsilon - 4,$$

so that

$$|x^2 + 1 - 5| < \epsilon,$$

as desired.

A2. Proof of a theorem on limits. Let us prove one of the results stated on page 10:

THEOREM 1. If

(1) $$\lim_{x \to a} f_1(x) = L_1$$

and

(2) $$\lim_{x \to a} f_2(x) = L_2,$$

then

(3) $$\lim_{x \to a} \left[f_1(x) + f_2(x) \right] = L_1 + L_2.$$

Proof: Because of (1) and the definition of a limit we know that for any $\epsilon_1 > 0$, there exists a δ_1 such that, if x satisfies

$$|x - a| < \delta_1, \qquad x \neq a,$$

then

$$|f_1(x) - L_1| < \epsilon_1.$$

Similarly, because of (2), for any $\epsilon_2 > 0$, there exists a δ_2 such that, if x satisfies

$$|x - a| < \delta_2, \qquad x \neq a,$$

then

$$|f_2(x) - L_2| < \epsilon_2.$$

Now suppose we are given an ϵ for which we wish to make

$$|\{f_1(x) + f_2(x)\} - (L_1 + L_2)| < \epsilon.$$

We can choose $\epsilon_1 = \frac{1}{2}\epsilon$, $\epsilon_2 = \frac{1}{2}\epsilon$, and let δ be smaller than either of δ_1 and δ_2, the δ's which correspond respectively to ϵ_1 and ϵ_2. Then for all x which satisfy

$$|x - a| < \delta, \qquad x \neq a,$$

it is also true that $|x - a| < \delta_1$ and $|x - a| < \delta_2$, and therefore that

(5)
$$|f_1(x) - L_1| < \frac{\epsilon}{2}$$

and

(6)
$$|f_2(x) - L_2| < \frac{\epsilon}{2},$$

using the specific ϵ_1 and ϵ_2 which we chose.

Since

$$|f_1(x) + f_2(x) - (L_1 + L_2)| \leqq |f_1(x) - L_1| + |f_2(x) - L_2|,$$

it follows, using (5) and (6), that

$$|f_1(x) + f_2(x) - (L_1 + L_2)| < \frac{\epsilon}{2} + \frac{\epsilon}{2}$$

or

$$|f_1(x) + f_2(x) - (L_1 + L_2)| < \epsilon,$$

as desired.

By similar, sometimes more complicated, devices, the other theorems on limits which are quoted in the text can be proved.

TABLES

INDEFINITE INTEGRALS

[In this table, integrals immediately reducible to a standard form (p. 226) are omitted.]

1. $\displaystyle \int \frac{x\,dx}{ax+b} = \frac{x}{a} - \frac{b}{a^2}\ln\,(ax+b) + C.$

2. $\displaystyle \int \frac{x\,dx}{(ax+b)^2} = \frac{b}{a^2(ax+b)} + \frac{1}{a^2}\ln\,(ax+b) + C.$

3. $\displaystyle \int x(ax+b)^n\,dx = \frac{x(ax+b)^{n+1}}{a(n+1)} - \frac{(ax+b)^{n+2}}{a^2(n+1)\,(n+2)} + C.$

4. $\displaystyle \int \frac{dx}{x(ax+b)} = \frac{1}{b}\ln\frac{x}{ax+b} + C.$

5. $\displaystyle \int \frac{dx}{x(ax+b)^2} = \frac{1}{b(ax+b)} + \frac{1}{b^2}\ln\frac{x}{ax+b} + C.$

6. $\displaystyle \int \frac{dx}{a^2-x^2} = \frac{1}{2a}\ln\frac{a+x}{a-x} + C.$ (See p. 258.)

7. $\displaystyle \int \frac{dx}{(ax^2+b)^2} = \frac{x}{2b(ax^2+b)} + \frac{1}{2b}\int\frac{dx}{ax^2+b}.$

8. $\displaystyle \int \frac{dx}{x(ax^2+b)} = \frac{1}{2b}\ln\frac{x^2}{ax^2+b} + C.$

9. $\displaystyle \int x\sqrt{ax+b}\,dx = \frac{2x}{3a}(ax+b)^{\frac{3}{2}} - \frac{4}{15a^2}(ax+b)^{\frac{5}{2}} + C.$

10. $\displaystyle \int \frac{x\,dx}{\sqrt{ax+b}} = \frac{2x}{a}(ax+b)^{\frac{1}{2}} - \frac{4}{3a^2}(ax+b)^{\frac{3}{2}} + C.$

11. $\displaystyle \int \sqrt{a^2-x^2}\,dx = \frac{1}{2}x\sqrt{a^2-x^2} + \frac{1}{2}a^2\,\text{Arcsin}\,\frac{x}{a} + C.$

12. $\int \sqrt{x^2 \pm a^2}\, dx = \frac{1}{2}x\sqrt{x^2 \pm a^2} \pm \frac{1}{2}a^2 \ln\left(x + \sqrt{x^2 \pm a^2}\right) + C.$

13. $\int \dfrac{dx}{\sqrt{x^2 \pm a^2}} = \ln\left(x + \sqrt{x^2 \pm a^2}\right) + C.$

14. $\int \dfrac{dx}{x\sqrt{a^2 \pm x^2}} = \dfrac{1}{a}\ln \dfrac{x}{a + \sqrt{a^2 \pm x^2}} + C.$

15. $\int \dfrac{dx}{x\sqrt{x^2 - a^2}} = -\dfrac{1}{a}\operatorname{Arcsin}\dfrac{a}{x} + C.$

16. $\int \dfrac{\sqrt{a^2 \pm x^2}}{x}\, dx = \sqrt{a^2 \pm x^2} + a \ln \dfrac{x}{a + \sqrt{a^2 \pm x^2}} + C.$

17. $\int \dfrac{\sqrt{x^2 - a^2}}{x}\, dx = \sqrt{x^2 - a^2} + a \operatorname{Arcsin}\dfrac{a}{x} + C.$

18. $\int (a^2 - x^2)^{\frac{3}{2}}\, dx$
$$= \frac{1}{4}x(a^2 - x^2)^{\frac{3}{2}} + \frac{3}{8}a^2 x\sqrt{a^2 - x^2} + \frac{3}{8}a^4 \operatorname{Arcsin}\frac{x}{a} + C.$$

19. $\int (x^2 \pm a^2)^{\frac{3}{2}}\, dx = \frac{1}{4}x(x^2 \pm a^2)^{\frac{3}{2}} \pm \frac{3}{8}a^2 x\sqrt{x^2 \pm a^2}$
$$+ \frac{3}{8}a^4 \ln\left(x + \sqrt{x^2 \pm a^2}\right) + C.$$

20. $\int \dfrac{dx}{(a^2 - x^2)^{\frac{3}{2}}} = \dfrac{x}{a^2\sqrt{a^2 - x^2}} + C.$

21. $\int \dfrac{dx}{(x^2 \pm a^2)^{\frac{3}{2}}} = \dfrac{\pm x}{a^2\sqrt{x^2 \pm a^2}} + C.$

22. $\int x^2\sqrt{a^2 - x^2}\, dx$
$$= -\frac{1}{4}x(a^2 - x^2)^{\frac{3}{2}} + \frac{1}{8}a^2 x\sqrt{a^2 - x^2} + \frac{1}{8}a^4 \operatorname{Arcsin}\frac{x}{a} + C.$$

23. $\int x^3\sqrt{a^2 - x^2}\, dx = \frac{1}{5}(a^2 - x^2)^{\frac{5}{2}} - \frac{1}{3}a^2(a^2 - x^2)^{\frac{3}{2}} + C.$

24. $\int x^2\sqrt{x^2 \pm a^2}\, dx = \frac{1}{4}x(x^2 \pm a^2)^{\frac{3}{2}} \mp \frac{1}{8}a^2 x\sqrt{x^2 \pm a^2}$
$$- \frac{1}{8}a^4 \ln\left(x + \sqrt{x^2 \pm a^2}\right) + C.$$

25. $\int \dfrac{x^2\,dx}{\sqrt{a^2 - x^2}} = -\dfrac{1}{2}x\sqrt{a^2 - x^2} + \dfrac{1}{2}a^2\,\text{Arcsin}\,\dfrac{x}{a} + C.$

26. $\int \dfrac{x^3\,dx}{\sqrt{a^2 - x^2}} = -x^2\sqrt{a^2 - x^2} - \dfrac{2}{3}(a^2 - x^2)^{\frac{3}{2}} + C.$

27. $\int \dfrac{x^2\,dx}{\sqrt{x^2 \pm a^2}} = \dfrac{1}{2}x\sqrt{x^2 \pm a^2} \mp \dfrac{1}{2}a^2\ln(x + \sqrt{x^2 \pm a^2}) + C.$

28. $\int \dfrac{dx}{\sqrt{2ax - x^2}} = 2\,\text{Arcsin}\,\sqrt{\dfrac{x}{2a}} + C.$

29. $\int \dfrac{x^n\,dx}{\sqrt{2ax - x^2}} = -\dfrac{x^{n-1}\sqrt{2ax - x^2}}{n}$

$$+ \dfrac{a(2n - 1)}{n}\int \dfrac{x^{n-1}\,dx}{\sqrt{2ax - x^2}}.$$

30. $\int \sqrt{2ax - x^2}\,dx$

$$= \dfrac{1}{2}(x - a)\sqrt{2ax - x^2} + \dfrac{1}{2}a^2\,\text{Arcsin}\,\dfrac{x - a}{a} + C.$$

31. $\int \sin^2 x\,dx = \tfrac{1}{2}x - \tfrac{1}{4}\sin 2x + C.$

32. $\int \cos^2 x\,dx = \tfrac{1}{2}x + \tfrac{1}{4}\sin 2x + C.$

33. $\int \sin^n x\,dx = -\dfrac{\sin^{n-1} x \cos x}{n} + \dfrac{n-1}{n}\int \sin^{n-2} x\,dx.$

34. $\int \cos^n x\,dx = \dfrac{1}{n}\cos^{n-1} x \sin x + \dfrac{n-1}{n}\int \cos^{n-2} x\,dx.$

35. $\int \cos^m x \sin^n x\,dx$

$$= \dfrac{\cos^{m-1} x \sin^{n+1} x}{m + n} + \dfrac{m-1}{m+n}\int \cos^{m-2} x \sin^n x\,dx.$$

36. $\int \cos^m x \sin^n x\,dx$

$$= -\dfrac{\sin^{n-1} x \cos^{m+1} x}{m + n} + \dfrac{n-1}{m+n}\int \cos^m x \sin^{n-2} x\,dx.$$

37. $\displaystyle\int \tan x \, dx = -\ln \cos x + C.$

38. $\displaystyle\int \cot x \, dx = \ln \sin x + C.$

39. $\displaystyle\int \tan^2 x \, dx = \tan x - x + C.$

40. $\displaystyle\int \cot^2 x \, dx = -\cot x - x + C.$

41. $\displaystyle\int \tan^n x \, dx = \frac{\tan^{n-1} x}{n-1} - \int \tan^{n-2} x \, dx.$

42. $\displaystyle\int \cot^n x \, dx = -\frac{\cot^{n-1} x}{n-1} - \int \cot^{n-2} x \, dx.$

43. $\displaystyle\int \sec x \, dx = \ln(\sec x + \tan x) + C.$

44. $\displaystyle\int \sec^3 x \, dx = \tfrac{1}{2}\sec x \tan x + \tfrac{1}{2}\ln(\sec x + \tan x) + C.$

45. $\displaystyle\int \csc x \, dx = \ln(\csc x - \cot x) + C.$

46. $\displaystyle\int \csc^3 x \, dx = -\tfrac{1}{2}\csc x \cot x + \tfrac{1}{2}\ln(\csc x - \cot x) + C.$

47. $\displaystyle\int \sec^n x \, dx = \frac{\tan x \sec^{n-2} x}{n-1} + \frac{n-2}{n-1}\int \sec^{n-2} x \, dx.$

48. $\displaystyle\int \csc^n x \, dx = -\frac{\cot x \csc^{n-2} x}{n-1} + \frac{n-2}{n-1}\int \csc^{n-2} x \, dx.$

49. $\displaystyle\int x \sin x \, dx = \sin x - x \cos x + C.$

50. $\displaystyle\int x \cos x \, dx = \cos x + x \sin x + C.$

51. $\displaystyle\int x^n \sin x \, dx = -x^n \cos x + n \int x^{n-1} \cos x \, dx.$

52. $\displaystyle\int x^n \cos x \, dx = x^n \sin x - n \int x^{n-1} \sin x \, dx.$

53. $\int x \sin^n x \, dx$

$$= \frac{\sin^{n-1} x \, (\sin x - nx \cos x)}{n^2} + \frac{n-1}{n} \int x \sin^{n-2} x \, dx.$$

54. $\int x \cos^n x \, dx$

$$= \frac{\cos^{n-1} x \, (\cos x + nx \sin x)}{n^2} + \frac{n-1}{n} \int x \cos^{n-2} x \, dx.$$

55. $\int \sin mx \sin nx \, dx = \dfrac{\sin (m-n)x}{2(m-n)} - \dfrac{\sin (m+n)x}{2(m+n)} + C.$

56. $\int \sin mx \cos nx \, dx = -\dfrac{\cos (m-n)x}{2(m-n)} - \dfrac{\cos (m+n)x}{2(m+n)} + C.$

57. $\int \cos mx \cos nx \, dx = \dfrac{\sin (m-n)x}{2(m-n)} + \dfrac{\sin (m+n)x}{2(m+n)} + C.$

58. $\int xe^{ax} \, dx = \dfrac{e^{ax}}{a^2} \, (ax - 1) + C.$

59. $\int x^2 e^{ax} \, dx = \dfrac{e^{ax}}{a^3} \, (a^2 x^2 - 2ax + 2) + C.$

60. $\int x^n e^{ax} \, dx = \dfrac{x^n e^{ax}}{a} - \dfrac{n}{a} \int x^{n-1} e^{ax} \, dx.$

61. $\int e^{ax} \sin mx \, dx = \dfrac{e^{ax}(a \sin mx - m \cos mx)}{m^2 + a^2} + C.$

62. $\int e^{ax} \cos mx \, dx = \dfrac{e^{ax}(m \sin mx + a \cos mx)}{m^2 + a^2} + C.$

63. $\int \sinh x \, dx = \cosh x + C.$

64. $\int \cosh x \, dx = \sinh x + C.$

65. $\int \tanh x \, dx = \ln \cosh x + C.$

66. $\int \sinh^2 x \, dx = \frac{1}{2} \sinh x \cosh x - \frac{1}{2}x + C.$

67. $\int \cosh^2 x \, dx = \frac{1}{2} \sinh x \cosh x + \frac{1}{2}x + C.$

68. $\displaystyle\int x \sinh x \, dx = x \cosh x - \sinh x + C.$

69. $\displaystyle\int x \cosh x \, dx = x \sinh x - \cosh x + C.$

70. $\displaystyle\int \ln x \, dx = x \ln x - x + C.$

71. $\displaystyle\int x^n \ln x \, dx = x^{n+1}\left[\frac{\ln x}{n+1} - \frac{1}{(n+1)^2}\right] + C.$

72. $\displaystyle\int (\ln x)^n \, dx = x(\ln x)^n - n\int (\ln x)^{n-1} \, dx.$

N	0	1	2	3	4	5	6	7	8	9
0.0		5.395	6.088	6.493	6.781	7.004	7.187	7.341	7.474	7.592
0.1	7.697	7.793	7.880	7.960	8.034	8.103	8.167	8.228	8.285	8.339
0.2	8.391	8.439	8.486	8.530	8.573	8.614	8.653	8.691	8.727	8.762
0.3	8.796	8.829	8.861	8.891	8.921	8.950	8.978	9.006	9.032	9.058
0.4	9.084	9.108	9.132	9.156	9.179	9.201	9.223	9.245	9.266	9.287
0.5	9.307	9.327	9.346	9.365	9.384	9.402	9.420	9.438	9.455	9.472
0.6	9.489	9.506	9.522	9.538	9.554	9.569	9.584	9.600	9.614	9.629
0.7	9.643	9.658	9.671	9.685	9.699	9.712	9.726	9.739	9.752	9.764
0.8	9.777	9.789	9.802	9.814	9.826	9.837	9.849	9.861	9.872	9.883
0.9	9.895	9.906	9.917	9.927	9.938	9.949	9.959	9.970	9.980	9.990
1.0	0.00000	0995	1980	2956	3922	4879	5827	6766	7696	8618
1.1	9531	*0436	*1333	*2222	*3103	*3976	*4842	*5700	*6551	*7395
1.2	0.1 8232	9062	9885	*0701	*1511	*2314	*3111	*3902	*4686	*5464
1.3	0.2 6236	7003	7763	8518	9267	*0010	*0748	*1481	*2208	*2930
1.4	0.3 3647	4359	5066	5767	6464	7156	7844	8526	9204	9878
1.5	0.4 0547	1211	1871	2527	3178	3825	4469	5108	5742	6373
1.6	7000	7623	8243	8858	9470	*0078	*0682	*1282	*1879	*2473
1.7	0.5 3063	3649	4232	4812	5389	5962	6531	7098	7661	8222
1.8	8779	9333	9884	*0432	*0977	*1519	*2058	*2594	*3127	*3658
1.9	0.6 4185	4710	5233	5752	6269	6783	7294	7803	8310	8813
2.0	9315	9813	*0310	*0804	*1295	*1784	*2271	*2755	*3237	*3716
2.1	0.7 4194	4669	5142	5612	6081	6547	7011	7473	7932	8390
2.2	8846	9299	9751	*0200	*0648	*1093	*1536	*1978	*2418	*2855
2.3	0.8 3291	3725	4157	4587	5015	5442	5866	6289	6710	7129
2.4	7547	7963	8377	8789	9200	9609	*0016	*0422	*0826	*1228
2.5	0.9 1629	2028	2426	2822	3216	3609	4001	4391	4779	5166
2.6	5551	5935	6317	6698	7078	7456	7833	8208	8582	8954
2.7	9325	9695	*0063	*0430	*0796	*1160	*1523	*1885	*2245	*2604
2.8	1.0 2962	3318	3674	4028	4380	4732	5082	5431	5779	6126
2.9	6471	6815	7158	7500	7841	8181	8519	8856	9192	9527
3.0	9861	*0194	*0526	*0856	*1186	*1514	*1841	*2168	*2493	*2817
3.1	1.1 3140	3462	3783	4103	4422	4740	5057	5373	5688	6002
3.2	6315	6627	6938	7248	7557	7865	8173	8479	8784	9089
3.3	9392	9695	9996	*0297	*0597	*0896	*1194	*1491	*1788	*2083
3.4	1.2 2378	2671	2964	3256	3547	3837	4127	4415	4703	4990
3.5	5276	5562	5846	6130	6413	6695	6976	7257	7536	7815
3.6	8093	8371	8647	8923	9198	9473	9746	*0019	*0291	*0563
3.7	1.3 0833	1103	1372	1641	1909	2176	2442	2708	2972	3237
3.8	3500	3763	4025	4286	4547	4807	5067	5325	5584	5841
3.9	6098	6354	6609	6864	7118	7372	7624	7877	8128	8379
4.0	8629	8879	9128	9377	9624	9872	*0118	*0364	*0610	*0854
4.1	1.4 1099	1342	1585	1828	2070	2311	2552	2792	3031	3270
4.2	3508	3746	3984	4220	4456	4692	4927	5161	5395	5629
4.3	5862	6094	6326	6557	6787	7018	7247	7476	7705	7933
4.4	8160	8387	8614	8840	9065	9290	9515	9739	9962	*0185
4.5	1.5 0408	0630	0851	1072	1293	1513	1732	1951	2170	2388
4.6	2606	2823	3039	3256	3471	3687	3902	4116	4330	4543
4.7	4756	4969	5181	5393	5604	5814	6025	6235	6444	6653
4.8	6362	7070	7277	7485	7691	7898	8104	8309	8515	8719
4.9	8924	9127	9331	9534	9737	9939	*0141	*0342	*0543	*0744
5.0	1.6 0944	1144	1343	1542	1741	1939	2137	2334	2531	2728
N	0	1	2	3	4	5	6	7	8	9

(Rows 0.1 through 0.9: Take tabular value − 10)

N	0	1	2	3	4	5	6	7	8	9
5.0	1.6 0944	1144	1343	1542	1741	1939	2137	2334	2531	2728
5.1	2924	3120	3315	3511	3705	3900	4094	4287	4481	4673
5.2	4866	5058	5250	5441	5632	5823	6013	6203	6393	6582
5.3	6771	6959	7147	7335	7523	7710	7896	8083	8269	8455
5.4	8640	8825	9010	9194	9378	9562	9745	9928	*0111	*0293
5.5	1.7 0475	0656	0838	1019	1199	1380	1560	1740	1919	2098
5.6	2277	2455	2633	2811	2988	3166	3342	3519	3695	3871
5.7	4047	4222	4397	4572	4746	4920	5094	5267	5440	5613
5.8	5786	5958	6130	6302	6473	6644	6815	6985	7156	7326
5.9	7495	7665	7834	8002	8171	8339	8507	8675	8842	9009
6.0	9176	9342	9509	9675	9840	*0006	*0171	*0336	*0500	*0665
6.1	1.8 0829	0993	1156	1319	1482	1645	1808	1970	2132	2294
6.2	2455	2616	2777	2938	3098	3258	3418	3578	3737	3896
6.3	4055	4214	4372	4530	4688	4845	5003	5160	5317	5473
6.4	5630	5786	5942	6097	6253	6408	6563	6718	6872	7026
6.5	7180	7334	7487	7641	7794	7947	8099	8251	8403	8555
6.6	8707	8858	9010	9160	9311	9462	9612	9762	9912	*0061
6.7	1.9 0211	0360	0509	0658	0806	0954	1102	1250	1398	1545
6.8	1692	1839	1986	2132	2279	2425	2571	2716	2862	3007
6.9	3152	3297	3442	3586	3730	3874	4018	4162	4305	4448
7.0	4591	4734	4876	5019	5161	5303	5445	5586	5727	5869
7.1	6009	6150	6291	6431	6571	6711	6851	6991	7130	7269
7.2	7408	7547	7685	7824	7962	8100	8238	8376	8513	8650
7.3	8787	8924	9061	9198	9334	9470	9606	9742	9877	*0013
7.4	2.0 0148	0283	0418	0553	0687	0821	0956	1089	1223	1357
7.5	1490	1624	1757	1890	2022	2155	2287	2419	2551	2683
7.6	2815	2946	3078	3209	3340	3471	3601	3732	3862	3992
7.7	4122	4252	4381	4511	4640	4769	4898	5027	5156	5284
7.8	5412	5540	5668	5796	5924	6051	6179	6306	6433	6560
7.9	6686	6813	6939	7065	7191	7317	7443	7568	7694	7819
8.0	7944	8069	8194	8318	8443	8567	8691	8815	8939	9063
8.1	9186	9310	9433	9556	9679	9802	9924	*0047	*0169	*0291
8.2	2.1 0413	0535	0657	0779	0900	1021	1142	1263	1384	1505
8.3	1626	1746	1866	1986	2106	2226	2346	2465	2585	2704
8.4	2823	2942	3061	3180	3298	3417	3535	3653	3771	3889
8.5	4007	4124	4242	4359	4476	4593	4710	4827	4943	5060
8.6	5176	5292	5409	5524	5640	5756	5871	5987	6102	6217
8.7	6332	6447	6562	6677	6791	6905	7020	7134	7248	7361
8.8	7475	7589	7702	7816	7929	8042	8155	8267	8380	8493
8.9	8605	8717	8830	8942	9054	9165	9277	9389	9500	9611
9.0	9722	9834	9944	*0055	*0166	*0276	*0387	*0497	*0607	*0717
9.1	2.2 0827	0937	1047	1157	1266	1375	1485	1594	1703	1812
9.2	1920	2029	2138	2246	2354	2462	2570	2678	2786	2894
9.3	3001	3109	3216	3324	3431	3538	3645	3751	3858	3965
9.4	4071	4177	4284	4390	4496	4601	4707	4813	4918	5024
9.5	5129	5234	5339	5444	5549	5654	5759	5863	5968	6072
9.6	6176	6280	6384	6488	6592	6696	6799	6903	7006	7109
9.7	7213	7316	7419	7521	7624	7727	7829	7932	8034	8136
9.8	8238	8340	8442	8544	8646	8747	8849	8950	9051	9152
9.9	9253	9354	9455	9556	9657	9757	9858	9958	*0058	*0158
10.0	2.3 0259	0358	0458	0558	0658	0757	0857	0956	1055	1154
N	0	1	2	3	4	5	6	7	8	9

x	e^x Value	e^x Log$_{10}$	e^{-x} Value	Sinh x Value	Sinh x Log$_{10}$	Cosh x Value	Cosh x Log$_{10}$	Tanh x Value
0.00	1.0000	.00000	1.0000	0.0000	$-\infty$	1.0000	.00000	.00000
0.01	1.0101	.00434	.99005	0.0100	.00001	1.0001	.00002	.01000
0.02	1.0202	.00869	.98020	0.0200	.30106	1.0002	.00009	.02000
0.03	1.0305	.01303	.97045	0.0300	.47719	1.0005	.00020	.02999
0.04	1.0408	.01737	.96079	0.0400	.60218	1.0008	.00035	.03998
0.05	1.0513	.02171	.95123	0.0500	.69915	1.0013	.00054	.04996
0.06	1.0618	.02606	.94176	0.0600	.77841	1.0018	.00078	.05993
0.07	1.0725	.03040	.93239	0.0701	.84545	1.0025	.00106	.06989
0.08	1.0833	.03474	.92312	0.0801	.90355	1.0032	.00139	.07983
0.09	1.0942	.03909	.91393	0.0901	.95483	1.0041	.00176	.08976
0.10	1.1052	.04343	.90484	0.1002	.00072	1.0050	.00217	.09967
0.11	1.1163	.04777	.89583	0.1102	.04227	1.0061	.00262	.10956
0.12	1.1275	.05212	.88692	0.1203	.08022	1.0072	.00312	.11943
0.13	1.1388	.05646	.87810	0.1304	.11517	1.0085	.00366	.12927
0.14	1.1503	.06080	.86936	0.1405	.14755	1.0098	.00424	.13909
0.15	1.1618	.06514	.86071	0.1506	.17772	1.0113	.00487	.14889
0.16	1.1735	.06949	.85214	0.1607	.20597	1.0128	.00554	.15865
0.17	1.1853	.07383	.84366	0.1708	.23254	1.0145	.00625	.16838
0.18	1.1972	.07817	.83527	0.1810	.25762	1.0162	.00700	.17808
0.19	1.2092	.08252	.82696	0.1911	.28136	1.0181	.00779	.18775
0.20	1.2214	.08686	.81873	0.2013	.30392	1.0201	.00863	.19738
0.21	1.2337	.09120	.81058	0.2115	.32541	1.0221	.00951	.20697
0.22	1.2461	.09554	.80252	0.2218	.34592	1.0243	.01043	.21652
0.23	1.2586	.09989	.79453	0.2320	.36555	1.0266	.01139	.22603
0.24	1.2712	.10423	.78663	0.2423	.38437	1.0289	.01239	.23550
0.25	1.2840	.10857	.77880	0.2526	.40245	1.0314	.01343	.24492
0.26	1.2969	.11292	.77105	0.2629	.41986	1.0340	.01452	.25430
0.27	1.3100	.11726	.76338	0.2733	.43663	1.0367	.01564	.26362
0.28	1.3231	.12160	.75578	0.2837	.45282	1.0395	.01681	.27291
0.29	1.3364	.12595	.74826	0.2941	.46847	1.0423	.01801	.28213
0.30	1.3499	.13029	.74082	0.3045	.48362	1.0453	.01926	.29131
0.31	1.3634	.13463	.73345	0.3150	.49830	1.0484	.02054	.30044
0.32	1.3771	.13897	.72615	0.3255	.51254	1.0516	.02187	.30951
0.33	1.3910	.14332	.71892	0.3360	.52637	1.0549	.02323	.31852
0.34	1.4049	.14766	.71177	0.3466	.53981	1.0584	.02463	.32748
0.35	1.4191	.15200	.70469	0.3572	.55290	1.0619	.02607	.33638
0.36	1.4333	.15635	.69768	0.3678	.56564	1.0655	.02755	.34521
0.37	1.4477	.16069	.69073	0.3785	.57807	1.0692	.02907	.35399
0.38	1.4623	.16503	.68386	0.3892	.59019	1.0731	.03063	.36271
0.39	1.4770	.16937	.67706	0.4000	.60202	1.0770	.03222	.37136
0.40	1.4918	.17372	.67032	0.4108	.61358	1.0811	.03385	.37995
0.41	1.5068	.17806	.66365	0.4216	.62488	1.0852	.03552	.38847
0.42	1.5220	.18240	.65705	0.4325	.63594	1.0895	.03723	.39693
0.43	1.5373	.18675	.65051	0.4434	.64677	1.0939	.03897	.40532
0.44	1.5527	.19109	.64404	0.4543	.65738	1.0984	.04075	.41364
0.45	1.5683	.19543	.63763	0.4653	.66777	1.1030	.04256	.42190
0.46	1.5841	.19978	.63128	0.4764	.67797	1.1077	.04441	.43008
0.47	1.6000	.20412	.62500	0.4875	.68797	1.1125	.04630	.43820
0.48	1.6161	.20846	.61878	0.4986	.69779	1.1174	.04822	.44624
0.49	1.6323	.21280	.61263	0.5098	.70744	1.1225	.05018	.45422
0.50	1.6487	.21715	.60653	0.5211	.71692	1.1276	.05217	.46212

x	e^x Value	e^x Log₁₀	e^{-x} Value	Sinh x Value	Sinh x Log₁₀	Cosh x Value	Cosh x Log₁₀	Tanh x Value
0.50	1.6487	.21715	.60653	0.5211	.71692	1.1276	.05217	.46212
0.51	1.6653	.22149	.60050	0.5324	.72624	1.1329	.05419	.46995
0.52	1.6820	.22583	.59452	0.5438	.73540	1.1383	.05625	.47770
0.53	1.6989	.23018	.58860	0.5552	.74442	1.1438	.05834	.48538
0.54	1.7160	.23452	.58275	0.5666	.75330	1.1494	.06046	.49299
0.55	1.7333	.23886	.57695	0.5782	.76204	1.1551	.06262	.50052
0.56	1.7507	.24320	.57121	0.5897	.77065	1.1609	.06481	.50798
0.57	1.7683	.24755	.56553	0.6014	.77914	1.1669	.06703	.51536
0.58	1.7860	.25189	.55990	0.6131	.78751	1.1730	.06929	.52267
0.59	1.8040	.25623	.55433	0.6248	.79576	1.1792	.07157	.52990
0.60	1.8221	.26058	.54881	0.6367	.80390	1.1855	.07389	.53705
0.61	1.8404	.26492	.54335	0.6485	.81194	1.1919	.07624	.54413
0.62	1.8589	.26926	.53794	0.6605	.81987	1.1984	.07861	.55113
0.63	1.8776	.27361	.53259	0.6725	.82770	1.2051	.08102	.55805
0.64	1.8965	.27795	.52729	0.6846	.83543	1.2119	.08346	.56490
0.65	1.9155	.28229	.52205	0.6967	.84308	1.2188	.08593	.57167
0.66	1.9348	.28663	.51685	0.7090	.85063	1.2258	.08843	.57836
0.67	1.9542	.29098	.51171	0.7213	.85809	1.2330	.09095	.58498
0.68	1.9739	.29532	.50662	0.7336	.86548	1.2402	.09351	.59152
0.69	1.9937	.29966	.50158	0.7461	.87278	1.2476	.09609	.59798
0.70	2.0138	.30401	.49659	0.7586	.88000	1.2552	.09870	.60437
0.71	2.0340	.30835	.49164	0.7712	.88715	1.2628	.10134	.61068
0.72	2.0544	.31269	.48675	0.7838	.89423	1.2706	.10401	.61691
0.73	2.0751	.31703	.48191	0.7966	.90123	1.2785	.10670	.62307
0.74	2.0959	.32138	.47711	0.8094	.90817	1.2865	.10942	.62915
0.75	2.1170	.32572	.47237	0.8223	.91504	1.2947	.11216	.63515
0.76	2.1383	.33006	.46767	0.8353	.92185	1.3030	.11493	.64108
0.77	2.1598	.33441	.46301	0.8484	.92859	1.3114	.11773	.64693
0.78	2.1815	.33875	.45841	0.8615	.93527	1.3199	.12055	.65271
0.79	2.2034	.34309	.45384	0.8748	.94190	1.3286	.12340	.65841
0.80	2.2255	.34744	.44933	0.8881	.94846	1.3374	.12627	.66404
0.81	2.2479	.35178	.44486	0.9015	.95498	1.3464	.12917	.66959
0.82	2.2705	.35612	.44043	0.9150	.96144	1.3555	.13209	.67507
0.83	2.2933	.36046	.43605	0.9286	.96784	1.3647	.13503	.68048
0.84	2.3164	.36481	.43171	0.9423	.97420	1.3740	.13800	.68581
0.85	2.3396	.36915	.42741	0.9561	.98051	1.3835	.14099	.69107
0.86	2.3632	.37349	.42316	0.9700	.98677	1.3932	.14400	.69626
0.87	2.3869	.37784	.41895	0.9840	.99299	1.4029	.14704	.70137
0.88	2.4109	.38218	.41478	0.9981	.99916	1.4128	.15009	.70642
0.89	2.4351	.38652	.41066	1.0122	.00528	1.4229	.15317	.71139
0.90	2.4596	.39087	.40657	1.0265	.01137	1.4331	.15627	.71630
0.91	2.4843	.39521	.40252	1.0409	.01741	1.4434	.15939	.72113
0.92	2.5093	.39955	.39852	1.0554	.02341	1.4539	.16254	.72590
0.93	2.5345	.40389	.39455	1.0700	.02937	1.4645	.16570	.73059
0.94	2.5600	.40824	.39063	1.0847	.03530	1.4753	.16888	.73522
0.95	2.5857	.41258	.38674	1.0995	.04119	1.4862	.17208	.73978
0.96	2.6117	.41692	.38289	1.1144	.04704	1.4973	.17531	.74428
0.97	2.6379	.42127	.37908	1.1294	.05286	1.5085	.17855	.74870
0.98	2.6645	.42561	.37531	1.1446	.05864	1.5199	.18181	.75307
0.99	2.6912	.42995	.37158	1.1598	.06439	1.5314	.18509	.75736
1.00	2.7183	.43429	.36788	1.1752	.07011	1.5431	.18839	.76159

x	e^x Value	e^x Log₁₀	e^{-x} Value	Sinh x Value	Sinh x Log₁₀	Cosh x Value	Cosh x Log₁₀	Tanh x Value
1.00	2.7183	.43429	.36788	1.1752	.07011	1.5431	.18839	.76159
1.01	2.7456	.43864	.36422	1.1907	.07580	1.5549	.19171	.76576
1.02	2.7732	.44298	.36059	1.2063	.08146	1.5669	.19504	.76987
1.03	2.8011	.44732	.35701	1.2220	.08708	1.5790	.19839	.77391
1.04	2.8292	.45167	.35345	1.2379	.09268	1.5913	.20176	.77789
1.05	2.8577	.45601	.34994	1.2539	.09825	1.6038	.20515	.78181
1.06	2.8864	.46035	.34646	1.2700	.10379	1.6164	.20855	.78566
1.07	2.9154	.46470	.34301	1.2862	.10930	1.6292	.21197	.78946
1.08	2.9447	.46904	.33960	1.3025	.11479	1.6421	.21541	.79320
1.09	2.9743	.47338	.33622	1.3190	.12025	1.6552	.21886	.79688
1.10	3.0042	.47772	.33287	1.3356	.12569	1.6685	.22233	.80050
1.11	3.0344	.48207	.32956	1.3524	.13111	1.6820	.22582	.80406
1.12	3.0649	.48641	.32628	1.3693	.13649	1.6956	.22931	.80757
1.13	3.0957	.49075	.32303	1.3863	.14186	1.7093	.23283	.81102
1.14	3.1268	.49510	.31982	1.4035	.14720	1.7233	.23636	.81441
1.15	3.1582	.49944	.31664	1.4208	.15253	1.7374	.23990	.81775
1.16	3.1899	.50378	.31349	1.4382	.15783	1.7517	.24346	.82104
1.17	3.2220	.50812	.31037	1.4558	.16311	1.7662	.24703	.82427
1.18	3.2544	.51247	.30728	1.4735	.16836	1.7808	.25062	.82745
1.19	3.2871	.51681	.30422	1.4914	.17360	1.7957	.25422	.83058
1.20	3.3201	.52115	.30119	1.5095	.17882	1.8107	.25784	.83365
1.21	3.3535	.52550	.29820	1.5276	.18402	1.8258	.26146	.83668
1.22	3.3872	.52984	.29523	1.5460	.18920	1.8412	.26510	.83965
1.23	3.4212	.53418	.29229	1.5645	.19437	1.8568	.26876	.84258
1.24	3.4556	.53853	.28938	1.5831	.19951	1.8725	.27242	.84546
1.25	3.4903	.54287	.28650	1.6019	.20464	1.8884	.27610	.84828
1.26	3.5254	.54721	.28365	1.6209	.20975	1.9045	.27979	.85106
1.27	3.5609	.55155	.28083	1.6400	.21485	1.9208	.28349	.85380
1.28	3.5966	.55590	.27804	1.6593	.21993	1.9373	.28721	.85648
1.29	3.6328	.56024	.27527	1.6788	.22499	1.9540	.29093	.85913
1.30	3.6693	.56458	.27253	1.6984	.23004	1.9709	.29467	.86172
1.31	3.7062	.56893	.26982	1.7182	.23507	1.9880	.29842	.86428
1.32	3.7434	.57327	.26714	1.7381	.24009	2.0053	.30217	.86678
1.33	3.7810	.57761	.26448	1.7583	.24509	2.0228	.30594	.86925
1.34	3.8190	.58195	.26185	1.7786	.25008	2.0404	.30972	.87167
1.35	3.8574	.58630	.25924	1.7991	.25505	2.0583	.31352	.87405
1.36	3.8962	.59064	.25666	1.8198	.26002	2.0764	.31732	.87639
1.37	3.9354	.59498	.25411	1.8406	.26496	2.0947	.32113	.87869
1.38	3.9749	.59933	.25158	1.8617	.26990	2.1132	.32495	.88095
1.39	4.0149	.60367	.24908	1.8829	.27482	2.1320	.32878	.88317
1.40	4.0552	.60801	.24660	1.9043	.27974	2.1509	.33262	.88535
1.41	4.0960	.61236	.24414	1.9259	.28464	2.1700	.33647	.88749
1.42	4.1371	.61670	.24171	1.9477	.28952	2.1894	.34033	.88960
1.43	4.1787	.62104	.23931	1.9697	.29440	2.2090	.34420	.89167
1.44	4.2207	.62538	.23693	1.9919	.29926	2.2288	.34807	.89370
1.45	4.2631	.62973	.23457	2.0143	.30412	2.2488	.35196	.89569
1.46	4.3060	.63407	.23224	2.0369	.30896	2.2691	.35585	.89765
1.47	4.3492	.63841	.22993	2.0597	.31379	2.2896	.35976	.89958
1.48	4.3929	.64276	.22764	2.0827	.31862	2.3103	.36367	.90147
1.49	4.4371	.64710	.22537	2.1059	.32343	2.3312	.36759	.90332
1.50	4.4817	.65144	.22313	2.1293	.32823	2.3524	.37151	.90515

x	e^x Value	e^x Log$_{10}$	e^{-x} Value	Sinh x Value	Sinh x Log$_{10}$	Cosh x Value	Cosh x Log$_{10}$	Tanh x Value
1.50	4.4817	.65144	.22313	2.1293	.32823	2.3524	.37151	.90515
1.51	4.5267	.65578	.22091	2.1529	.33303	2.3738	.37545	.90694
1.52	4.5722	.66013	.21871	2.1768	.33781	2.3955	.37939	.90870
1.53	4.6182	.66447	.21654	2.2008	.34258	2.4174	.38334	.91042
1.54	4.6646	.66881	.21438	2.2251	.34735	2.4395	.38730	.91212
1.55	4.7115	.67316	.21225	2.2496	.35211	2.4619	.39126	.91379
1.56	4.7588	.67750	.21014	2.2743	.35686	2.4845	.39524	.91542
1.57	4.8066	.68184	.20805	2.2993	.36160	2.5073	.39921	.91703
1.58	4.8550	.68619	.20598	2.3245	.36633	2.5305	.40320	.91860
1.59	4.9037	.69053	.20393	2.3499	.37105	2.5538	.40719	.92015
1.60	4.9530	.69487	.20190	2.3756	.37577	2.5775	.41119	.92167
1.61	5.0028	.69921	.19989	2.4015	.38048	2.6013	.41520	.92316
1.62	5.0531	.70356	.19790	2.4276	.38518	2.6255	.41921	.92462
1.63	5.1039	.70790	.19593	2.4540	.38987	2.6499	.42323	.92606
1.64	5.1552	.71224	.19398	2.4806	.39456	2.6746	.42725	.92747
1.65	5.2070	.71659	.19205	2.5075	.39923	2.6995	.43129	.92886
1.66	5.2593	.72093	.19014	2.5346	.40391	2.7247	.43532	.93022
1.67	5.3122	.72527	.18825	2.5620	.40857	2.7502	.43937	.93155
1.68	5.3656	.72961	.18637	2.5896	.41323	2.7760	.44341	.93286
1.69	5.4195	.73396	.18452	2.6175	.41788	2.8020	.44747	.93415
1.70	5.4739	.73830	.18268	2.6456	.42253	2.8283	.45153	.93541
1.71	5.5290	.74264	.18087	2.6740	.42717	2.8549	.45559	.93665
1.72	5.5845	.74699	.17907	2.7027	.43180	2.8818	.45966	.93786
1.73	5.6407	.75133	.17728	2.7317	.43643	2.9090	.46374	.93906
1.74	5.6973	.75567	.17552	2.7609	.44105	2.9364	.46782	.94023
1.75	5.7546	.76002	.17377	2.7904	.44567	2.9642	.47191	.94138
1.76	5.8124	.76436	.17204	2.8202	.45028	2.9922	.47600	.94250
1.77	5.8709	.76870	.17033	2.8503	.45488	3.0206	.48009	.94361
1.78	5.9299	.77304	.16864	2.8806	.45948	3.0492	.48419	.94470
1.79	5.9895	.77739	.16696	2.9112	.46408	3.0782	.48830	.94576
1.80	6.0496	.78173	.16530	2.9422	.46867	3.1075	.49241	.94681
1.81	6.1104	.78607	.16365	2.9734	.47325	3.1371	.49652	.94783
1.82	6.1719	.79042	.16203	3.0049	.47783	3.1669	.50064	.94884
1.83	6.2339	.79476	.16041	3.0367	.48241	3.1972	.50476	.94983
1.84	6.2965	.79910	.15882	3.0689	.48698	3.2277	.50889	.95080
1.85	6.3598	.80344	.15724	3.1013	.49154	3.2585	.51302	.95175
1.86	6.4237	.80779	.15567	3.1340	.49610	3.2897	.51716	.95268
1.87	6.4883	.81213	.15412	3.1671	.50066	3.3212	.52130	.95359
1.88	6.5535	.81647	.15259	3.2005	.50521	3.3530	.52544	.95449
1.89	6.6194	.82082	.15107	3.2341	.50976	3.3852	.52959	.95537
1.90	6.6859	.82516	.14957	3.2682	.51430	3.4177	.53374	.95624
1.91	6.7531	.82950	.14808	3.3025	.51884	3.4506	.53789	.95709
1.92	6.8210	.83385	.14661	3.3372	.52338	3.4838	.54205	.95792
1.93	6.8895	.83819	.14515	3.3722	.52791	3.5173	.54621	.95873
1.94	6.9588	.84253	.14370	3.4075	.53244	3.5512	.55038	.95953
1.95	7.0287	.84687	.14227	3.4432	.53696	3.5855	.55455	.96032
1.96	7.0993	.85122	.14086	3.4792	.54148	3.6201	.55872	.96109
1.97	7.1707	.85556	.13946	3.5156	.54600	3.6551	.56290	.96185
1.98	7.2427	.85990	.13807	3.5523	.55051	3.6904	.56707	.96259
1.99	7.3155	.86425	.13670	3.5894	.55502	3.7261	.57126	.96331
2.00	7.3891	.86859	.13534	3.6269	.55953	3.7622	.57544	.96403

x	e^x Value	e^x Log₁₀	e^{-x} Value	Sinh x Value	Sinh x Log₁₀	Cosh x Value	Cosh x Log₁₀	Tanh x Value
2.00	7.3891	.86859	.13534	3.6269	.55953	3.7622	.57544	.96403
2.01	7.4633	.87293	.13399	3.6647	.56403	3.7987	.57963	.96473
2.02	7.5383	.87727	.13266	3.7028	.56853	3.8355	.58382	.96541
2.03	7.6141	.88162	.13134	3.7414	.57303	3.8727	.58802	.96609
2.04	7.6906	.88596	.13003	3.7803	.57753	3.9103	.59221	.96675
2.05	7.7679	.89030	.12873	3.8196	.58202	3.9483	.59641	.96740
2.06	7.8460	.89465	.12745	3.8593	.58650	3.9867	.60061	.96803
2.07	7.9248	.89899	.12619	3.8993	.59099	4.0255	.60482	.96865
2.08	8.0045	.90333	.12493	3.9398	.59547	4.0647	.60903	.96926
2.09	8.0849	.90768	.12369	3.9806	.59995	4.1043	.61324	.96986
2.10	8.1662	.91202	.12246	4.0219	.60443	4.1443	.61745	.97045
2.11	8.2482	.91636	.12124	4.0635	.60890	4.1847	.62167	.97103
2.12	8.3311	.92070	.12003	4.1056	.61337	4.2256	.62589	.97159
2.13	8.4149	.92505	.11884	4.1480	.61784	4.2669	.63011	.97215
2.14	8.4994	.92939	.11765	4.1909	.62231	4.3085	.63433	.97269
2.15	8.5849	.93373	.11648	4.2342	.62677	4.3507	.63856	.97323
2.16	8.6711	.93808	.11533	4.2779	.63123	4.3932	.64278	.97375
2.17	8.7583	.94242	.11418	4.3221	.63569	4.4362	.64701	.97426
2.18	8.8463	.94676	.11304	4.3666	.64015	4.4797	.65125	.97477
2.19	8.9352	.95110	.11192	4.4116	.64460	4.5236	.65548	.97526
2.20	9.0250	.95545	.11080	4.4571	.64905	4.5679	.65972	.97574
2.21	9.1157	.95979	.10970	4.5030	.65350	4.6127	.66396	.97622
2.22	9.2073	.96413	.10861	4.5494	.65795	4.6580	.66820	.97668
2.23	9.2999	.96848	.10753	4.5962	.66240	4.7037	.67244	.97714
2.24	9.3933	.97282	.10646	4.6434	.66684	4.7499	.67668	.97759
2.25	9.4877	.97716	.10540	4.6912	.67128	4.7966	.68093	.97803
2.26	9.5831	.98151	.10435	4.7394	.67572	4.8437	.68518	.97846
2.27	9.6794	.98585	.10331	4.7880	.68016	4.8914	.68943	.97888
2.28	9.7767	.99019	.10228	4.8372	.68459	4.9395	.69368	.97929
2.29	9.8749	.99453	.10127	4.8868	.68903	4.9881	.69794	.97970
2.30	9.9742	.99888	.10026	4.9370	.69346	5.0372	.70219	.98010
2.31	10.074	.00322	.09926	4.9876	.69789	5.0868	.70645	.98049
2.32	10.176	.00756	.09827	5.0387	.70232	5.1370	.71071	.98087
2.33	10.278	.01191	.09730	5.0903	.70675	5.1876	.71497	.98124
2.34	10.381	.01625	.09633	5.1425	.71117	5.2388	.71923	.98161
2.35	10.486	.02059	.09537	5.1951	.71559	5.2905	.72349	.98197
2.36	10.591	.02493	.09442	5.2483	.72002	5.3427	.72776	.98233
2.37	10.697	.02928	.09348	5.3020	.72444	5.3954	.73203	.98267
2.38	10.805	.03362	.09255	5.3562	.72885	5.4487	.73630	.98301
2.39	10.913	.03796	.09163	5.4109	.73327	5.5026	.74056	.98335
2.40	11.023	.04231	.09072	5.4662	.73769	5.5569	.74484	.98367
2.41	11.134	.04665	.08982	5.5221	.74210	5.6119	.74911	.98400
2.42	11.246	.05099	.08892	5.5785	.74652	5.6674	.75338	.98431
2.43	11.359	.05534	.08804	5.6354	.75093	5.7235	.75766	.98462
2.44	11.473	.05968	.08716	5.6929	.75534	5.7801	.76194	.98492
2.45	11.588	.06402	.08629	5.7510	.75975	5.8373	.76621	.98522
2.46	11.705	.06836	.08543	5.8097	.76415	5.8951	.77049	.98551
2.47	11.822	.07271	.08458	5.8689	.76856	5.9535	.77477	.98579
2.48	11.941	.07705	.08374	5.9288	.77296	6.0125	.77906	.98607
2.49	12.061	.08139	.08291	5.9892	.77737	6.0721	.78334	.98635
2.50	12.182	.08574	.08208	6.0502	.78177	6.1323	.78762	.98661

x	e^x Value	e^x Log$_{10}$	e^{-x} Value	Sinh x Value	Sinh x Log$_{10}$	Cosh x Value	Cosh x Log$_{10}$	Tanh x Value
2.50	12.182	.08574	.08208	6.0502	.78177	6.1323	.78762	.98661
2.51	12.305	.09008	.08127	6.1118	.78617	6.1931	.79191	.98688
2.52	12.429	.09442	.08046	6.1741	.79057	6.2545	.79619	.98714
2.53	12.554	.09877	.07966	6.2369	.79497	6.3166	.80048	.98739
2.54	12.680	.10311	.07887	6.3004	.79937	6.3793	.80477	.98764
2.55	12.807	.10745	.07808	6.3645	.80377	6.4426	.80906	.98788
2.56	12.936	.11179	.07730	6.4293	.80816	6.5066	.81335	.98812
2.57	13.066	.11614	.07654	6.4946	.81256	6.5712	.81764	.98835
2.58	13.197	.12048	.07577	6.5607	.81695	6.6365	.82194	.98858
2.59	13.330	.12482	.07502	6.6274	.82134	6.7024	.82623	.98881
2.60	13.464	.12917	.07427	6.6947	.82573	6.7690	.83052	.98903
2.61	13.599	.13351	.07353	6.7628	.83012	6.8363	.83482	.98924
2.62	13.736	.13785	.07280	6.8315	.83451	6.9043	.83912	.98946
2.63	13.874	.14219	.07208	6.9008	.83890	6.9729	.84341	.98966
2.64	14.013	.14654	.07136	6.9709	.84329	7.0423	.84771	.98987
2.65	14.154	.15088	.07065	7.0417	.84768	7.1123	.85201	.99007
2.66	14.296	.15522	.06995	7.1132	.85206	7.1831	.85631	.99026
2.67	14.440	.15957	.06925	7.1854	.85645	7.2546	.86061	.99045
2.68	14.585	.16391	.06856	7.2583	.86083	7.3268	.86492	.99064
2.69	14.732	.16825	.06788	7.3319	.86522	7.3998	.86922	.99083
2.70	14.880	.17260	.06721	7.4063	.86960	7.4735	.87352	.99101
2.71	15.029	.17694	.06654	7.4814	.87398	7.5479	.87783	.99118
2.72	15.180	.18128	.06587	7.5572	.87836	7.6231	.88213	.99136
2.73	15.333	.18562	.06522	7.6338	.88274	7.6991	.88644	.99153
2.74	15.487	.18997	.06457	7.7112	.88712	7.7758	.89074	.99170
2.75	15.643	.19431	.06393	7.7894	.89150	7.8533	.89505	.99186
2.76	15.800	.19865	.06329	7.8683	.89588	7.9316	.89936	.99202
2.77	15.959	.20300	.06266	7.9480	.90026	8.0106	.90367	.99218
2.78	16.119	.20734	.06204	8.0285	.90463	8.0905	.90798	.99233
2.79	16.281	.21168	.06142	8.1098	.90901	8.1712	.91229	.99248
2.80	16.445	.21602	.06081	8.1919	.91339	8.2527	.91660	.99263
2.81	16.610	.22037	.06020	8.2749	.91776	8.3351	.92091	.99278
2.82	16.777	.22471	.05961	8.3586	.92213	8.4182	.92522	.99292
2.83	16.945	.22905	.05901	8.4432	.92651	8.5022	.92953	.99306
2.84	17.116	.23340	.05843	8.5287	.93088	8.5871	.93385	.99320
2.85	17.288	.23774	.05784	8.6150	.93525	8.6728	.93816	.99333
2.86	17.462	.24208	.05727	8.7021	.93963	8.7594	.94247	.99346
2.87	17.637	.24643	.05670	8.7902	.94400	8.8469	.94679	.99359
2.88	17.814	.25077	.05613	8.8791	.94837	8.9352	.95110	.99372
2.89	17.993	.25511	.05558	8.9689	.95274	9.0244	.95542	.99384
2.90	18.174	.25945	.05502	9.0596	.95711	9.1146	.95974	.99396
2.91	18.357	.26380	.05448	9.1512	.96148	9.2056	.96405	.99408
2.92	18.541	.26814	.05393	9.2437	.96584	9.2976	.96837	.99420
2.93	18.728	.27248	.05340	9.3371	.97021	9.3905	.97269	.99431
2.94	18.916	.27683	.05287	9.4315	.97458	9.4844	.97701	.99443
2.95	19.106	.28117	.05234	9.5268	.97895	9.5791	.98133	.99454
2.96	19.298	.28551	.05182	9.6231	.98331	9.6749	.98565	.99464
2.97	19.492	.28985	.05130	9.7203	.98768	9.7716	.98997	.99475
2.98	19.688	.29420	.05079	9.8185	.99205	9.8693	.99429	.99485
2.99	19.886	.29854	.05029	9.9177	.99641	9.9680	.99861	.99496
3.00	20.086	.30288	.04979	10.018	.00078	10.068	.00293	.99505

[Characteristics of Logarithms omitted—determine by the usual rule from the value]

Radians	Degrees	Sine Value	Sine Log₁₀	Tangent Value	Tangent Log₁₀	Cotangent Value	Cotangent Log₁₀	Cosine Value	Cosine Log₁₀		
.0000	0° 00′	.0000	——	.0000	——	——	——	1.0000	.0000	90° 00′	1.5708
.0029	10	.0029	.4637	.0029	.4637	343.77	.5363	1.0000	.0000	50	1.5679
.0058	20	.0058	.7648	.0058	.7648	171.89	.2352	1.0000	.0000	40	1.5650
.0087	30	.0087	.9408	.0087	.9409	114.59	.0591	1.0000	.0000	30	1.5621
.0116	40	.0116	.0658	.0116	.0658	85.940	.9342	.9999	.0000	20	1.5592
.0145	50	.0145	.1627	.0145	.1627	68.750	.8373	.9999	.0000	10	1.5563
.0175	1° 00′	.0175	.2419	.0175	.2419	57.290	.7581	.9998	.9999	89° 00′	1.5533
.0204	10	.0204	.3088	.0204	.3089	49.104	.6911	.9998	.9999	50	1.5504
.0233	20	.0233	.3668	.0233	.3669	42.964	.6331	.9997	.9999	40	1.5475
.0262	30	.0262	.4179	.0262	.4181	38.188	.5819	.9997	.9999	30	1.5446
.0291	40	.0291	.4637	.0291	.4638	34.368	.5362	.9996	.9998	20	1.5417
.0320	50	.0320	.5050	.0320	.5053	31.242	.4947	.9995	.9998	10	1.5388
.0349	2° 00′	.0349	.5428	.0349	.5431	28.636	.4569	.9994	.9997	88° 00′	1.5359
.0378	10	.0378	.5776	.0378	.5779	26.432	.4221	.9993	.9997	50	1.5330
.0407	20	.0407	.6097	.0407	.6101	24.542	.3899	.9992	.9996	40	1.5301
.0436	30	.0436	.6397	.0437	.6401	22.904	.3599	.9990	.9996	30	1.5272
.0465	40	.0465	.6677	.0466	.6682	21.470	.3318	.9989	.9995	20	1.5243
.0495	50	.0494	.6940	.0495	.6945	20.206	.3055	.9988	.9995	10	1.5213
.0524	3° 00′	.0523	.7188	.0524	.7194	19.081	.2806	.9986	.9994	87° 00′	1.5184
.0553	10	.0552	.7423	.0553	.7429	18.075	.2571	.9985	.9993	50	1.5155
.0582	20	.0581	.7645	.0582	.7652	17.169	.2348	.9983	.9993	40	1.5126
.0611	30	.0610	.7857	.0612	.7865	16.350	.2135	.9981	.9992	30	1.5097
.0640	40	.0640	.8059	.0641	.8067	15.605	.1933	.9980	.9991	20	1.5068
.0669	50	.0669	.8251	.0670	.8261	14.924	.1739	.9978	.9990	10	1.5039
.0698	4° 00′	.0698	.8436	.0699	.8446	14.301	.1554	.9976	.9989	86° 00′	1.5010
.0727	10	.0727	.8613	.0729	.8624	13.727	.1376	.9974	.9989	50	1.4981
.0756	20	.0756	.8783	.0758	.8795	13.197	.1205	.9971	.9988	40	1.4952
.0785	30	.0785	.8946	.0787	.8960	12.706	.1040	.9969	.9987	30	1.4923
.0814	40	.0814	.9104	.0816	.9118	12.251	.0882	.9967	.9986	20	1.4893
.0844	50	.0843	.9256	.0846	.9272	11.826	.0728	.9964	.9985	10	1.4864
.0873	5° 00′	.0872	.9403	.0875	.9420	11.430	.0580	.9962	.9983	85° 00′	1.4835
.0902	10	.0901	.9545	.0904	.9563	11.059	.0437	.9959	.9982	50	1.4806
.0931	20	.0929	.9682	.0934	.9701	10.712	.0299	.9957	.9981	40	1.4777
.0960	30	.0958	.9816	.0963	.9836	10.385	.0164	.9954	.9980	30	1.4748
.0989	40	.0987	.9945	.0992	.9966	10.078	.0034	.9951	.9979	20	1.4719
.1018	50	.1016	.0070	.1022	.0093	9.7882	.9907	.9948	.9977	10	1.4690
.1047	6° 00′	.1045	.0192	.1051	.0216	9.5144	.9784	.9945	.9976	84° 00′	1.4661
.1076	10	.1074	.0311	.1080	.0336	9.2553	.9664	.9942	.9975	50	1.4632
.1105	20	.1103	.0426	.1110	.0453	9.0098	.9547	.9939	.9973	40	1.4603
.1134	30	.1132	.0539	.1139	.0567	8.7769	.9433	.9936	.9972	30	1.4573
.1164	40	.1161	.0648	.1169	.0678	8.5555	.9322	.9932	.9971	20	1.4544
.1193	50	.1190	.0755	.1198	.0786	8.3450	.9214	.9929	.9969	10	1.4515
.1222	7° 00′	.1219	.0859	.1228	.0891	8.1443	.9109	.9925	.9968	83° 00′	1.4486
.1251	10	.1248	.0961	.1257	.0995	7.9530	.9005	.9922	.9966	50	1.4457
.1280	20	.1276	.1060	.1287	.1096	7.7704	.8904	.9918	.9964	40	1.4428
.1309	30	.1305	.1157	.1317	.1194	7.5958	.8806	.9914	.9963	30	1.4399
.1338	40	.1334	.1252	.1346	.1291	7.4287	.8709	.9911	.9961	20	1.4370
.1367	50	.1363	.1345	.1376	.1385	7.2687	.8615	.9907	.9959	10	1.4341
.1396	8° 00′	.1392	.1436	.1405	.1478	7.1154	.8522	.9903	.9958	82° 00′	1.4312
.1425	10	.1421	.1525	.1435	.1569	6.9682	.8431	.9899	.9956	50	1.4283
.1454	20	.1449	.1612	.1465	.1658	6.8269	.8342	.9894	.9954	40	1.4254
.1484	30	.1478	.1697	.1495	.1745	6.6912	.8255	.9890	.9952	30	1.4224
.1513	40	.1507	.1781	.1524	.1831	6.5606	.8169	.9886	.9950	20	1.4195
.1542	50	.1536	.1863	.1554	.1915	6.4348	.8085	.9881	.9948	10	1.4166
.1571	9° 00′	.1564	.1943	.1584	.1997	6.3138	.8003	.9877	.9946	81° 00′	1.4137
		Value Cosine	Log₁₀	Value Cotangent	Log₁₀	Value Tangent	Log₁₀	Value Sine	Log₁₀	Degrees	Radians

[Characteristics of Logarithms omitted—determine by the usual rule from the value]

RADIANS	DEGREES	SINE Value	SINE Log₁₀	TANGENT Value	TANGENT Log₁₀	COTANGENT Value	COTANGENT Log₁₀	COSINE Value	COSINE Log₁₀		
.1571	9° 00′	.1564	.1943	.1584	.1997	6.3138	.8003	.9877	.9946	81° 00′	1.4137
.1600	10	.1593	.2022	.1614	.2078	6.1970	.7922	.9872	.9944	50	1.4108
.1629	20	.1622	.2100	.1644	.2158	6.0844	.7842	.9868	.9942	40	1.4079
.1658	30	.1650	.2176	.1673	.2236	5.9758	.7764	.9863	.9940	30	1.4050
.1687	40	.1679	.2251	.1703	.2313	5.8708	.7687	.9858	.9938	20	1.4021
.1716	50	.1708	.2324	.1733	.2389	5.7694	.7611	.9853	.9936	10	1.3992
.1745	10° 00′	.1736	.2397	.1763	.2463	5.6713	.7537	.9848	.9934	80° 00′	1.3963
.1774	10	.1765	.2468	.1793	.2536	5.5764	.7464	.9843	.9931	50	1.3934
.1804	20	.1794	.2538	.1823	.2609	5.4845	.7391	.9838	.9929	40	1.3904
.1833	30	.1822	.2606	.1853	.2680	5.3955	.7320	.9833	.9927	30	1.3875
.1862	40	.1851	.2674	.1883	.2750	5.3093	.7250	.9827	.9924	20	1.3846
.1891	50	.1880	.2740	.1914	.2819	5.2257	.7181	.9822	.9922	10	1.3817
.1920	11° 00′	.1908	.2806	.1944	.2887	5.1446	.7113	.9816	.9919	79° 00′	1.3788
.1949	10	.1937	.2870	.1974	.2953	5.0658	.7047	.9811	.9917	50	1.3759
.1978	20	.1965	.2934	.2004	.3020	4.9894	.6980	.9805	.9914	40	1.3730
.2007	30	.1994	.2997	.2035	.3085	4.9152	.6915	.9799	.9912	30	1.3701
.2036	40	.2022	.3058	.2065	.3149	4.8430	.6851	.9793	.9909	20	1.3672
.2065	50	.2051	.3119	.2095	.3212	4.7729	.6788	.9787	.9907	10	1.3643
.2094	12° 00′	.2079	.3179	.2126	.3275	4.7046	.6725	.9781	.9904	78° 00′	1.3614
.2123	10	.2108	.3238	.2156	.3336	4.6382	.6664	.9775	.9901	50	1.3584
.2153	20	.2136	.3296	.2186	.3397	4.5736	.6603	.9769	.9899	40	1.3555
.2182	30	.2164	.3353	.2217	.3458	4.5107	.6542	.9763	.9896	30	1.3526
.2211	40	.2193	.3410	.2247	.3517	4.4494	.6483	.9757	.9893	20	1.3497
.2240	50	.2221	.3466	.2278	.3576	4.3897	.6424	.9750	.9890	10	1.3468
.2269	13° 00′	.2250	.3521	.2309	.3634	4.3315	.6366	.9744	.9887	77° 00′	1.3439
.2298	10	.2278	.3575	.2339	.3691	4.2747	.6309	.9737	.9884	50	1.3410
.2327	20	.2306	.3629	.2370	.3748	4.2193	.6252	.9730	.9881	40	1.3381
.2356	30	.2334	.3682	.2401	.3804	4.1653	.6196	.9724	.9878	30	1.3352
.2385	40	.2363	.3734	.2432	.3859	4.1126	.6141	.9717	.9875	20	1.3323
.2414	50	.2391	.3786	.2462	.3914	4.0611	.6086	.9710	.9872	10	1.3294
.2443	14° 00′	.2419	.3837	.2493	.3968	4.0108	.6032	.9703	.9869	76° 00′	1.3265
.2473	10	.2447	.3887	.2524	.4021	3.9617	.5979	.9696	.9866	50	1.3235
.2502	20	.2476	.3937	.2555	.4074	3.9136	.5926	.9689	.9863	40	1.3206
.2531	30	.2504	.3986	.2586	.4127	3.8667	.5873	.9681	.9859	30	1.3177
.2560	40	.2532	.4035	.2617	.4178	3.8208	.5822	.9674	.9856	20	1.3148
.2589	50	.2560	.4083	.2648	.4230	3.7760	.5770	.9667	.9853	10	1.3119
.2618	15° 00′	.2588	.4130	.2679	.4281	3.7321	.5719	.9659	.9849	75° 00′	1.3090
.2647	10	.2616	.4177	.2711	.4331	3.6891	.5669	.9652	.9846	50	1.3061
.2676	20	.2644	.4223	.2742	.4381	3.6470	.5619	.9644	.9843	40	1.3032
.2705	30	.2672	.4269	.2773	.4430	3.6059	.5570	.9636	.9839	30	1.3003
.2734	40	.2700	.4314	.2805	.4479	3.5656	.5521	.9628	.9836	20	1.2974
.2763	50	.2728	.4359	.2836	.4527	3.5261	.5473	.9621	.9832	10	1.2945
.2793	16° 00′	.2756	.4403	.2867	.4575	3.4874	.5425	.9613	.9828	74° 00′	1.2915
.2822	10	.2784	.4447	.2899	.4622	3.4495	.5378	.9605	.9825	50	1.2886
.2851	20	.2812	.4491	.2931	.4669	3.4124	.5331	.9596	.9821	40	1.2857
.2880	30	.2840	.4533	.2962	.4716	3.3759	.5284	.9588	.9817	30	1.2828
.2909	40	.2868	.4576	.2994	.4762	3.3402	.5238	.9580	.9814	20	1.2799
.2938	50	.2896	.4618	.3026	.4808	3.3052	.5192	.9572	.9810	10	1.2770
.2967	17° 00′	.2924	.4659	.3057	.4853	3.2709	.5147	.9563	.9806	73° 00′	1.2741
.2996	10	.2952	.4700	.3089	.4898	3.2371	.5102	.9555	.9802	50	1.2712
.3025	20	.2979	.4741	.3121	.4943	3.2041	.5057	.9546	.9798	40	1.2683
.3054	30	.3007	.4781	.3153	.4987	3.1716	.5013	.9537	.9794	30	1.2654
.3083	40	.3035	.4821	.3185	.5031	3.1397	.4969	.9528	.9790	20	1.2625
.3113	50	.3062	.4861	.3217	.5075	3.1084	.4925	.9520	.9786	10	1.2595
.3142	18° 00′	.3090	.4900	.3249	.5118	3.0777	.4882	.9511	.9782	72° 00′	1.2566
		Value COSINE	Log₁₀	Value COTANGENT	Log₁₀	Value TANGENT	Log₁₀	Value SINE	Log₁₀	DEGREES	RADIANS

[Characteristics of Logarithms omitted—determine by the usual rule from the value]

RADIANS	DEGREES	SINE Value	Log₁₀	TANGENT Value	Log₁₀	COTANGENT Value	Log₁₀	COSINE Value	Log₁₀		
.3142	18° 00′	.3090	.4900	.3249	.5118	3.0777	.4882	.9511	.9782	72° 00′	1.2566
.3171	10	.3118	.4939	.3281	.5161	3.0475	.4839	.9502	.9778	50	1.2537
.3200	20	.3145	.4977	.3314	.5203	3.0178	.4797	.9492	.9774	40	1.2508
.3229	30	.3173	.5015	.3346	.5245	2.9887	.4755	.9483	.9770	30	1.2479
.3258	40	.3201	.5052	.3378	.5287	2.9600	.4713	.9474	.9765	20	1.2450
.3287	50	.3228	.5090	.3411	.5329	2.9319	.4671	.9465	.9761	10	1.2421
.3316	19° 00′	.3256	.5126	.3443	.5370	2.9042	.4630	.9455	.9757	71° 00′	1.2392
.3345	10	.3283	.5163	.3476	.5411	2.8770	.4589	.9446	.9752	50	1.2363
.3374	20	.3311	.5199	.3508	.5451	2.8502	.4549	.9436	.9748	40	1.2334
.3403	30	.3338	.5235	.3541	.5491	2.8239	.4509	.9426	.9743	30	1.2305
.3432	40	.3365	.5270	.3574	.5531	2.7980	.4469	.9417	.9739	20	1.2275
.3462	50	.3393	.5306	.3607	.5571	2.7725	.4429	.9407	.9734	10	1.2246
.3491	20° 00′	.3420	.5341	.3640	.5611	2.7475	.4389	.9397	.9730	70° 00′	1.2217
.3520	10	.3448	.5375	.3673	.5650	2.7228	.4350	.9387	.9725	50	1.2188
.3549	20	.3475	.5409	.3706	.5689	2.6985	.4311	.9377	.9721	40	1.2159
.3578	30	.3502	.5443	.3739	.5727	2.6746	.4273	.9367	.9716	30	1.2130
.3607	40	.3529	.5477	.3772	.5766	2.6511	.4234	.9356	.9711	20	1.2101
.3636	50	.3557	.5510	.3805	.5804	2.6279	.4196	.9346	.9706	10	1.2072
.3665	21° 00′	.3584	.5543	.3839	.5842	2.6051	.4158	.9336	.9702	69° 00′	1.2043
.3694	10	.3611	.5576	.3872	.5879	2.5826	.4121	.9325	.9697	50	1.2014
.3723	20	.3638	.5609	.3906	.5917	2.5605	.4083	.9315	.9692	40	1.1985
.3752	30	.3665	.5641	.3939	.5954	2.5386	.4046	.9304	.9687	30	1.1956
.3782	40	.3692	.5673	.3973	.5991	2.5172	.4009	.9293	.9682	20	1.1926
.3811	50	.3719	.5704	.4006	.6028	2.4960	.3972	.9283	.9677	10	1.1897
.3840	22° 00′	.3746	.5736	.4040	.6064	2.4751	.3936	.9272	.9672	68° 00′	1.1868
.3869	10	.3773	.5767	.4074	.6100	2.4545	.3900	.9261	.9667	50	1.1839
.3898	20	.3800	.5798	.4108	.6136	2.4342	.3864	.9250	.9661	40	1.1810
.3927	30	.3827	.5828	.4142	.6172	2.4142	.3828	.9239	.9656	30	1.1781
.3956	40	.3854	.5859	.4176	.6208	2.3945	.3792	.9228	.9651	20	1.1752
.3985	50	.3881	.5889	.4210	.6243	2.3750	.3757	.9216	.9646	10	1.1723
.4014	23° 00′	.3907	.5919	.4245	.6279	2.3559	.3721	.9205	.9640	67° 00′	1.1694
.4043	10	.3934	.5948	.4279	.6314	2.3369	.3686	.9194	.9635	50	1.1665
.4072	20	.3961	.5978	.4314	.6348	2.3183	.3652	.9182	.9629	40	1.1636
.4102	30	.3987	.6007	.4348	.6383	2.2998	.3617	.9171	.9624	30	1.1606
.4131	40	.4014	.6036	.4383	.6417	2.2817	.3583	.9159	.9618	20	1.1577
.4160	50	.4041	.6065	.4417	.6452	2.2637	.3548	.9147	.9613	10	1.1548
.4189	24° 00′	.4067	.6093	.4452	.6486	2.2460	.3514	.9135	.9607	66° 00′	1.1519
.4218	10	.4094	.6121	.4487	.6520	2.2286	.3480	.9124	.9602	50	1.1490
.4247	20	.4120	.6149	.4522	.6553	2.2113	.3447	.9112	.9596	40	1.1461
.4276	30	.4147	.6177	.4557	.6587	2.1943	.3413	.9100	.9590	30	1.1432
.4305	40	.4173	.6205	.4592	.6620	2.1775	.3380	.9088	.9584	20	1.1403
.4334	50	.4200	.6232	.4628	.6654	2.1609	.3346	.9075	.9579	10	1.1374
.4363	25° 00′	.4226	.6259	.4663	.6687	2.1445	.3313	.9063	.9573	65° 00′	1.1345
.4392	10	.4253	.6286	.4699	.6720	2.1283	.3280	.9051	.9567	50	1.1316
.4422	20	.4279	.6313	.4734	.6752	2.1123	.3248	.9038	.9561	40	1.1286
.4451	30	.4305	.6340	.4770	.6785	2.0965	.3215	.9026	.9555	30	1.1257
.4480	40	.4331	.6366	.4806	.6817	2.0809	.3183	.9013	.9549	20	1.1228
.4509	50	.4358	.6392	.4841	.6850	2.0655	.3150	.9001	.9543	10	1.1199
.4538	26° 00′	.4384	.6418	.4877	.6882	2.0503	.3118	.8988	.9537	64° 00′	1.1170
.4567	10	.4410	.6444	.4913	.6914	2.0353	.3086	.8975	.9530	50	1.1141
.4596	20	.4436	.6470	.4950	.6946	2.0204	.3054	.8962	.9524	40	1.1112
.4625	30	.4462	.6495	.4986	.6977	2.0057	.3023	.8949	.9518	30	1.1083
.4654	40	.4488	.6521	.5022	.7009	1.9912	.2991	.8936	.9512	20	1.1054
.4683	50	.4514	.6546	.5059	.7040	1.9768	.2960	.8923	.9505	10	1.1025
.4712	27° 00′	.4540	.6570	.5095	.7072	1.9626	.2928	.8910	.9499	63° 00′	1.0996
		Value Log₁₀ COSINE		Value Log₁₀ COTANGENT		Value Log₁₀ TANGENT		Value Log₁₀ SINE		DEGREES	RADIANS

[Characteristics of Logarithms omitted—determine by the usual rule from the value]

Radians	Degrees	Sine Value	Sine Log₁₀	Tangent Value	Tangent Log₁₀	Cotangent Value	Cotangent Log₁₀	Cosine Value	Cosine Log₁₀		
.4712	27° 00′	.4540	.6570	.5095	.7072	1.9626	.2928	.8910	.9499	63° 00′	1.0996
.4741	10	.4566	.6595	.5132	.7103	1.9486	.2897	.8897	.9492	50	1.0966
.4771	20	.4592	.6620	.5169	.7134	1.9347	.2866	.8884	.9486	40	1.0937
.4800	30	.4617	.6644	.5206	.7165	1.9210	.2835	.8870	.9479	30	1.0908
.4829	40	.4643	.6668	.5243	.7196	1.9074	.2804	.8857	.9473	20	1.0879
.4858	50	.4669	.6692	.5280	.7226	1.8940	.2774	.8843	.9466	10	1.0850
.4887	28° 00′	.4695	.6716	.5317	.7257	1.8807	.2743	.8829	.9459	62° 00′	1.0821
.4916	10	.4720	.6740	.5354	.7287	1.8676	.2713	.8816	.9453	50	1.0792
.4945	20	.4746	.6763	.5392	.7317	1.8546	.2683	.8802	.9446	40	1.0763
.4974	30	.4772	.6787	.5430	.7348	1.8418	.2652	.8788	.9439	30	1.0734
.5003	40	.4797	.6810	.5467	.7378	1.8291	.2622	.8774	.9432	20	1.0705
.5032	50	.4823	.6833	.5505	.7408	1.8165	.2592	.8760	.9425	10	1.0676
.5061	29° 00′	.4848	.6856	.5543	.7438	1.8040	.2562	.8746	.9418	61° 00′	1.0647
.5091	10	.4874	.6878	.5581	.7467	1.7917	.2533	.8732	.9411	50	1.0617
.5120	20	.4899	.6901	.5619	.7497	1.7796	.2503	.8718	.9404	40	1.0588
.5149	30	.4924	.6923	.5658	.7526	1.7675	.2474	.8704	.9397	30	1.0559
.5178	40	.4950	.6946	.5696	.7556	1.7556	.2444	.8689	.9390	20	1.0530
.5207	50	.4975	.6968	.5735	.7585	1.7437	.2415	.8675	.9383	10	1.0501
.5236	30° 00′	.5000	.6990	.5774	.7614	1.7321	.2386	.8660	.9375	60° 00′	1.0472
.5265	10	.5025	.7012	.5812	.7644	1.7205	.2356	.8646	.9368	50	1.0443
.5294	20	.5050	.7033	.5851	.7673	1.7090	.2327	.8631	.9361	40	1.0414
.5323	30	.5075	.7055	.5890	.7701	1.6977	.2299	.8616	.9353	30	1.0385
.5352	40	.5100	.7076	.5930	.7730	1.6864	.2270	.8601	.9346	20	1.0356
.5381	50	.5125	.7097	.5969	.7759	1.6753	.2241	.8587	.9338	10	1.0327
.5411	31° 00′	.5150	.7118	.6009	.7788	1.6643	.2212	.8572	.9331	59° 00′	1.0297
.5440	10	.5175	.7139	.6048	.7816	1.6534	.2184	.8557	.9323	50	1.0268
.5469	20	.5200	.7160	.6088	.7845	1.6426	.2155	.8542	.9315	40	1.0239
.5498	30	.5225	.7181	.6128	.7873	1.6319	.2127	.8526	.9308	30	1.0210
.5527	40	.5250	.7201	.6168	.7902	1.6212	.2098	.8511	.9300	20	1.0181
.5556	50	.5275	.7222	.6208	.7930	1.6107	.2070	.8496	.9292	10	1.0152
.5585	32° 00′	.5299	.7242	.6249	.7958	1.6003	.2042	.8480	.9284	58° 00′	1.0123
.5614	10	.5324	.7262	.6289	.7986	1.5900	.2014	.8465	.9276	50	1.0094
.5643	20	.5348	.7282	.6330	.8014	1.5798	.1986	.8450	.9268	40	1.0065
.5672	30	.5373	.7302	.6371	.8042	1.5697	.1958	.8434	.9260	30	1.0036
.5701	40	.5398	.7322	.6412	.8070	1.5597	.1930	.8418	.9252	20	1.0007
.5730	50	.5422	.7342	.6453	.8097	1.5497	.1903	.8403	.9244	10	.9977
.5760	33° 00′	.5446	.7361	.6494	.8125	1.5399	.1875	.8387	.9236	57° 00′	.9948
.5789	10	.5471	.7380	.6536	.8153	1.5301	.1847	.8371	.9228	50	.9919
.5818	20	.5495	.7400	.6577	.8180	1.5204	.1820	.8355	.9219	40	.9890
.5847	30	.5519	.7419	.6619	.8208	1.5108	.1792	.8339	.9211	30	.9861
.5876	40	.5544	.7438	.6661	.8235	1.5013	.1765	.8323	.9203	20	.9832
.5905	50	.5568	.7457	.6703	.8263	1.4919	.1737	.8307	.9194	10	.9803
.5934	34° 00′	.5592	.7476	.6745	.8290	1.4826	.1710	.8290	.9186	56° 00′	.9774
.5963	10	.5616	.7494	.6787	.8317	1.4733	.1683	.8274	.9177	50	.9745
.5992	20	.5640	.7513	.6830	.8344	1.4641	.1656	.8258	.9169	40	.9716
.6021	30	.5664	.7531	.6873	.8371	1.4550	.1629	.8241	.9160	30	.9687
.6050	40	.5688	.7550	.6916	.8398	1.4460	.1602	.8225	.9151	20	.9657
.6080	50	.5712	.7568	.6959	.8425	1.4370	.1575	.8208	.9142	10	.9628
.6109	35° 00′	.5736	.7586	.7002	.8452	1.4281	.1548	.8192	.9134	55° 00′	.9599
.6138	10	.5760	.7604	.7046	.8479	1.4193	.1521	.8175	.9125	50	.9570
.6167	20	.5783	.7622	.7089	.8506	1.4106	.1494	.8158	.9116	40	.9541
.6196	30	.5807	.7640	.7133	.8533	1.4019	.1467	.8141	.9107	30	.9512
.6225	40	.5831	.7657	.7177	.8559	1.3934	.1441	.8124	.9098	20	.9483
.6254	50	.5854	.7675	.7221	.8586	1.3848	.1414	.8107	.9089	10	.9454
.6283	36° 00′	.5878	.7692	.7265	.8613	1.3764	.1387	.8090	.9080	54° 00′	.9425
		Value Log₁₀ Cosine		Value Log₁₀ Cotangent		Value Log₁₀ Tangent		Value Log₁₀ Sine		Degrees	Radians

[Characteristics of Logarithms omitted—determine by the usual rule from the value]

RADIANS	DEGREES	SINE Value	SINE Log₁₀	TANGENT Value	TANGENT Log₁₀	COTANGENT Value	COTANGENT Log₁₀	COSINE Value	COSINE Log₁₀		
.6283	36° 00′	.5878	.7692	.7265	.8613	1.3764	.1387	.8090	.9080	54° 00′	.9425
.6312	10	.5901	.7710	.7310	.8639	1.3680	.1361	.8073	.9070	50	.9396
.6341	20	.5925	.7727	.7355	.8666	1.3597	.1334	.8056	.9061	40	.9367
.6370	30	.5948	.7744	.7400	.8692	1.3514	.1308	.8039	.9052	30	.9338
.6400	40	.5972	.7761	.7445	.8718	1.3432	.1282	.8021	.9042	20	.9308
.6429	50	.5995	.7778	.7490	.8745	1.3351	.1255	.8004	.9033	10	.9279
.6458	37° 00′	.6018	.7795	.7536	.8771	1.3270	.1229	.7986	.9023	53° 00′	.9250
.6487	10	.6041	.7811	.7581	.8797	1.3190	.1203	.7969	.9014	50	.9221
.6516	20	.6065	.7828	.7627	.8824	1.3111	.1176	.7951	.9004	40	.9192
.6545	30	.6088	.7844	.7673	.8850	1.3032	.1150	.7934	.8995	30	.9163
.6574	40	.6111	.7861	.7720	.8876	1.2954	.1124	.7916	.8985	20	.9134
.6603	50	.6134	.7877	.7766	.8902	1.2876	.1098	.7898	.8975	10	.9105
.6632	38° 00′	.6157	.7893	.7813	.8928	1.2799	.1072	.7880	.8965	52° 00′	.9076
.6661	10	.6180	.7910	.7860	.8954	1.2723	.1046	.7862	.8955	50	.9047
.6690	20	.6202	.7926	.7907	.8980	1.2647	.1020	.7844	.8945	40	.9018
.6720	30	.6225	.7941	.7954	.9006	1.2572	.0994	.7826	.8935	30	.8988
.6749	40	.6248	.7957	.8002	.9032	1.2497	.0968	.7808	.8925	20	.8959
.6778	50	.6271	.7973	.8050	.9058	1.2423	.0942	.7790	.8915	10	.8930
.6807	39° 00′	.6293	.7989	.8098	.9084	1.2349	.0916	.7771	.8905	51° 00′	.8901
.6836	10	.6316	.8004	.8146	.9110	1.2276	.0890	.7753	.8895	50	.8872
.6865	20	.6338	.8020	.8195	.9135	1.2203	.0865	.7735	.8884	40	.8843
.6894	30	.6361	.8035	.8243	.9161	1.2131	.0839	.7716	.8874	30	.8814
.6923	40	.6383	.8050	.8292	.9187	1.2059	.0813	.7698	.8864	20	.8785
.6952	50	.6406	.8066	.8342	.9212	1.1988	.0788	.7679	.8853	10	.8756
.6981	40° 00′	.6428	.8081	.8391	.9238	1.1918	.0762	.7660	.8843	50° 00′	.8727
.7010	10	.6450	.8096	.8441	.9264	1.1847	.0736	.7642	.8832	50	.8698
.7039	20	.6472	.8111	.8491	.9289	1.1778	.0711	.7623	.8821	40	.8668
.7069	30	.6494	.8125	.8541	.9315	1.1708	.0685	.7604	.8810	30	.8639
.7098	40	.6517	.8140	.8591	.9341	1.1640	.0659	.7585	.8800	20	.8610
.7127	50	.6539	.8155	.8642	.9366	1.1571	.0634	.7566	.8789	10	.8581
.7156	41° 00′	.6561	.8169	.8693	.9392	1.1504	.0608	.7547	.8778	49° 00′	.8552
.7185	10	.6583	.8184	.8744	.9417	1.1436	.0583	.7528	.8767	50	.8523
.7214	20	.6604	.8198	.8796	.9443	1.1369	.0557	.7509	.8756	40	.8494
.7243	30	.6626	.8213	.8847	.9468	1.1303	.0532	.7490	.8745	30	.8465
.7272	40	.6648	.8227	.8899	.9494	1.1237	.0506	.7470	.8733	20	.8436
.7301	50	.6670	.8241	.8952	.9519	1.1171	.0481	.7451	.8722	10	.8407
.7330	42° 00′	.6691	.8255	.9004	.9544	1.1106	.0456	.7431	.8711	48° 00′	.8378
.7359	10	.6713	.8269	.9057	.9570	1.1041	.0430	.7412	.8699	50	.8348
.7389	20	.6734	.8283	.9110	.9595	1.0977	.0405	.7392	.8688	40	.8319
.7418	30	.6756	.8297	.9163	.9621	1.0913	.0379	.7373	.8676	30	.8290
.7447	40	.6777	.8311	.9217	.9646	1.0850	.0354	.7353	.8665	20	.8261
.7476	50	.6799	.8324	.9271	.9671	1.0786	.0329	.7333	.8653	10	.8232
.7505	43° 00′	.6820	.8338	.9325	.9697	1.0724	.0303	.7314	.8641	47° 00′	.8203
.7534	10	.6841	.8351	.9380	.9722	1.0661	.0278	.7294	.8629	50	.8174
.7563	20	.6862	.8365	.9435	.9747	1.0599	.0253	.7274	.8618	40	.8145
.7592	30	.6884	.8378	.9490	.9772	1.0538	.0228	.7254	.8606	30	.8116
.7621	40	.6905	.8391	.9545	.9798	1.0477	.0202	.7234	.8594	20	.8087
.7650	50	.6926	.8405	.9601	.9823	1.0416	.0177	.7214	.8582	10	.8058
.7679	44° 00′	.6947	.8418	.9657	.9848	1.0355	.0152	.7193	.8569	46° 00′	.8029
.7709	10	.6967	.8431	.9713	.9874	1.0295	.0126	.7173	.8557	50	.7999
.7738	20	.6988	.8444	.9770	.9899	1.0235	.0101	.7153	.8545	40	.7970
.7767	30	.7009	.8457	.9827	.9924	1.0176	.0076	.7133	.8532	30	.7941
.7796	40	.7030	.8469	.9884	.9949	1.0117	.0051	.7112	.8520	20	.7912
.7825	50	.7050	.8482	.9942	.9975	1.0058	.0025	.7092	.8507	10	.7883
.7854	45° 00′	.7071	.8495	1.0000	.0000	1.0000	.0000	.7071	.8495	45° 00′	.7854
		Value Log₁₀ COSINE		Value Log₁₀ COTANGENT		Value Log₁₀ TANGENT		Value Log₁₀ SINE		DEGREES	RADIANS

x Radians	Sin x	Cos x	Tan x	Equivalent of x	x Radians	Sin x	Cos x	Tan x	Equivalent of x
.00	.00000	1.0000	.00000	0° 00'.0	.50	.47943	.87758	.54630	28° 38'.9
.01	.01000	.99995	.01000	0° 34'.4	.51	.48818	.87274	.55936	29° 13'.3
.02	.02000	.99980	.02000	1° 08'.8	.52	.49688	.86782	.57256	29° 47'.6
.03	.03000	.99955	.03001	1° 43'.1	.53	.50553	.86281	.58592	30° 22'.0
.04	.03999	.99920	.04002	2° 17'.5	.54	.51414	.85771	.59943	30° 56'.4
.05	.04998	.99875	.05004	2° 51'.9	.55	.52269	.85252	.61311	31° 30'.8
.06	.05996	.99820	.06007	3° 26'.3	.56	.53119	.84726	.62695	32° 05'.1
.07	.06994	.99755	.07011	4° 00'.6	.57	.53963	.84190	.64097	32° 39'.5
.08	.07991	.99680	.08017	4° 35'.0	.58	.54802	.83646	.65517	33° 13'.9
.09	.08988	.99595	.09024	5° 09'.4	.59	.55636	.83094	.66956	33° 48'.3
.10	.09983	.99500	.10033	5° 43'.8	.60	.56464	.82534	.68414	34° 22'.6
.11	.10978	.99396	.11045	6° 18'.2	.61	.57287	.81965	.69892	34° 57'.0
.12	.11971	.99281	.12058	6° 52'.5	.62	.58104	.81388	.71391	35° 31'.4
.13	.12963	.99156	.13074	7° 26'.9	.63	.58914	.80803	.72911	36° 05'.8
.14	.13954	.99022	.14092	8° 01'.3	.64	.59720	.80210	.74454	36° 40'.2
.15	.14944	.98877	.15114	8° 35'.7	.65	.60519	.79608	.76020	37° 14'.5
.16	.15932	.98723	.16138	9° 10'.0	.66	.61312	.78999	.77610	37° 48'.9
.17	.16918	.98558	.17166	9° 44'.4	.67	.62099	.78382	.79225	38° 23'.3
.18	.17903	.98384	.18197	10° 18'.8	.68	.62879	.77757	.80866	38° 57'.7
.19	.18886	.98200	.19232	10° 53'.2	.69	.63654	.77125	.82534	39° 32'.0
.20	.19867	.98007	.20271	11° 27'.5	.70	.64422	.76484	.84229	40° 06'.4
.21	.20846	.97803	.21314	12° 01'.9	.71	.65183	.75836	.85953	40° 40'.8
.22	.21823	.97590	.22362	12° 36'.3	.72	.65938	.75181	.87707	41° 15'.2
.23	.22798	.97367	.23414	13° 10'.7	.73	.66687	.74517	.89492	41° 49'.6
.24	.23770	.97134	.24472	13° 45'.1	.74	.67429	.73847	.91309	42° 23'.9
.25	.24740	.96891	.25534	14° 19'.4	.75	.68164	.73169	.93160	42° 58'.3
.26	.25708	.96639	.26602	14° 53'.8	.76	.68892	.72484	.95045	43° 32'.7
.27	.26673	.96377	.27676	15° 28'.2	.77	.69614	.71791	.96967	44° 07'.1
.28	.27636	.96106	.28755	16° 02'.6	.78	.70328	.71091	.98926	44° 41'.4
.29	.28595	.95824	.29841	16° 36'.9	.79	.71035	.70385	1.0092	45° 15'.8
.30	.29552	.95534	.30934	17° 11'.3	.80	.71736	.69671	1.0296	45° 50'.2
.31	.30506	.95233	.32033	17° 45'.7	.81	.72429	.68950	1.0505	46° 24'.6
.32	.31457	.94924	.33139	18° 20'.1	.82	.73115	.68222	1.0717	46° 59'.0
.33	.32404	.94604	.34252	18° 54'.5	.83	.73793	.67488	1.0934	47° 33'.3
.34	.33349	.94275	.35374	19° 28'.8	.84	.74464	.66746	1.1156	48° 07'.7
.35	.34290	.93937	.36503	20° 03'.2	.85	.75128	.65998	1.1383	48° 42'.1
.36	.35227	.93590	.37640	20° 37'.6	.86	.75784	.65244	1.1616	49° 16'.5
.37	.36162	.93233	.38786	21° 12'.0	.87	.76433	.64483	1.1853	49° 50'.8
.38	.37092	.92866	.39941	21° 46'.3	.88	.77074	.63715	1.2097	50° 25'.2
.39	.38019	.92491	.41105	22° 20'.7	.89	.77707	.62941	1.2346	50° 59'.6
.40	.38942	.92106	.42279	22° 55'.1	.90	.78333	.62161	1.2602	51° 34'.0
.41	.39861	.91712	.43463	23° 29'.5	.91	.78950	.61375	1.2864	52° 08'.3
.42	.40776	.91309	.44657	24° 03'.9	.92	.79560	.60582	1.3133	52° 42'.7
.43	.41687	.90897	.45862	24° 38'.2	.93	.80162	.59783	1.3409	53° 17'.1
.44	.42594	.90475	.47078	25° 12'.6	.94	.80756	.58979	1.3692	53° 51'.5
.45	.43497	.90045	.48306	25° 47'.0	.95	.81342	.58168	1.3984	54° 25'.9
.46	.44395	.89605	.49545	26° 21'.4	.96	.81919	.57352	1.4284	55° 00'.2
.47	.45289	.89157	.50797	26° 55'.7	.97	.82489	.56530	1.4592	55° 34'.6
.48	.46178	.88699	.52061	27° 30'.1	.98	.83050	.55702	1.4910	56° 09'.0
.49	.47063	.88233	.53339	28° 04'.5	.99	.83603	.54869	1.5237	56° 43'.4
.50	.47943	.87758	.54630	28° 38'.9	1.00	.84147	.54030	1.5574	57° 17'.7

x Radians	Sin x	Cos x	Tan x	Equivalent of x	x Radians	Sin x	Cos x	Tan x	Equivalent of x
1.00	.84147	.54030	1.5574	57° 17'.7	1.30	.96356	.26750	3.6021	74° 29'.1
1.01	.84683	.53186	1.5922	57° 52'.1	1.31	.96618	.25785	3.7471	75° 03'.4
1.02	.85211	.52337	1.6281	58° 26'.5	1.32	.96872	.24818	3.9033	75° 37'.8
1.03	.85730	.51482	1.6652	59° 00'.9	1.33	.97115	.23848	4.0723	76° 12'.2
1.04	.86240	.50622	1.7036	59° 35'.3	1.34	.97348	.22875	4.2556	76° 46'.6
1.05	.86742	.49757	1.7433	60° 09'.6	1.35	.97572	.21901	4.4552	77° 21'.0
1.06	.87236	.48887	1.7844	60° 44'.0	1.36	.97786	.20924	4.6734	77° 55'.3
1.07	.87720	.48012	1.8270	61° 18'.4	1.37	.97991	.19945	4.9131	78° 29'.7
1.08	.88196	.47133	1.8712	61° 52'.8	1.38	.98185	.18964	5.1774	79° 04'.1
1.09	.88663	.46249	1.9171	62° 27'.1	1.39	.98370	.17981	5.4707	79° 38'.5
1.10	.89121	.45360	1.9648	63° 01'.5	1.40	.98545	.16997	5.7979	80° 12'.8
1.11	.89570	.44466	2.0143	63° 35'.9	1.41	.98710	.16010	6.1654	80° 47'.2
1.12	.90010	.43568	2.0660	64° 10'.3	1.42	.98865	.15023	6.5811	81° 21'.6
1.13	.90441	.42666	2.1198	64° 44'.7	1.43	.99010	.14033	7.0555	81° 56'.0
1.14	.90863	.41759	2.1759	65° 19'.0	1.44	.99146	.13042	7.6018	82° 30'.4
1.15	.91276	.40849	2.2345	65° 53'.4	1.45	.99271	.12050	8.2381	83° 04'.7
1.16	.91680	.39934	2.2958	66° 27'.8	1.46	.99387	.11057	8.9886	83° 39'.1
1.17	.92075	.39015	2.3600	67° 02'.2	1.47	.99492	.10063	9.8874	84° 13'.5
1.18	.92461	.38092	2.4273	67° 36'.5	1.48	.99588	.09067	10.983	84° 47'.9
1.19	.92837	.37166	2.4979	68° 10'.9	1.49	.99674	.08071	12.350	85° 22'.2
1.20	.93204	.36236	2.5722	68° 45'.3	1.50	.99749	.07074	14.101	85° 56'.6
1.21	.93562	.35302	2.6503	69° 19'.7	1.51	.99815	.06076	16.428	86° 31'.0
1.22	.93910	.34365	2.7328	69° 54'.1	1.52	.99871	.05077	19.670	87° 05'.4
1.23	.94249	.33424	2.8198	70° 28'.4	1.53	.99917	.04079	24.498	87° 39'.8
1.24	.94578	.32480	2.9119	71° 02'.8	1.54	.99953	.03079	32.461	88° 14'.1
1.25	.94898	.31532	3.0096	71° 37'.2	1.55	.99978	.02079	48.078	88° 48'.5
1.26	.95209	.30582	3.1133	72° 11'.6	1.56	.99994	.01080	92.621	89° 22'.9
1.27	.95510	.29628	3.2236	72° 45'.9	*1.57	*1.0000	*.00080	*1255.8	89° 57'.3
1.28	.95802	.28672	3.3413	73° 20'.3	1.58	.99996	−.00920	−108.65	90° 31'.6
1.29	.96084	.27712	3.4672	73° 54'.7	1.59	.99982	−.01920	−52.067	91° 06'.0
1.30	.96356	.26750	3.6021	74° 29'.1	1.60	.99957	−.02920	−34.233	91° 40'.4

π radians = 180°   1 radian = 57° 17' 44".806 = 57.°2957795

π = 3.14159265   3600" = 60' = 1° = 0.01745329 radian

*1 right angle = 90° = $\pi/2$ radians = 1.5707963 radians

INDEX

(The references are to pages.)